WRENS, DIPPERS AND THRASHERS

WRENS, DIPPERS AND THRASHERS

DAVID BREWER

ILLUSTRATED BY BARRY KENT MACKAY

CHRISTOPHER HELM
LONDON

Published 2001 by Christopher Helm, an imprint of A & C Black (Publishers) Ltd.,
37 Soho Square, London W1D 3QZ

ISBN 1-873403-95-X

A CIP catalogue record for this book is available from the British Library

10 9 8 7 6 5 4 3 2 1

Production and design by Fluke Art, Looe, Cornwall
Printed in Hong Kong through Phoenix Offset Ltd

CONTENTS

ACKNOWLEDGEMENTS

During the writing of this book I have received much generous help from many people. I hope that I have acknowledged all of my many helpers; if I have omitted anybody I apologise.

Access to museum material was of paramount importance and I am very grateful to Dr Ross James and Mark Peck of the Royal Ontario Museum, Dr John Bates and Dr David Willard of the Field Museum of Natural History, David Agro, Dr Nate Rice, Dr Robert Ridgely and Dr Leo Joseph of the Academy of Natural Sciences of Philadelphia and Dr François Vuilleumier, Dr Mary LeCroy and Paul Sweet of the American Museum of Natural History for access to their respective collections. I would also like to thank Dr Bates and Dr Shannon Hackett for their hospitality on earlier visits to New York.

Equally important was access to the literature, in which I received great help and many courtesies from the staffs of the libraries of the Universities of Guelph and Waterloo, the Royal Ontario Museum and the Field Museum. I am also particularly grateful to many individuals who gave me access to unpublished material or who allowed me sneak previews of papers in the process of publication. These include many people who are the acknowledged authorities in their areas; Dr Dan Christian, Dr Tara Robinson and Dr Mathilde Jullien on *Microcerculus*, Dr Martin Cody on California Thrasher, Dr Susan Farabaugh on *Thryothorus*, Dr Hector Gómez de Silva on *Hylorchilus*, Dr Sallie Hejl on Winter Wren, Dr Scott Johnson and Dr Charles Thompson on House and Brown-throated Wrens, Dr Donald Kroodsma on *Cistothorus*, Dr Kerry Rabenold on Fasciated Wren, Dr Tim Reynolds on Sage Thrasher and Robin Woods on Cobb's Wren. I also thank Dr Kroodsma for the loan of a tape of the song of Cobb's Wren. I very much appreciate the help of a number of people in getting for me copies of papers in less accessible journals; Simon and Richard Aspinall, Dr George Barraclough, Dr Keith Barker, Dr John Bates, Professor Donald Broom, Jenny Friend, Dr Jurgen Haffer, Christopher Helm, Dr David Hussell, Bob McGowan, Séan McMinn, Mark Peck, Dr Van Remsen, Dr Nate Rice and Dr Bernard Zonfrillo. I am especially indebted to Dr Robert Ridgely and Paul Greenfield for their courtesy in providing me with relevant parts of the manuscript of their upcoming book on the birds of Ecuador. Dr Barker I particularly thank for his generously-given help on taxonomic issues and other technical matters.

On issues of conservation I received willing help from Dr Nigel Collar, Jeremy Speck and David Capper. I was also greatly assisted in a variety of ways, mostly by the provision of information based on personal field experience, by David Agro, Phil Atkinson, David Bacab, Dr Robert Bates, Peter Burke, Jon Curson, Luc Fazio, Dr Rosendo Fraga, Dr Steve Gnadiek, Clive Green, Steve Howell, Peter Hubbell, Alvaro Jaramillo, Marc Johnson, Stephanie Jones, Dr M. Kestenholz, Dr Niels Krabbe, Greg Lasley, Tania Macouzet, Dr Sandy Middleton, Paul Prior, Dr Ron Orenstein, Dr Kerry Rabenold, Herbert Raffaele, Don Roberson, Dina Roberts, Graham Speight, Ron Scovell, the late Betsy Thomas, Dr Vern Thomas and Dr George Wallace.

For access to bird-banding data I am indebted to Louise Laurin and Lucie Métras of the Canadian Wildlife Service, Ottawa and to Mary Gustafsonof the U.S. Bird-banding Laboratory; the maps of recoveries were kindly provided by Eric Woodsworth, CWS Saskatoon, using a programme which he himself invented for our recently published *Canadian Atlas of Bird-banding*. Dr David Shepherd manipulated data from CWS tapes. Dr Rinse Wassenaar of the Nederlands Instituut voor Oecologisch Onderzoek very kindly coordinated the provision of recovery data from various European ringing schemes, who are also thanked for their cooperation.

I owe a great debt of gratitude to Dr Roman Jaschenko and Dr Victoria Kovshar for their kindness and hospitality during my visits to Kazakhstan and for providing me with transportation up into the Tien Shan Mountains where I was able to make observations of the Brown Dipper. I am also grateful to Dr Eduard Gavrilov for giving me access to the unrivalled collection of Central Asian dippers in the Academy of Natural Sciences of Kazakhstan and for obtaining for me a number of Russian-language publications not easily found in Canada. Dr Pavel Tomkovich kindly arranged access to specimens in the Zoological Museum of Moscow State University. My travel in Central Asia was greatly facilitated by the help of Lori Nicol, Andrei Malygin and Andrei Slivkin.

For secretarial help I am much indebted to my daughters Jenny and Hazel and to Norah Lea.

Many of the observations which are included in this book arose from personal experience in the field. I thank the following companions on numerous trips to various crannies of Central and South America over many years, often under very trying physical conditions. David Agro, Paul Eagles, Larry Hubble, Peter Hubbell, Niels Krabbe, Barry MacKay, Bill McIlveen, Xavier Muñoz, Lelis Navarrete, Robert Ridgely, John Schmeleski, Nigel Simpson, Francisco Sornoza, Graham Watkin, Doug Wechsler and Bernard Zonfrillo. I appreciate their help and companionship in the field and especially their tolerance of my numerous foibles and eccentricities which I well appreciate become more extreme and obnoxious the further removed I am from a paved road, a bug-free bed and a supply of cold beer.

I must conclude by recognising my debt to my wife Margaret; for her support and companionship on many trips in the field; for the enormous amount of secretarial work and cryptographic analysis required to turn my long-hand script into an acceptable document; for her heroic efforts to achieve the ultimately unachievable objective of keeping me organised; for her resolute determination, born of many years in the Ontario school system, to ruthlessly and totally eliminate the split infinitive, the dangling participle and similar grievous insults to the English language from my prose; and above all, for her encouragement during the long gestation of this book; for all these – and much more – I am infinitely grateful.

Barry MacKay would like to acknowledge the invaluable assistance of Mark Peck, Ross James, James Dick, Glenn Murphy and Allan Baker of the Royal Ontario Museum, Toronto; John Bates and Dave Willard of the Field Museum of Natural History, Chicago; Leo Joseph, Nathaniel Rice and David Agro of the Philadelphia Academy of Natural Sciences; Paul Sweet and Christine Blake of the American Museum of Natural History; and Janet Hinshaw and Robert Storer of the University of Michigan Museum of Zoology, all of whom kindly provided specimens and/or photographs. He would also like to thank David Brewer, Alvaro Jaramillo, Phyllis E. MacKay, John P. O'Neill and Ronald I. Orenstein for advice or reference materials, and Alan Berger of the Animal Protection Institute, for facilitating the degree of flexibility required to complete the project. Finally, he thanks his long-suffering editors at Pica Press and Christopher Helm for their understanding and accommodation of unfortunate delays in completing the work.

*I dedicate this book to my wife Margaret, not only in thanks for her
immense help in its production but, far more, in recognition of those
sterling Caledonian qualities of fortitude, endurance and good humour
that have allowed her to survive, with her sanity pretty much unscathed,
more than three decades of marriage to a fanatical birdwatcher.*

INTRODUCTION

This book deals with three families: the wrens, comprising rather more than eighty species, the mimids (mockingbirds, thrashers and allies) at about thirty-five, and the dippers, the smallest family, with just five species. Of these, to our knowledge, only the last has been the subject of an extensive monograph, namely Tyler and Ormerod's detailed study *The Dippers*, published in London in 1994. Although two individual species of wren have been the subject of books (the Reverend E. A. Armstrong's classic, *The Wren* published almost fifty years ago, and the Andersons' study of the Cactus Wren in Southern Arizona), there have been no comprehensive reviews of either the wrens or the mimids as groups, an omission that we hope will be rectified by the present work.

Our objective has been to review all the available literature, in whatever language, on the species concerned and to give a comprehensive summary of the plumage, systematics, voice, habits, habitat, breeding biology, movements and food for each. The literature was reviewed up to 31 December 1999 although, for some journals which are slow in being abstracted, some 1999 references may have been missed. Major journals were reviewed in hard copy up to 1 June 2000. In certain cases, mainly the well-investigated species found in North America and Europe, there is such a wealth of published material that we have had to be very selective, while not, we hope, omitting much of significance to the general purpose of the book; for many species, however, there is remarkably little information recorded of even their most basic biology. For example, there are seventy-three species of wren occurring only to the south of the US-Mexican border. The nests and eggs of no fewer than twenty-three of these have never been described, while several more were recorded for the first time during the actual writing of this book. For a further twenty species only the sketchiest details of breeding biology are available, with no information recorded about such fundamental aspects as egg colour, clutch size, or incubation or fledging periods. An equal lack of information exists in many other basic areas of biology and behaviour. This remarkable paucity of information is doubtless a product of the very nature of wrens; typically secretive (although the flamboyant genus *Campylorhynchus* is anything but retiring) inhabitants most frequently of dense vegetation and understorey, often in country which is physically difficult for the observer to penetrate. The mimids, by contrast, even those of restricted Neotropical distribution, are generally much better known, again as a result of the inherent nature of the family. The five species of dipper are well-studied, with the single exception of the highly-restricted Rufous-throated Dipper of Argentina and Bolivia.

EXPLANATION OF THE SPECIES ACCOUNTS

We have generally followed the pattern of previous books in this series in the treatment of species in the systematic section. Before the individual species accounts, each genus is accorded a brief description of characteristics and salient features.

NOMENCLATURE

The scientific name, with naming authority and type location, is given, followed by alternative names and common names in some other relevant languages. Where appropriate a note of the etymology of the common name is given. This is followed by some general comments on the overall nature of the species and, again where relevant, its taxonomic relationships.

IDENTIFICATION

This section is designed to highlight the distinctions from other species that are sympatric – that is, found in the same geographical area – or nearly or potentially sympatric. No effort has been made to make distinctions from species which are widely separated geographically. An overall length – that is, bill-tip to tail tip – is given, although it should be borne in mind that there may be considerable variation in size between individuals, or between races of the same species.

DESCRIPTION

A detailed description is given for adult birds. In all the families treated, male and female plumages are essentially identical, with a couple of trivial exceptions, and therefore no distinction is given in the description section. Following the detailed description of the adult, a more abbreviated note on the immature plumage is provided. In some cases information on immature plumages is not available. Generally, the description relates to the nominate race; however, in a few instances we have deliberately strayed from this, usually where for geographic reasons a race other than the nominate is the one most likely to be encountered by birdwatchers.

GEOGRAPHICAL VARIATION

All races are listed, with scientific trinomial names and a brief description of their distinctive features, which will help distinguish them from the nominate or from adjacent races. Although we deplore the practice of giving races full English names, since this confuses subspecies and species, much of the older literature does so, and so we have listed such names in inverted commas. Subspecies are taken from Howard and Moore (1984), with additions for new subspecies described in the abstracted literature up to 31 December 1999.

VOICE

Describing calls and songs is one of the most difficult and subjective tasks facing a birdwatcher. This is especially the case with species with – as is typical of wrens and mimids, perhaps less so for dippers – long and complex songs with many notes per second and much variation. To complicate matters further, for many wrens the audible songs are in fact the product of a pair, or even a group, of birds, sometimes singing in unison (duetting song), sometimes with one bird taking over at certain points or filling in (antiphonal song). In addition, there is much individual variation as well as, in some cases, substantial differences in different geographical parts of one species' range. We have done the best that we can to give an objective description of songs and calls, based on our own observations and on published descriptions. Fortunately there are excellent and nearly complete sets of recordings of the mimids (Hardy, Barlow and Coffey 1987) and the wrens (Hardy and Coffey 1991). Even with these recordings, some caution is required because of individual and geographical variation; but songs are worthy of close attention, since in the tropical forest wrens, above almost all other species, they are usually the first, and sometimes the only, indications that a birdwatcher gets of the presence of a species. For mimids songs are of lesser importance in finding or identifying a species, while for the dippers, the songs, usually muffled by the sound of running water, are rarely useful for locating birds and never helpful for identification.

HABITAT

Many species of wrens, especially, are habitat specialists; a knowledge of habitat types is frequently useful in ascertaining which species is likely to be found in an area. In South and Central America, habitat types are overwhelmingly the result of two factors; precipitation and altitude. A detailed analysis of habitat types is beyond the scope of this book; the interested reader is referred to some excellent summaries, some with photographs, in Ridgely and Tudor (1989), Howell and Webb (1995), Stiles and Skutch (1989) and Hilty and Brown (1986). For readers not familiar with the terms, *várzea* is forest, typically close to watercourses, which is seasonally inundated, often to a very substantial depth. *Páramo* is a high-altitude habitat, a cold, often wet grassland above the treeline. Characteristic plants of the *páramo* are the members of the genus *Espletia*, a tall composite. *Páramo* occurs in the mountains of Venezuela south to northern Peru; further south the corresponding high-altitude habitat is drier, much more sparsely vegetated and is called *puna*. *Llanos* refers to the lowland savannas of Venezuela, an area predominantly of grassland but with frequent islands of trees and brush. *Caatinga*, a Brazilian word, is an area of deciduous forest characterised by succulents, cacti and terrestrial bromeliads, and frequently spiny trees; herbaceous plants tend to grow only after rains and there is little grass. *Huiscoyol* refers to the impenetrable thickets of the palm *Bactris subglobosa* found in Central America. *Yungas* are forested steeply-sloping areas, usually at elevations of about 2,300–2,500m, in the temperate zones of Bolivia and Argentina.

HABITS

For many species there has been remarkably little published on habits and behaviour. We have included such information as we have, based on personal observation as well as the published literature, while fully recognising the paucity of data for so many species. This, we might add, is an area where casual observations of visiting birdwatchers could add substantially to the pool of knowledge of, especially, the wrens.

STATUS AND DISTRIBUTION

We have relied very heavily on published data for this section. We have included range maps for all species. The maps show the ranges of the various species, differentiating where appropriate between breeding and wintering ranges and areas where the species is found throughout the year. Rare extralimital breeding records and other vagrancies are not shown, but are instead dealt with in the text. It should be understood that the depiction of an area as the range of a species does not mean that it occurs everywhere in the given area, or even in all suitable patches of habitat in the area, but merely that habitual occurrences are within the limits of the area. Many species are uncommon and sporadic and may well not be found in apparently prime habitat in many parts of their overall range. It should also be noted that the scale of the maps precludes the fine detail necessary to indicate more precisely the areas of suitable habitat. This is especially true of tropical species found within narrow altitudinal ranges in complex mountainous areas. The maps should be interpreted in combination with the sections in the text on habitat and status and distribution.

   In some cases, where there are sufficient data, we have given maps showing recoveries of banded birds. In these maps the recovery location is indicated by the symbol at the end of the line. In some instances, where there are a number of similar (but not identical) recoveries, recoveries have been combined; in these cases the banding and recovery locations are not exact, but are approximations of the combined recoveries, the location then being indicated by a larger symbol (Brewer *et al.* 2000).

The following sources were used in drawing the maps.

Individual species accounts available as of 1 May, 2000 in the series *Birds of North America*, The Academy of Natural Sciences of Philadelphia and The American Ornithologists' Union, Washington DC.

Cadman, M.D., Eagles, P.J.F. & Helleine,r F.M. 1987. *Atlas of the Breeding Birds of Ontario*, University of Waterloo Press, Waterloo, Ontario.

Cheng Tso-Hsin 1987. *A Synopsis of the Avifauna of China*, Science Press, Beijing.

Cramp, S. *et al.* (eds.) 1988. *Handbook of the Birds of Europe, The Middle East and North Africa, Vol. 5*. Oxford University Press, Oxford.

Fjeldså, J. & Krabbe, N. 1990. *Birds of the High Andes*, Zoological Museum, University of Copenhagen.

Flint, V.E., Boehme, R.L., Kostin, Y.V., & Kuznetsov, A.A. 1984. *A Field Guide to the Birds of the USSR*, Princeton University Press, Princeton, New Jersey.

Harris, M. 1974. *A Field Guide to the Birds of the Galapagos*, Collins, London.

Harrison, C. 1982. *An Atlas of the Birds of the Western Palearctic*, Collins, London.

Hilty, S.L. & Brown, W.L. 1986. *A Guide to the Birds of Colombia*, Princeton University Press, Princeton, New Jersey.

Howell, S.N.G. & Webb, S. 1995. *A Guide to the Birds of Mexico and Northern Central America*, Oxford University Press, Oxford.

Land, H.C. 1970. *Birds of Guatemala*, Livingston, Wynnewood, Pennsylvania.

Narosky, T. & Yzurieta, D. 1987. *Guía para la identificación de las Aves de Argentina y Uruguay*, Vasquez Mazzini, Buenos Aires.

National Geographic Society 1983. *A Field Guide to the Birds of North America*, National Geographic Society, Washington DC.

Peterson, R.T. 1980. *A Field Guide to the Birds*. Houghton Mifflin, San Diego, California.

Peterson, R.T. 1990. *A Field Guide to Western Birds.* Houghton Mifflin, Boston, Massachusetts.

Price, J., Droege, S. & Price, A. 1995. *The Summer Atlas of North American Birds,* Academic Press, San Diego, California.

Raffaele, H., Wiley, J., Garrido, O., Keith, A. & Raffaele, J. 1988. *A Guide to the Birds of the West Indies,* Princeton University Press, Princeton, New Jersey.

Ridgely, R.S. 1976. *A Guide to the Birds of Panama,* Princeton University Press, Princeton, New Jersey.

Ridgely, R.S. & Tudor G. 1989. *The Birds of South America, Vol. 1,* University of Texas Press, Austin, Texas.

Russell, S.M. 1964. *A Distributional Study of the Birds of British Honduras,* American Ornithologists' Union, Allen Press, Lawrence, Kansas.

Russell, S.M. & Monson, G. 1998. *The Birds of Sonora,* University of Arizona Press, Tucson, Arizona.

Stiles, F.G. & Skutch, A.F. 1989. *A Guide to the Birds of Costa Rica,* Cornell University Press, Ithaca, New York.

Sonobe, K. (ed.) 1982. *A Field Guide to the Birds of Japan,* Wild Bird Society of Japan, Tokyo.

In addition, some maps have been modified on the basis of personal experience or from personal communications from several sources who are appropriately referenced in the text. It should be noted that phrases such as "fairly common" or "rather sparsely distributed" which we have had to accept from published data are very subjective and imprecise. Readers not totally familiar with the geography of Central and South America are referred to the regional maps, on pp. 271–272, of the states, provinces and departments of the relevant countries. It should also be realised that there is much to be discovered about the ranges of many species in the Neotropics; birdwatchers who discover inaccuracies in our accounts (as they undoubtedly will) or who find range extensions for any species are encouraged to publish their discoveries.

BREEDING

It is truly remarkable how little is known about the breeding biology of, especially, the wrens; for more than half the species found in Central and South America, the nests are either totally unknown (or totally undescribed in the literature, not necessarily the same thing), or there remain major gaps of published knowledge of elementary facets of breeding biology. This must surely be an irresistible challenge to any birdwatcher worth his (or her) salt. In the "Breeding" section we have given as complete an account as the data allow of nest type and siting, descriptions of eggs, clutch size, incubation and fledging periods and other related details. Even in those cases where nests have been described, in many instances our knowledge is based on a tiny handful of observations. If nothing else, we hope that this section will alert birdwatchers to the gaps in the recorded data and, surely, encourage them to go out and fill them.

MOVEMENTS

The majority of the species in this book are sedentary; that is to say, the species is found in the same area year-round, and in all probability it is the same individual birds which remain in a particular spot. This is typical of species found in tropical areas without extremes of climate. In our case, the tropical species seem to be sedentary even in areas with marked wet and dry seasons. For a few species in mountainous regions there is some evidence of altitudinal movement. However, most of the populations of wrens and mimids found in temperate zones are highly migratory. In North America there is a wealth of information, not only on the simple presence or absence of a species throughout the year but also for population densities, arising from breeding bird surveys, Christmas Counts and similar activities. An analysis of these is well beyond the scope of this book. In addition, in Europe and North America there is a considerable body of information arising from the recoveries of banded birds. We have examined these in a very simple and crude manner for half a dozen species, without making any pretence of doing a thorough analysis. Some populations of wrens and mimids in temperate South America are also migratory, albeit usually for much shorter distances. However, in these cases the data available are very scanty; there are no banding recoveries and even the limits of winter distribution for many species are imperfectly known.

MEASUREMENTS

Standard measurements (natural or unflattened wing-chord, tail, exposed culmen and tarsus) are given for males and females. These are either taken from the literature, in which case the relevant reference is given, or were made from museum specimens. The following abbreviations have been used for museums; ROM, Royal Ontario Museum, Toronto; AMNH, American Museum of Natural History, New York; ANSP, The Academy of Natural Sciences, Philadelphia; FMNH, The Field Museum of Natural History, Chicago; ANRK, Academy of Sciences, Republic of Kazakhstan, Almaty; MGUZM, Moscow State University, Museum of Zoology; BMNH, British Museum (Natural History).

REFERENCES

The sources of statements made in the text are given in parentheses at the appropriate points; there is a complete bibliography at the end.

PLATES

The plates are arranged approximately in the same order as the species accounts in the text, with occasional modifications for convenience and to put species which occur in the same geographic areas together, or to put species of a similar appearance on the same plate. Each species is referred to by a species number, the various plumages or races being differentiated by lower case letters of the alphabet. Although there is very rarely any difference in the plumages of the sexes, we have noted in the plate captions the sex of the actual specimens that were used as models for individual figures, when this was recorded on the museum label. On the plate captions are given the common and scientific names of each species, followed by a brief desciption of habitat, geographic range and (in some cases) a very short desciption of the salient features of the species, all of which is dealt with in much greater detail in the text. There then follows a brief note on each of the figures, giving the race involved and its range and the distinction between that race and, usually, the nominate race. Not all races are individually figured; in most cases we chose the races to illustrate the greatest diversity of plumage types within a species. In all cases the text is much more exhaustive than the plate captions.

CLASSIFICATION AND RELATIONSHIPS

Serious attempts to classify birds, in a manner that we would now regard as 'scientific', first began in the seventeenth century with Willughby and Ray's classical *Ornithologiae*, published by the Royal Society in 1676. In it the authors, basing their arguments on obvious observable features such as legs and bill, gave a framework to the logical arrangements of bird families which greatly influenced the monumental work of Linnaeus almost a century later. With the general acceptance among zoologists, following the publication of Darwin's *Origin of Species* in 1859, of the principles of evolution and descent from common ancestors there was, in the second half of the nineteenth century, an outburst of work designed to unravel and systematise the interrelationships of the known families of birds. This was almost entirely based upon anatomical features observable from dead specimens in museums. Resulting from the studies of anatomists such as Fürbringer and Gadow, a classification system was produced; not universally accepted in all its aspects, but with much general agreement among most of the leading contemporary authorities. This is largely the foundation on which the famous 'Wetmore Order' was based.

From these approaches there was constructed a tree of relationships which might be called 'traditional'. It was accepted therein that wrens and dippers were very closely related (indeed, some authorities went so far as to place them within one family, albeit a view not widely held even then), and the mockingbirds and allies were, along with thrushes, not far removed. From a strictly anatomical viewpoint, buttressed by other relevant features (such as the nest-type of wrens and dippers), this seemed eminently reasonable. However, more recent work based on the comparative study of nucleic acids in the various families strongly indicate that these conclusions were erroneous, and that the similar features shared by members of the different families are more the result of chance and convergent evolution than any true close taxonomic relationship.

Based on their DNA hybridisation studies, Sibley and Ahlquist (1990) concluded that mockingbirds and dippers were members of a large monophyletic assemblage, along with thrushes, Old World flycatchers and starlings. Mockingbirds (mimids) are a sister-group to starlings, while dippers are closer to thrushes and other members of the assemblage than they are to wrens. Wrens, by contrast, are closely associated with the New World gnatcatchers and gnatwrens, and not at all close to mimids or dippers. Later work by Sheldon & Gill (1996; see also Barker 1999) has supported Sibley & Ahlquist's additional suggestion that the creepers (*Certhia*) and nuthatches (*Sitta*) are successive sister-taxa to the wren/gnatcatcher assemblage.

The extraordinary and enigmatic Donacobius, whose eventful taxonomic career has included many return journeys between the wren and mockingbird families, as well as brief excursions in other directions, may very well be a member of neither family; its final taxonomic resting-place is not entirely clear but on DNA evidence it appears to be closest to the Sylvioids (Old World warblers and the babblers).

Thus the birds dealt with in this work are a very diverse group, not very closely associated with each other.

WRENS

The largest family covered in this book are the wrens, comprising between seventy-five and about ninety species, depending on the taxonomy of different authorities. We have recognised eighty-three species, giving reasons for this treatment.

There is an opinion widespread among birdwatchers that wrens are small, brown and uninteresting. It is indeed true that wrens are small; the Giant Wren of southern Mexico is the size of a thrush and the only temperate birds lighter in weight than the smallest wrens are gnatcatchers, kinglets and a few warblers (Old and New World) and hummingbirds. Wrens do indeed eschew gaudy colours; they are plumaged variously in brown, white and black, although some of the tropical members of the genus *Thryothorus* have managed to use this combination to remarkably attractive effect. But they are most certainly not uninteresting. Within the diverse members of the family occur some of the most advanced and complex systems of social breeding to be found in the passerines, and in some species uniquely complicated and highly developed mutual singing patterns of the sexes (duetting) occur with regularity. The family has evolved to occupy a wide variety of ecological niches in habitats as varied as boreal and sub-arctic scrubland, coniferous forest, reed-beds, cliff-faces, cactus desert, rock-falls, arid scrub, dense lowland tropical rainforest and high-altitude montane forest. In the course of adapting to these different requirements the family has diversified in a remarkable manner, and has developed very different patterns of behaviour. At the one extreme we have the boisterous and conspicuous members of the genus *Campylorhynchus*, typified by a Cactus Wren belting out its apology for a song from the top of a street light in downtown Tucson; at the other, the obsessively stealthy Nightingale-Wrens, whose presence would rarely be detected but for a song of unearthly and ethereal beauty emanating unseen from dense lowland rainforest. Most wrens fall somewhere between these extremes. Typically they are highly active, enormously busy little birds, frequently difficult to observe but in many cases with musical (and sometimes stunningly beautiful) songs of a volume out of all proportion to the size of the singer.

16

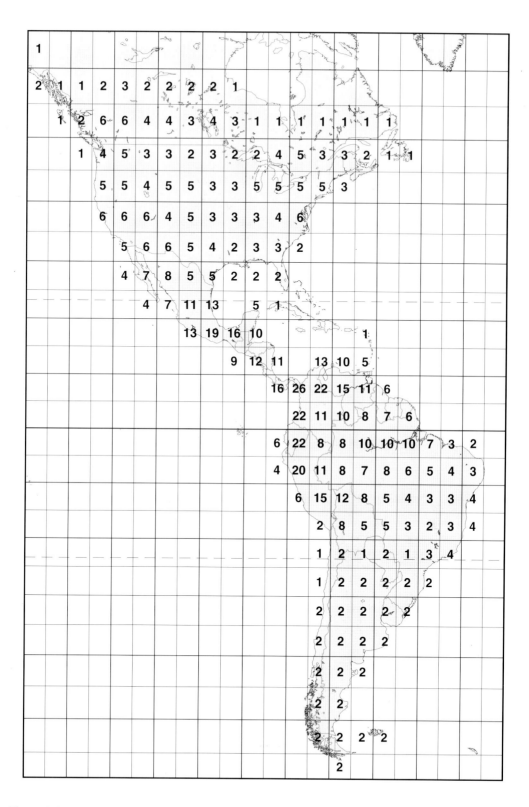

Figure 1. Species adundance of wrens.

The greatest diversity of wren species is to be found in Central America and northwestern South America. If we divide the New World up into blocks of five degrees latitude and longitude and then plot the number of species to be found in each block (a pretty crude technique, since it makes no allowance for the areas of the blocks shrinking as one moves away from the equator, nor for the amount of open water in a block [fig. 1]), some interesting facts emerge. Species diversity is greatest in the mountainous regions of both continents, as might be expected since different species have different altitudinal requirements. The number of species increases sharply as one moves down the Central American isthmus, reaching a total of over twenty in five-degree blocks in southern Panama and northern Colombia. To some extent this is a reflection of the fact that many species have a predominantly Central American or northern South American distribution, and in the Isthmus area they reach their southern, or northern, limits. Species diversity drops off sharply away from the western mountain chains as well as with increasing latitude; much of lowland Brazil is very poor in wren species, and South America south of the Tropic of Capricorn has only two. Rather remarkably most of the West Indies, including the largest islands which would seem to be prime wren habitat, have no wrens at all, the only species being the peculiar Zapata Wren found in a few square kilometres of Cuban swampland and the Southern House Wren in some of the Windward Islands. By contrast the Winter Wren in the Northern Hemisphere has managed to colonise the most remote islands in the North Pacific and North Atlantic Oceans.

The Winter Wren is the only species to invade the Old World, possibly in more than one colonisation. In the absence of competition from close relatives it has become very catholic in its habitat, being found in a variety of situations from low wind-blown scrub on oceanic islands to mountain forests in central Asia and semi-arid bush in the Mediterranean basin. It is also one of the most successful species of the family, having demonstrated an ability to adapt to habitats greatly changed by human activities, and in some areas, such as the British Isles, is one of the three or four most abundant birds. Conspicuous by virtue of its loud song, it has given rise to an abundance of folk-legend in almost all cultures.

The ancestral homeland of the wrens is clearly in the New World, but it is not proven, in the absence of any significant fossil record, exactly where. Geological evidence suggests that for most of the time during which passerines were evolving into approximately their present families, there was no land connection between the Americas; instead, a series of gaps existed at different times and in different places between the present Mexico and Colombia, the final continuous land connection only arising during the upper Pliocene period, about two million years ago. Based on studies of phylogeny, Mayr (1946) suggests an origin for wrens in southern North America (which had at that time a more tropical climate), followed by an invasion of South America when a route was available. More recent studies are somewhat equivocal on this score.

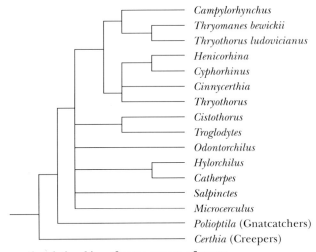

Figure 2. Phylogenetic relationships of some genera of wrens.

The relationships of different genera within the wren family has over the years been the subject of considerable, and sometimes contradictory, debate. Earlier work, based entirely on morphology, gave rise to the genus order used in Peters' *Check-list of the Birds of the World*. Intuitively, some groups are obviously closely related – for example the rock-creeping species of the genera *Catherpes* and *Hylorchilus* – but in many cases the relationships are neither clear nor obvious. In some ways the timing of this book is unfortunate, since at the time of writing much information (and some further controversy) is arising from ongoing biochemical studies; without doubt in the near future the evolutionary relationships of the wrens will be clarified and many outstanding questions settled. Figure 2 is a phylogenetic framework of some genera based on the studies of Dr F. K. Barker and kindly provided by him. Although not complete, due to unavailability of some material for study, it does illustrate some interesting features. The close relationship of *Hylorchilus* and *Catherpes* is confirmed, and preliminary evidence indicates that these genera form part of the earliest radiation of wrens, along with *Salpinctes* (another rock-dwelling species) and the forest understorey specialists of the genus *Microcerculus*. The short-tailed *Troglodytes* and *Cistothorus* are closely related but distant from the superficially similar *Henicorhina*, which is closer to the ground-dwelling *Cyphorhinus* and, more distantly, *Cinnycerthia*. Interestingly, the sole North American member of the large neotropical genus *Thryothorus*, the Carolina Wren, appears to be closer to the genus *Thryomanes*, which currently contains the temperate Bewick's Wren, than to the other members of the genus. The whole area of wren relationships is clearly in a state of flux and will doubtless shortly settle in a different form from that currently accepted. For the purposes of this book we have been forced to accept the current Peters ordering of genera and species (with a couple of obvious modifications, such as putting the Socorro Wren into *Troglodytes* from *Thryomanes* and bringing the Carolina Wren closer to Bewick's Wren), while at the same time realising that this treatment is very likely to be overtaken by current studies in the very near future.

MIMIDS

The family *Mimidae* contains some thirty-six species, the great majority of which fall into the categories of Mockingbirds and Thrashers, two groups which are relatively homogeneous. The mimids are clearly of North American origin; performing the same exercise of plotting the number of species per five-degree block (fig. 3) it is obvious that the greatest species diversity is found in the American southwest and in the Windward Islands, though species abundance in an area of numerous small islands is something of an artefact, since there are several insular forms which are not truly sympatric. Unlike the wrens, the mimids have successfully colonised the West Indies, a colonisation that is clearly of considerable antiquity since there are three very divergent and highly modified genera endemic to the area as well as several endemic species. Again in contrast to the wrens, colonisation of South America is incomplete and of relatively recent origin; mainland South America has only one breeding genus, *Mimus*, and seven species which closely resemble each other in plumage and habits. Some of the island groups west of the American mainlands have been colonised, sufficiently long ago for the insular forms to be generically separated: *Mimodes* on Socorro Island off Mexico and *Nesomimus* on the Galápagos.

Mimids are typically relatively large passerines, usually with long tails, heavy legs and strong, often decurved bills. Nests, with a couple of exceptions, are bulky open cups placed in vegetation, and in strong contrast to the wrens, breeding is 'conventional' – a pair, acting alone, raises a brood which then disperses. With one exception, 'helpers at the nest' do not occur, and the antiphonal or duetting song collaborations between the sexes which are such a feature of the behaviour of many tropical wrens do not exist. The exception to this rule is the genus *Nesomimus* in the Galápagos, where a complex breeding society involving many birds and group defence of territory has evolved, perhaps as a response to a harsh and rather variable habitat. The Galápagos group of mockingbirds has also developed some bizarre feeding habits found nowhere else in the family, or in the passerines for that matter.

DIPPERS

The family *Cinclidae*, the dippers, is completely unique among passerines in its distribution. We have here five very similar species, differing in plumage but with a remarkably homogeneous physical form, lifestyle, food, song and nesting behaviour, found in the same very specialised habitat on five separate continents. Dippers have been successful colonists; the only broad geographic areas where suitable habitat occurs, and they do not, are eastern North America, sub-Saharan Africa and the Antipodes. Where they are absent other species have learnt to exploit the food-supply of the family but without the unique adaptations of the dippers, and probably less efficiently. The geographical origin of the dippers is by no means a source of agreement among ornithologists. When it was believed that dippers were closely related to wrens, a New World origin was unarguable. Since recent evidence, however, clearly shows a closer relationship to the thrushes than to the wrens, this simplistic approach is on shaky ground. Based on the arguments of plumage, in 1905 Steineger surmised that the ancestral dipper stock arose in eastern Asia, crossing the Bering land-bridge and colonising the uplifting mountains of North and South America. By contrast, Sibley *et al.* (1974) suggest almost the precise opposite; that dippers arose in western North America, and invaded Eurasia via the Bering bridge and South America via the recently uplifted Panamanian isthmus. The fossil record is of no help in elucidating the geographic origins of the dippers, since there is none; the habitat of dippers is hardly conducive to fossil formation or preservation. What is clear is that the apparent physical similarities of wrens and dippers are the result of convergent evolution, not of a common close ancestry.

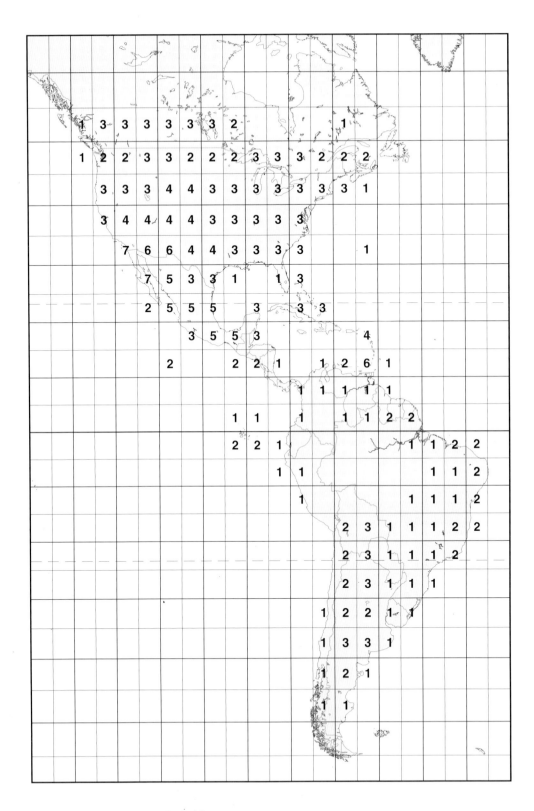

Figure 3. Species adundance of mimids.

CONSERVATION ISSUES

Given that the majority of the 124 species covered in this work inhabit Central and South America, an area where habitat modification and outright destruction is rampant, and that several forms are restricted to small islands, traditionally vulnerable faunistically, it might be expected that there would be some serious conservation issues. This is indeed the case, although several species with very restricted ranges do seem to be locally abundant and of no great conservation concerns.

There have been no known extinctions of full species in the wrens in historic times, but some races have been lost. Two insular subspecies of Bewick's Wren, *Thryomanes bewickii leucophrys* and *T. b. brevicauda*, formerly found on islands off the Californias, are gone, as is the Martinique race of Southern House Wren *Troglodytes musculus martinicus*. The race *Salpinctes obsoletus exsul* of the Rock Wren became extinct in the most spectacular manner in 1952 when its island home, San Benedicto in the Revillagigedo group, erupted catastrophically; this is perhaps one of the few recent extinctions for which Man can completely disclaim any responsibility! Virtually all the other conservation issues related to our species are man-made.

Two races of the Southern House Wren in the West Indies, *Troglodytes musculus guadelupensis* on Guadeloupe and *T. m. mesoleucus* on St. Lucia are in a very parlous state; indeed both were at one time believed already extinct, and their future will depend on prompt and effective conservation measures.

Also in the West Indies, the unique and highly aberrant Zapata Wren has a tiny population, probably below one hundred individuals, and a very restricted geographic distribution. Nevertheless there is good reason to hope its survival will be ensured by sensible (and perfectly feasible) conservation measures, involving mainly the suppression of fires in its habitat and the control of introduced predators. The recent discovery of an unsuspected population some distance away from the traditional areas is a hopeful sign.

In Central America, two unusual species of the genus *Hylorchilus*, Sumichrast's Wren (*H. sumichrasti*) and Nava's Wren (*H. navai*) are causes for worry. Both have tiny, fragmented geographic ranges which are largely or wholly unprotected and which could very easily be destroyed below the point of viability. Both are to a degree protected by the nature of their habitat, weird convoluted karst outcrops crowned by forests which are unattractive to agriculture, but the future of both species can only be assured with certainty by the acquisition and protection of adequate amounts of habitat

In South America, three species cause concern. In Colombia, Apolinar's Wren is found only in specialised lake-side habitat in the central region, most of it not far from the capital, Bogotá, an area under much pressure. The species has disappeared from several known sites and could easily be lost if the remaining locations are significantly changed. Again, the only certain solution appears to be the acquisition or formal protection of the few remaining locations.

Niceforo's Wren was found in 1945 near Bucaramanga in Colombia and not observed again until 1989. The population is obviously tiny, in habitat very vulnerable to destruction; without strong conservation measures the extinction of this bird is very probable.

Cobb's Wren of the Falkland Islands has obviously undergone a major contraction in its range due to the introduction of rats and cats and the destruction of its habitat by unwise grazing practices. Nevertheless it seems abundant on some of about thirty offshore islands. It would be highly desirable to exterminate alien predators from some other small islands on which it does not now occur, but the total elimination of rats from the large islands of the group would seem to be an impossible task.

It should be noted that some species of wren have very small ranges but nevertheless seem to be abundant, or at least reasonably common, in much of the range. Thus the Cozumel Wren is common on much of Cozumel Island; the Giant and Yucatan Wrens, each inhabiting a narrow coastal strip on opposite coasts of Mexico, are reasonably common; and the insular species in the Revillagigedo group, the Socorro and Clarion Wrens, seem at this time fairly secure. The Inca Wren, though found only in a small area of Peru, may actually be benefitting from some man-made habitat changes, and the Bar-winged Wood Wren of Ecuador and Peru is probably secure as a result of the remoteness of its habitat.

Several insular races of the Winter Wren fluctuate in an apparently alarming manner – the Fair Isle race *Troglodytes troglodytes fridariensis* has been as low as ten breeding pairs in recent years – but appear to be able to bounce back in a rapid manner.

Although the majority of the tropical, forest-specialising wrens of Central and South America are in no way endangered, major population losses of some species have occurred and continue to occur as a result of habitat destruction. Ranges are also fragmented as intervening areas of habitat are destroyed. This process is still continuing apace.

Among the mimids, all of the concerns relate to island species. Probably the saddest case is that of the Socorro Mockingbird; saddest because it was totally unnecessary, totally avoidable and happened quite recently when modern conservation values were in existence. Formerly one of the most common species on the island of Socorro in the Revillagigedo group, it suffered catastrophically after the establishment of a military garrison in 1957, which brought with them cats that were allowed to run wild. The species (the only member of its genus) is probably saveable with prompt action but it will be the nearest run thing.

In the West Indies, the White-breasted Thrasher *Ramphocinclus brachyurus* occurs as two races on the islands of St Lucia and Guadeloupe and is in a critical condition on both. Here the main causes appear to be the traditional ones of habitat destruction and introduced predators – in this case, mongooses, a problem not easily solved. Several other mimids have disappeared from some islands but remain reasonably common on others. There seems to be no recent information on the San Andres Mockingbird, found (along with an endemic vireo) on the tiny island of San Andrés, a location which is undergoing rapid development.

Most puzzling is the case of the Cozumel Thrasher; formerly abundant, it has become very rare following devastating hurricanes of 1988 and 1995. The habitat, however, does not look excessively damaged. There is plenty of it and no other endemic species has suffered in any permanent way. There is an urgent need for a comprehensive census of this species.

In the Galápagos Islands, the endemic mockingbirds generally seem to have withstood man-made changes reasonably well, with the notable exception of the Charles Mockingbird, which was eliminated from its main stronghold on Charles (Floreana) Island, probably by rats, and is now restricted to two small islands nearby. Given the natural fluctuations in population due to climatic and other changes the future of these populations is by no means assured; the large size of Charles Island would make rat elimination a difficult task.

The dippers are, by virtue of their requirement for unpolluted, clear, rushing water, (a commodity which mankind has a consistent tendency to muddy, contaminate or impound), inherently vulnerable. However, the only species which is in immediate hazard is the Rufous-throated Dipper of northern Argentina and adjacent Bolivia, with a population of about 1,000 pairs. Developments which would result in loss of water quality along a relatively few watercourses could make this situation critical.

Most of the other dipper species have shown range contractions as a result of watercourse degradation, but the only actual extinction is the loss some fifty years ago of the Cyprus race of the Eurasian Dipper *Cinclus cinclus olympicus*.

TOPOGRAPHY

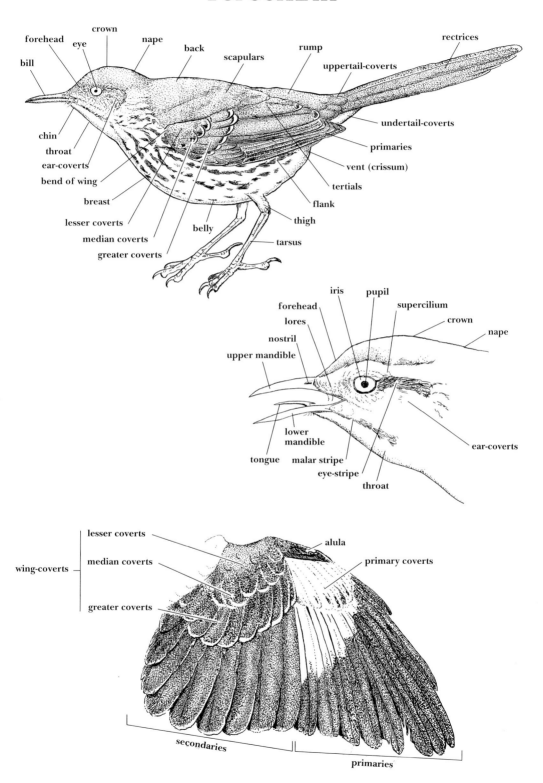

forehead
crown
eye
nape
back
scapulars
rump
rectrices
uppertail-coverts
bill
undertail-coverts
chin
primaries
throat
vent (crissum)
ear-coverts
bend of wing
tertials
breast
flank
lesser coverts
thigh
median coverts
belly
greater coverts
tarsus

iris
pupil
forehead
supercilium
lores
crown
nostril
nape
upper mandible

lower
mandible
ear-coverts
tongue
malar stripe
eye-stripe
throat

lesser coverts
alula
wing-coverts
median coverts
primary coverts
greater coverts
secondaries
primaries

4   Cactus Wren *Campylorhynchus brunneicapillus*   **Text and map page 92**

Arid brushland and desert, sea-level to 2,000m. South-western United States, northern and central Mexico.

    4a   **Adult female** (*anthonyi*; south-western United States from Texas to Arizona, northern Baja California) Very large; heavily spotted below, the spots coalescing to form a chest-patch; brown cap, prominent   supercilium; tail with conspicuous pale sides.

    4b   **Immature male** (*anthonyi*) Markings on chest less prominent, eye muddy grey-brown.

    4c   **Adult female** (*affinis*; southern Baja California) Paler than *anthonyi*; underparts less strongly marked.

    4d   **Adult female** (*purus*; northern Baja California) Smaller than *anthonyi*; underparts with little buff.

2   Spotted Wren *Campylorhynchus gularis*   **Text and map page 90**

Woodland, rocky slopes with palm trees, shrubland, 800–2,500m. Western and central Mexico.

    2a   **Adult male** White eyestripe; throat and chest whitish, with discrete circular black spots at sides of chest and flanks; lower flanks obscurely barred.

    2b   **Immature female** Underparts buffy without spots, eyestripe buff.

1   Boucard's Wren *Campylorhynchus jocosus*   **Text and map page 89**

Open dry forest and scrubland, 800–2,500m. South-western Mexico.

    1a   **Adult male** Dark cap, white supercilium. Throat white, chest and upper belly white with prominent black spots.

    1b   **Immature** Eyestripe buffy, underparts dull greyish, the spots much smaller and more diffuse than in adult.

3   Yucatán Wren *Campylorhynchus yucatanicus*   **Text and map page 91**

Low coastal scrub with scattered bushes and cacti, always close to the coastline. Northern Yucatán peninsula.

    3a   **Adult female** Crown blackish-brown, supercilium white, underparts off-white with longitudinal streaks, flanks with obscure darker bars.

    3b   **Immature male** More buff below, markings on underparts more diffuse.

PLATE 2: *CAMPYLORHYNCHUS* WRENS 2

5   **Giant Wren** *Campylorhynchus chiapensis*   **Text and map page 94**

Scattered woodland, bush and scrub, entirely within the coastal regions of the state of Chiapas, Mexico. Sea-level to 300m.

    5   **Adult female** Very large; unmarked black cap, rufous back, white chest; white supercilium.

---

6   **Bicolored Wren** *Campylorhynchus griseus*   **Text and map page 96**

Scattered bush and scrubland, northern Colombia, Venezuela. Sea-level to 2,100m.
Very large; unmarked black cap, brown back and white underparts (nominate race). Allopatric from *C. chiapensis*.

    6a   **Adult** (*bicolor*; western Colombia [Río Magdalena, Santander, Boyacá]) Darker on back than nominate race.

    6b   **Adult female** (*albicilius*; northern Colombia and north-western Venezuela) Lower back, rump and uppertail-coverts deeper rufous colour than in nominate.

    6c   **Immature** (*albicilius*) Generally duller than adult, underparts less pure white.

---

7   **Rufous-naped Wren** *Campylorhynchus rufinucha*   **Text and map page 97**

Arid or semi-arid scrubland; Mexico, on the western drainage from Colima south to north-western Costa Rica.

    7a   **Adult female** (nominate; Veracruz, Mexico) Strongly rufous on nape and shoulders, underparts white with small dark spots.

    7b   **Adult female** (*capistratus*; eastern Guatemala to Costa Rica) Underparts without spots, rufous on back more extensive than in nominate.

    7c   **Adult female** (*humilis*; western Mexico as far south as western Chiapas) Smaller than nominate, with solid chestnut-brown extending further down back.

    7d   **Adult** (*nigricaudatus*; Pacific coast from El Salvador to north-western Costa Rica) Larger than *humilis*, with streaks on back further reduced, tail appearing largely black from above.

PLATE 3: *CAMPYLORHYNCHUS* WRENS 3

8 Thrush-like Wren *Campylorhynchus turdinus*   Text and map page 99

Forest edge, clearings, second growth, palm groves, sea-level to 1,300m. Amazonia from southern Colombia to southern Brazil, disjunctly in coastal southern Brazil.

8a **Adult male** (nominate; eastern Brazil) Very large, dull scalloped brown on back, pale underparts with prominent spots.

8b **Adult male** (*hypostictus*; south-eastern Colombia to northern Bolivia and central Brazil) Underparts more heavily and more extensively spotted than in nominate.

8c **Adult female** (*unicolor*; eastern Bolivia and adjacent Brazil and Paraguay) Underparts largely unspotted, upperparts more grey-brown than brown, supercilium more pronounced.

9 White-headed Wren *Campylorhynchus albobrunneus*   Text and map page 100

Humid epiphytic forest, sea-level to 1,500m. Panama and north-western Colombia.

9a **Adult male** (nominate; Panama from the Canal Zone to western Darién) Unique plumage; pure white head and underparts, back blackish-brown.

9b **Adult female** (*harterti*; eastern Panama to west-central Colombia) Upperparts darker than in nominate, undertail-coverts more coarsely spotted.

PLATE 4: *CAMPYLORHYNCHUS* WRENS 4

13   **Grey-barred Wren** *Campylorhynchus megalopterus*   **Text and map page 105**

Mountain forests; pine, fir and oak, 2,100–3,150m. South-central Mexico.

13a   **Adult male** (nominate; western Mexican highlands) Largely greyish-black and white, back heavily barred, underparts prominently spotted.

13b   **Immature** (nominate) Very distinct; crown solid blackish, upperparts streaked buffy-brown, chest unspotted, diffuse barring on flanks.

---

11   **Fasciated Wren** *Campylorhynchus fasciatus*   **Text and map page 102**

Arid scrubland, sea-level to 1,500m, rarely higher. Western Ecuador and northern Peru. Allopatric from *C. megalopterus*.

11a   **Adult female** (nominate; southern Peru) Plumage largely blackish, grey and white. Back strongly barred, underparts prominently spotted.

11b   **Adult male** (*pallescens*; Ecuador and northern Peru) Generally paler than nominate, crown more blackish, markings on underparts more diffuse.

11c   **Immature** (nominate) Similar to adult female but markings more diffuse, cap darker.

---

10   **Stripe-backed Wren** *Campylorhynchus nuchalis*   **Text and map page 101**

Bush and open forest. Northern Colombia and Venezuela. Allopatric from *C. fasciatus* and *C. zonatus*.

10a   **Adult male** (nominate; eastern and central Venezuela) Strikingly marked with dull black and white, heavily barred on back and spotted below.

10b   **Adult male** (*pardus*; western Colombia) Underparts with less prominent markings than in nominate, bill heavier.

---

12   **Band-backed Wren** *Campylorhynchus zonatus*   **Text and map page 104**

Varied forest types; lowland humid forest to high-altitude pine and epiphytic woodlands. Sea-level to 3,000m.
Upperparts with heavy black barring, chest prominently spotted, flanks and belly rich cinnamon (nominate race).

12a   **Adult male** (*vulcanius*; southern Mexico to Nicaragua) Differs from nominate race in having weaker buff on underparts, bars on back more narrow.

12b   **Adult male** (*brevirostris*; northern and north-central Colombia, disjunctly in western Ecuador) Belly much paler than in nominate race; marks on underparts more extensive and more brown rather than black.

12c   **Immature male** (*restrictus*; Mexico from southern Veracruz, Oaxaca and Campeche to Belize and Guatemala) Differs from adult in having a capped appearance, streaked buffish rather than barred blackish back, no spots on chest and belly much weaker in colour.

13a

11a

11b

13b

11c

10a

12a

10b

12b

12c

PLATE 5: *ODONTORCHILUS* WRENS, ROCK AND CANYON WRENS

15   **Grey-mantled Wren** *Odontorchilus branickii*   **Text and map page 107**

Humid subtropical and upper tropical forest, 1,400–2,200m, southern Colombia, Ecuador, Peru and Bolivia.

15   **Adult male** (nominate; southern Andes of Colombia, Ecuador, Peru and Bolivia) Very slight and long-tailed; plain grey above, white below, crown tawny-brown, tail grey with blackish bars.

---

14   **Tooth-billed Wren** *Odontorchilus cinereus*   **Text and map page 106**

Lowland forest of western Amazonian Brazil; near sea-level to 500m.
Allopatric from *O. branickii*.

14   **Adult male** Differs from *O. branickii* by having a more brownish-grey back, and a buff-tinged throat and breast.

---

17   **Canyon Wren** *Catherpes mexicanus*   **Text and map page 110**

Rocky canyons, rarely sea-cliffs. Western Canada, western United States south to southern Mexico.

17a   **Adult male** (*conspersus*; southern British Colombia to north-western Mexico) Warm rusty-brown underparts with white throat and upper chest, grey-brown head and warm brown back with fine whitish-buff speckles. Long decurved bill.

17b   **Adult female** (*albifrons*; northern Mexico) More grey-brown above than *conspersus* with narrower rectrix bars.

17c   **Adult male** (nominate; Central and southern Mexico) Larger and darker than *conspersus*.

---

16   **Rock Wren** *Salpinctes obsoletus*   **Text and map page 108**

Barren rocky areas. Western Canada to Mexico, Guatemala and Costa Rica. Sea-level to 3,500m.

16a   **Adult male** (nominate; western Canada to southern Mexico) Grey-brown above, becoming warm chestnut-brown on rump; tail with prominent buff corners. Underparts dull grey with obscure streaking.

16b   **Immature female** (nominate) Duller than adult with reduced markings on underparts and obscure barring on back.

16c   **Adult female** (*guttatus*; El Salvador to Costa Rica) Heavily barred above and below.

16d   **Immature male** (*guttatus*) Markings on underparts less well defined, wing coverts with grey-buff spots.

16e   **Adult male** (*guadeloupensis*; Guadelupe Island, off Baja California) Darker than nominate with heavier bill and longer tarsi.

15

14

17b

17a

16c

16d

17c

16e

16a

16b

18   Sumichrast's Wren *Hylorchilus sumichrasti*   **Text and map page 112**

Forest on karst limestone, southern Mexico.

    18   **Adult male** Plump, long-billed; dark brown with white speckles on lower belly.

---

22   Peruvian Wren *Cinnycerthia peruana*   **Text and map page 116**

Wet mountain forest and forest-edge, 1,500–3,300m, Andean Peru.

    22a   **Adult male** More rufescent than *C. olivascens*; post-ocular area more prominent.

    22b   **Adult male** With white facial plumage.

    22c   **Adult male** With white head.

---

20   Rufous Wren *Cinnycerthia unirufa*   **Text and map page 114**

Wet mountain forests from Colombia to northern Peru, 2,200–3,800m.

    20a   **Adult female** (nominate; western Venezuela to central Colombia) Medium to large size, plumage entirely chestnut-brown, more reddish on lower back and rump.

    20b   **Adult female** (*unibrunnea*; western Colombia through Ecuador to northern Peru) Darker and duller than nominate race.

    20c   **Immature** (*unibrunnea*) Barring on wings and tail less pronounced than in adult.

---

19   Nava's Wren *Hylorchilus navai*   **Text and map page 113**

Forest on karst limestone, southern Mexico.
Allopatric from *H. sumichrasti*.

    19   **Adult male** Differs from *H. sumichrasti* by having a much paler throat and upper chest.

---

21   Sharpe's Wren *Cinnycerthia olivascens*   **Text and map page 115**

Wet mountain forest and cloud forest, from central Colombia south to northern Peru, mostly 1,500–3,100m.

    21   **Adult male** (nominate; western Colombia, Ecuador to northern Peru) Darker and less rufous than *C. unirufa*, with barring on wings and tail more prominent.

---

23   Fulvous Wren *Cinnycerthia fulva*   **Text and map page 117**

Wet mountain forest, 1,500–3,300m, central Peru to central Bolivia.

    23a   **Adult male** (nominate; central Peru) Prominent pale supercilium, more obvious than other members of the genus.

    23b   **Adult male** (nominate) With white facial plumage.

    23c   **Adult male** (*fitzpatricki*; Cordillera de Villabamba, Peru) Crown darker and supercilium paler than in nominate race.

    23d   **Adult male** (*gravesi*; southern Peru to Bolivia) Paler below than nominate race.

18

22b

22a

22c

20c

20b

21

19

23c

23b

23a

23d

20a

PLATE 7: MARSH, SEDGE AND GRASS WRENS

27   **Marsh Wren** *Cistothorus palustris*   **Text and map page 124**

Reed-beds in standing water. North America and central Mexico.
Prominent whitish supercilium, black and white longitudinal streaks on shoulders (nominate race).

> **27a**   **Adult female** (*plesius*; south-eastern Idaho to New Mexico) Underparts paler and duller than adjacent races, crown duller and nape more brown.
>
> **27b**   **Adult male** (*dissaeptus*; southern Ontario to New England, Ohio and West Virginia) Differs from nominate race in having sides and flanks dull brownish, not barred or spotted.
>
> **27c**   **Adult male** (*paludicola*; south-western Washington, north-western Oregon) Darker than *plesius* with more extensive black on crown.

24   **Sedge Wren** *Cistothorus platensis*   **Text and map page 118**

Damp sedge meadows, dry grasslands, flooded forest, *páramo*. North, Central and South America, sea-level to 4,000m.

> **24a**   **Adult** (nominate; Eastern Argentina) Small, short-tailed. with streaks on shoulders (less conspicuous than in *C. palustris*) and rather obscure buff supercilium. Crown darker than in North American races (e.g. *stellaris*).
>
> **24b**   **Adult male** (*stellaris*; eastern North America from southern Canada to Mississippi and Kentucky) Smaller than Marsh Wren, lacks the prominent supercilium; streaks on shoulders much less conspicuous.
>
> **24c**   **Immature female** (*stellaris*) Differs from adult in having reduced streaking on crown and back, and with paler underparts.
>
> **24d**   **Adult** (*alticola*; northern Colombia, northern Venezuela) Flanks darker brown and more rufescent than in adjacent races, supercilium less prominent.
>
> **24e**   **Adult** (*tamae*; eastern Colombia, south-western Venezuela) More rufescent than adjacent races.
>
> **24f**   **Adult female** (*lucidus*; Costa Rica and (formerly) Panama) Rump more cinnamon than in *stellaris*.
>
> **24g**   **Adult** (*aequatorialis*; high altitudes in Ecuador and Colombia) Supercilia broad and buff, heavier bars on rectrices.

26   **Apolinar's Wren** *Cistothorus apolinari*   **Text and map page 122**

Reed-beds around a few lakes in Colombia.

> **26**   **Adult male** Larger than sympatric *C. platensis* (race *C. p. tamae*), grey eyestripe, dingy grey underparts.

25   **Merida Wren** *Cistothorus meridae*   **Text and map page 121**

High-altitude *páramo* in western Venezuela.

> **25**   **Adult** Differs from sympatric *C. platensis* (race *C. p. alticola*) by having a paler and more pronounced supercilium, and heavier barring on flanks.

27a

27b

27c

24g

24c

24b

24d

24a

24e

24f

26

25

28   Bewick's Wren *Thryomanes bewickii*   **Text and map page 128**

Bushy areas, abandoned farmland and various types of brushland, sea-level to 3,000m. North America, mostly western, from British Columbia south to Oaxaca, Mexico.

28a   **Adult male** (nominate; eastern North America from Nebraska and Illinois south to Georgia and Alabama) A distinctive long-tailed wren, with obvious white supercilium and conspicuous white corners to the tail.

28b   **Adult male** (*calophonus*; south-western British Columbia to western Oregon) Sides and flanks stronger brown than in nominate.

28c   **Adult male** (*cryptus*; Central United States from south-central Kansas south to northern Mexico [Nuevo León and Tamaulipas]) Larger than nominate race, underparts whiter, upperparts more grey.

28d   **Adult male** (*leucophrys*; San Clemente Island, California) Larger and more grey than races on mainland. Probably extinct.

28e   **Adult male** (*spilurus*; California from San Francisco Bay to Monterrey County) Smaller and less brown than *calophonus*.

28f   **Adult male** (*correctus*; coastal California from San Benito to San Diego) Upperparts lighter brown than *spilurus*, tail longer.

28g   **Adult female** (*drymoecus*; south-central Oregon south to San Joaquin and Sacramento valleys, California) Somewhat larger than *spilurus*, and duller and paler.

28h   **Adult male** (*charienturus*; northern Baja California south to 30°N) Less brown than *drymoecus*, tail longer, bill shorter.

28i   **Adult male** (*marinensis*; north-western California) Brighter brown on back and flanks than *spilurus*.

28j   **Adult female** (*eremophilus*; Eastern California to western Texas, south to west-central Mexico) More grey above and white below than adjacent races.

31   White-browed Wren *Thryothorus albinucha*   **Text and map page 134**

Dry scrub and forest, Yucatán Peninsula, Guatemala, western Nicaragua.

31   **Adult male** (nominate; Yucatán and northern Guatemala) Prominent white supercilium, unbarred flanks, less rufous above than *T. ludovicianus*.

30   Carolina Wren *Thryothorus ludovicianus*   **Text and map page 132**

Varied habitat; woodlands, suburban gardens, abandoned farmland, etc. Eastern North America from southern Canada to north-eastern Mexico.

30a   **Adult male** (nominate; eastern North America from Ontario south to northern Florida) Warm rufous above and buff below, conspicuous white supercilium.

30b   **Adult male** (*lomitensis*; southern Texas and northern Tamaulipas, Mexico) Duller above than nominate, with paler underparts.

30c   **Juvenile male** (nominate) Generally paler than adult, wing-coverts with buff tips.

30d   **Adult male** (*miamensis*; Florida from 30°N southwards) Larger than nominate, upperparts a darker rusty chestnut, underparts more richly coloured.

28a

28b

31

28c

28d

28e

28f

28g

28h

28j

28i

30b

30a

30c

30d

PLATE 9: *THRYOTHORUS* WRENS 1

34   Black-bellied Wren *Thryothorus fasciatoventris*   **Text and map page 137**

Humid forest, sea-level to (mostly) 500m. Costa Rica, Panama and northwestern Colombia.

    34a   **Adult female** (nominate; Colombia south of Chocó) White chest, black belly with transverse white bars.

    34b   **Immature** (nominate) Chin and throat dull white, chest and belly brownish.

---

35   Plain-tailed Wren *Thryothorus euophrys*   **Text and map page 138**

Dense undergrowth in mountain woodland, mostly 2,000–3,300m, southern Colombia to Peru.

    35a   **Adult male** (nominate; southern Colombia, western Andes of Ecuador) Unbarred tail, prominent white supercilium and black malar stripe, spotted chest.

    35b   **Adult** (*schulenbergi*; northern Peru, south of Río Marañon) Larger and duller than nominate.

    35c   **Adult** (*atriceps*; northern Peru, north of the Río Marañon) Less spotting on chest than nominate, crown blackish.

    35d   **Adult male** (*longipes*; eastern Andes of Ecuador) Underparts more grey than in nominate, fewer spots on chest.

    35e   **Immature female** (*longipes*) Crown more olive-grey than in adult, throat more rufous.

---

33   Sooty-headed Wren *Thryothorus spadix*   **Text and map page 136**

Forest-edge, humid forest and cloud-forest, mostly 800–1,800m, extreme E Panama and W Colombia.

    33   **Adult** Diagnostic black face with white markings, black throat and unmarked chestnut chest.

---

32   Black-throated Wren *Thryothorus atrogularis*   **Text and map page 135**

Lowland forest and forest-edge, sea-level to 1100m. Costa Rica and western Panama.

    32   **Adult** Very dark, with black throat and chest and dark reddish-brown back.

---

38   Whiskered Wren *Thryothorus mystacalis*   **Text and map page 141**

Humid forest-edges, mostly 1,200–2,400m, Andes from central Venezuela through Colombia to southern Ecuador.

Large, prominent supercilium, facial markings and malar stripe; back bright chestnut (nominate race).

    38a   **Adult male** (*consobrinus*; western Venezuela) Bill more slender than in nominate, supercilia tinged buff, foreneck and chest more buffy.

    38b   **Adult male** (*saltuensis*; western Colombia) Differs from nominate race by having clearer grey crown, greyer chest and less distinct tail barring.

---

36   Inca Wren *Thryothorus eisenmanni*   **Text and map page 139**

Bamboo thickets, 1,830–3,350m, central Peru.

    36a   **Adult male** Similar to *T. euophrys*, but underparts much more heavily marked; tail with transverse bars.

    36b   **Adult female** Markings on underparts reduced, belly usually unstreaked, crown charcoal grey, tail usually without bars.

---

37   Moustached Wren *Thryothorus genibarbis*   **Text and map page 140**

Forest and forest-edge, sea-level to 1,500m. Amazonian Peru and Bolivia across Brazil to Atlantic coast.

    37a   **Adult male** (nominate; eastern Brazil) Sharply-marked facial pattern, white supercilium and moustachial stripe, black malar stripe.

    37b   **Adult female** (*bolivianus*; Amazonian Bolivia) Underparts deeply ochraceous, sides of neck darker grey than in nominate.

34a

34b

35a

38a

33

35b

38b

32

35c

36a

37a

35d

35e

36b

37b

40   **Happy Wren** *Thryothorus felix*   **Text and map page 144**

Dry deciduous forest, thorn scrub and open woodland, eastern Mexico.

  40a   **Adult male** (nominate; western Mexico from southern Jalisco to western Oaxaca) Medium-sized; warm rufous-brown above, well-marked facial pattern, warm buff underparts. See *T. sinoloa* (Plate 12).

  40b   **Adult male** (*pallidus*; north-western Mexico from central Sinaloa to Michoacán) Smaller than nominate race, upperparts less rufescent, underparts paler.

41   **Spot-breasted Wren** *Thryothorus maculipectus*   **Text and map page 145**

Forest, forest-edge and plantations, sea-level to 1,300m, from north-eastern Mexico to northern Costa Rica.
Diagnostic; warm chestnut back and heavily spotted underparts (nominate race).

  41a   **Adult male** (*canobrunneus*; Yucatán peninsula and northern Guatemala) Paler than nominate race, pileum light cinnamon-brown.

  41b   **Immature male** (*canobrunneus*) Markings on underparts much less well-defined, diffuse markings on cheek.

39   **Coraya Wren** *Thryothorus coraya*   **Text and map page 142**

Wet forest and second growth, northern Amazonia.
Large, deep reddish-brown on back, heavily-marked face (nominate race).

  39a   **Adult male** (*cantator*; central Peru) Differs from nominate race in lacking white streaks on sides of head.

  39b   **Adult female** (*ridgwayi*; western Guyana, eastern Venezuela) Similar to nominate race but underparts deep ochraceous to bright brown.

  39c   **Adult female** (*griseipectus*; north-eastern Peru, eastern Ecuador) Chest pale grey with dark rufescent-brown flanks.

42   **Rufous-breasted Wren** *Thryothorus rutilus*   **Text and map page 146**

Thickets, forest edge, tall second growth, sea-level to 1,900m. Costa Rica and Panama, and eastern Colombia to Trinidad and Tobago.

  42   **Adult male** (nominate; northern Venezuela and Trinidad) Diagnostic; densely-speckled throat and face, bright rufous chest.

43   **Speckle-breasted Wren** *Thryothorus sclateri*   **Text and map page 147**

Dense undergrowth in semi-humid forest, 1,100–2,000m. Western Ecuador, northern Peru and central Colombia.

  43a   **Adult male** (nominate; southern Ecuador and northern Peru) Conspicuous facial markings and supercilium, heavily speckled or barred below.

  43b   **Adult male** (*paucimaculatus*; western Ecuador) Markings on underparts less prominent.

46 **Stripe-breasted Wren** *Thryothorus thoracicus* Text and map page 151

Lowland forest and forest-edge, eastern Nicaragua to central Panama.

46a **Adult male** Characteristic tear-drop shaped stripes on underparts.

46b **Juvenile** More russet above than adult, throat and chest greyish-brown with whitish stripes.

47 **Stripe-throated Wren** *Thryothorus leucopogon* Text and map page 152

Borders of secondary forest, eastern Panama, western Colombia, to western Ecuador.

47 **Adult** (nominate; Pacific slope of eastern Panama to northern Ecuador) Rufescent-buff chest, face and throat striped black and white.

49 **Rufous-and-white Wren** *Thryothorus rufalbus* Text and map page 154

Mostly dry deciduous forest, Central America, from southern Mexico, disjunctly southwards to Panama, northern Colombia and northern Venezuela.
Warm brown above, white below, conspicuous supercilium and facial markings (nominate race).

49a **Adult male** (*castanonotus*; Nicaragua, Costa Rica, western Panama) Similar to nominate race but upperparts lighter rufous, flanks grey.

49b **Immature female** (*castanonotus*) Facial markings more obscure, underparts less pure white.

49c **Adult** (*cumanensis*; northern Venezuela) Similar to nominate race but generally paler.

48 **Banded Wren** *Thryothorus pleurostictus* Text and map page 153

Scrub, second growth and tropical deciduous forest, from central Mexico to north-western Costa Rica.
Diagnostic dark bars on flanks (nominate race).

48a **Adult male** (*ravus*; western Nicaragua to western Costa Rica) Smaller than nominate race, brighter above, barring on wings less prominent.

48b **Immature** (*ravus*) Facial markings reduced, bars on flanks absent.

50 **Niceforo's Wren** *Thryothorus nicefori* Text and map page 156

Tiny range in dry scrubland in eastern central Colombia.

50 **Adult male** Similar to *T. rufalbus*, but back much less rufous.

44 **Bay Wren** *Thryothorus nigricapillus* Text and map page 148

Humid forest-edge and second growth, sea-level to 1,200m, central Nicaragua to southern Ecuador.

44a **Adult male** (nominate; western Ecuador) Black cap, white facial markings and barred underparts.

44b **Adult female** (*costaricensis*; Nicaragua to western Panama) Lacks barring on underparts.

44c **Immature female** (*costaricensis*) Generally duller in colour than adult.

45 **Riverside Wren** *Thryothorus semibadius* Text and map page 150

Dense forest and wet woodland, south-eastern Costa Rica and north-western Panama.

45 **Adult** Bright chestnut upperparts, barred wings and tail, ear-coverts streaked black and white, underparts heavily barred.

46a

46b

47

49a

48a

48b

49b

49c

44b

44c

50

44a

45

51   Sinaloa Wren *Thryothorus sinaloa*   Text and map page 157

Scrubland, tropical deciduous forest and scattered bush, sea-level to 2,000m. Western Mexico from southern Sonora to Oaxaca.

> **51   Adult female** (nominate; north-western Mexico south to Michoacán) Unmarked pale underparts, prominent supercilium, obscure facial markings (compare with *T. felix*).

52   Plain Wren *Thryothorus modestus*   Text and map page 158

Forest-edge, overgrown farmland, sea-level to 2,000m. Southern Mexico to central Panama.

> **52   Adult male** (nominate; southern Mexico to Costa Rica) Rather featureless, lacking prominent markings apart from obvious plain supercilium (compare with *Uropsila leucogastra*).

53   Canebrake Wren *Thryothorus zeledoni*   Text and map page 159

Scrubby second-growth and wild cane-brakes, Caribbean coast from Nicaragua to western Panama.

> **53   Adult male** Larger than *T. modestus*, the upperparts less rufous and more grey.

54   Buff-breasted Wren *Thryothorus leucotis*   Text and map page 160

Forest, forest-edge, sea-level to 950m. Northern South America from Colombia to south-central Brazil. Warm brown above, buff below, white supercilium (nominate race).

> **54a   Adult male** (*conditus*; islands off Panama) Larger than nominate race, deeper in colour.
>
> **54b   Adult male** (*venezuelanus*; northern Colombia and western Venezuela) Less rufescent than nominate race, paler underneath.

55   Superciliated Wren *Thryothorus superciliaris*   Text and map page 161

Dry woodland, arid scrub and brushy areas, sea-level to 1,850m; western-central Ecuador and north-western Peru.

> **55a   Adult** (nominate; western Ecuador south to Guayas) Prominent white supercilium, white chest and throat.
>
> **55b   Adult** (*baroni*; southern Ecuador and northern Peru) More rufescent than nominate, back and rump brighter tawny.

56   Fawn-breasted Wren *Thryothorus guarayanus*   Text and map page 162

Thickets near water, forest-edge, near sea-level to 400m. Eastern Bolivia and south-western Brazil.

> **56a   Adult male** Brown and rufescent-brown above, ear-coverts marked with blackish-grey and whitish, chest and belly orange-buff (compare with allopatric *T. leucotis*).
>
> **56b   Immature male** Facial pattern more obscure.

57   Long-billed Wren *Thryothorus longirostris*   Text and map page 163

Secondary forest and forest-edge, sea-level to 900m, eastern Brazil.

> **57a   Adult male** (nominate; south-eastern Brazil) Rufescent-brown above, reddish-buff below with white throat, prominent supercilium, obscure cheek markings and long bill.
>
> **57b   Adult male** (*bahiae*; north-eastern Brazil) Paler than nominate race.

58   Grey Wren *Thryothorus griseus*   Text and map page 164

Tangled undergrowth at forest-edge and in clearings , near sea-level to 200m, western Brazil.

> **58   Adult female** Diagnostic; grey without any brown or chestnut, short barred tail.

59   Winter Wren *Troglodytes troglodytes*   Text and map page 165

Very varied in habitat, from suburban gardens to boreal forest and low brush on oceanic islands. Northern North America, most of temperate Europe including many isolated islands, North Africa, Middle East, Central Asia, east to Japan and Taiwan.

59a   **Adult male** (nominate; Europe, from Scandinavia east to the Ural Mountains, south to Spain, Italy and Greece) Small, very short-tailed, dark brown or rufescent brown with barred flanks. Compare with *T. aedon, Cistothorus platensis* and *C. palustris.*

59b   **Adult male** (*hiemalis*; eastern North America from Newfoundland west to Alberta and south to Georgia) More reddish-brown, pale throat.

59c   **Immature male** (*hiemalis*) Barring on flanks less distinct, some mottling on breast.

59d   **Adult male** (*pacificus*; western North America from south-western Alaska to California) Throat rufous-brown, short bill.

59e   **Adult female** (*kiskensis*; Kiska and Little Kiska Islands, Alaska) Underparts light, with little rufescent.

59f   **Adult** (*zetlandicus*; Shetland Islands) Darker above and below than mainland races.

59g   **Immature male** (*indigenus*; British Isles except western Scotland, Hebrides and other island groups with endemic races) Duller and darker above than nominate race, less rufous.

59h   **Adult female** (*fumigatus*; southern Kurile Islands, Russia/Japan) Darker than adjacent races, bill short.

59i   **Adult** (*hirtensis*; St. Kilda, Outer Hebrides) Substantially larger, more grey-brown above and paler below than mainland races.

59j   **Adult male** (*alascensis*; Pribilof Islands, Alaska) Rather larger than adjacent mainland race, upperparts medium-brown, throat and breast medium pale-brown.

59k   **Adult male** (*tianschianicus*; Central Asia from north-eastern Iran to Chinese Turkestan) Distinctly paler and more grey than adjacent races.

59l   **Adult** (*cypriotes*; Cyprus) Bars on flanks heavier and more obvious.

59a

59k

59b

59c

59d

59e

59f

59g

59h

59i

59j

59l

PLATE 14: HOUSE WRENS

60 **Northern House Wren** *Troglodytes aedon* **Text and map page 169**

Varied habitats, sea-level to 3,000m. Canada and United States.

60a **Adult male** (nominate; eastern North America) Grey-brown above, rufous-buff below, long tail.

60b **Adult male** (*parkmanii*; western Ontario to British Columbia, south to Baja California) Larger than nominate race, more pale below and more grey above.

60c **Immature** (*parkmanii*) Differs from adult by dusky mottling on breast and less distinct barring on flanks.

---

61 **Brown-throated Wren** *Troglodytes brunneicollis* **Text and map page 171**

Mountain woodland, 1,600–3,000m, southern Arizona to south-central Mexico.

61a **Adult female** (nominate; central and southern Mexico) More rusty than *T. musculus*, buff supercilium.

61b **Adult female** (*cahooni*; Arizona to north-central Mexico) Greyer above and paler below than nominate.

---

62 **Southern House Wren** *Troglodytes musculus* **Text and map page 172**

Varied habitats, sea-level to 4,000m. Southern Mexico, Central and South America, some islands in West Indies.
Nominate race is more warmly rufous than *T. aedon* with buffy eyestripe.

62a **Adult male** (*mesoleucus*; St Lucia) Very pale below, rufescent above.

62b **Adult male** (*tobagensis*; Tobago, West Indies) Paler underparts than nominate.

62c **Adult male** (*intermedius*; Mexico to Costa Rica) Ventral surface deep cinnamon-buff.

62d **Adult male** (*guadeloupensis*; Guadeloupe, West Indies) Smaller and more rufescent than adjacent island races.

62e **Adult female** (*martinicensis*; Martinique, West Indies [probably extinct]) Upperparts dark brown, narrowly lined with black.

62f **Adult female** (*rufescens*; Dominica, West Indies) Crissum with black bars.

62g **Adult male** (*albicans*; south-western Colombia and western Ecuador) Sandy-coloured underparts.

62h **Adult male** (*puna*; Peru and north-western Bolivia) Larger than nominate race, underparts deeper cinnamon-buff.

62i **Adult female** (*columbae*; eastern Colombia and western Venezuela) Upperparts dark greyish-brown with fine dusky bars.

62j **Adult male** (*atacamensis*; northern Chile) Upperparts pale with barring reduced.

62k **Adult female** (*striatulus*; western Colombia) Large, whitish underparts, greyish-brown above.

62l **Immature** (*striatulus*)

62m **Adult male** (*chilensis*; southern Chile and Argentina) Pale underparts.

60b

60c

61b

61a

60a

62b

62a

62d

62c

62e

62f

62h

62i

62g

62m

62j

62k

62l

70   **Rufous-browed Wren** *Troglodytes rufociliatus*   **Text and map page 181**

Mountain forest and epiphytic forest, southern Mexico to Nicaragua, mostly 1,700–3,500m.

> **70a**   **Adult female** (nominate; eastern Guatemala to El Salvador) Warm rufous-brown face with conspicuous supercilium.

> **70b**   **Adult male** (*nannoides*; Volcán Santa Ana, El Salvador) Darker above than nominate race, with heavier barring on flanks.

69   **Ochraceous Wren** *Troglodytes ochraceus*   **Text and map page 180**

Humid mountain forest with extensive epiphytic growth, mostly 900–2,450m, Costa Rica to western Panama, disjunctly in eastern Panama.

> **69a**   **Adult male** (nominate; Costa Rica [Cordilleras de Tilarán and Talamanca]) Richly-coloured face, ochraceous supercilium.

> **69b**   **Adult female** (*ligea*; mountains of western Panama) Duller than nominate race, bill heavier.

67   **Mountain Wren** *Troglodytes solstitialis*   **Text and map page 179**

Humid forest, forest-edge and cloud-forest, Andes from Colombia and Venezuela to northwestern Argentina.

> **67a**   **Adult female** (nominate; Southern Colombia, Ecuador and north-western Peru) Warm buff below, conspicuous supercilium.

> **67b**   **Adult female** (*frater*; southern Peru, Bolivia) Supercilia white or whitish-buff.

> **67c**   **Adult male** (*macrourus*; eastern Peru) Larger than nominate race, centre of belly whitish.

71   **Tepui Wren** *Troglodytes rufulus*   **Text and map page 182**

Tepui mountain-slopes of Venezuela and western Guyana, 1,000–2,800m.
Relatively large, intensely-coloured with conspicuous buff supercilium (nominate race).

> **71a**   **Adult female** (*wetmorei*; Cerro de la Neblina, Venezuela) Similar to nominate race; centre of belly whitish.

> **71b**   **Adult** (*fulvigularis*; south-eastern Bolívar, Venezuela) Darker and less rufous than nominate race.

68   **Santa Marta Wren** *Troglodytes monticola*   **Text and map page 180**

Páramo and high-altitude forest, upper levels of Volcán Santa Marta, Colombia.

> **68**   **Adult** Warm buff supercilium, buffy-white eye-ring, flanks with dark brown bars.

70a

69b

69a

70b

67a

67b

67c

71a

71b

68

PLATE 16: *TROGLODYTES* WRENS, ZAPATA & WHITE-BELLIED WRENS

29   Zapata Wren *Ferminia cerverai*   Text and map page 130

Marshland, Ciénaga de Zapata, Cuba.

> **29**   **Adult male** Unique; large size, long tail, prominently barred upperparts.

---

63   Clarion Wren *Troglodytes tanneri*   Text and map page 175

Scrub and cactus bush on Isla Clarión, Mexico.

> **63**   **Adult male** Large, greyish, only wren in its range.

---

64   Cozumel Wren *Troglodytes beani*   Text and map page 175

Scrub and low woodland, Cozumel Island, Yucatán Peninsula.

> **64**   **Adult male** Paler below than *T. musculus*; only wren in its range.

---

65   Cobb's Wren *Troglodytes cobbi*   Text and map page 176

Tussac grasslands, islets in Falklands archipelago.

> **65**   **Adult male** Large, grey face and sides of head.

---

66   Socorro Wren *Troglodytes sissonii*   Text and map page 178

Woodlands and brushy hillsides, Socorro Island, Revillagigedo group, western Mexico.
Only wren on Socorro Island.

> **66**   **Adult female** Grey-brown above, pale supercilium, no white edges to tail.

---

73   White-bellied Wren *Uropsila leucogastra*   Text and map page 184

Woodland, both dry and moist; from sea-level to 500m.

> **73a** **Adult male** (nominate; north-western Mexico from Tamaulipas to Oaxaca) Small and
> featureless with pale supercilium and lores, short tail, unmarked above and below.

> **73b** **Adult female** (*brachyurus*; Yucatán Peninsula and Belize) Bars on tail better defined than in
> nominate, undertail-coverts barred dusky.

29

63

65

64

66

73a

73b

PLATE 17: TIMBERLINE WREN AND WOOD WRENS

72   Timberline Wren *Thryorchilus browni*   **Text and map page 183**

Forest-edge and *páramo* at high altitudes of Costa Rica and Panama, 2,800–3,600m.
Small, short-tailed, with prominent white supercilium and white on outer webs of primaries.

   72   **Adult female** (*ridgwayi*; Highlands of central Costa Rica) Larger than nominate race, deeper
             rufous-brown above.

---

75   White-breasted Wood Wren *Henicorhina leucosticta*   **Text and map page 188**

Low altitude tropical forest, sea-level to 1,100m, rarely higher. Eastern Mexico to northern Ecuador
and northern Brazil.
Small, stumpy-tailed, with white chest and prominent markings on cheeks (nominate race).

   75a   **Adult male** (*tropaea*; Honduras and Nicaragua) Differs from nominate race in having brown
             on cap.

   75b   **Juvenile male** (*tropaea*) Crown duller, breast less clear white, belly more grey.

   75c   **Adult male** (*hauxwelli*; southern Colombia, eastern Ecuador and northeastern Peru) More
             rufous above and darker rufous below than nominate race.

---

74   Grey-breasted Wood Wren *Henicorhina leucophrys*   **Text and map page 186**

Mountain forest, mostly 1,500–3,000m. Central Mexico, disjunctly through Central America to central
Bolivia.

   74a   **Adult female** (nominate; Peru, western Colombia, Ecuador except south-western and north-
             western sections) Small, stumpy-tailed, with grey chest, prominent supercilium and
             conspicuously-marked cheeks.

   74b   **Juvenile** (nominate) Facial markings more obscure than in adult.

   74c   **Adult female** (*collina*; central Costa Rica and western Panama) Paler on back than adjacent
             races.

   74d   **Adult male** (*capitalis*; Pacific slopes of southern Mexico and Guatemala) Centre of crown
             greyish.

---

76   Bar-winged Wood Wren *Henicorhina leucoptera*   **Text and map page 190**

Restricted to a few mountains in northern Peru and southern Ecuador, 1,350–2,450m.

   76   **Adult** Diagnostic double white wing-bars.

PLATE 18: NIGHTINGALE WRENS

77 **Southern Nightingale Wren** *Microcerculus marginatus* **Text and map page 191**

Lower levels of humid tropical and sub-tropical forest, sea-level to 1,700m, central Costa Rica, northern and western Colombia, north-western Peru and Amazonia.

> **77a** **Adult male** (nominate; western Amazonia from southern Venezuela to north-eastern Bolivia and north-western Brazil) Small, dark, with tiny tail and long bill, heavily scalloped below.
>
> **77b** **Immature female** (nominate) Crown and back with obscure dark barring.
>
> **77c** **Adult male** (*taeniatus*; western Ecuador) Scaly marks on underparts, upperparts deep rufous-brown.
>
> **77d** **Adult male** (*luscinia*; central Costa Rica to eastern Panama) Pale throat, rich brown back.
>
> **77e** **Immature** (*squamulatus*; north-western Venezuela and north-eastern Colombia) Scaly marks below.

78 **Northern Nightingale Wren** *Microcerculus philomela* **Text and map page 193**

Humid forest, sea-level to 1,200m. Southern Mexico to central Costa Rica.

> **78** **Adult** Small, very dark above and below, with tiny tail and long bill.

79 **Flutist Wren** *Microcerculus ustulatus* **Text and map page 194**

Dense wet mountain forests, 860–2,100m, southern and eastern Venezuela, north-western Brazil, western Guyana.
Very short tail. Rich chocolate-brown above, lighter below with darker edges to body feathers (nominate race).

> **79** **Adult male** (*duidae*; Cerro Duida, Venezuela) Paler above and below than nominate race; upperparts less rufous, underparts less amber.

80 **Wing-banded Wren** *Microcerculus bambla* **Text and map page 195**

Lowland rainforest, sea-level to 1,100m. Guianas, Venezuela and northern Brazil; disjunctly in Ecuador and Peru.
Diagnostic double wing-bar (nominate race). Allopatric from *Henicorhina leucoptera*.

> **80** **Adult male** (*caurensis*; eastern Venezuela) Upperparts brighter rufous than nominate race.

PLATE 19: *CYPHORHINUS* WRENS

81   Chestnut-breasted Wren *Cyphorhinus thoracicus*   Text and map page 196

Wet mountain forests, mostly 1,300–2,100m, Andes from Colombia disjunctly to Peru.
Similar in shape to *C. aradus*, but unbarred wings and tail, no bare skin around eye (nominate race).

   81   **Adult male** (*dichrous*; Colombia, disjunctly through Ecuador to northern Peru) Darker on
   head, wings and abdomen than nominate race.

82   Song Wren *Cyphorhinus phaeocephalus*   Text and map page 197

Lowland humid forest, from sea-level to 1,000m, from eastern Honduras through Central America to
southern Ecuador.

   82a   **Adult female** (nominate; western slopes in Colombia to southern Ecuador) Bulky body, bare
   blue skin around eye, bizarre arched bill, warm orange-brown chest.

   82b   **Adult female** (*infuscata*; Caribbean slopes of Costa Rica and western Panama) Darker above
   than nominate, especially on crown.

83   Musician Wren *Cyphorhinus aradus*   Text and map page 198

Lowland humid forest, from sea-level to 1,000m (usually lower), from the Guianas south through
Amazonia to northern Bolivia.

   83a   **Adult male** (nominate; Guianas, eastern Venezuela, north-eastern Brazil) Similar in shape to
   C. phaeocephalus, but orange on chest brighter, supercilium more orange, bare skin around
   eye less extensive, conspicuous collar of brownish-black and buff-white stripes.

   83b   **Adult female** (*salvini*; south-eastern Colombia and eastern Ecuador) Differs from nominate in
   having no collar; cheeks and auriculars uniform dark brown.

   83c   **Adult male** (*modulator*; Amazonian Bolivia and Peru) No collar, lighter above than *salvini*.

81

82a

82b

83a

83b

83c

PLATE 20: OLD WORLD DIPPERS

84 **Eurasian Dipper** *Cinclus cinclus*   **Text and map page 199**

Fast-flowing streams. Europe, North Africa, Asia south to Himalayas and east to Western China.

- **84a** **Adult male** (nominate; western Europe from Scandinavia south to Spain, Corsica and Sardinia) Unmistakable. Plump, dumpy shape, chocolate-brown above, chin, throat and chest gleaming white.

- **84b/c Adult male** (*persicus*; south-western Iran) Generally larger, greyer and paler than nominate race.

- **84d** **Adult male** (*przewalski*; mountains of western China, south-eastern Tibet and Nepal) Belly wholly dark.

- **84e** **Adult male** (*przewalski*) Dark variant.

- **84f** **Adult male** (*aquaticus*; central and southern Europe from Belgium to Greece and Poland) Broad band of rufous on upper belly.

- **84g** **Juvenile** (*aquaticus*) Quite distinct from adult; mottled dark grey and black above, underparts down to belly dirty white with blackish-brown speckles.

- **84h** **Adult male** (*gularis*; England, Wales, Scotland except Hebrides and western Highlands) Bright rufous belly-band.

- **84i** **Adult male** (*leucogaster*; Central Asia from northern Afghanistan to eastern Siberia) Distinctive Central Asian race; entire underparts white.

- **84j** **Adult male** (*cashmeriensis*; Himalayas and Nepal) Upper belly with pale shading.

- **84k** **Juvenile male** (*cashmeriensis*) Mottled grey and black above, dirty white below with brownish scaling.

---

85 **Brown Dipper** *Cinclus pallasii*   **Text and map page 202**

Fast-flowing streams, from Central Asia south to northern India, east to Kamchatka and Japan.

- **85a** **Adult female** (nominate; Japan, west to western China, south to northern Thailand) Unmistakable: shape and form similar to *C. cinclus*, but uniform brownish or chocolate above and below.

- **85b** **Adult female** (*dorjei*; south-eastern Tibet to northern Burma) Darker above than *tenuirostris*.

- **85c** **Immature female** (*dorjei*) Mottled grey-brown above and below. More rufous than immature of nominate race.

- **85d** **Adult female** (*tenuirostris*; Kazakhstan, Kyrgyzstan, Uzbekistan, northern Tibet) Generally rather paler than nominate.

- **85e** **Juvenile male** (*tenuirostris*) Less rufous than young *dorjei*.

84a

84b

84c

84d

84f

84e

84g

84h

84i

84j

84k

85b

85c

85a

85d

85e

86   American Dipper *Cinclus mexicanus*   **Text and map page 203**

Rushing streams, sea-level to 3,500m. North and Central America.
Uniformly dark grey above and below, paler on chin. Nominate race with brownish tinge.

> **86a**   **Adult male** (*unicolor*; western North America from Alaska to New Mexico) Lacks brownish tinge of nominate race, head and neck paler.

> **86b**   **Immature female** (*unicolor*) Differs from adult in having underparts extensively scalloped with greyish-white.

> **86c**   **Adult male** (*ardesiacus*; Costa Rica and western Panama) Substantially paler than races further north.

87   White-capped Dipper *Cinclus leucocephalus*   **Text and map page 205**

Rushing mountain streams, 1,000–3,900m. Western Venezuela to Bolivia.

> **87a**   **Adult male** (nominate; Peru and Bolivia) Unmistakable, but very variable. White cap and chest, black back.

> **87b**   **Immature male** (nominate) Pale tips to feathers of lower back, rump and belly; streaked breast feathers.

> **87c**   **Adult male** (*leuconotus*; Venezuela to Ecuador) White patch on back, white flanks.

> **87d**   **Immature male** (*rivularis*; Santa Marta mountains, Colombia) Differs from nominate race by having spotted throat and grey rather than blackish-brown plumage.

88   Rufous-throated Dipper *Cinclus schulzi*   **Text and map page 206**

Mountain streams, northern Argentina and southern Bolivia, 1,400–2,500m.

> **88a/b** **Adult male** Diagnostic rufous throat, remainder of plumage grey-brown, white flash on extended wing.

86a

86b

86c

87d

87c

88a

88b

87b

87a

PLATE 22: BLUE MOCKINGBIRDS AND CATBIRDS

92   **Blue-and-white Mockingbird** *Melanotis hypoleucus*   **Text and map page 211**

Open woodland, scrub and brushland, 1,000–3,000m. Southern Mexico, Guatemala and Honduras.

     92a   **Adult female** Unmistakable; blue above, white below, red eye.

     92b   **Immature male** Quite different from adult, dull blackish-grey above, underparts grey with variable amount of whitish markings.

---

91   **Blue Mockingbird** *Melanotis caerulescens*   **Text and map page 210**

Woods, humid forest, thickets and second-growth; sea-level to 3,000m.

     91a   **Adult male** (nominate; eastern and south-central Mexico) Totally blue with blackish mask and red eyes.

     91b   **Immature** (nominate) Quite different from adult; dull blackish-grey with little hint of blue.

---

90   **Black Catbird** *Melanoptila glabrirostris*   **Text and map page 209**

Scrubland, abandoned farmland, wood-edge. Yucatán peninsula.

     90   **Adult male** Unmistakable; the only jet-black mimid.

---

89   **Grey Catbird** *Dumetella carolinensis*   **Text and map page 207**

Scrubland, wood-edges, overgrown farmland. Southern Canada, northern and eastern United States, Bermuda.

     89a   **Adult female** Unique; soft grey plumage, blackish cap, chestnut crissum.

     89b   **Immature male** Crissum colour less intense, feathers loose and fluffy.

     89c   **Fledgling female**

93   **Northern Mockingbird** *Mimus polyglottos*   **Text and map page 212**

Brushland, abandoned farmland, suburbs. North America from southern Canada south to the Isthmus of Tehuantepec, Mexico; Bahamas and Greater Antilles.

93a   **Adult male** (nominate; eastern North America from the Maritimes to Florida, west to Nebraska) Large, long-tailed, conspicuous white wing flash and white sides to tail.

93b   **Juvenile female** (nominate) Similar to adult but with indistinct streaking on back; more heavily marked below.

93c   **Adult female** (*orpheus*; Bahamas, Greater Antilles east to the Virgin Islands) Smaller than nominate race, paler grey on back, little buff on underparts.

93d   **Juvenile male** (*orpheus*) Underparts with diffuse spots and streaks.

93e   **Adult male** (*leucopterus*; western North America from north-western Nebraska to the Pacific coast, south through Mexico to the Isthmus of Tehuantepec) Larger than nominate race, upperparts paler and with buffy tinge, underparts more buff.

94   **Tropical Mockingbird** *Mimus gilvus*   **Text and map page 213**

Open and semi-open country, sea-level to 2,500m. Central America (Isthmus of Tehuantepec southwards); northern South America, coastal Brazil, West Indies.

Distinguished from *Mimus polyglottos* by lack of white wing flash and lesser amount of white on tail (nominate race).

94a   **Adult** (*leucophaeus*; Yucatán Peninsula, Belize, Campeche and Tabasco, Mexico) Upperparts clear grey, extensive white on lateral rectrices.

94b   **Adult male** (*antelius*; eastern Brazil) Longer-tailed than nominate race, less white on rectrices, flanks more heavily streaked.

94c   **Adult male** (*tolimensis*; Colombia) Larger than nominate race, underparts whiter, upperparts paler grey.

96   **Bahama Mockingbird** *Mimus gundlachii*   **Text and map page 215**

Scrubland, woodland. Bahamas, islands off northern Cuba, Jamaica.

96a   **Adult male** (nominate; Bahamas, Turks and Caicos Islands, cays off northern coast of Cuba) Large, streaked flanks, dark whisker mask, no white wing flash.

96b   **Immature female** (nominate) Underparts obscurely streaked, malar stripe diffuse.

95   **San Andrés Mockingbird** *Mimus magnirostris*   **Text and map page 215**

Copses, orchards. Isla San Andrés (St Andrew Island), western Caribbean.

95   **Adult female** Much larger than *M. gilvus*, heavier bill.

PLATE 24: SOUTH AMERICAN MOCKINGBIRDS 1

98   **Long-tailed Mockingbird** *Mimus longicaudatus*   **Text and map page 217**

Arid brushland in western Ecuador and north-western Peru, sea-level to 2,000m.

     98a   **Adult male** (nominate; western Peru) Large, conspicuous facial markings with black malar stripe, small white patch at base of primaries; notably long-tailed.

     98b   **Immature male** (nominate) Differs from adult in having obvious dark markings on chest.

     98c   **Adult male** (*albogriseus*; western Ecuador) Smaller than nominate, with more white on tail and blacker ear-coverts and lores.

99   **Chalk-browed Mockingbird** *Mimus saturninus*   **Text and map page 218**

Suburban areas, open bushy areas, bushy scrub. Sea-level to (mostly) 1,000m, rarely to 2,500m; central Argentina north to Bolivia and Brazil; southern Guianas.
Brown back with obvious streaks, conspicuous broad pale supercilium, no white flash on wing (nominate race).

     99a   **Adult male** (*frater*, eastern Bolivia, Brazil from Maranhão south to Rio de Janeiro and Matto Grosso) Differs from nominate race in having a less buffy rump and generally more brown upperparts.

     99b   **Immature male** (*frater*) Iris grey or grey-yellow, supercilium less obvious, streaks on chest.

     99c   **Adult female** (*arenaceus*; eastern Brazil [Bahia]) Browner on back than nominate race, bill larger.

97   **Chilean Mockingbird** *Mimus thenca*   **Text and map page 216**

Scrubland and brushy areas, sea-level to 700m, Chile from Antofagasta to Valdivia.

     97   **Adult female** Most resembles *M. longicaudatus*, but smaller, shorter-tailed, browner above and more uniform buff below.

98c

99a

98a

99b

98b

99c

97

101 White-banded Mockingbird *Mimus triurus* Text and map page 220

Brushland, steppes with scattered bushes, etc. Sea-level to (mostly) 500m. Central Argentina, wintering north to Bolivia and southern Brazil.

101 **Adult female** Diagnostic large white wing patches and extensive white sides to the tail; unmarked brown back and rusty rump.

100 Patagonian Mockingbird *Mimus patagonicus* Text and map page 219

Arid and semi-arid bushy scrub, mostly below 500m. Southern Argentina, eastern Chile, wintering north to Bolivia.

100 **Adult female** Most resembles *M. saturninus*, but supercilium less obvious, back without streaks and narrow black malar stripe.

102 Brown-backed Mockingbird *Mimus dorsalis* Text and map page 221

Arid mountain scrubland, 1,700–4,200m, Bolivia and northern Argentina.

102a **Adult female** Differs from the partially sympatric *M. saturninus* in having more white on sides of tail, less streaky upperparts and large white patch on wing.

102b **Juvenile female** Chest diffusely spotted with brown, tertials and secondary coverts with rusty tips.

101

100

102a

102b

PLATE 26: MOCKINGBIRDS OF THE GALÁPAGOS ISLANDS

103 Galapagos Mockingbird *Nesomimus parvulus*   **Text and map page 222**

Scrubland and forest on most islands of the Galápagos except where occupied by one of the other species.

103a Adult male (nominate; specimen from Isabella) Large, greyish-brown with chocolate-brown ear-coverts contrasting with chin and supercilium.

103b Immature (nominate; specimen from Santa Cruz) Spotting and streaking on breast.

103c Adult male (*bauri*; Tower Island) Slightly larger than nominate race.

106 Chatham Mockingbird *Nesomimus melanotis*   **Text and map page 225**

Scrubland and semi-desert, San Cristobal.

106a Adult male Small bill, dark ear-coverts contrasting with pale throat, spots at sides of chest.

106b Immature female Underparts more heavily marked, tawny edges to back feathers.

105 Hood Mockingbird *Nesomimus macdonaldi*   **Text and map page 224**

Scrubland and seabird colonies, Hood (Española) Island.

105 Adult Larger than other species; bill longer, more robust and decurved; dark ear-coverts and diffuse malar stripe.

104 Charles Mockingbird *Nesomimus trifasciatus*   **Text and map page 223**

Arid scrubland, Champion and Gardner-near-Floreana.

104 Adult Diagnostic dark marks at sides of chest.

PLATE 27: GREY AND SAGE THRASHERS, SOCORRO MOCKINGBIRD

112 Grey Thrasher *Toxostoma cinereum*   Text and map page 233

Desert and semi-desert, sea-level to 1,500m, Baja California.
Distinctive combination of grey overall plumage with conspicuous blackish spots on chest and flanks.

    112   **Adult female** (nominate; Baja California south of 28°30' N)

108 Sage Thrasher *Oreoscoptes montanus*   Text and map page 228

Arid sagebrush areas; winters in various desert habitats. Western North America from southern British Columbia to northern Arizona; winters from California and Arizona to central Mexico.

    108a   **Adult** (worn plumage) Small, small-billed, heavily streaked below, with diagnostic white corners to tail.

    108b   **Adult** (fresh plumage) Upperparts with pale edgings.

    108c/d Juvenile Eye colour duller than in adult, wing-coverts and tertials with pale buff-brown edgings.

107 Socorro Mockingbird *Mimodes graysoni*   Text and map page 226

Woodland and scrub, Socorro Island, Revillagigedo group, Mexico. Critically endangered.

    107   **Adult male** Rather featureless, dull grey-brown above and buffy-grey below with no wing-flash. Diagnostic short bill.

76

112

108a

108b

108c

108d

107

110 Long-billed Thrasher *Toxostoma longirostre*   **Text and map page 231**

Woodland, mesquite thickets, scrubland. Southern Texas and northeastern Mexico.

> **110a** **Adult male** (nominate; north-eastern Mexico south to Veracruz) Rufous above, double whitish
> wing-bar, conspicuous blackish streaks on pale underparts; differs from *T. rufum* by grey sides
> to the head, orange eye and all-dark, longer and more decurved bill.
>
> **110b** **Adult male** (*sennetti*; Texas, Mexico south to San Luis Potosí) Larger than nominate, paler
> above and less rufescent.
>
> **110c** **Adult** (nominate) Head.
>
> **110d** **Adult** (*sennetti*) Head.

109 Brown Thrasher *Toxostoma rufum*   **Text and map page 229**

Brushy areas, abandoned farmland, orchards, etc. Eastern North America from New Brunswick south to
Florida, west to Oklahoma. Winters from New England southwards.

> **109a** **Adult male** (nominate, worn plumage; eastern North America from New Brunswick to
> Florida) Warm rufous-brown above, double white wing-bar, long rufous tail, conspicuous
> spotting on pale underparts; differs from *T. longirostre* by yellow eye, brown sides of face.
>
> **109b** **Adult male** (nominate, fresh plumage) Brighter; more prominent wing-bars.
>
> **109c** **Adult male** (*longicauda*; western part of range from western Ontario to Alberta, south to
> north-eastern New Mexico) Differs from nominate in more cinnamon-rufous upperparts,
> whiter wing-bars.
>
> **109d** **Adult** (*longicauda*) Head.

111 Cozumel Thrasher *Toxostoma guttatum*   **Text and map page 232**

Brush, low woodland. Cozumel Island, Yucatán Peninsula, Mexico.
Allopatric from *T. rufum* and *T. longirostre*.

> **111a** **Adult** Rufous above, heavily spotted black on white underparts.
>
> **111b** **Adult** Head.

110a

110b

109a

109c

109b

111a

110c

110d

111b

109d

PLATE 29: NORTH AMERICAN DESERT THRASHERS

115 Curve-billed Thrasher *Toxostoma curvirostre*   **Text and map page 236**

Dry areas, including different desert types, also oak and pinyon woodland, sea-level to 3,000m.

115a   **Adult male** (nominate; central and south-central Mexico) Uniformly grey-brown above, obscurely but extensively spotted below, pale corners to tail, orange eye, long decurved bill.

115b   **Adult male** (*celsum*; United States from south-eastern Arizona and southern New Mexico south to central Mexico [Jalisco]) Larger, more buff below, the pale corners of the tail more white.

115c   **Juvenile** (*celsum*) Feathers of lower abdomen and vent more fluffy in texture, rectrices with pale tips reduced or absent.

115d   **Adult** (*palmeri*; southern Arizona, northern Mexico. Spotting on underparts less distinct, pale on corners of tail reduced in extent.

115e   **Adult** (*oberholseri*; south-eastern Texas, north-eastern Mexico) General body-colour more slaty than nominate, wings and tail shorter.

113 Bendire's Thrasher *Toxostoma bendirei*   **Text and map page 234**

Arid country, from sea-level to 1,800m. South-western United States and north-western Mexico.

113a   **Adult female** Similar to *T. curvirostre*, but spots on chest smaller, better-defined and arrowhead shaped instead of round; eye usually paler yellow, bill shorter and less decurved.

113b   **Immature** Spots on chest usually smaller and less extensive.

116 Le Conte's Thrasher *Toxostoma lecontei*   **Text and map page 238**

Waterless desert, sea-level (and below) to 1,600m. South-western United States, north-western Mexico.

116a   **Adult male** (nominate; California, Nevada, Arizona, Sonora and northern Baja California) Diagnostic; very pale, unspotted, long decurved bill, dark eye.

116b   **Immature female** (nominate) Darker brown above than adult, feathers of underparts fluffy in texture.

115e

115b

115d

115c

115a

113b

113a

116a

116b

PLATE 30: OCELLATED, CALIFORNIA AND CRISSAL THRASHERS

114 Ocellated Thrasher *Toxostoma ocellatum*   **Text and map page 235**

Dry brushland of central Mexico plateau, 1,400–3,000m.

   114   Adult male Diagnostic: grey upperparts, heavy large circular black spots on underparts.

---

117 California Thrasher *Toxostoma redivivium*   **Text and map page 239**

Dry chaparral brushland from north-central California to central Baja California, sea-level to 2,000m.

   117a   Adult male (nominate; California, Monterrey Bay south to Baja California) Large, dark with
           cinnamon underparts, long decurved bill, brown eye.

   117b   Adult female (*sonomae*, California from Santa Cruz county northwards) Larger and darker
           than nominate; pale chest-band, belly darker.

---

118 Crissal Thrasher *Toxostoma crissale*   **Text and map page 240**

Brushland and valley bottoms from south-eastern California and western Texas to central Mexican
plateau. Sea-level to 2,500m.

   118a   Adult male (nominate; Arizona, southern New Mexico, western Texas) Diagnostic deep
           reddish-brown crissum, diffuse malar stripe.

   118b   Adult male (*coloradense*, south-eastern California, southern Nevada, south-western Utah to
           northern Mexico) Paler above than nominate.

114

117a

117b

118a

118b

PLATE 31: ENDEMIC WEST INDIAN MIMIDS

119 Brown Trembler *Cinclocerthia ruficauda*   **Text and map page 242**

Wet epiphytic forest, Lesser Antilles.

    119a Adult male (nominate; Dominica, West Indies) Browner than *C. gutteralis*, belly orange-brown.

    119b Adult male (*tenebrosa*; St Vincent, West Indies) Darker above than nominate race.

---

120 Grey Trembler *Cinclocerthia gutteralis*   **Text and map page 243**

Forest and scrubland, Martinique and St Lucia, Lesser Antilles.

    120 Adult female (nominate; Martinique) Unique in shape and habits (along with *C. ruficauda*). Sooty-grey above, grey below, pale chin, white or yellow eye.

---

122 Scaly-breasted Thrasher *Margarops fuscus*   **Text and map page 245**

Forests, open woodlands and settled areas, Lesser Antilles from Barbuda to Grenada.
Dark greyish-brown above, underparts off-white with brownish scallopings; obvious white wing-bar, extensive white on tail-feathers, white or yellow eye (nominate race).

    122a Adult male (*vincenti*; St Vincent) Differs from nominate race in having darker underparts with larger flank spots.

    122b Immature male (*vincenti*) Dark eye.

---

123 Pearly-eyed Thrasher *Margarops fuscatus*   **Text and map page 245**

Varied habitat, including woods of various types, scrubland, fruit plantations, suburban areas. Eastern Bahamas, Puerto Rico to St Lucia.
Large, streaky brown above, whitish below with coarse brown markings, yellow bill, whitish eye (nominate race). Compare with *M. fuscus*.

    123 Adult male (*densirostris*; southern Lesser Antilles) Darker on upperparts than nominate race, streaks on underparts broader.

119b

119a

122a

120

122b

123

PLATE 32: WHITE-BREASTED THRASHER AND DONACOBIUS

121 **White-breasted Thrasher** *Ramphocinclus brachyurus*   **Text and map page 244**

Dense thickets in semi-arid woodland, Lesser Antilles. Critically endangered.

121a **Adult male** (nominate; Martinique, West Indies) Unmistakable; striking contrast of white underparts with blackish-brown upperparts, dark ear-coverts and red eye.

121b **Adult male** (*santaeluciae*, St Lucia, West Indies) Larger and darker than the nominate race.

124 **Donacobius** *Donacobius atricapillus*   **Text and map page 247**

Marshlands and river-edge, sea-level to (mostly) 600m, South America from extreme eastern Panama to northern Argentina.

124a **Adult female** (nominate; Eastern Venezuela,the Guianas south through eastern Brazil to Paraguay and Argentina.) On nest. Unmistakable; large size, staring yellow eye, black cap, white wing flash and long white-tipped tail.

124b **Adult male** (*nigrodorsalis*; south-eastern Colombia to Peru) Darker above than nominate race.

124c **Adult** (*nigrodorsalis*) Dorsal view of tail.

124d **Adult female** (*brachypterus*; northern Colombia, Panama) Slightly smaller than nominate, rump paler, underparts lighter.

124e **Immature** (*brachypterus*) Generally duller. Crown dusky brown, underparts less bright yellow, brown edgings to back feathers.

124f **Adult male** (*albovittatus*; eastern Bolivia and western Brazil) Differs from nominate and other races by having a prominent white supercilium.

121b

121a

124f

124b

124d

124c

124a

124e

CAMPYLORHYNCHUS

The largest wrens, ranging from 16–22cm in length. Bills always moderately decurved, quite heavy and stout in some species, more delicate in others. Legs and feet heavy and powerful. Wings rounded, fifth to seventh primaries longest. Tail as long as wing, heavily rounded. Plumage usually brown, in most species heavily barred or spotted, with conspicuous eye-stripes. Nests (where known) domed, with an entrance in the side; eggs 2–6, unmarked to quite heavily speckled, on a buff, pinkish or dull white ground. 12 or 13 species according to taxonomy, ranging from Utah and Nevada to northern Paraguay; species diversity greatest in southern Mexico and north-eastern South America. Raucous, demonstrative and not at all secretive in behaviour. Songs in most species tend to be harsh and innocent of any hint of musical accomplishment; antiphonal song and cooperative breeding common, especially in tropical species.

Selander (1964), using morphological and ecological, rather than biochemical, data divides the genus into two groups. The *Heleodytes* grouping (using an obsolete generic name) consists of the Cactus, Spotted, Boucard's, Rufous-naped, Giant, Bicolored and Yucatan Wrens. They are primarily located in northern Central America and Mexico, with one species only in South America. Wrens of this group tend to be relatively short-winged and short-tailed, lay eggs with brown markings on a usually buff or pinkish ground, and tend to inhabit semi-desert, or at least arid, habitats. The *Campylorhynchus* group comprises the Grey-barred, Band-backed, White-headed, Stripe-backed, Fasciated and Thrush-like Wrens. These species are longer-winged and -tailed, lay eggs which, (where described), are whitish with either no markings or very light speckles, and tend to live in more humid zones, including rainforest. Many (perhaps all) of the *Campylorhynchus* group indulge in duetting or chorus song, and some, at least, nest cooperatively, with non-breeding birds assisting in the rearing of young.

1   BOUCARD'S WREN
Campylorhynchus jocosus   Plate 1

Campylorhynchus jocosus Sclater 1859 Oaxaca, Mexico.

Alternative name: Boucard's Cactus Wren; Spanish *Matraca alacranera, Matraca del Balsas*; Mixteco, *Lasimi*

Etymology: named after A. Boucard (1839–1904), a French collector and author.

An endemic Mexican species, quite common in certain locations in arid areas, less abundant in oak scrub and pine-oak forest.

IDENTIFICATION Length 16–18cm. Confusion with other species is unlikely; obviously a *Campylorhynchus* wren, with so far as is known no overlap in range or habitat with other members of the genus. Spotted Wren, which approaches the range of Boucard's Wren in central Mexico, is smaller, with a finer, shorter bill and with no spots on the belly.

DESCRIPTION
Adult Crown dark chocolate-brown; nape more rufescent. Shoulders dull blackish, with prominent longitudinal off-white streaks. Back reddish-brown with streaks reduced to scattered whitish spotting. Rump and uppertail-coverts dull rufescent-brown with obscure transverse bars. Rectrices grey-brown above with dull bars (broader at the base) of blackish-brown. Underside of rectrices blackish-brown, with conspicuous off-white bars, one on central rectrice, two or three on lateral rectrices. Outerweb of outer rectrix with four or five alternate blackish and white bars. Lores and area behind eye dull blackish, eye-stripe between eye and bill dull white, behind eye broader and whiter. Ear-coverts grey. Chin and throat unmarked white, chest and stomach white with prominent circular black spots, becoming larger on lower chest. Ground-colour of flanks and belly buffish, becoming deeper laterally. Markings on lower belly and thighs widen out to diffuse dull blackish bars. Primaries and secondaries dull blackish-brown with buffy-white markings on outerweb forming seven or

eight conspicuous bars on closed wing. Underwing dull whitish-grey. The spots on the underparts tend to be smaller in the female than the male (Selander 1964). Iris reddish-brown, bill black or dark brownish-black, pale bluish-grey at base of lower mandible, legs greyish-slate.
Juvenile Streaks on shoulders much less well-defined than adult; underparts dull greyish, spots much smaller and much less conspicuous than adult; throat with numerous dull blackish speckles. Crown dull black.

GEOGRAPHICAL VARIATION None; monotypic.

VOICE A series of grating notes repeated up to a dozen times, each note sometimes ascending slightly at the end, or descending; also a more rapid harsh chatter largely on one note. Both sexes sing in simultaneous duets (K. Barker pers. comm.).

HABITAT Various types of open forest and bush, generally of a dry or actually arid nature. In Oaxaca, common in arid subtropical scrub, less so in oak scrub and pine-oak forest (Binford 1989). In some areas found in association with scattered giant cactus of several species (Selander 1964). Sometimes in quite disturbed areas. Usually 800m to 2,500m, occasionally as low as 600m.

HABITS Forages from ground level to tops of trees and cacti, but generally less terrestrial than the Cactus Wren. On ground hops with tail held at a slight angle above the horizontal, when perched the tail is held down. Stated to be more wary than other members of the genus (Selander 1964).

STATUS AND DISTRIBUTION Fairly common in some parts of its restricted range, less so in others. Endemic to south-central Mexico, mostly within the states of Guerrero and Oaxaca, marginally in southern Mexico, Puebla and Morelos; records from the Federal District somewhat dubious (Selander 1964). Readily observed around the ruins at Monte Albán, Oaxaca (Wheatley & Brewer in press).

Boucard's Wren

and grey. Nest construction 10 April, nest with four eggs 14 June, nest with three eggs 8 July, nest and eggs 4 July Oaxaca (two specimens) (Rowley 1984); pre-juvenile 14 July (Binford 1989). Probably single-brooded. Incubation and fledging periods unknown. Apparently birds other than the breeding pair will help at the nest (K. Barker pers. comm.). One instance of parasitism by Brown-headed Cowbird *Molothrus ater* recorded (Rowley 1984).

FOOD Quite varied; invertebrates, but a substantial a-mount of vegetable matter is also taken. Stomach contents of various specimens taken in May consisted of 50% cactus seeds, as well as insect remains and several small pebbles (Selander 1964). The Spanish name *Matraca alacranera* suggests that it eats scorpions; whether this has any basis in fact is not known.

MOVEMENTS Apparently totally sedentary.

MEASUREMENTS (Guerrero State) (Means) Wing of male 73.1, of female 70.3; tail of male 67.9, of female 64.5; bill of male 16.4, of female 15.5; tarsus of male 22.9, of female 22.2 (19 male and 10 female specimens) (Selander 1964).

BREEDING No detailed description of nest recorded. Eggs three to four, whitish, densely speckled with brown

---

2 SPOTTED WREN
Campylorhynchus gularis

Plate 1

Campylorhynchus gularis Sclater 1860 'Mexico'.

Alternative names: Spotted Cactus Wren; Spanish *Matraca Manchada, Matraca Serrana*

A Mexican endemic, the Spotted Wren is found in a variety of habitats in the north-west of the country. It has from time to time been regarded as conspecific with Boucard's Wren, a larger and quite distinct bird.

IDENTIFICATION Length 16–18cm. It most closely resembles Boucard's Wren, from which it is distinguished in the adult plumage by having much less extensive spotting on the underparts (largely confined to the flanks and upper chest); the two species are in any case allopatric. The only *Campylorhynchus* with extensive sympatry is the Cactus Wren, which is larger, and has much heavier black markings on the chest. Juvenile Spotted Wrens are quite distinct from the adults, having essentially unmarked buff underparts; juvenile Cactus Wrens have fine darker markings over much of the chest and belly. In a limited area of central Mexico (for example in northern Michoacán) Spotted Wren is sympatric with Grey-barred Wren, which is totally distinct in adult plumage; the juvenile Grey-barred Wren has no malar stripe and indistinct barring on the flanks.

DESCRIPTION
Adult Crown chestnut-brown, shoulders and back rufescent-brown with broken transverse markings of dull black and buffy-white. Rump medium-brown with diffuse bars of dark brown and buff. Shoulders and wing-coverts rufescent-brown with bars of dull black and buff, with some lateral whitish streaking on shoulders. Primaries and secondaries dull grey-brown with alternating dark and buff markings on outerwebs giving a strongly barred appearance to the closed wing. Upper surface of tail

grey-brown with numerous narrow transverse bars on both webs; underside of outer rectrices dark brownish-black, broadly tipped with grey-white, the tips with two or three very diffuse greyish bars. Supercilium buffy-white, lores and area behind eye medium-brown, ear-coverts buffy-white. Chin, throat and chest off-white, narrow blackish malar stripe, chest with sharp circular blackish spots, more numerous on sides than centre, becoming bars on sides of lower flanks. Ground-colour of flanks cinnamon-buff; belly and vent unmarked rufescent-buff. Underwing buffy. Iris red, upper mandible black or dark brownish-black; lower surface of lower mandible pale bluish-grey, yellowish at base; legs greyish-slate.
Juvenile Very different. Crown unmarked dull black, back rufescent-buff with numerous longitudinal streaks of dull black, bars on closed wing broader and more conspicuous, supercilium broader and cinnamon-buff, underparts pale buff on chin and throat, shading to cinnamon-buff on belly and flanks, but totally lacking any spots or bars.

GEOGRAPHICAL VARIATION None; monotypic. There is considerable variation in different populations in characters such as the degree of spotting (Selander 1964) but not, apparently, with sufficient constancy to justify subspecific distinction.

VOICE Song is a series of harsh churring notes, of various speeds, also a series of gurgling phrases only scarcely more musical. Call is a gruff, dry and fairly quiet *cheh-cheh-cheht* and longer scolding and chattering series (Howell & Webb 1995).

HABITAT Quite varied. Primarily in oak or pine-oak woodland, usually fairly dry in nature; also mixed stands of tuna cactus and leguminous shrubs (Lea & Edwards 1950); at the northern end of the range, in Sonora, on rocky slopes with palms. Although the ranges of Cactus Wren and Spotted Wren overlap extensively, they rarely occupy the same habitat, the Spotted preferring areas with much denser vegetation (Russell & Monson 1998).

HABITS Typical of the genus, active and conspicuous. Forages mostly close to or on the ground, searching for food in bark crevices and on and under rocks; more rarely higher in fir trees, up to 15m above ground level. Will also forage in cornstalks and edges of fields near cover. The bill of the Spotted Wren is shorter and stouter than that of epiphyte specialists such as the Band-backed Wren; nevertheless Spotted Wrens do forage in epiphytic clumps. Usually found in small parties of four to six birds; occasionally up to ten. Groups of birds will cooperatively defend a territory of more than 20ha (Farley 1995), a much larger area than Boucard's Wren, for example.

STATUS AND DISTRIBUTION Two disjunct populations, separated by unsuitable habitat. Western Mexico from south-eastern Sonora through western Durango to northern Michoacán and western México; and eastern Mexico from south-western Tamaulipas through San Luis Potosí to Hidalgo. 800 to 2,500m, locally to 3,000m in Colima. Abundance varies from quite sparse and uncommon to very common in suitable habitat (Selander 1964).

BREEDING Little published information. Nest is similar in shape to that of the Cactus Wren; one active nest (in Sonora) was located on the underside of a dead palm frond. Eggs undescribed, incubation and fledging periods unknown. Up to four fledglings seen. Breeding

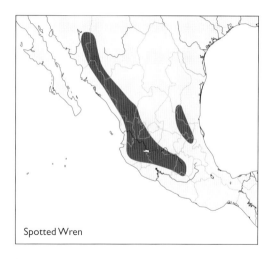

Spotted Wren

in Sonora in June and July. One instance recorded of parasitism by Brown-headed Cowbird *Molothrus ater* (Russell & Monson 1998).

FOOD Very little information recorded; doubtless similar to other members of the genus in similar habitats, i.e. invertebrate with substantial amounts of vegetable matter in the form of cactus seeds. Has been seen to take small lizards (Edwards & Martin 1955).

MOVEMENTS Probably entirely sedentary.

MEASUREMENTS Wing of male 70–74, of female 69.5–74; tail of male 66–74, of female 65–71; exposed culmen of male 18–21, of female 17–21; tarsus of male 23–25, of female 22–26 (Ridgway 1904).

---

3 YUCATAN WREN
Campylorhynchus yucatanicus

Plate 1

Campylorhynchus guttatus Lawrence 1869, Progresso and Celestia (sic), Yucatán.

Heleodytes brunneicapillus yucatanicus Hellmayr 1934, Río Lagartos, Yucatán, Mexico.

Alternative names: Yucatan Cactus Wren; Spanish *Matraca Yucateca*

An isolated *Campylorhynchus*, found in a very limited area of coastal Yucatán, Mexico. Considered by many authorities to be a race of the Cactus Wren; however, since it has little resemblance to that species in either plumage, song or nest-type that view is surely untenable.

IDENTIFICATION Length 17–18.5cm. Within its range totally distinct; obviously a *Campylorhynchus* wren, with no members of the genus occurring within 600km; the closest population of the Cactus Wren is almost 1,000km removed.

DESCRIPTION
Adult Crown blackish-brown, becoming more rufous towards nape. Shoulders and back dark brown, with many conspicuous longitudinal white streaks extending

across entire shoulder region. Streaks less conspicuous on lower back; rump and uppertail-coverts obscurely barred with dull blackish-brown. Greater and lesser coverts with alternate bands of dull black and off-white forming conspicuous light and dark bars across whole closed wing. Primaries and secondaries dull blackish with off-white markings on outerwebs forming seven to nine conspicuous bars on closed wing. Upper surface of rectrices are alternately barred with blackish-brown and dull grey-white, giving 12–14 transverse bars across tail; underside with prominent white bars forming whitish tips. Chin, throat and chest off-white, with longitudinal streaks, smaller on chin and throat, larger and longer on chest, becoming lateral bars on lower flanks. Undertail-coverts with several dull blackish bars. Underwing dull greyish-white with some darker streaks on contour feathers. Iris reddish-brown, bill grey or grey-black above, pale grey-horn at base, legs dark grey.
Juvenile Markings on back and shoulders much less well-defined; bars on wing-coverts buffy-brown, not white. Markings on underparts inconspicuous and diffuse.

GEOGRAPHICAL VARIATION None; monotypic.

VOICE Song is a repeated series of four or five notes, *chick che-wa chooo, kee kaa chewick,* etc. In contrast to all races of the Cactus Wren, whose songs are repetitions of a single harsh note, the song of the Yucatan Wren is a varied series of notes. Again in distinction from the Cactus Wren, duetting song is very common. Other calls are harsh gruff growls.

HABITAT Confined entirely to low coastal scrub, typically consisting of scattered bushes about 3–6m in height with some occasional *Opuntia* cacti. Also found in semi-disturbed habitat such as bushy edges to pasture.

HABITS Conspicuous, noisy and demonstrative. Usually found in pairs and family parties. Mated pairs of birds sing together, often sitting side by side. Display consists of neck-stretching, tail-fanning, wing-vibrating and bowing and bobbing. Sometimes one bird of a singing pair will hang head-downwards with vibrating wings without interruption in song. Feeds on the ground as well as in low vegetation. Tail is frequently fanned and flirted sideways when birds hop around on the ground. Fond of dust-bathing.

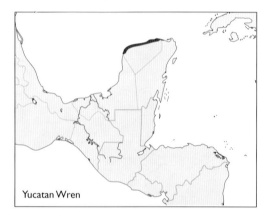

Yucatan Wren

STATUS AND DISTRIBUTION Confined almost entirely to coastal Yucatán State in Mexico (may just get across the border into northern Campeche, but only for a few kilometres). Edges of range approximately Celestún in the west and El Cuyo in the east. Extends only a few kilometres inland (records from Mérida [Ridgway 1904] are dubious). In much of this area it seems to be quite abundant. In scrubland north of Celestún it is one of the commonest species encountered (Wheatley & Brewer in press). However, given the extreme limited range, in an area where coastal vacation development is prominent and increasing, complacency for the species' welfare is not justified.

BREEDING Nest is an ovoid ball of grass, lined with fine plant fibres. Dimensions are; length, 25cm; height and breadth, 15cm; entrance hole, width 5.0cm, height 4.5cm, overhung by a portal about 6.5cm in length. Nests are typically situated about 2–3m above the ground in bushes with no attempt at concealment; although cacti are usually present in the area, nests are not (in contrast with the habits of the Cactus Wren) preferentially built in cacti. The nest shape is also substantially different from that of the Cactus Wren, being more ovoid with a tendency to have an entrance portal (A. D. Brewer pers. obs.). Nests are built by both sexes; in suitable habitat nests are very numerous, suggesting the existence of multiple nests for roosting. Completed nests have been found in March and May, with nest construction still going on in May (Paynter 1955, Zimmerman 1957). Eggs not described; incubation and fledging periods unknown.

FOOD No data available.

MOVEMENTS Presumably totally sedentary.

MEASUREMENTS Wing of male 74.6–78.5, of female 69.6–73.1; tail of male 72.7–76.0, of female 65.4–72.2; bill of male 17.1–20.8, of female 15.5–17.7; tarsus of male 24.1–26.1, of female 22.3–24.9 (Selander 1964).

4   CACTUS WREN
Campylorhynchus brunneicapillus   Plate 1

Picocolaptes brunneicapillus Lafresnaye 1835, Guaymas, Sonora, Mexico.

Alternative names: Spanish *Matraca Desértica, Matraca Grande*

A characteristic and conspicuous part of the fauna of the arid South-west, the Cactus Wren is the largest United States wren, and the only member of its genus to range north of the Mexican border. The State Bird of Arizona.

IDENTIFICATION Length 18–19cm. In most of its range, totally distinct from all other species. It is set apart from all other sympatric wrens by its much larger size, heavily barred wings and tail, large amount of white on the tips of the rectrices and heavy dark markings on the underparts, especially the chest. The only possible confusion is with Sage Thrasher *Oreoscoptes montanus* which is distinguished by its unmarked back, lack of

barring on flight feathers and double wing-bar. May be sympatric with Spotted Wren *C. gularis* in parts of western Mexico; see under that species for distinctions.

DESCRIPTION *C. b. anthonyi*
Adult Crown chocolate-brown, largely unmarked; nape same colour, some feathers with prominent white centre streaks; back more grey-brown, centre streaks larger, longer and with black sides, centre streaks continuing down to rump and uppertail-coverts; tertiary coverts broadly barred pale buff to dark brown; primaries and secondaries, outerweb strongly barred buff and black and white, giving five or six prominent bars on closed wing; coverts mottled brownish-buff; central rectrices barred brownish-black and pale grey-brown, outer four rectrices with white subterminal bars, otherwise dark brownish-black with prominent white bars; prominent white supercilium from bill to behind ear-coverts; ear-coverts obscurely streaked grey and black; chin white,

throat and upper chest heavily patterned with black on whitish background, which becomes buff to orange-buff on undertail-coverts; centre chest, belly and vent with small black speckles; iris deep reddish-brown, bill dull blackish, paler at base of lower mandible, legs brown or pinkish-brown.

Juvenile Differs by having the black chest-markings much less prominent, no white streaks on nape or back, orange-buff of vent duller, iris colour muddy grey-brown.

GEOGRAPHICAL VARIATION Seven races (Ridgway 1904; Miller *et al.* 1957; Anderson & Anderson 1973).

C. b. brunneicapillus (central and southern Sonora and northern Sinaloa, Mexico) Similar to *anthonyi*, but smaller, with posterior underparts a darker buff.

C. b. bryanti 'Bryant's Cactus Wren' (west coast of Baja California in region of San Quintén between approximate latitudes of 31° to 29° 30'N) Similar to *brunneicapillus*, but darker and browner above, and with back, scapulars and rump always conspicuously streaked with white; three lateral rectrices distinctly barred white; underparts more distinctly and heavily marked with black, posterior underparts very slight buff tinge.

C. b. purus 'San Ignacio Cactus Wren' (both coasts of Baja California between about 29° to 25°N) Underparts pure black and white, with only the slightest traces of buff on the flanks. Upperparts more grey, less reddish, than *C. b. affinis*, its neighbour southwards in the Baja California peninsula. Differs from its northern neighbour *C. b. bryanti* in having broader dorsal streaking and little buff on underparts; smaller than both *affinis* and *bryanti*, and with smaller bill.

C. b. affinis 'San Lucas Cactus Wren' (Baja California south of 25°N to Cabo San Lucas) Much like *bryanti*, but much paler, underparts more sparsely marked with black. Pileum and hindneck more reddish brown. All rectrices except middle pair with distinct white bars. Underparts paler.

C. b. seri (Tiburón Island, Gulf of California) Back greyer than *bryanti*, crown less rufous. Abdominal spotting wider than on *brunneicapillus*, cinnamon-buff on abdomen reduced.

C. b. guttatus (central Mexican plateau from southern Chihuahua and Coahuila, Nuevo León and Tamaulipas to Michoacán and Hidalgo; southern and central Texas) Similar to *brunneicapillus*, but generally duller and more grey, with white markings of upperparts less conspicuous.

C. b. anthonyi (includes *C. b. couesi*) (western Texas, southern New Mexico at lower elevations, southern Arizona, south-western Utah, Baja California south to about 31°N) Described above.

C. b. sandiegense (north-western Baja California and south-western California on coast) Crown less rufescent than *anthonyi*; more rich brown and less grey on back, lighter and more rufescent above than *bryanti*.

VOICE Song, a harsh series of unmusical notes, *jar-jar-jar-jar*, of a dozen or so syllables, becoming more emphatic and louder towards the end. Alarm call a low buzz, also a staccato *tek* repeated several times. A growling call is used as part of pair-recognition display, and harsh scratchy notes during territorial disputes.

HABITAT Permanent resident of semi-desert of various vegetation types, from sea-level to about 1,400m in Arizona, sparsely up to almost 2,000m in New Mexico and the central Mexican plateau. It requires the presence of spiny cacti, such as various species of cholla and prickly pear (*Opuntia* sp.) to provide nesting sites. Absent from associations of pure creosote bush without such cacti. It adapts quite well to suburban landscapes as well as very degraded habitat, such as gravel pits and junkyards, albeit in lower density, so long as some suitable cacti for nesting remain (Anderson & Anderson 1957). In prime habitat breeding territories may be as small as 1.5ha (Anderson & Anderson 1973).

HABITS A demonstrative and noisy bird, not at all shy or secretive. It feeds much of the time low down in vegetation or on the ground, turning over large pieces of leaf-litter and other debris, and sometimes overturning rocks and stones heavier than the bird itself to search for invertebrate prey underneath. It moves rapidly on the ground, often sprinting between the cover of adjacent cacti; in suburban locations often forages on lawns and in gutters. Flight is usually short, direct and low down. Tail is frequently quivered and flirted, but not cocked over the back in the manner of *Troglodytes* wrens. Frequently bathes in dust, but rarely in water. Song is usually delivered from a conspicuous perch such as the top of a cactus, or in suburban locations from such places as telephone poles, street lights or gable ends. Nests are built for roosting throughout the year.

Cactus Wren

STATUS AND DISTRIBUTION Resident, from southern and south-eastern Arizona, extreme southern Nevada, southern New Mexico and Texas through Mexico from Baja California, eastwards to Tamaulipas and south to Sinaloa and the central Mexican plateau to Michoacán and Hidalgo. Over much of its range common or abundant.

BREEDING Builds large and conspicuous nests, usually in spiny cactus; in Arizona the majority are in cholla sp., especially jumping cholla *Opuntia fulgida* and staghorn cholla *O. versicolor*. Also quite frequently in crotches of saguaro *Carnegia gigantea*, less often in dead stumps or in holes in saguaro. Other bushes, such as palo verde *Cercidium* sp. and leafless mistletoe *Phoradendron* *californicum* used less often (Anderson & Anderson 1957). Rarely in artificial situations such as cavities under eaves of buildings. Nests in cholla typically 1–2m above ground level, in palo verde 2–3.7m, and in giant saguaro up to 6m (Anderson & Anderson 1959, 1973). Nests are usually about 30cm in length, sloping downward from the entrance at a 30° angle. They have an entrance roughly 3.8cm in diameter, and a well-defined cylindrical vestibule of the same diameter, but of varying length, leading to a nest cavity, into which it drops abruptly. The cavity may be 7.5cm in diameter. In profile the exterior is pouch-shaped; the interior is formed like a retort (Anderson & Anderson 1973). Nests are made mostly of dried grasses and other fibres and lined with feathers; in suburban locations various items of artificial debris also used. Several nests in Nuevo León, Mexico were built very largely of fibreglass taken from a nearby dump; in one instance where the nest was used for breeding the chicks did not survive, possibly due to contact with the glass fibres (Guzmán-Velasco, in press). In Arizona, at low elevations, egg laying may begin in January, but more usually in late February or March; at higher elevations usually a month later. Multibrooded; may attempt up to six clutches a year, but only three successful broods reared, and in some years, according to weather conditions, only two (Anderson & Anderson 1959). May lay up to seven eggs (rarely), but three to five most usual; The race *affinis* in Baja California averages smaller clutches, typically two eggs (Bancroft 1930; Rowley 1935). Eggs have a buff or pinkish ground colour, more or less covered with fine speckles of brown or reddish-brown. Some geographic variation: eggs of *C. b. affinis* tend to be paler, those in coastal California darker, and those of the Colorado basin more brightly coloured, on a paler background (Bancroft 1946). Incubation by female alone, for about 16 days, young often hatching over a period of two to three days. Young fed almost entirely on insects; fledging period in Arizona usually 19–23 days, average 21 (Anderson & Anderson 1962). Males start to build a secondary nest as soon as female is laying. When the first brood is fledged the female assists in completing the second nest and lays a second clutch in it; only rarely are second broods raised in the first nest. Second laying usually begins about one week after the first brood fledges. In contrast to several tropical members of the genus, non-breeding birds only rarely aid in the feeding of nestlings; in Arizona, juveniles of one brood have observed feeding young in subsequent nests, but this seems exceptional (Anderson & Anderson 1973).

Cactus Wrens build roosting nests throughout the year and older birds sleep singly in them. Fledged broods roost communally, sometimes in roosting nests or old breeding nests, neither of their own construction, before roosting singly. Tentative attempts at nest building by juveniles may occur as soon as ten days after fledging, but more usually at two months or so. Young birds may begin serious nest construction within ten weeks of the fledging date.

The situation of most nests, in the savagely spiny cholla cactus or similar situations, gives protection against many predators. Nests may be raided by snakes or raptors such as Harris' Hawk *Parabuteo unicinctus*. Roosting nests, but not breeding nests in use, are routinely vandalised by Curve-billed Thrashers *Toxostoma curvirostre*. In ranching areas cattle may snack on grass nests, removing them from cacti.

FOOD In a study in southern California, animal matter was 83% of the total, vegetable 17% (Bent 1964). Prey includes ants, wasps, grasshoppers, bugs, caterpillars and spiders. Cactus Wrens have been seen to take small frogs and lizards, and will occasionally feed at bird tables. Birds may learn to pry squashed insects off car radiators (Philips *et al.* 1964). Adults drink frequently in winter if water is available, but apparently can obtain adequate water from prey in summer; however, juveniles drink in summer.

MOVEMENT Appears to be entirely sedentary; no evidence of movement, even altitudinal movement from higher elevations in winter. Of 126 recoveries of ringed birds, in Arizona, California and Texas, 125 showed zero movement; the single exception was recovered 80km from the banding site, in southern Arizona (data from Bird-banding Laboratory). No records outside the known breeding range, apart from one bizarre occurrence in south-western Saskatchewan, Canada, in a late May blizzard (Wapple & Smith 1982).

MEASUREMENTS (*C. b. anthonyi*) Wing of male 80–92, of female 79–88; tail of male 76–86, of female 70–84; exposed culmen of male 20.5–26, of female 19.5–24; tarsus of male 26.5–30, of female 25.5–29 (Ridgway 1904).

---

5 GIANT WREN
Campylorhynchus chiapensis   Plate 2

Campylorhynchus chiapensis Salvin and Godman 1891.

Alternative names: Chiapas Wren; Spanish *Matraca Chiapeneca, Chupahuevo*

One of the largest wrens, rivalled only by the closely related Bicolored Wren of northern South America, with a very restricted distribution in southern Mexico.

IDENTIFICATION Length 20.5–22cm. Distinctive and unmistakable. The large size, prominent head markings and unmarked bright chestnut upperparts make confusion with other wrens or any other bird in its limited geographic range unlikely. The sympatric Rufous-naped Wren, while having a similar head-pattern, is considerably smaller and has prominent barring on wings and tail, and no buff belly.

DESCRIPTION
Adult Sexes similar. Crown and nape black. Upper back deep chestnut-brown without streaking, becoming paler and more rufous on upper tail-coverts. Wings; shoulders immaculate chestnut-brown, contrasting with darker alula. Primaries dark grey-black contrasting with chestnut edged secondaries with very obscure barring, not

visible in the field; coverts rufous-brown with very obscure darker bars. Tail; central rectrices dark chestnut-brown with very obscure fine darker barring, not visible in the field; lateral rectrices darker and less chestnut. Four outer rectrices with white subterminal band becoming broader and more prominent on outer feathers, forming a bold white tail-band (interrupted in the centre of the tail) in flight. Prominent buff supercilium. Lores and stripe behind eye black, merging into chestnut of shoulders; underparts usually immaculate; chin, throat and chest white, becoming pale buff on belly, deeper buff on vent and medium buff on lower flanks. A majority of females have underparts without dark spots, but in some cases flanks and under tail-coverts are spotted with black or dark brown; such markings more frequent and heavier in males. Iris reddish-brown, upper mandible black, lower mandible grey, paler at base; legs pale slate-blue to greyish-brown.

Juvenile Very similar to adult; chin, throat and chest slightly less pure white.

GEOGRAPHICAL VARIATION Monotypic; however, birds from the south-eastern part of the range are somewhat smaller, both in overall size and bill-length, than those in the north-western section (Selander 1964). Sometimes considered conspecific with Bicolored Wren (q.v.).

VOICE Bizarre, hollow, gurgling rhythmic chortling and rollicking phrases, repeated, *kar-a-u'too*, or *kar-rale-du-ow*, etc. (Howell & Webb 1995). Both sexes sing in unison (Skutch 1940). Calls; a variety of harsh churrs and grating noises.

HABITAT A variety of habitat types, including those much modified by human activity. Farmland with trees and bushes, fence rows and hedges and more rarely in clearings in forest. Ideal habitat includes groves of mangoes or guanacastes, with denser patches of smaller trees and with bull's horn acacias for nesting (Skutch 1940). When their ranges overlap, lives in more humid areas than Rufous-naped Wren; the two species are rarely found together (Brodkorb 1939).

Giant Wren

HABITS Relatively little recorded. An active and noisy bird with little fear of humans. Feeds on or near the ground, rarely at great height, often on the bases of trees and on fallen dead trees. Probably differentiated from, and therefore not competitive with, Rufous-naped Wren in feeding habits; the latter species, being less heavy, forages more in the lighter vegetation near the ends of branches (Selander 1964).

STATUS AND DISTRIBUTION Confined entirely to the Pacific lowlands of the Mexican state of Chiapas, from about Puerto Arista in the north to Puerto Madero in the south, (a distance of about 200km), and extending no more than 50km inland. Has not been recorded in adjacent Guatemala (Land 1970). Occurs from sea-level to 300m; in some locations very common. Despite its very limited geographic distribution, not apparently in any danger. One of the commonest birds in some parts of its range, with groups of wrens spaced at intervals of 100 to 150 yards (Selander 1964). Has also adapted well to local farming practices.

BREEDING Builds a very bulky roofed nest with little effort at concealment. Nests may measure up to 35cm in depth and 25cm in diameter, with usually one, sometimes two, circular entrances in the side. Frequently, located in bull's horn acacias, a tree noted for symbiotic ants which will attack intruding predators such as snakes or squirrels, but apparently do not touch the wren nestlings, or even invade the nest. Nests are made of straws, weed stems, bits of vine and the like; two described examples were located 3–4m above ground level (Skutch 1960). Eggs, clutch of three recorded (one nest), light buff with heavy brown mottling, especially at larger end. Incubation and fledging periods unknown. Possibly double-brooded, since full-grown young were seen on 27 June (Brodkorb 1939) and eggs in mid-July (Skutch 1960). During incubation and brooding, males roost alone in separate nests some distance from the breeding nest. Possibly a cooperative breeder with immature birds helping at the nest (Skutch 1976).

FOOD Nothing recorded, but presumably predominantly invertebrates. Has been seen to enter chicken coops, and the local name *chupahuevos* means literally 'egg-sucker'. Wrens of several genera, including Rufous-naped Wren, are known to attack eggs of other species, but usually only during the breeding season around nesting territory rather than as a food source.

MOVEMENTS Apparently totally sedentary.

MEASUREMENTS Northern population: wing of male 90-96, of female 82–92; tail of male 79–90, of female 79–86; bill of male 18–22, of female 17–20; tarsus of male 27.5, female 26–29, (37 male, 38 female specimens).

Southern population: wing of male 89–92, of female 85–86; tail of male 92–86, of female 80–82; bill of male 17–20, of female 16–19; tarsus of male 28–31, of female 27–29 (11 male, 4 female specimens) (Selander 1964).

Furnarius griseus Swainson 1837, Savannas of Guiana.

Alternative names: Guyanan Cactus Wren (nominate race); Spanish *Cucarachero Palmero, Cucarachero Curru-cuchu, Cuchica* (Colombia), *Chupahuevo* (Venezuela)

A large and unmistakable wren confined to northern South America, with some interesting behavioural characteristics involving cooperative breeding.

IDENTIFICATION Length 21–22cm. Within its range, not confusable with any other species of wren. The large size, prominent eye-stripe and unmarked white under-parts distinguished it from all other sympatric species. Donacobius, which has different habitat requirements, has buff underparts, a prominent yellow eye, no supercilium and a conspicuous white wing-flash at the base of the primaries.

DESCRIPTION *C. g. griseus*
Adult Crown and nape dark chocolate-brown, forehead slightly lighter. Back paler brown, contrasting with darker nape and shoulders; lower back more russet-brown. Rump and upper tail-coverts with obscure transverse barring. Rectrices dull brownish-black, the outer five with white tips, more than half the feather-length in outermost, narrowing to about 8mm on inner feather; each feather tipped with dark brown on outerweb; central rectrices dull brownish-black with very obscure transverse barrings. Broad supercilium off-white, contrasting strongly with cap; dark chocolate-brown eye-stripe narrowing and becoming buffy in front of eye. Lores dull dark brown. Chin, throat, ear-coverts, chest, belly, flanks, thighs and vent white. Remiges dull brown on innerweb, grey-brown on outer, with obscure barring on outerwebs of tertials; primary and secondary coverts dull grey-brown with very obscure transverse barring. Underwing-coverts off-white. Iris reddish-chestnut, legs and feet slate-grey. Bill black, base of lower mandible grey.
Juvenile Differs from adult by having greyer, less rufes-cent back, cap with grey-brown mottling without sharp differentiation from shoulders, underparts duller white.

GEOGRAPHICAL VARIATION
C. g. griseus (eastern Venezuela, Guyana, northern Brazil) Described above.
C. g. minor 'Lesser Cactus Wren' (lowlands of north-ern Venezuela from the Orinoco delta westwards to eastern Colombia, Arauca) Smaller than *C. g. griseus*; hindneck and upper back blackish-brown like crown; lower back more russet; flanks and under wing-coverts strongly washed buff.
C. g. albicilius 'White-browed Cactus Wren' (northern Colombia and extreme north-western Venezuela) Lower back and rump and upper tail-coverts deeper rufous. Bars at base of tail absent or much reduced.
C. g. bicolor 'Bicolored Cactus Wren' (Colombia, upper valley of the Río Magdalena, Santander and Boyacá) Similar to *albicilius* but rusty-edges wing-coverts and flight feathers much reduced; rump and upper tail-coverts much less bright rufous. Almost

black back; cap, back and tail uniform.
C. g. pallidus (restricted to Amazonas, Venezuela) Differs from other members of the group by grey colour of back, rump and wings, instead of buffy-olivaceous, rufous or brown. Crown darker than *griseus*, mantle mottled with dark brown (Phelps & Phelps 1947).
C. g. zimmeri (Huila and Tolima, Colombia) may be regarded as an intergrade between *bicolor* and *albicilius* (Selander 1964).

VOICE Song is a series of loud gurgling multiple notes, two to five in a phrase, with a harsh grating undertone, *chook-acha-chak* etc., usually repeated in a long series. Songs may be solos, one bird of either sex singing; duets, of a pair; or choruses, with three or more birds singing. In the case of solos, male birds sing with a series of short simple notes, whereas females invariably include at least one trill (Austad & Rabenold 1986). Calls are varied, frequently harsh or grating, *awk-chook, ook-a-chuk*, etc. Scolding a harsh *rud* (Hilty & Brown 1986).

HABITAT Inhabits areas of scattered bush and trees, both xeric and semi-humid, being absent both from thick forest and totally open pasture. In Venezuela, common in seasonally flooded savanna woodland where the dominant vegetation types are palms and legum-inous trees. Adapts well to disturbed habitat such as the environs of ranch-houses and stock-yards, so long as there is an adequate number of trees or large bushes. In Guyana, largely confined to savannas. In Colombia, the race *C. g. bicolor* occurs in quite arid vegetation communities dominated by organ-pipe cacti and thorn-trees (Miller 1947). Sea-level to 2,100m in Colombia; in Venezuela, to 1,600m north of the Orinoco, to 400m south of it (Meyer de Schauensee & Phelps 1978).

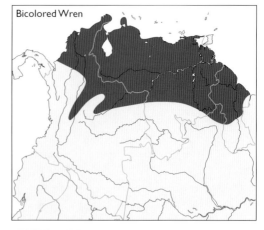
Bicolored Wren

STATUS AND DISTRIBUTION Common or abundant in suitable habitat in many areas of its range. Northern Colombia south to Huila, northern Venezuela, northern and western Guyana, marginally in northern Brazil (Roraima).

HABITS Noisy and conspicuous. Forages both in trees,

especially palms, and on the ground: flights are usually direct and of short duration. Can be very noisy and aggressive, joining other birds such as Kiskadees *Pitangus* sp. to mob predators such as snakes. Sometimes enters houses and other buildings to forage; has been seen to pick up insects attracted to artificial light. Roosts in dormitory nests which do not differ from breeding nests.

BREEDING Pairs defend territories year-round, but nesting is synchronised with the wet season, which usually begins in late March or early April in northern Venezuela. (Thomas 1979). In Colombia, nests between February and July. The nest is a domed structure with a relatively small side-entrance built mostly of grasses and plant fibres; in the *llanos* mostly in palm trees, at heights of 3.5m or more. Since the species does not routinely take advantage of trees infested by aggressive ants, in contrast to several other members of the genus, nests are better concealed. In Colombia, frequently appropriates second-hand nests of other species, such as Kiskadees *Pitangus* sp. or *Myiozetetes* flycatchers, which build domed nests; in Venezuelan *llanos* apparently does so less commonly, there usually using the pendant nests of Plain Thornbird *Phacellodomus rufifrons*. Eggs three to five, buffy or cinnamon-buff ground colour, more or less heavily speckled with brown. Incubation 17 days, by female only. Fledging period also about 17 days; after leaving the nest young are fed for up to a further 30 days, with decreasing regularity (Austad & Rabenold 1986).

A cooperative breeder, although in terms of sheer numbers of helpers apparently less so than the Stripe-backed Wren. In a study in Venezuela, one population reared young with little external help, only 15% of nests having an assistant, usually a single young male; by contrast, in an adjacent population most nests had helpers, and in more than half there were several helpers of both sexes (Austad & Rabenold 1986). Helpers are invariably blood-relations of the actual breeding pair, in the majority of cases full brothers and sisters of the brood being assisted, more rarely half-siblings or nephews. Nests with helpers are up to three times more successful than unassisted nests; interestingly, the actual number of helpers at a nest did not affect success, there being no apparent advantage in having more than one. The mechanism of enhanced success in assisted nests seems to lie in better defence of the nest.

FOOD Mostly invertebrates. However, a fair amount of vegetable matter may be taken. In Venezuela, reported to eat berries (B. T. Thomas pers. comm.). In Colombia, it may be occasionally destructive to mangoes and *avocates* (Darlington 1931). According to local Colombian folklore, will enter henhouses to pierce and suck eggs (hence the dialect name *chupahuevo*, also given to the closely related Giant Wren in southern Mexico).

MOVEMENTS Totally sedentary so far as can be determined.

MEASUREMENTS Wing of male 92–96, of female 86.5–91.8; tail of male 92.2, of female 82.7–87.7; bill of male 19.1–20.1, of female 18.7–19.6; tarsus of male 29.9–30.2, of female 28.3–29.0.

---

7 RUFOUS-NAPED WREN
Campylorhynchus rufinucha

Plate 2

Picocolaptes rufinucha Lesson 1838 Vera Cruz (sic), Mexico.

Alternative names: Rufous-backed Wren; Spanish *Matraca Nuquirufa, Soterrey Nuquirufa*

A conspicuous and noisy resident of arid and semi-arid regions on the Pacific coast of Central America, with isolated populations in the Caribbean drainage, from about 19°N in Mexico to 9°N in Costa Rica.

IDENTIFICATION Length 15–19cm. In most of its range essentially unmistakable, since it cannot be confused with any species of other families, and is largely allopatric with numbers of its own genus. In southern Mexico and Guatemala it overlaps with the Giant Wren *C. chiapensis*, from which it differs in its smaller size and heavily barred flight feathers and wing-coverts. Rufous-and-white Wren *Thryothorus rufalbus* is sympatric over parts of its range from southern Mexico (Chiapas) to Costa Rica; that species is smaller, with less pronounced barring on the wings, no white on tail and has a conspicuous black malar stripe and black and white patterned ear-coverts.

DESCRIPTION *C. r. rufinucha*
Adult Crown blackish, contrasting with chestnut-brown, shoulders with prominent black and white longitudinal streaks; back medium brown, less chestnut than upper back. Wing-coverts heavily barred with greyish-black and reddish-buff. Primaries blackish with outerweb spotted with pale buff, giving five or six prominent bars on closed wing. Uppertail-coverts medium brown barred with brownish-black. Lateral rectrices blackish-brown with prominent white tips on outer three, the white darkening to dusky at the very tip. Outerwebs with buff-white spots forming three or four pale bars. Central rectrices grey-brown with six or seven diffuse darker bars, but no white tips. Prominent whitish supercilium from bill to past ear-coverts. Lores and eye-stripe blackish. Ear-coverts greyish-white. Slight black malar stripe (not prominent). Chin and throat off-white; chest pale buffy white speckled with very small round brownish-black dots. Belly buffy-white with diffuse blackish bars on flanks. Iris reddish-brown, bill blackish with pale slate or horn blue at base of lower mandible, legs pale slate-blue.
Juvenile Similar to adult; hind-crown with rufescent edgings, supercilium more buffy, markings on shoulders and primaries less sharply demarcated and more buffy, back duller rufous.

GEOGRAPHICAL VARIATION Different authorities recognise between five and seven races, a number so widely different from each other as to have been formerly granted full specific status.

C. r. rufinucha (Veracruz State, Mexico) Described above.

C. r. humilis 'Sclater's Cactus Wren' (West Mexico from Colima and southern Jalisco to western Chiapas) Small, streaks on upper back of *rufinucha* replaced by solid chestnut brown, crown rufous-brown, back streaked and spotted dark brown and whitish to pale cinnamon, tail barred blackish-brown and pale grey. No spots on underparts except in northern parts of range where there may be some spotting on sides of chest and barring on flanks. Malar stripe.

C. r. nigricaudatus 'Black-tailed Cactus Wren', 'Rufous-backed Wren' (southern coastal Mexico to western Guatemala) Intergrades with *humilis* in Chiapas (Selander 1965). Substantially larger than *humilis*, unmarked chestnut of upperparts extending further down back, crown and eye-stripe almost black, central rectrices black apart from tips, outer rectrices barred pale grey and with broad sub-terminal white band. Underparts without spots, no malar stripe.

C. r. capistratus 'Hooded Cactus Wren' (E Guatemala, Pacific coastal Honduras and El Salvador to north-west Costa Rica) Differs from *nigricaudatus* in paler chestnut back and upper rump, and central rectrices with light brownish-grey bars.

C. r. xerophilum (interior Guatemala) Similar to *rufinucha*, but rarely show malar stripe, underparts unspotted and undertail-coverts rarely with dark spots or bars (Howell & Webb 1995).

C. r. nicaraguae (interior West Nicaragua) Similar to *xerophilum* but back and rump less well-marked.

C. r. castaneus 'Chestnut Cactus Wren' (isolated population in west-central Honduras, Sula valley) Back plain rufous-chestnut.

VOICE Sings in duets, both sexes being equally accomplished. The song, more melodious than that of most *Campylorhynchus* wrens, is a series of rich, chortling phrases, typically three to eight notes, interspersed with harsher sounds and chatters, often repeated almost continuously. Contact calls short and harsh, *kr-r-r, kr-r-r*, etc. Pairs greet each other with simultaneous song while quivering wings and fanning tail.

HABITAT Largely confined to arid or semi-arid areas; dry scrub, especially where cacti (such as *Opuntia* spp.) are present, second growth and deciduous xerophytic forest, including areas much modified by human activity, such as farm edges and abandoned pastures, where sufficient bushes and large cacti remain. Less commonly to lower edge of cloud forest zone (in El Salvador) and in mangroves (Dickey & Van Rossem 1938). Sea-level to 1,400m in El Salvador, 800m (rarely higher) in Costa Rica (Stiles & Skutch 1989) and 1,200m in Mexico (Howell & Webb 1995).

HABITS Noisy, demonstrative and conspicuous, and not at all shy of human beings, sometimes foraging in buildings and on verandahs. Usually found in pairs or small noisy groups of up to five or six individuals moving through scrubland giving constant short harsh contact notes. Feeds on the ground in low vegetation, but will sing from conspicuous elevated perches. Flight typically direct and low. Does not cock tail over back.

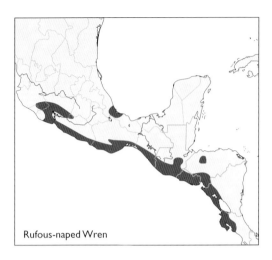

Rufous-naped Wren

STATUS AND DISTRIBUTION Common, sometimes abundant, in suitable habitat on the Pacific drainage of Central America from Colima State in Mexico through Guatemala, El Salvador, Honduras, Nicaragua to NW Costa Rica. Isolated populations in Veracruz State, Mexico, and the Sula valley, Honduras.

BREEDING Nests, built by both sexes, are bulky, conspicuous, globular structures, 20–25cm in length, made of grasses, straw and plant fibres, with an upward-directed tunnel entrance at one side, leading into a deep pocket copiously lined with feathers or plant down. In the northern race *humilis* shorter, more open and more highly domed (Skutch 1960b). Sited in cacti, thorn bushes, etc., at heights of 1.5–10m above the ground; also, however, in artificial sites such as cavities under roof eaves, drain spouts, and occasionally in the abandoned hanging nests of species such as Spot-breasted Oriole *Icterus pectoralis* which are relined for the purpose. In Costa Rica and doubtless other areas, nests deliberately in close proximity to wasps' nests or in acacia trees inhabited by aggressive stinging ants, e.g. *Pseudomyrmex spinicola*, thereby gaining vicarious protection against the depredations of nest-predators such as White-faced Monkeys *Cebus capucinus* (Joyce 1993). Nests close to wasps' nests are significantly more successful than those not so protected; in acacia trees, Rufous-naped Wrens deliberately seek out those with the most aggressive and active ants, and discourage birds of other species from using the same tree by attacking their eggs (Young *et al.* 1990). Eggs whitish or buffy-white, marked with small speckles to larger blotches of brown, lilac or blackish: in El Salvador, three to six, with four or five most common (Dickey & Van Rossem 1938), in Costa Rica usually four. Probably single-brooded; young are fed by both sexes and occasionally by helpers at the nest (Joyce 1993). Family parties may remain together with young still being fed by both sexes, until almost the next breeding season. In El Salvador (race *capistratus*) eggs laid mid-March to July, but mostly in April–June. Young fed by both sexes. Nests are built throughout the year for roosting purposes, with perhaps only one nest in eight or so actually used for breeding (Dickey & Van Rossem 1938); groups of wrens, possibly families, may roost communally in these nests.

FOOD Predominantly invertebrate, especially small insects, larvae and spiders. Since individuals are seen with forehead and face stained with purple juice, doubtless also vegetable matter including berries (Dickey & Van Rossem 1938).

MOVEMENTS None; apparently totally sedentary.

MEASUREMENTS (*C. r. rufinucha*) (Means) Wing of male 72.4, of female 67.3; tail of male 67.2, of female 62.7; bill of male 15.6, of female 14.7; tarsus of male 22.6, of female 21.5 (22 male and 19 female specimens) (Selander 1964).

---

8   THRUSH-LIKE WREN
Campylorhynchus turdinus   Plate 3

Opetiorhynchus turdinus Wied 1821 Rio Catole, Bahia, Brazil.

Alternative names: Spanish *Soterrey Mirlo*, *Chupachoro* (Bolivia); Portuguese, *Catatau*, *Garrinchao*

A widely distributed species, found over a huge area of lowland South America, but one curiously little-known or studied. Within its range there are major differences in plumage between the races.

IDENTIFICATION Length 20.5cm. Not very like any other wren in its range; the combination of large size, unbarred back and heavy spotting on the underparts distinguishes it from other *Campylorhynchus* wrens, none of which are in any case sympatric. The race *unicolor* (in Bolivia and the Matto Grosso) is very different in appearance, being greyish above and lacking spots below; on a poor view it is more likely to be confused with a *Turdus* thrush such as the Creamy-bellied *T. amaurochalinus* or Pale-breasted *T. leucomelas*, but aside from the obvious differences in shape and 'jizz', these thrushes have streaked throats.

DESCRIPTION *C. t. turdinus*
Adult Crown dull blackish-grey with pale grey-brown scalloping. Shoulders and back similar, the scalloping becoming broader and more diffuse posteriorly. Lower back and rump blackish-grey with diffuse lateral bars of buffy-grey. Primaries and secondaries dull blackish with dull reddish-brown spots on outerwebs giving six or seven inconspicuous bars on closed wing. Rectrices dull blackish-brown, unmarked except some slight, inconspicuous, barring in outerwebs of outer feathers. Lores greyish, narrow grey supercilium, ear-coverts mottled grey-brown, throat and upper chest dull white, becoming slightly buffy on chest and belly; throat largely unmarked, chest with conspicuous circular blackish spots, becoming more diffuse and coalescing into bars on lower flanks and vent. Thighs dull barred blackish-brown and buff-brown. Iris pale orange-rufous, legs and feet dusky-grey, bill blackish or brownish above, ivory below.
Juvenile Duller, spots on underparts reduced and much less well-marked.

GEOGRAPHICAL VARIATION
  C. t. turdinus 'Spotted Cactus Wren' (eastern Brazil from Maranhão to Espirito Santo) Described above.
  C. t. hypostictus 'Amazonian Spotted Cactus Wren' (includes *C. t. chanchamayoensis*) (Amazonia, from south-eastern Colombia [Meta], eastern Ecuador and Peru to northern Bolivia, eastwards across central Brazil to the Rio Tocantins) Similar to *turdinus* but more heavily spotted on underparts, the spots extending up onto most of the throat.
  C. t. unicolor 'Brown Cactus Wren' (lowlands of eastern Bolivia and adjacent Brazil, marginally into northern Paraguay) Very different from other races; underparts unspotted or nearly so, upperparts grey rather than brown, superciliary more pronounced.

VOICE A very vocal bird, giving rise to the local Brazilian dialect name of *Rouxinol* (Nightingale). Song is a loud series of cheerful chortling notes, *chew yoo choop*, *chew yu yu yu chup*, etc., repeated frequently, often with a preface, of variable length, of harsh scratchy chittering notes. Sings from prominent perches such as upper portions of trees and telephone wires. The sexes apparently duet, the contribution of the female differing slightly from the male's.

HABITAT Lowlands, though locally up to 1,300m along eastern foothills of the Andes. Generally humid forest, including seasonally flooded forest, clearings and roadsides with secondary growth; in the Matto Grosso, among palms.

HABITS Usually found in small flocks, doubtless extended family parties. Feeds mostly higher up, in upperparts of trees and lower canopy. Not excessively shy, although more often heard than seen; will perch and sing from quite exposed sites.

STATUS AND DISTRIBUTION Common or moderately common over much of its range. Lowland South America east of the Andes, south-eastern Colombia

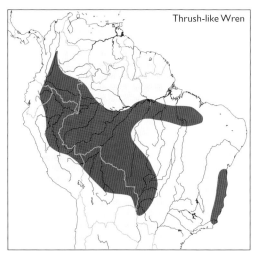
Thrush-like Wren

(Meta, Caqueta), eastern Ecuador (Napo, Pastaza), eastern Peru, north-eastern Bolivia (Beni, Santa Cruz), northern Paraguay, across Brazil as far west as Maranhão; apparently disjunctly in eastern Brazil, but distribution not entirely clear; Bahia, Espirito Santo, one record in Rio Grande do Sul. Appears to be colonising northern Argentina; about a dozen recent records (R. Fraga, pers. comm.).

BREEDING Little known. Nests from eastern Brazil have been described as domed, round or oval in shape, built of grass, with an inner breeding chamber and an outside ante-chamber, situated in trees and quite frequently near houses (J. Steinbach, on labels of specimens, AMNH); also described as a 'great ball of soft material, including rags and tow, high in trees'. In the Matto Grosso (race *unicolor*) it may use the nests of Thornbirds *Phacello-* *dromus* as a base, 'stuffing everything generously with feathers and other flexible material' (Sick 1993). A pair (race *hypostictus*) in Tingo María, Peru on 17 August 1968 were seen to enter repeatedly, over a two-hour period, a natural cavity about 10m up in a dead tree; it seemed likely that they were nesting in the cavity, and the female had a brood-patch (Short & Morony 1969). Eggs, clutch size, incubation and fledging periods unknown; it is also not known if it is a cooperative breeder.

FOOD No information recorded.

MOVEMENTS Apparently sedentary.

MEASUREMENTS (*C. t. hypostictus*) Wing of male 84–89, of female 78–87; tail of male 74–79, of female 71–74; exposed culmen of male 21–21, of female 20–21; tarsus of male 27–29, of female 25.5–27.5.

---

9   WHITE-HEADED WREN
Campylorhynchus albobrunneus   Plate 3

Heleodytes albo-brunneus Lawrence 1862. Routes of transisthmian railway, Panama.

Alternative names: White-headed Cactus Wren

The most distinctive in plumage of all the wrens, the White-headed Wren has nevertheless been regarded from time to time as conspecific with either the Thrushlike Wren or the Band-backed Wren. Given the very different vocalisations of the former, and their total allopatry, conspecificity with Thrush-like Wren seems very unlikely.

IDENTIFICATION Length 18.5–19cm. Quite unlike any other wren, or indeed any other species in its range. However, in south-western Colombia the race *aenigmaticus* has a dusky head and the underparts are white, grey and dusky; these may in fact be a hybrid between Bandbacked and White-headed Wrens. They may be distinguished from Band-backed Wrens by the lack of strong sharp barring on the back.

DESCRIPTION *C. a. albobrunneus*
Adult Entire head, nape, throat, chest and most of belly immaculate white without markings. Thighs and vent diffuse grey-brown. Shoulders, back, rump and upper tail-coverts uniform dull blackish-brown, sometimes with a few white feathers on shoulders. Rectrices dull dark brown with fine very inconspicuous narrow dark bars on upper surfaces. Primaries and secondaries unmarked dull brownish-black, concolour with back and tail. Underwing dull greyish-white. Iris dark brown to red, upper mandible dark brown, lower mandible greyish. Upper mandible dark brown, lower mandible greyish, legs lead-grey; white of head and face is frequently soiled and stained brown.
Juvenile Crown streaky grey-brown, diffuse paler speckling on shoulders, underparts and face buffy and duller than adult, belly with distinct buff-cinnamon, thighs darker grey-brown. Iris dark grey.

GEOGRAPHICAL VARIATION
    C. a. albobrunneus (Panama, from the Canal Zone eastwards to western Darién) Described above.
C. a. harterti 'Hartert's White-headed Cactus Wren' (eastern Panama [eastern Darién] through the Pacific slope of Colombia south to Valle) Upperparts darker than the nominate race, undertail-coverts more coarsely spotted.
C. a. aenigmaticus (Nariño, Colombia) Very probably a hybrid between White-headed and Band-backed Wrens (Haffer 1967). Head more or less brownish, belly buffy with barred flanks, some spotting on breast.

VOICE Song is a series of harsh scratchy notes, quite similar to that of the Band-backed Wren, and totally distinct from the explosive chortling of the Thrush-like Wren. Both sexes sing. Call is a harsh scratchy *kahk*.

HABITAT Humid forest with epiphytes, including areas somewhat disturbed, to 1,500m. In drier areas tends to be replaced by Band-backed Wren (Hilty & Brown 1986).

HABITS Mostly seen in the upper or middle levels of trees, rarely lower. Often in small parties, possibly extended families. Forages especially in epiphytic tangles.

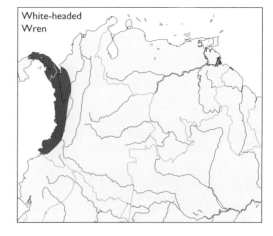
White-headed Wren

STATUS AND DISTRIBUTION Central Panama (Western Colón) eastwards through Darién; Colombia from Chocó and Antioquia south along Pacific slope to Nariño. Not generally common; in Panama fairly sparse, more abundant in Darién (Ridgely 1976); in Colombia uncommon and local (Ridgely & Tudor 1989).

BREEDING Little known. One nest in late February in Darién was described as globular with side entrance set at base of an epiphyte on a dead snag (R. S. Ridgely pers. comm.). At the same time birds in probable juvenile plumage were seen. In north-western Colombia a nest was located in a low tree next to an Indian hut in an abandoned clearing (Haffer 1975). An adult was noted feeding a juvenile on 25 November (Darién,

Panama) (C. Green pers. comm.). Colour and number of eggs, incubation and fledging periods, and general nesting behaviour (including if a cooperative nester) all undescribed. Nests may be used for group roosting (Farley 1995).

FOOD Stomach contents of a specimen taken near Cana, Panama in May included beetles, Orthoptera and ants (Wetmore 1984). No other published information.

MOVEMENTS Probably sedentary.

MEASUREMENTS (*C. a. harterti*) Wing of male 79–87.5, of female 79–85; tail of male 71–78, of female 71–74; exposed culmen of male 19–23, of female 16.5–21; tarsus of male 26–28, of female 27–29.5.

---

10   STRIPE-BACKED WREN
Campylorhynchus nuchalis

Plate 4

Campylorhynchus nuchalis Cabinis 1847 Venezuela.

Alternative names: Banded Wren; Spanish *Cucarachero chocorocoy* (Venezuela)

A distinctively-plumaged wren of northern South America, with a very highly developed system of co-operative nesting.

IDENTIFICATION Length 17.5cm. Noisy and conspicuous. A large, grey-black and white wren. The only other species in its range with which it can be confused is the Band-backed Wren, from which it differs by lacking buff underparts, by having lateral stripes rather than longitudinal bars on the upper back, and by its broader, more conspicuous barring on primaries and rectrices. The two species tend not to overlap, with Stripe-backed favouring drier habitats (Hilty & Brown 1986).

DESCRIPTION *C. n. nuchalis*
Adult Crown, centres of feathers dull black, broadly edged with buffy-grey, giving a buffy-grey mottled with dark appearance in fresh plumage; nape and shoulders with conspicuous broad, longitudinal streaks of dull black and white, becoming more diffuse and duller on lower back and rump. Rectrices dull black, the outerwebs with triangular indentations of white, giving the appearance of white bars on the closed tail. Throat grey-white, with diffuse greyish spots on lower throat, becoming darker and more conspicuous on chest, coalescing to form bars on lower chest and flanks. Vent grey-white. Primaries and secondaries dull black with white spots on outerwebs giving about four white bars on closed wing; greater or lesser coverts also dull black, tipped with off-white, giving bars on shoulders. Iris white or straw-yellow, upper mandible blackish or bluish-black with pale edges, lower mandible greyish, pale flesh-colour or white, legs and feet slate-grey.
Juvenile Differs from adult by having solid blackish crown, colour of back, wings and tail more brownish-black, spotting on underparts much reduced with little barring on belly. Markings on crown and back more diffuse. Iris grey.

GEOGRAPHICAL VARIATION
   C. n. nuchalis 'Orinocan Banded Wren' (eastern and

central Venezuela from Bolívar westwards to Barinas extending to the Caribbean coast in Sucre) Described above.
   C. n. brevipennis (Caribbean coast of Venezuela from Miranda and Carabobo south to Guarico) Similar to *nuchalis* but much more heavily spotted below, blackish crown markings, more extensive and more prominent, grey of crown darker (Hilty & Brown 1986).
   C. n. pardus (western part of range; Caribbean coast of Colombia south through the lower Magdalena valley to about 8°N) Similar to *nuchalis*, but black spottings on lower surface reduced, no trace of bars (in contrast to *C. n. nuchalis*.), pileum lighter grey, bill large and heavy (Hilty & Brown 1986).

VOICE Song is a series of hollow scratchy notes, half a dozen or more in sequence. The principal pair of a group of wrens occupying a territory (see below) sing vigorously in duet, frequently sitting near each other on a branch. The duets consist of precisely timed repeated cadences of harsh notes, the duetters alternating, or at least intercalating, their individual contributions (Wiley & Wiley 1977). Frequently, other members of the group will then join in, with at times, up to five birds singing simultaneously. A variety of other notes, typically harsh and rasping, used to maintain contact and during aggressive or defensive activities against predators.

HABITAT Bush and open forest, both dry and semi-humid, including gallery forest. In Colombia occupies both very dry and very wet areas (Darlington 1931), but generally in drier areas than Band-backed Wren. Frequently associated with ponds and small lakes (Barnés 1939).

HABITS In general behaviour, typical of the genus; a noisy and demonstrative bird, not at all secretive. Forages in all levels of vegetation and on tree trunks. Has what is probably the most developed and complex breeding and social behaviour of any wren. A co-operative polyandrous breeder, with groups of up to 14 individuals defending territories , usually, in the region of 1–4ha in extent (Piper & Slater 1993). In the group, there will be one principle pair, which are the most persistent singers in duet, and which alone will breed (Rabenold 1985). The remaining birds are mostly offspring produced by the dominant pair which have not yet dispersed (Rabenold 1990). Most birds will participate in breeding only as assistants; elevation to breeding status is strictly age-determined. Assistants may contribute as much to the feeding of young as the actual parents. Breeding success is strongly correlated with the number of assistants; furthermore, only pairs with at least two auxiliaries will attempt a second brood (Rabenold 1984). Young birds of both sexes usually remain in their natal groups for about a year, after which all females, and a majority of males, disperse to breed with nearby groups; those males which remain in the group, although initially of subordinate rank, may later rise to a senior and hence breeding status (Rabenold 1984, Piper & Slater 1993). There is thus a mechanism to minimise incest. Vacancies in large groups are much sought-after and are the object of much competition; by contrast, vacancies in smaller groups are little desired and may not be taken up (Zack & Rabenold 1989). Predators and other species may be attacked and harassed by most individuals of a group; Shiny Cowbirds *Molothrus bonariensis*, which are brood parasites, are usually attacked with vigour. Groups and individuals are able to recognise the songs of neighbours, which receive a less vigorous response, than the songs of strangers, which might indicate a new group with potential territorial ambitions; these tend to elicit a very energetic reaction (Wiley & Wiley 1977).

STATUS AND DISTRIBUTION In suitable habitat very common; territories of 1–4ha may be contiguous, each with a group of 5 to 14 birds. Breeds from northern Colombia (Córdoba) through northern Venezuela east to the Orinoco delta, but absent from the Maracaibo basin; sea-level to 800m.

BREEDING Only the dominant pair in a group breed. Nests are of two types; if built by the wrens themselves, a large, untidy domed structure, built of grass, fibres, string and other debris, copiously lined with feathers, at heights of 2–10m above the ground, in leguminous (most frequently) or palm trees, usually located near the end of slim branches for protection against monkey predators. Frequently usurps the nests of other species, most especially the pendant twig nests of the Plain-fronted Thornbird *Phacellodomus rufifrons*, but also other

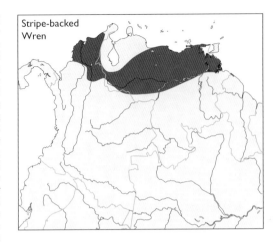

roofed nests with entrances in the side, such as those of Kiskadees *Pitangus* sp.; in these cases the nest is relined with feathers. When disturbed, blocks up the nest entrance with feathers (Cherrie 1916). Eggs usually four, unmarked white. Egg-laying is triggered by the onset of heavy rains at the beginning of the wet season, which in Venezuela is usually late March to early June; clutches are usually started 5–19 days after the first heavy precipitation (Thomas 1979). Incubation, by dominant female only, 18–21 days. Young are fed by entire group and fledge probably in 19 days; in larger groups, individuals apparently work less hard, each bird making fewer feeding visits than in small groups. Brood-parasitism by Shiny Cowbirds may occur in 10–30% of observed nests, and may be a limiting factor in population; the wrens accept and brood cowbird eggs without question. May be multiple-brooded, with second or even third clutches; however, only larger groups are able to rear multiple clutches successfully.

FOOD Mostly invertebrate.

MOVEMENTS None; dispersal of young birds (see above) is short-range, otherwise totally sedentary.

MEASUREMENTS Wing of male 74–77, of female 71.5–73.5; tail of male 71–74, of female 66–70; exposed culmen of male 17-18, of female 16.5–17.5; tarsus of male 25–25.5, of female 23–24.

---

11 FASCIATED WREN
Campylorhynchus fasciatus

Plate 4

Furnarius fasciatus Swainson 1837, Peru.

Alternative names: Banded Wren; Spanish *Soterrey Ondeado*

A little-studied species, in spite of the fact that within its rather limited range it is a common and conspicuous bird.

IDENTIFICATION Length 19cm. Within its range unmistakable, the only member of its genus. Similar to the Stripe-backed Wren of northern South America, but widely separated geographically from that species. The

Band-backed Wren, from which it differs by its greyer crown, lack of ochraceous tinge on the lower belly and generally more diffuse, less sharp, markings, is also geographically separate; the Fasciated Wren also occurs only in the more arid areas.

DESCRIPTION *C. f. fasciatus*
Adult Crown medium grey with conspicuous black speckles; shoulders, back and rump blackish-grey with prominent off-white speckles tending to coalesce as bars on lower back and rump. Wing-coverts strongly marked

with bars of buffy-white and blackish brown. Primaries and secondaries blackish-brown, the outerwebs having four or five large patches of buffy-white, the whole giving prominent and obvious bars on the closed wing. Rectrices blackish-brown with about nine well-marked lateral bars of buffy-white. Supercilium greyish-white, not particularly well-defined. Ear-coverts mottled grey-buff. Chin and chest off-white, belly pale buff-white, heavily marked with round blackish-grey spots which coalesce into transverse bars on the belly and flanks. Thighs and vent barred dull buff and dull blackish-brown. Bill notably long and thin. Iris red-brown to pale whitish-tan, upper mandible dark grey or dark brown, lower mandible greyish-horn, legs dark tan to dull yellowish.

Juvenile Very similar; markings on underparts less heavy and more diffuse, cap darker, iris slate-grey.

GEOGRAPHICAL VARIATION

C. f. fasciatus (arid coastal regions of Peru, from north-western Lima north to Piura) Described above.

C. f. pallescens 'Ecuadorian Banded Wren' (northern Peru [northern Piura, Tumbes] to central Ecuador [Guayas, El Oro, Loja]) Very similar to *fasciatus*. Bill shorter, plumage generally much paler, whitish supercilia wider with dusky edges; markings on underparts less pronounced.

VOICE Song is a series of short, harsh churring notes, repeated many times, often interspersed with a series of more gurgling notes. A duetting singer; in a group, birds invariably duet with an individual of the opposite sex. Calls are sharp *churrs* and other harsh notes.

HABITAT Arid and semi-arid areas. Thorny scrubland, including much disturbed areas such as the edges of cropland, grazing paddocks, gardens and around farmhouses. Seems to adapt well to human disturbance so long as some bushy areas remain and is common in citrus orchards. Usually in valley bottoms rather than more sparse habitat further up (K. N. Rabenold pers. comm.). Sea-level to 1,500m, rarely to 2,500m (Cajamarca, Peru). In Ecuador, second growth of humid tropical forest, Bombax-dominated deciduous forest, tall shrubby deciduous woodland (Selander 1964).

HABITS Very noisy and demonstrative, with little fear of humans; frequently found in boisterous parties (presumably extended family groups). Forages in bushes, occasionally on the ground, and on roofs of huts and farmhouses; will enter buildings to take insects from spider webs (Taczanowski 1884).

STATUS AND DISTRIBUTION In much of its range quite common. Arid areas of Ecuador from Los Ríos and Guayas southwards (avoiding the more humid coastline north of Guayas), inland to Azuay, El Oro and Loja; northern Peru from Tumbes south to Lima, east to San Martín. In spite of the somewhat limited range, not apparently in any hazard due to its compatibility with general farming in arid areas.

BREEDING No published data; the following information comes from field work by Dr K. N. Rabenold in northern Peru (pers. comm.).

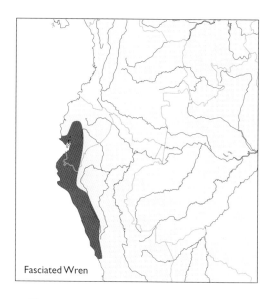

Fasciated Wren

The nest is a typical *Campylorhynchus* structure, domed with a side entrance, made of grass with a lining of feathers and cotton. Nests are located in a variety of sites; in mesquite trees, in lemon trees in a citrus orchard and in columnar cacti. Frequently builds in the disused mud-oven nests of the Pale-legged Hornero *Furnarius leucopus*; one nest located on a porch under the eaves of a house. Eggs not described, probably spotted; incubation period about 17 days. Brood size probably usually three or four; from one to four juveniles seen with parents. Breeding season probably from May to August; nests in June and July still had fledglings. Certainly a cooperative breeder, although out of 20 territories studied, two were occupied by single, unaided pairs. In other cases up to 10 birds occupied a territory, but only one female had a brood patch. In each group one pair of birds was clearly dominant. The offspring of a pair tend to remain to assist in at least the next year; thereafter females tend to disperse to other groups but males usually remain with the natal group, graduating to breeding rank as vacancies occur. Birds roost communally in nests.

FOOD Little information recorded; presumably typical of the genus (i.e. invertebrate, with substantial amounts of vegetable matter in the form of seeds and fruit). Stomach contents 'insect remains and vegetative matter'.

MOVEMENTS Apparently sedentary.

MEASUREMENTS (*C. f. pallescens*) Wing of male 82.4–91.9, of female 81.7–82.5; tail of male 84.0–92.2, of female 81.3–90.7; bill of male 14.7–16.8, of female ; tarsus of male 24.3–27.3, of female 22.4–25.9 (Selander 1964).

Picocolaptes zonatus Lesson 1832 'California' (obviously in error).

Alternative names: Banded Cactus Wren, Barred Wren; Spanish *Carrasquita, Cucarachero Listado, Matraca-barrada Tropical;* Cakchiquel, *Zorochuc;* Nahuatl, *Ayacatcho*

An abundant, widely distributed and generally unmistakable wren which forms a noisy and conspicuous element of the fauna of a variety of habitats from central Mexico to Ecuador.

IDENTIFICATION Length 18.5–20.5cm. A distinctive species which cannot be confused with any other wren in its extensive range. In Mexico, it most closely resembles Grey-barred Wren, from which it differs in having cinnamon belly and no bars on the flanks; juveniles more closely resemble each other, but Grey-barred juvenile is paler below and has obscure flank bars. There may be a small area of sympatry in Veracruz state, but over most of the two species' range there is no overlap. In Colombia, the two most similar species are Thrush-like Wren, which has a uniform dark back, and Stripe-backed Wren, which has longitudinal stripes rather than lateral bars on the upper back, and no buff on the underparts. The Thrush-like Wren is geographically separated from Band-backed, and the Stripe-backed and Band-backed do not apparently occur together (Hilty & Brown 1986). In Ecuador, Fasciated Wren is similar, but is more diffusely patterned and lacks the buffy underparts; the two species' ranges approach each other in western Ecuador, but do not overlap.

DESCRIPTION *C. z. zonatus*
Adult Head and crown dark blackish-grey, each feather broadly edged with lighter grey giving a speckled appearance. Shoulders and back dull black with prominent broad off-white streaks, forming broad bars further down, the bars extending sideways onto the shoulders and greater coverts as prominent bands of dull black and off-white. On lower back and rump bars become more diffuse and strongly suffused with orange-brown, especially at the sides. Rectrices dull black with prominent off-white bars on both webs, the markings stronger on the lateral feathers; central rectrices with dull, diffuse, buff-brown bars on outerwebs. No white tips to rectrices. Primaries and secondaries dull black with heavy off-white spotting on outerwebs, forming four or five obvious white bars on closed wing. Throat and upper chest very pale buff-white with circular dull black spots on throat, becoming larger and more obvious on chest. Belly immaculate orange-buff, the colour being richer on flanks and lower belly. Iris reddish-brown, bill black or dark dusky horn, legs yellowish-flesh to yellowish-olive.
Juvenile Very distinctive from adult plumage. Crown blackish, contrasting strongly with cinnamon-buff nape (giving a strongly capped appearance). Back reddish-brown with numerous blackish-brown spots, not forming prominent transverse bars. Chest buffy-white, totally lacking spots. Belly pale cinnamon-buff, much less strongly coloured than adult.

GEOGRAPHICAL VARIATION
C. z. zonatus (Puebla and Veracruz, Mexico) Described above.
C. z. restrictus 'Tabasco Cactus Wren' (southern Mexico [southern Veracruz and northern Oaxaca] to Belize and Guatemala) Underparts more heavily spotted than *zonatus*, with the markings extending onto the cinnamon belly and flanks, often forming conspicuous bars. Substantially larger than *zonatus*.
C. z. vulcanius (South Mexico from Chiapas through central Guatemala, central Honduras to central Nicaragua) Belly less strongly buff than *zonatus* with no spots; barring on upper back narrower; juvenile paler. Relatively small.
C. z. costaricensis 'Costa Rican Banded Wren' (Caribbean drainage of central Costa Rica to coastal regions of north-west Panama) Similar to *restrictus*, but belly without spots or bars, and with a deeper cinnamon colour than *zonatus*. Much smaller than *zonatus*.
C. z. panamensis 'Panama Banded Wren' (western Panama only [Veraguas]) Very similar to *costaricensis* with which it intergrades in western Panama. Abdomen deeper colour than *costaricensis*, smaller black centres on feathers of pileum.
C. z. brevirostris 'Short-billed Banded Wren' (two disjunct populations; northern and north-central Colombia, and north-western Ecuador) Belly much paler than *zonatus*; dark markings extend over most of lower abdomen, with bars brownish, not black; sides of neck ochraceous. Juvenile paler than *zonatus*.
C. z. curvirostris 'Curve-billed Banded Wren' (Santa Marta region, Colombia) Very similar to, and possibly indistinguishable from, *brevirostris*. Smaller than *brevirostris*, posterior upperparts deeper buff (Hellmayr 1924–1949, Selander 1964).

In south-west Colombia (Nariño) apparently hybridises with White-headed Wren (q.v.) (Haffer 1975).

VOICE Song is a jumbled series of harsh scratchy notes, usually in phrases of about two to three seconds, frequently repeated many times. Male and female sing duets in unison (Skutch 1960). Call is a *churring* somewhat Jay-like note, used incessantly when birds are in flocks. During courtship pairs make low, soft calls to each other.

HABITAT The most catholic of its genus as regards both vegetation-type and climate. In Mexico and Guatemala from sea-level to more than 3,000m, but to only 1,700m in Costa Rica and Colombia and 1,000m in Panama and Ecuador. At lower altitudes lives in humid forest, including areas much modified and cut-over, in palm groves, in trees bordering farm fields and forest clearings. At intermediate altitudes in both relatively dry oak and pine forest, and in very wet epiphytic forest. In Guatemala at 3,000m in cypress forest edge.

HABITS A rambunctious and demonstrative bird. Usually encountered in parties of up to a dozen individuals, probably based on families, which move through the forest as a scattered group, keeping contact constantly with raucous calls. Forages in all levels of forest, turning over leaf-litter on the ground and prising apart lichens and loose bark of trees, occasionally hanging head downwards in the manner of a nuthatch. On occasion feeds in mixed flocks with other species. Birds routinely roost in groups in nests, sometimes with up to a dozen individuals crammed together, sometimes only a pair. Roosting nests are usually built at a considerable height (up to 30m, rarely as low as 4m) in trees. Birds may sometimes sing from the interior of a nest, even one shared with other individuals. In groups, mutual preening is common.

Band-backed Wren

STATUS AND DISTRIBUTION Four disjunct populations; mostly Caribbean drainage of Mexico, from north-

ern Veracruz through Guatemala, southern Belize, Honduras to central Nicaragua; central Costa Rica and Atlantic coast of Panama, stopping about 150km west of canal; North Colombia; and north-west Ecuador.

BREEDING The nest is a rather untidy globular structure, made of plant fibres, straw and moss, and lined with wool and hair, about 25–30cm in diameter, with a lateral entrance about 10cm in diameter, protected by a short porch above. Nests are located in trees or bushes, 2–30m from the ground, but usually at a good height, 8m or more. In dryer highland areas, nests are placed conspicuously in oak or pine trees; in wetter areas, often under cover of epiphytes. Nest-building may be by male or by both sexes. Roosting nests are the same as breeding nests, and in this case construction may be a cooperative affair involving several birds. Eggs three to five, white, either unmarked or with a few pale brown speckles, laid from March to August. Apparently, at least double-brooded in lowlands; attempts at third broods usually abandoned. In highland areas single-brooded. Incubation period unknown, but probably in region of 20 days. Young are fed not only by both sexes, but also a variable number of 'helpers', from one to five, which are presumably immature birds. Helpers bring food, but female alone broods the young. After fledging which occurs at about 18–19 days the family usually moves out and roosts communally, usually in another dormitory nest. Dormitory nests are changed quite frequently.

FOOD Mostly invertebrate.

MOVEMENTS Apparently totally sedentary, without even altitudinal movement.

MEASUREMENTS (Means) Wing of male 84.8, of female 83.5; tail of male 87.8, of female 87.5; bill of male 17.0, of female 15.4; tarsus of male 25.2, of female 24.3 (10 male and 6 female specimens) (Selander 1964).

13   GREY-BARRED WREN
Campylorhynchus megalopterus

Plate 4

Campylorhynchus megalopterus Lafresnaye 1845 'Mexique'.

Alternative names: Grey Wren, Grey Cactus Wren; Spanish *Sonaja parda, Matraca-barrada Serrana*

A very distinctive wren, endemic to the higher altitudes of the Central Mexican plateau, where it is common in some forested locations.

IDENTIFICATION Length 17–19.5cm. The adult is essentially unmistakable. The largely grey plumage, heavily barred back, spotted throat and general lack of brown or buff tones is unlike any other species in its limited range. The juvenile plumage is quite different and is not dissimilar to the juvenile Band-backed Wren, with which it may be sympatric in parts of Oaxaca, Veracruz and Puebla. It differs from that species in having traces of darker bars on the flanks, less prominently marked nape and shoulders, and in being generally paler on the underparts.

DESCRIPTION *C. m. megalopterus*
Adult Crown blackish, with broad grey-brown edgings

on all feathers. Shoulders and back blackish, with prominent white markings, forming a collar of lateral streaks on shoulders and becoming broad transverse bars on back. Wing-coverts heavily barred buffy-white and blackish. Primaries and secondaries blackish-brown with four or five buff-white spots on outerwebs forming bars on closed wing. Rectrices blackish-grey with seven or eight transverse bars of off-white, giving a strongly barred appearance to the whole tail. Supercilium off-white, lores and ear-coverts speckled greyish-buff. Chin, throat and chest off-white becoming buffy on lower belly; prominent circular blackish spots on throat, chest and belly, becoming transverse bars on flanks and lower belly. Underwing whitish-grey. Iris reddish-brown, bill blackish above, grey-black below, legs brownish-flesh colour, feet somewhat darker.
Juvenile Quite different. Crown solid black, shoulders and back diffusely patterned with blackish and buffy-brown, wings with transverse bars of buff-brown and blackish-brown, tails with buffy bars, underparts almost without markings except for diffuse and ill-defined barring on the flanks and lower belly.

GEOGRAPHICAL VARIATION

C. m. megalopterus 'Huitzilac Cactus Wren' (central Mexican highlands from Jalisco through Michoacán to western Puebla) Described above.

C. m. nelsoni 'Grey Cactus Wren' (disjunct from *megalopterus*; eastern Puebla, Veracruz and Oaxaca) Differs from *megalopterus* by smaller size, with markings on underparts much paler, brown or greyish brown instead of blackish (Hellmayr 1934).

VOICE Song is quite similar to that of Band-backed Wren, a rapid harsh chattering described as a 'varied and rollicking *ke wook'a ke wook'a* or *kurr-e te-rek* etc.' (Howell & Webb 1995). Sings in simultaneous duet between sexes (K. Barker pers. comm.). Calls a loud harsh *karr.* Contact notes among a group a low *rrt-trrrt.*

HABITAT Generally montane forest of various kinds. It occurs in a variety of forest types, including epiphytic forest, from pure stands of tall fir in Michoacán (Lea & Edwards 1950) to humid pine-oak forest (Binford 1989). It seems to be able to tolerate a moderate amount of disturbance, since it appears to be as common in cut-over areas as in virgin forest (Selander 1964). From about 2,100m to 3,150m (Davis & Russell 1953).

HABITS Typical of its genus; noisy and not shy. Usually found in small parties from 6–12 birds, moving through higher and medium levels of forest, although it will descend to the understorey. Does not apparently forage on the ground. Spends most of its time probing among epiphytes, mosses and lichens and in pine cones; it has a somewhat finer bill than most *Campylorhynchus* wrens. The race *nelsoni* is said to be less wary than *megalopterus* (Selander 1964).

STATUS AND DISTRIBUTION In many areas of suitable habitat quite common; since it appears to be somewhat tolerant of disturbance, not apparently in hazard notwithstanding its restricted range. Two disjunct populations; from the Sierra de Colima, Jalisco and higher peaks through northern Michoacán, México, Morelos to western Puebla (*megalopterus*); and marginally in Veracruz (west of Orizaba), eastern Puebla and in high mountains of northern Oaxaca (Cerro San

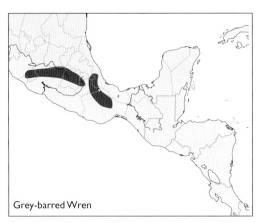

Grey-barred Wren

Felipe, Sierra Aloapaneca, etc.). Readily found at La Cumbre, Cerro San Felipe (Wheatley & Brewer in press).

BREEDING The few nests so far described have been domed constructions, built of mosses, with an entrance hole midway up one side, situated 15 to 20m up in oak, conifer or madrono trees (Rowley 1984, S. Howell pers. comm.). Eggs not described. An adult female feeding three full-sized juveniles on 26 April; females in breeding condition 27 April; nests, either for breeding or as a dormitory in construction, 8 and 27 June (Rowley 1984). Breeding pairs are assisted by helpers (K. Barker pers. comm.). Incubation and fledgling periods unknown.

FOOD No information; presumably predominantly invertebrate.

MOVEMENTS Probably largely sedentary; no information on altitudinal movements if any.

MEASUREMENTS (*C. m. megalopterus*, north-eastern Michoacán) Wing of male 91, of female 86.7; tail of male 86.6, of female 82.6; bill of male 15.1, of female 13.7; tarsus of male 24.9, of female 24.4.

(*C. m. nelsoni*, Sierra Madre, Veracruz) Wing of male 89.8, of female 78.0; tail of male 80.0, of female 78.0; bill of male 14.4, of female 13.1; tarsus of male 26.4, of female 25.3 (Selander 1964).

ODONTORCHILUS

An aberrant genus consisting of two, or possibly one, species found in central South America. Very small, but with an exceptionally long tail; wings short and rounded, feet and legs rather thin and delicate. Rictal bristles strongly developed. Bill long, fine and decurved, the upper mandible having a unique notch about two-thirds of the way to the top. Possibly most closely related to *Campylorhynchus*, but very different in size, pattern and habits.

14   TOOTH-BILLED WREN
Odontorchilus cinereus   Plate 5

Odontorhynchus cinereus Pelzeln 1868 Salto do Girao, Rio Madera, Brazil.

Alternative name: Portuguese *Cambaxirra-cinzenta*

The lowland congener of the better-known Grey-mantled Wren, the Tooth-billed Wren has been very little

studied and is confined entirely to western Amazonian Brazil and adjacent Bolivia. The two birds have been considered to be conspecific; however, the widely separated ranges, the somewhat different habitats and, perhaps more significant, the substantially different songs suggest that the two are distinct species.

IDENTIFICATION Length 12cm. Not likely to be confused with any other wren (the Grey-mantled Wren being allopatric) due to its general grey colour and long tail. Distinguished from the sympatric Gnatcatchers (*Polioptila*) (Tropical and, barely, Guianian) by the barred rectrices without prominent white at the sides.

DESCRIPTION
Adult Crown almost cinnamon-grey-brown; back and shoulders mid-grey. Primaries and secondaries somewhat darker grey, tertials the same with extremely diffuse darker bars on innerwebs. Rump and uppertail-coverts grey-brown with about six broad, dark greyish-black bands. Outer rectrices, barring restricted to outerweb, but on both webs on central rectrices. Outer three rectrices with pale tips, with penultimate dark band. Ear-coverts and sides of neck grey-brown. Throat and chest buffy-grey. Flanks greyish-white. Centre of belly pale-buff. Undertail-coverts greyish-white, strongly barred with greyish-black. Underwing-coverts greyish-white. Vague suggestion of small greyish-brown streaks, but no defined superciliary. Iris dark brown to brick-red. Upper mandible black. Lower mandible black with grey base. Legs dark grey.
Juvenile Lower mandible with brownish base.

GEOGRAPHICAL VARIATION None; monotypic.

VOICE Song is a long series of single notes, ten or more, on the same pitch, the notes being much longer and more distinct than the rapid trill of the Grey-mantled Wren; also a high-pitched series of *swee* notes (Bates *et al.* 1992). Both sexes sing.

HABITAT Lowland forest below 500m.

HABITS Little known. Occurs in pairs or small groups, sometimes in association with flycatchers, tanagers, furnariids etc. in mixed flocks. Forages in the upper forest canopy at heights of up to 30m.

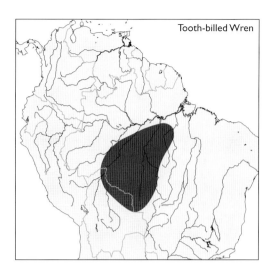

Tooth-billed Wren

STATUS AND DISTRIBUTION Central Brazil from just south of the Amazon in Pará and Amazonas south to central Mato Grosso and westwards to eastern Rondônia; also eastern Bolivia (Santa Cruz). Apparently relatively uncommon over much of its range, although fairly common in a narrow zone of forest in eastern Bolivia (Bates *et al.* 1992).

BREEDING Nest and eggs unknown. One female collected in eastern Bolivia on 1 September was in laying condition (Bates *et al.* 1992).

FOOD Not recorded; presumably predominantly or entirely invertebrate.

MOVEMENTS Not known; presumably largely sedentary.

MEASUREMENTS No data available.

---

15   GREY-MANTLED WREN
Odontorchilus branickii   Plate 5

Odontorhynchus branickii Taczanowski and Berlepsch, 1885, Machay and Mapoto, eastern Ecuador.

Alternative name: Spanish *Soterrey Dorsigris*

A very unusual wren, light and fairy-like with a long tail which is constantly twitched and cocked.

IDENTIFICATION Length 12cm. Not likely to be confused with any other wren, the very similar (and possibly conspecific) Tooth-billed Wren being widely separated both geographically and altitudinally. The long tail, constantly in motion and frequently cocked over the back gives it the appearance of a Gnatcatcher (*Polioptila*); however, the heavy bars on the tail and lack of white rectrices distinguishes it from all members of that genus (Ridgely & Tudor 1989).

DESCRIPTION *O. b. branickii*
Adult Forehead tawny-brown, becoming darker brown on crown, merging into mid-grey shoulders and upper back. Crown feathers, especially at front, with diffuse

buff streaking. Back medium grey blending to medium brown rump and uppertail-coverts. Primaries and secondaries slightly darker. Tertials with very ill-defined, slightly darker barring (not normally visible in field). Rectrices mid-grey with six or seven prominent black bars on outerwebs of feathers, more simply patterned and more boldly contrasted than in *cinereus*. Outer rectrices with subterminal white bar visible from below. Chin, chest and belly white with slight buff tinge (less buff than *cinereus*). Flanks greyish white. Undertail-coverts with strong black bars. Obscure grey-brown supercilium; ear-coverts grey-brown, diffusely streaked whitish-grey. Iris brown, upper mandible black, lower mandible silvery-grey, legs and feet grey.
Juvenile Very similar to adult; upper chest with more pronounced buff wash, markings on ear-coverts more diffuse, brown on forehead more dull.

GEOGRAPHICAL VARIATION
   O. b. branickii 'Branicki's Tooth-billed Wren' (south-

ern Andes of Colombia (Caqueta, Putumayo), central Ecuador on both Andean slopes to northern Peru; central Peru; and north-eastern Bolivia) Described above.

O. b. minor 'Lesser Tooth-billed Wren' (western Andes of southern Colombia and extreme northern Ecuador) Slightly smaller; central rectrices without strong bars.

VOICE Song is a high, weak, very rapid and rather metallic trill, all on one pitch, more reminiscent of some of the North American warblers than of a wren. No evidence of antiphonal or duetting song. Call when foraging, a high *si-si-si.*

HABITAT Humid subtropical and humid upper-tropical forest, mostly 1,400–2,200m, occasionally higher; on Pacific slope 800–1,100m (Ridgely & Tudor 1989).

HABITS Usually found singly or in pairs, but very frequently in mixed flocks of *Tanagra* tanagers, becards, Toucan-barbets etc. Atypically for a wren, feeds high up in the trees, in the canopy or below the canopy. Very active; emphasises its superficial resemblance to a Gnatcatcher by constantly twitching and cocking its tail.

STATUS AND DISTRIBUTION Western Colombia (Valle, Cauca, Nariño) and adjacent Ecuador to north-western Pichincha; disjunctly, eastern slopes of eastern Andes in Colombia through Ecuador, mostly on eastern Andes, rarely on western Andes (Ridgely and Greenfield 2001) to northern Peru (Cajamarca); disjunctly, north-eastern Bolivia (La Paz) (Parker *et al.* 1980). Not generally common; most readily seen in Ecuador on the Loreto Road and at the San Raphael (Coca) Falls (Green 1996).

Grey-mantled Wren

BREEDING Nest and eggs unknown.

FOOD Presumably mainly or entirely invertebrate. 'Insect remains', 'insects', 'insect parts' (stomach contents of museum specimens).

MOVEMENTS Apparently sedentary.

MEASUREMENTS Males, wing 58–61, exposed culmen 12–14, tarsus 16.5–19, tail 49–51 (4 specimens). Females, wing 55–57, exposed culmen 12.5–13, tarsus 16.5–18, tail 46–50 (3 specimens).

SALPINCTES

Medium-sized wren (wing 64–75mm, length 14–16cm). Bill straight, decurved slightly at tip, shorter than head, fairly slender (though stouter than *Catherpes*). Wings moderately rounded, rather long, sixth to eighth primaries longest. Rectrices very broad, tail moderately rounded. Legs and feet fairly sturdy. Probably most closely related to *Catherpes* and *Hylorchilus*. One species, with some geographic variation in southern populations, ranging from western Canada (British Columbia, Alberta, western Saskatchewan) to southern Mexico, with disjunct populations in Guatemala, Honduras and El Salvador, Nicaragua and in north-eastern Costa Rica.

16   ROCK WREN
Salpinctes obsoletus   Plate 5

Troglodytes obsoletus Say, 1823, South Platte, Colorado.

Alternative names: French *Troglodyte de rochers*; Spanish *Saltapared Roquero, Saltaladera, Chinchirivín de las Rocas, Saltapared comesebo*; Navajo *Tse Noolch 'Oshiibahi*

A characteristic and cheerful feature of the fauna of arid or semi-arid areas of western North America and central America, often inhabiting dry rocky areas where few other species of birds are found.

IDENTIFICATION Length 13.5–14.5cm. In most of its range and habitat, not likely to be confused with other species. The grey-brown adult plumage, with prominent buff eye-stripe, fine streaks on the breast and unique buff sides to the tail are unlike any other wren. Frequently

shares habitat with Canyon Wren, which is immediately distinguished by sharply contrasting white bib and chestnut belly, and reddish-brown upperparts. Juvenile Rock Wrens more closely resemble House Wrens, from which they differ in possessing buffy tail-edgings and buffy rump.

DESCRIPTION *S. o. obsoletus*
Adult Head, crown, nape and back grey-brown, thickly patterned with dark spots; on the crown each spot with minute white edging. Markings less thick and more diffuse on back, forming obscure dark bars on mid-back, continuing over onto shoulders and greater coverts. Tertials pale grey-brown with prominent darker brown bars on both webs, giving a strongly barred appearance

on closed wing. Secondaries grey-brown, outerweb with light grey-brown bars. Lower back chestnut-brown, contrasting with grey-brown upper back, colour becoming less intense and more buff-brown on lower rump and uppertail-coverts. Rectrices buff-brown, prominently barred with blackish-brown, the bars being broader on outer rectrices. All rectrices except centre two with prominent buff tips, largest on outermost rectrices, giving a wide buff bar on the spread tail. Underparts dull grey, becoming rufous-buff on belly, the colour richer on the flanks. Obvious grey-buff supercilium, contrasting with grey-black streaking, becoming more spotted on chest; belly largely unmarked, although some individuals have diffuse barring on flanks. Underwing-coverts buffy-brown. Iris brown, upper mandible dark horn with pale base, mandible pale pinkish-grey, legs blackish-brown.

Juvenile Generally duller, spots on upper and lower parts much reduced and less prominent, obscure barring on back; underparts paler than adult, with more brownish tinge on undertail-coverts.

GEOGRAPHICAL VARIATION There has been substantial debate about the recognisable races of the Rock Wren, various authorities separating, or merging, different populations according to plumage and measurements (Linton 1908, Swarth 1914, Grinnell 1928, Griscom 1928). We have followed the lead of Peters (1931–1986) in recognising six races.

S. o. obsoletus (breeds across western North America, from the southern parts of British Columbia, Alberta and Saskatchewan east to Oklahoma and Texas and south through highland areas of Mexico to central Oaxaca. Withdraws in winter from the area north of southern Nevada and Colorado. Synonyms, *S. o. notius*, Mexico from Jalisco and Puebla to Oaxaca, *S. o. pulverius*, San Nicholas Island, California) Described above.

S. o. exsul 'San Benedicto Rock Wren' (formerly, San Benedicto Island, Revillagigedo group, Mexico) San Benedicto was devastated by a catastrophic volcanic eruption on 1 August 1952; a few wrens survived the initial eruption but by December 1952 all were gone (Brattstrom 1990). Similar to *obsoletus*, but with lateral rectrices more numerously barred with cinnamon-buff (the outermost with one or two distinct bands on innerweb and three or four on outer), wing shorter, tail longer, bill and feet larger (Hellmayr 1924–1949).

S. o. guadeloupensis 'Guadelupe Rock Wren' (Guadelupe Island, off Baja California) Darker than *obsoletus*, heavier bill, legs longer; juveniles have upperparts darker with heavier barring.

S. o. tenuirostris 'San Benito Rock Wren' (San Benito Islands, Baja California) Identical in plumage to *obsoletus*, but bill longer and more slender.

S. o. neglectus 'Chancol Rock Wren', 'Spotted Rock Wren' (Highlands of Central America from Chiapas to central Honduras) Darker than *obsoletus* with heavier markings.

S. o. guttatus 'Salvador Rock Wren', 'Nicaraguan Rock Wren' (El Salvador to Guanacaste province, north-western Costa Rica) Very different from *obsoletus*, underparts heavily barred to lower belly, generally very dark.

VOICE Song loud and carrying. Usual song is a series of loud simple whistles, with a slight burry tone, often interspersed with gurgles, short polysyllabic phrases and buzzy trills. Calls are short and buzzy, *chick-urrr* etc., also harsh scolding notes when alarmed.

HABITAT Barren rocky areas, including boulder-falls and screes, usually with little vegetation; also bare areas of sun-baked mud in canyons. Will colonise areas of clear-cut forest (Marshall & Horn 1973) as well as artificial sites such as quarries and areas of mining tailings (Renaud 1979). In vagrant situations it seems frequently to search out artificial areas such as concrete structures that resemble its natural habitat.

HABITS An active and busy bird, scurrying mouse-like among the boulders of its barren habitat. Flights are usually short and low. Not at all difficult to observe, although when alarmed it is very adept at disappearing in areas with little vegetation cover. Roosts in a vertical posture propped up by the tail in the manner of a woodpecker (Bond 1940).

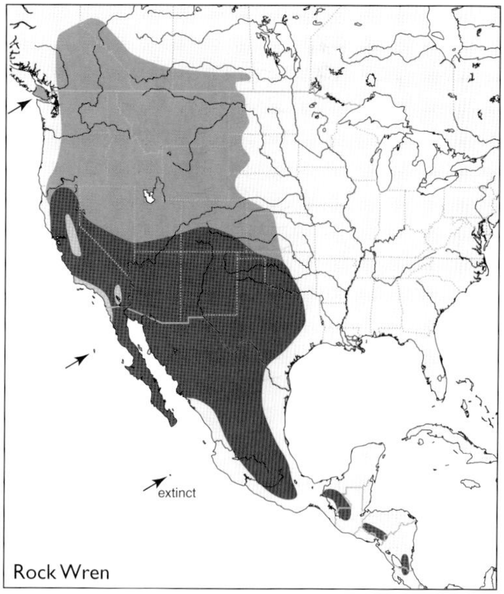

Rock Wren

STATUS AND DISTRIBUTION Breeds from British Columbia (southern Vancouver Island, mountains north to about 54°N), adjacent Alberta, southern Saskatchewan, east as far as western section of both Dakotas, western Oklahoma, central Texas, the central highlands of Mexico as far south as Oaxaca; absent from the lowlands of western Mexico, south of central Sinaloa; north-western Mexico including Baja California and most adjacent islands, California, Oregon and Washington, but absent from the wetter regions of coastal north-western United States. Disjunct populations in highlands of Chiapas State, Mexico and adjacent Guatemala; central Honduras and northern El Salvador; and Nicaragua and extreme north-western Costa Rica.

BREEDING In cavities and crevices in rock-piles, in abandoned gopher-holes and occasionally in artificial sites in abandoned buildings. Nests are made of grasses, straw and rootlets, and lined with horsehair, feathers or sheep's wool (Bent 1948). One measured nest was 14cm external size, with a cavity 7.5 x 3.75cm. Like the Canyon Wren, will sometimes accumulate all sorts of extraneous matter in the nest; one nest in the Farallone Islands, California contained 1,665 miscellaneous objects, including nails, rabbit bones, shell fragments and bits of rusty iron (Ray 1904). A characteristic of Rock Wrens' nests is the foundation, of small stones and pebbles. The nest usually rests upon a base of small flat stones, which may be very extensive, and which usually extends in front of the nest provided there is space in the site; occasionally forming a pavement as much as 25cm long. These stone bases represent a substantial expenditure of energy on the part of the birds; the total weight of stones in one nest was 2.2kg, about one hundred and twenty times the average body weight (18g) of a Rock Wren. The average weight of stones used was 2.85g, and the heaviest, at 6.1g, was one-third the weight of the builder (Merola 1995). The siting of this nest required the birds to fly, carrying the stones in their bills. No very convincing explanation of the value of this stone base to the Rock Wrens' nest has been advanced (Bailey 1904, Smith 1904, Moreno 1994), but given the effort involved it must have some selective advantage. Similar behaviour is observed in the Black Wheatear *Oenanthe leucura* of Spain and Morocco, but in this case, unlike the Rock Wren, it is mainly the male which does the stone construction (Richardson 1965).

Clutches of the race *obsoletus* are usually five or six, more rarely four to eight, and occasionally as many as ten (Bent 1948). *Guadeloupensis* has smaller clutches, the usual number being four, sometimes five (Bryant 1887). Ground colour of eggs glossy white, sparingly speckled with fine reddish-brown markings. Dates of nesting vary according to latitude and altitude; in Baja California nesting may begin as early as mid-January, in California the first week of February, in New Mexico early March, and at higher elevations in Colorado and Saskatchewan not until late May (Renaud, Bent). Nest construction is probably by both sexes, but incubation by female alone, for 12–14 days (Merola 1995). Males feed the incubating female in a desultory manner, but she also leaves the nest to forage on her own. Young fledge after 14–16 days. Over much of its range double or triple-brooded, although northern populations do not have sufficient time for third broods.

FOOD Predominantly invertebrate. Known prey includes locusts and grasshoppers, earthworms and grubs, and spiders. The race *guadeloupensis* was seen to frequent slaughtering yards to glean insects from the offal (Ridgway 1876). Has been known to take young lizards (Contreras & Trevino 1987).

MOVEMENTS In winter, withdraws from northern positions of range; occurs from north-central California, southern Nevada, Utah and Colorado and extreme south-western Oklahoma. Southern populations and island populations appear to be sedentary. There are no significant banding recoveries for Rock Wren which would illustrate migration routes. Has occurred as a vagrant across virtually the entire North American continent. Frequent records in mid-western states; easternmost sites include coastal Nova Scotia, Massachusetts, New York, New Jersey, Florida and Louisiana. The great majority of vagrancies in the east occur between October and December. Has occurred in Mackenzie District, Northwest Territories, and has bred near Churchill, Manitoba, in sub-arctic tundra. It has been suggested that these latter birds may have been accidentally transported in railway boxcars (Seutin & Chartier 1989), but in view of the well documented long-distance wanderings of the species this explanation seems superfluous.

MEASUREMENTS Wing of male 68–74, of female 66-72; tail of male 47-52, of female 47–51; bill of male 16.5–19.0, of female 17.0–19.0; tarsus of male 20.5–23, of female 20.5–21.5 (Ridgway 1904).

CATHERPES

A monotypic genus, highly specialised for a life spent foraging on rock-faces and canyon walls. Modifications for this lifestyle include a long, fine, slightly decurved bill, which with the low flattened cranium and unique attachment of the cervical vertebrae to the skull allow the bird to reach into narrow crevices in rocks (Mirsky 1976). Short legs and large feet with long claws facilitate the exploitation of the same ecological niche. Tail is relatively long, wings also rather long and less rounded than *Troglodytes*, sixth and seventh primaries longest. Sexes similar though female has substantially shorter bill (Ridgway 1904). Probably most closely related to *Hylorchilus* of southern Mexico, a genus comprising two species confined to limestone karst habitat (Hardy & Delaney 1987).

17 CANYON WREN
Catherpes mexicanus
Plate 5

Thryothorus mexicanus Swainson 1829 Real del Monte, Hidalgo, Mexico.

Alternative names: Cañon Wren; Spanish, *Saltapared Barraquero, Saltapared risquero*; French, *Troglodyte des Canons*; Tarasco, *Katzas*; Navajo, *Tse Noolch Oshil*

An unusual species confined to cliffs and canyons in semi-arid or desert country, from Canada to southern Mexico. The song, a beautiful series of clear descending whistles, is a characteristic sound of the south-western canyonlands.

IDENTIFICATION Length 12.5–14cm. Cannot be confused with any other species in its range or habitat; may frequently be found with Rock Wren, from which it is immediately distinguished by the combination of a rich chestnut-back and belly contrasting with white throat and chest, and tail without buffy tips to outer rectrices.

DESCRIPTION *C. m. conspersus*
Adult Crown, forehead and nape grey-brown, thickly marked with fine off-white speckles. Shoulders and back becoming more rufous, shading into chestnut rump. Back with numerous darker brown spots, each spot terminating in a pale buff-white edging. Rectrices chestnut-brown, each feather with about eight narrow black bands forming parallel bars across entire tail. Primaries and secondaries chestnut-brown, with about ten dark brown bars on outerweb, giving a barred appearance to the closed wing. Shoulder and greater coverts medium-brown with fine off-white speckles. Chin, throat and chest grey-white, contrasting sharply with chestnut-brown belly, which deepens in colour to rich red-brown on lower belly and crissum. Mid-belly feathers with dark brown tips, each with narrow white edge, giving a loosely barred appearance. Ear-coverts grey-brown with fine whitish spots. Underwing-coverts mid-brown, with diffuse darker brown bars. Iris dark brown, bill greyish-black, paler at base of lower mandible; legs dull grey-black.
Juvenile Differs from adult in having pale speckles on upperparts extremely obscure and colour of underparts less bright with little barring. Upper mandible blackish-grey, lower mandible vinaceous-flesh, basal half paler.

GEOGRAPHICAL VARIATION There is much disagreement between various authorities as to the number of recognisable races. There is substantial, but inconsistent, variation in the plumage characteristics of the population in the United States; birds from the Pacific Coast tend to be predominately a darker, richer brown colour, in Utah a paler, tawny colour, and in the high northern plains ashy-grey; nevertheless the fluctuations in colour are 'spotty or local', without clear-cut clines (Miller 1948). We have followed the conservative approach of the fifth AOU Checklist (1957) and recognised three races only.

C. m. conspersus (southern British Columbia, through western United States to north-western Mexico [Sonora]) Described above.

C. m. mexicanus 'Mexican Canyon Wren' (Mexico, from southern Chihuahua to Oaxaca and Isthmus of Tehuantepec) Larger than *conspersus* and generally darker, with substantially longer bill.

C. m. albifrons 'Giraud's Canyon Wren', 'White-throated Canyon Wren' (northern Mexico, from Nuevo León and Coahuila to San Luis Potosí and Zacatecas; south-western Texas) Paler and more grey-brown on upperparts than *mexicanus*, chestnut of underparts paler, and bars on rectrices narrower.

VOICE Song is a descending trill, becoming slower and finishing in a beautiful series of six or seven pure clear whistles; occasionally with some burry notes at the end. Both sexes sing, but the song of the female tends to be shorter, less frequent and less pure, with more of a buzzing overtone (Tramontano 1964). Song is heard throughout the year, but less frequently in winter. Call is a loud metallic buzz (Jones & Dieni 1995). Nestlings make high-pitched begging calls when soliciting food.

HABITAT Essentially confined to areas with rock faces and cliffs, such as canyons, bluffs and more rarely sea-cliffs (locally, in California). Given the requirement of large rocky areas, found in several different vegetation types, including various western coniferous zones, as well as oak woodlands and desert washes. Frequently, in association with water, although it has not been observed to drink; also, however, in very arid habitat. Also found in stone buildings and ruins, especially in the Mexican part of its range (Bent 1964). In some areas of southern Mexico in humid areas as low as 200m (Gómez de Silva 1995).

HABITS Forages on rocks when it climbs much in the manner of a creeper (*Certhia*), rapidly crawling over faces both flat, inverted and horizontal, the body pressed close to the rocks, but without using the tail as a prop. Makes frequent short flights from rock face to rock face, as well as longer excursions across canyons. Frequently forages in narrow cracks and crevices, where the low posture, made still lower by angling the legs out sideways, and flattened body allows access to narrow openings. Sometimes flycatches. More rarely forages on ground or in vegetation.

Canyon Wren

STATUS AND DISTRIBUTION Fairly common in suitable habitat from extreme southern British Columbia (southern Okanagan Valley) through the mountain states as far east as western Texas, with disjunct populations in south-western South Dakota, north-eastern Wyoming and south-eastern Montana; Western California from about 40°N to Baja California, including some islands in the Gulf of California; most of Mexico, excluding two coastal strips on the Caribbean and Pacific lowlands, from the U.S. border south to Oaxaca, the Isthmus of Tehuantepec and western Chiapas. Mostly from about 200 to 1,850m, although locally to sea-level in California, and up to 3,000m in New Mexico.

BREEDING Nests are built by both sexes. In 'natural' habitat usually in crevices in rock-faces and cliffs; also in artificial sites, such as on eaves of buildings, ruins and in holes in cedar fence posts (Bent 1964). Nest is an open cup of wool, hair and feathers, built on a base of coarser twigs, moss, etc. Average nest size; diameter 14.2cm, depth 9.5cm, cup diameter 5.6cm, depth 3.9cm (Jones & Dieni 1995). Frequently incorporates debris; one nest in an artificial site in California contained among other items 600 paper clips, 500 pins, almost 100 matches and a number of pen nibs, screws, drawing pins and miscellaneous office sundries, to the total of 1,791 countable objects (all stolen from a nearby office), with a total weight of more than a kilogram (Lofberg 1931). Nesting time varies with geographic location and attitude; nest-building from mid-March (in the south) to early June (further north and at higher altitudes). Eggs three to seven, frequently six (Jones & Dieni 1995); the race *mexicanus* may average fewer (Bent 1964). Ground colour glossy white with fine reddish-brown speckles, more rarely with heavier brown dots. Incubation by female alone, 12–18 days, average 16 (Jones & Dieni 1995); male feeds incubating female. Young fledge in 12–17 days, average 15. Does not, apparently, build subsidiary nests for roosting.

FOOD Entirely invertebrate. Spiders, beetles, bugs, plant-hoppers, ants, termites, etc. (Tramontano 1964). Has been observed to pilfer paralysed spiders from the nests of mud-dauber wasps (Martin 1971).

MOVEMENTS Largely sedentary, with some apparent altitudinal movement in northerly populations. However, several records outside normal breeding-range indicate some degree of mobility; has occurred as a vagrant in north-eastern Nebraska and south-western Kansas, South Dakota and Saskatchewan.

MEASUREMENTS (*C. m. mexicanus*) Wing of male 64.5–74, of female 60–66; tail of male 53–60.5, of female 51–55; exposed culmen of male 23–24.5, of female 19.5–23; tarsus of male 19.5–21, of female 18.5–20 (Hellmayr 1924–1949).

HYLORCHILUS

Two very specialised and local species, found only in very limited areas of Mexico. Relatively large, terrestrial wrens (15–16.5cm) with plump, heavy bodies and notably long, slender and only slightly decurved bills. Legs and feet heavy and substantial, tarsus 30mm or more. Wings short and very rounded with second to fifth primaries longest. Tails medium length, rather soft and fluffy. Plumage largely dark brown with very little barring.

Probably closest to *Catherpes*; indeed, Sumichrast's Wren was initially ascribed to that genus, based on a specimen lacking a tail. However, there are major differences between the two genera; the tail in *Hylorchilus* is shorter, rounded and with ten, not twelve, feathers; the eggs of *Hylorchilus* are plain white, those of *Catherpes* speckled with brown and grey; and there are major anatomical differences in the feet and legs. The similarity in song between Sumichrast's Wren and Canyon Wren has variously been argued as indicating a close relationship (Hardy & Delaney 1987) or as being merely coincidental (Gómez de Silva 1997).

18   SUMICHRAST'S WREN
Hylorchilus sumichrasti   Plate 6

Catherpes sumichrasti Lawrence, 1871, Mato Bejuco, Veracruz, Mexico.

Alternative names: Slender-billed Wren; Spanish *Cuevero de Sumichrast, Saltapared de Sumichrast, Chinchirivín de Sumichrast*

Etymology: Named after Professor F. Sumichrast (1828–1882), a pioneer of Mexican ornithology.

An extraordinary and distinctive large terrestrial wren with a very short tail, restricted to a very small geographic area of limestone karst country of southern Mexico.

IDENTIFICATION Length 15–16.5cm. Unmistakable: quite unlike any other wren (apart from the allopatric Nava's Wren), and not likely to be confused with any other species in the same habitat. Superficially similar to Tawny-throated Leaftosser *Sclerurus mexicanus*, which differs by having a rufous throat and rump.

DESCRIPTION
Adult Upperparts unmarked deep chocolate-brown, becoming slightly more rufescent on back and darker on rump. Rectrices unmarked dark chocolate-brown. Wing-coverts uniform with back. Primaries and secondaries dull blackish-brown, outerwebs with dull rufescent-brown markings, giving extremely obscure barring on closed wing. Throat whitish-brown, becoming orange-brown on chest and rich chocolate-brown on belly, darkening on lower belly and undertail-coverts. Belly and lower flanks with small, distinct white spots. Iris brown, bill blackish, lower mandible dull orange-yellow at base. Legs dark grey.
Juvenile Throat dull buff with diffuse scales, belly with whitish flecks.

GEOGRAPHICAL VARIATION None; monotypic. An isolated population on the other side of the Isthmus of Tehuantepec, discovered in 1969–1971, was originally described as a second race (Crossin & Ely 1973), but is now given full specific status under the name of Nava's Wren *Hylorchilus navai* (q.v.) (Whittingham & Atkinson 1996, AOU 1998).

VOICE Males have two types of song; a loud, clear series of ringing whistles, starting with a short series of notes and continuing without a break into a longer series of slower, descending notes, and a shorter song, usually of three to five notes, alternating in pitch, seemingly at random, with the last notes usually doubled (Howell & Webb 1995; Gómez de Silva 1997b). The female also sings, in a manner distinct from the male (Pérez-Villafana *et al.* 1997). The female song is a simple phrase consisting of a single syllable repeated in a series. There are usually between 4 and 22 syllables per song. The pause between the first and second syllable, and the pause before the last syllable, are the longest. Females will sing synchronously with males. Calls are an emphatic *chewk*, a squealing *wheeo* and a scolding *keh-keh-keh*, a soft *kr-kr* and a descending *karr-karr-karr*.

HABITAT Found in humid and semi-deciduous forest on limestone outcrops; it is also found in shaded coffee plantations on limestone: 75 to 1,000m altitude.

HABITS Usually detected by its song. Mostly terrestrial, hopping over boulders with cocked tail, bobbing like a dipper. Solitary, usually single or more rarely in pairs; may counter-sing. Forages on mosses and lichens on rocks, frequently disappearing into crevices. Not

excessively secretive; will disappear on being alarmed, but frequently returns, thrusting its head and beak out of rock crevices to peek inquisitively at the passer-by.

STATUS AND DISTRIBUTION Restricted to a small area within the states of Veracruz, Puebla and Oaxaca, Mexico; the total range is in an area of about 6,000km², but within that it only occurs in scattered locations, typically residual forest on outcrops of karst limestone which are unsuitable for clearing or farming (Gómez de Silva 1997a). It does seem to be able to withstand some habitat disturbance. For example, a readily accessible population near Amatlán, Veracruz lives in karst forest heavily planted with coffee, although the shade trees remain undisturbed (Wheatley & Brewer in press). No portion of its range is formally protected; classified as Vulnerable (Collar *et al.* 1994, Gómez de Silva 1997a).

BREEDING Very imperfectly known. Breeding seems to be between May and July. Three nests were found in 1925, each with three white eggs, on 6, 17 and 20 May; the last two clutches were near hatching, suggesting a laying date in the first week of May. Of these three nests, one was in the roof of a limestone cave, the other two in crevices in rocks. Incubation and fledging periods not known. No evidence of multiple-brooding is presently known.

FOOD Mainly or entirely invertebrates.

MOVEMENTS Appears to be entirely sedentary.

MEASUREMENTS Wing of male 64.0–70.6, of female 62.2–70.5; tail of male 39.0–47.5, of female 39.0–47.8; exposed culmen of male 25.0–26.9, of female 25.2–27.4; tarsus of male 28.5–30.2, of female 27.5–29.1 (8 specimens for each sex) (Crossin & Ely 1973).

Sumichrast's Wren

---

19   NAVA'S WREN
Hylorchilus navai

Plate 6

Hylorchilus sumichrasti navai Crossin & Ely 1973, 26km N [sic] of Ocozocoautla, Chiapas, Mexico.

Alternative names: Crossin's Wren; Spanish *Cuevero de Nava*

Etymology: Named after Sr. Juan Nava S., 'who, through his devotion to learning the birds of his native Mexico, has earned the admiration and respect of numerous American ornithologists' (Crossin & Ely 1973).

A recent 'split'; originally described, in 1973, as a well-marked and very local race of Sumichrast's Wren *H. sumichrasti*; recent careful studies of vocalisations clearly indicate that it is a distinct species.

IDENTIFICATION Length 15–16.5cm. Very similar in appearance to Sumichrast's Wren; has an obviously whiter throat and upper chest; rectrices with fewer, broader and more prominent bars, spots on belly and flanks much larger. The ranges of the two species do not overlap; within its own range most likely to be confused with the Scaly-throated Leaftosser *Sclerurus guatemalensis*, which, however, is a somewhat larger bird with a dark throat and chest.

DESCRIPTION
Adult Head and upperparts rich dark brown, face tawny-brown with slightly greyer lores; remiges faintly barred black. Throat and upper chest whitish becoming pale grey, faintly scalloped spots offset by subterminal dark crescents; sides and flanks dark sooty-brown, undertail-coverts dusky grey brown. Bill blackish, pale orange-yellow at base, legs dark grey.
Juvenile Plumage undescribed (Howell & Webb 1995).

GEOGRAPHICAL VARIATION None; monotypic.

VOICE Call is a characteristic metallic *tink*, entirely different from the hoarse *chuk* and the disyllabic *wheeo* of Sumichrast's Wren (Gómez de Silva 1997b). Song is also quite different: a varied, often slightly jerky warble of rich whistles, may be introduced by a few soft slightly accelerating notes and end with a strongly upslurred note (Howell & Webb 1995). Individual males of Nava's Wren do not respond to tape-recordings of the songs of Sumichrast's Wren, and vice-versa. So far no female song of Nava's Wren has been observed.

HABITAT Nava's Wren seems to be very demanding, being essentially confined to forest on outcrops of limestone; it seems likely that even when the forest was continuous, it was confined to such karst islands. Over much of its range intervening forest has since been destroyed. So far no evidence of colonisation of disturbed secondary habitat, as is the case with Sumichrast's Wren.

HABITS Much as Sumichrast's Wren; somewhat secretive, terrestrial, spends most of its time foraging on rocky ground and among boulders and crevices. The statement that there is a consistent distinction from Sumichrast's Wren in the body posture when singing (Atkinson *et al.* 1993) is apparently not true (Gómez de Silva pers. comm.). Flights are always of short duration and near the ground.

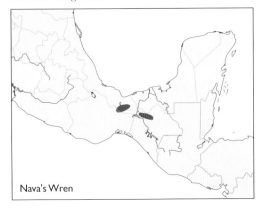

Nava's Wren

STATUS AND DISTRIBUTION Confined to a very restricted area of less than 5,000km² in the Mexican states of Veracruz and Chiapas, and very marginally in Oaxaca. Within this range it is confined to forest on limestone outcrops so actually inhabits a much smaller area. In the years since its discovery much of the forest joining these 'islands' has been destroyed for the creation of cattle-pasture; the karst islands have largely been saved because of their unsuitability for such purposes, although they may be cut for firewood. Nevertheless quite small patches of forest (less than 4ha) can support the species, albeit in isolation. Population density seems to be lower than for Sumichrast's Wren. Part of the range is protected in the El Ocote reserve, although even here there was a proposal to build a road, which was in fact diverted (Gómez de Silva 1997a). May readily be found near Colonia Cuauhtémoc, Oaxaca (Wheatley & Brewer in press). Status of Nava's Wren is presently given as Vulnerable (Collar *et al.* 1994). It has been suggested, however, that it should be reclassified as Endangered (Gómez de Silva 1997a).

BREEDING Nest and eggs presently undescribed; presumably similar to those of Sumichrast's Wren.

FOOD Nothing recorded; presumably largely or wholly invertebrate.

MOVEMENTS Apparently entirely sedentary.

MEASUREMENTS Wing of male 67.1–68.0, of female 64.0–65.7; tail of male 39.2–43.4, of female 39.5–40.6; exposed culmen of male 27.2–28.0, of female 26.2–26.7; tarsus of male 29.7–31.5, of female 27.5–30.0; (males, 6 specimens; females, 2 specimens) (Crossin & Ely 1973).

CINNYCERTHIA

An unusual genus, confined to montane forest in the northern Andes, consisting of two (or four) species with uniform brown or rufous plumage, heavy short bill and notably sturdy feet and thick legs. Unusual in wrens in being gregarious, with parties larger than can be accounted for by parents and young frequently encountered. The taxonomy of the group is fluid and debatable: the more conservative approach, e.g. Meyer de Schauensee (1964), treating the genus as two species only while Brumfield & Remsen (1996), in a very detailed analysis, convincingly argue that the 'Sepia-brown Wren' is, in fact, three distinct and separate species (*C. peruana*, *C. olivascens* and *C. fulva*), an approach that we have followed in this book.

20   RUFOUS WREN
Cinnycerthia unirufa   Plate 6

Limnornis unirufus Lafresnaye 1840, Santa-Fe-de-Bogotá, Colombia.

Alternative names: Brown Wren; Spanish *Soterrey Rufo, Cucarachero Bayo*

A common and rather conspicuous, by virtue of its behaviour, inhabitant of wet mountain forest in Venezuela, Ecuador and Peru.

IDENTIFICATION Length 16.5cm. Among wrens only confusable with the Sepia-brown Wren complex, from which it differs from having almost no bars on wings and tail (totally absent in juveniles), darker tones and more rufous, less chocolate, colour especially in the

nominate race of north-eastern Colombia and western Venezuela. Perhaps as likely to be confused with the sympatric Rufous Spinetail *Synallaxis unirufa*, which differs in having a characteristic long 'spinetail' tail.

DESCRIPTION *C. u. unirufa*
Adult Plumage entirely shades of chestnut-brown. Crown and ear-coverts orange-brown, paler above bill. Nape and shoulders deeper chestnut-brown, the colour becoming more intense and reddish on lower back and rump. Rectrices red-brown with numerous very obscure darker bars, not visible in field. Primaries and secondaries darker chestnut-brown on outerwebs, with numerous (12–15) narrow blackish bars, giving a barred appear-

ances to closed wing. Innerwebs greyish-black, concealed on closed wing. Chin whitish-buff, shading into pale orange-brown on chest, this colour becoming steadily more intense on belly and bright reddish-brown on vent. Lores, and a diffuse malar stripe, greyish-black. Underwing chestnut-brown. Eyes brown, bill and legs black.
Juvenile Very similar but barring on wings and tail largely absent.

GEOGRAPHICAL VARIATION
 C. u. unirufa 'Bay Wren' (extreme western Venezuela (Táchira) and Colombia east of the Río Magdalena south to Cundinamarca) Described above.
 C. u. chakei (Perijá mountains on border of Colombia [Cesar] and Venezuela [Zulia]) Similar to *unirufa*; eyes whitish or grey.
 C. u. unibrunnea 'Brown Wren' (Colombia west of the Río Magdalena south through central Ecuador to northern Peru [Piura, Cajamarca]) Similar to *unirufa* but substantially darker and duller.

VOICE Call is a soft *churr* or short *whit-whit*. The song is startling and arresting, typically produced in duet by a pair, consisting of a rapidly repeated two or three-note motif *chew-tu*, *chew-tu*, *whoo-he*, etc., overlaid with a loud metallic trill, the whole continuing for ten or more seconds; sometimes other members of the group will join in with short *whit-whit* call-notes.

HABITAT Wet mountain forest and forest edge, from 2,200m to shrub forest at 3,800m; frequently in association with *Chusquea* bamboo.

HABITS Notably gregarious; parties of up to 20 birds may be encountered, though frequently found in somewhat smaller groups. Not excessively shy; groups may surround the quiet observer, curiously examining him while calling all the time. May follow mixed flocks or on its own. Feeds mostly low down or on the ground, turning over debris in search of food. Duetting pairs often sit side by side.

STATUS AND DISTRIBUTION In suitable habitat can

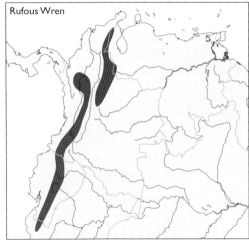

Rufous Wren

be quite common. Extreme western Venezuela in Zulia (Cerro Tetari, Sierra de Perijá) and Táchira (Páramo de Tania); Colombia, eastern Andes from the Venezuelan border through Santander and Boyacá south to Cundinamarca; disjunctly west of the Río Magdalena from Antioquia through eastern Nariño, Ecuador from Carchí and Imbabura to Zamora-Chinchipe and Loja; northern Peru (Piura and Cajamarca).

BREEDING Nest and eggs not described; presumably similar to that of Peruvian Wren. Birds in breeding condition (*chakei*) in June to August; juvenile (*unibrunnea*) in south-western Colombia in March.

FOOD From stomach contents of museum specimens apparently entirely invertebrates (FMNH data).

MOVEMENTS Apparently sedentary.

MEASUREMENTS Males, wing 80–85, exposed culmen 15·5–16, tarsus 27–28.5, tail 82 (2 specimens). Females, wing 76–83, exposed culmen 15.5–16.5, tarsus 28–30, tail 71–79 (6 specimens).

---

21 SHARPE'S WREN
Cinnycerthia olivascens
Plate 6

Cinnicerthia (sic) *olivascens* Sharpe 1881. Santa Elena, Antioquia, Colombia.

Alternative name: Spanish *Soterrey Caferrojizo*

Etymology: Named after Dr R. Bowdler Sharpe (1847–1904), head of the Bird department of the British Museum (Natural History) and one of the most influential British taxonomic ornithologists of the late nineteenth century. 'Nobody ...could fail to remember the bustling, energetic and impressive figure of R. Bowdler Sharpe ...a tonic to all zealous ornithologists.' (Manson-Bahr 1959).

The northernmost member of the Sepia-brown Wren complex, originally described as a full species, later subsumed into *C. peruana*, and now resurrected.

IDENTIFICATION Length 16cm. Over much of its

range sympatric with Rufous Wren, although that species tends to occur at higher elevations; nevertheless they coexist in the same habitat in locations such as the Cordillera de Sabanilla in Ecuador (A.D. Brewer pers. obs.). Distinguished from that species by having the barring on wings and tail more prominent, and by darker and less rufous overall appearance, especially in comparison with the eastern Andean race of Rufous Wren. See also Peruvian Wren.

DESCRIPTION *C. o. olivascens*
Adult Entire plumage shades of reddish-brown. Crown dark grey-brown, becoming more red-brown on back and rump. Primaries and secondaries slightly brighter reddish-brown with dull black bars on outerwebs, forming 10–12 transverse bars on closed wing; similar bars on greater coverts. Innerwebs of flight feathers

115

brownish-black without bars. Rectrices chestnut-brown with 20–25 narrow black bars on both webs. Chin and throat pale greyish-brown, darkening over chest to a deep reddish-brown on belly and vent. Underwing dull rufous-brown. Iris light brown or grey. Bill dark grey-brown. Legs and feet grey.

Juvenile Similar to adult; postocular area grey.

GEOGRAPHICAL VARIATION

C. o. olivascens 'Salmon's Brown Wren' (central and western Andes of Colombia from Antioquia to Nariño, central Ecuador and extreme northern Peru) Described above.

C. o. bogotensis 'Bogota Brown Wren' (Western slope of eastern Andes of Colombia [Santander to Cundinamarca]) Much darker than nominate race. White-faced birds do not occur.

VOICE Complex and variable song consists of a series of variable, musical phrases with changing emphasis (Ridgely & Greenfield 2001). Call is a low, soft *wurt*.

HABITAT Wet mossy forest, cloudforest and forest edges, frequently associated with *Chusquea* bamboo, mostly 1,500–3,100m, locally in Colombia down to 900m (Cauca, on Pacific slope).

HABITS Similar to other members of genus. Usually found in small flocks of up to ten birds, often in association with other species. Feeds low down in dense vegetation or actually on ground.

STATUS AND DISTRIBUTION Fairly common in suitable habitat. Colombia, western slope of eastern Andes, east of the Río Magdalena (Santander, Boyacá, Cundinamarca); disjunctly west of the Río Magdalena from Antioquia southwards through western Andes through Ecuador south to Zamora-Chinchipe (on

Sharpe's Wren

western slope south to Pichincha); extreme northern Peru (Piura and Cajamarca).

BREEDING Nest and eggs unknown; presumably very similar to those of Peruvian Wren. Birds in breeding condition in June–August in Colombia (Fjeldså & Krabbe 1990).

FOOD No information; presumably largely or entirely invertebrate.

MOVEMENTS Apparently entirely sedentary.

MEASUREMENTS (*C. o. olivascens*) (Means) Wing of male 69.5, of female 65.9; tail of male 65.4, of female 62.5; bill of male 14.1, of female 14.0; tarsus of male 24.6, of female 23.5 (42 male and 49 female specimens) (Brumfield & Remsen 1996).

---

22 PERUVIAN WREN
Cinnycerthia peruana   **Plate 6**

Presbys peruanus Cabanis 1873, Maraynioc, Peru.

Alternative names: Peruvian Brown Wren, Sepia-brown Wren

An inhabitant of wet mountain forest, endemic to the Peruvian Andes; formerly regarded as conspecific with Sharpe's Wren and Fulvous Wren.

IDENTIFICATION Length 15.5cm. Leaving aside the recently separated species (Sharpe's Wren to the north and Fulvous Wren to the south), Peruvian Wren is unlike any other sympatric species, the Rufous Wren not over-lapping in range. More likely to be confused with similarly-plumaged species of other families, such as the Rufous Spinetail *Synalaxis unirufa*. There appears to be a limited area of sympatry with Sharpe's Wren in northern Peru south of the Río Marañón. Peruvian Wren tends to have a more prominent, pale postocular area and to be more rufescent. Fulvous Wren, from extreme southern Peru to Bolivia, is quite distinct by virtue of its conspicuous pale postocular area, darker

lores and generally paler underparts.

DESCRIPTION

Adult Crown rich chestnut-brown, becoming less rufescent on nape and back. Rump and uppertail-coverts more rufescent. Wing-coverts and primaries and secondaries rich chestnut, conspicuously barred with sharp, narrow black bars, giving about 20–24 bars on closed wing. Rectrices rich chestnut-brown with numerous (25–30) narrow blackish bars. Throat and chin orange-brown becoming darker and duller on chest, belly and flanks. Iris chestnut, bill dark brown with pale yellow gape, legs and feet black.

In many (apparently always adult) birds there is an indeterminate amount of white feathering on the head, which can vary from none, through a white eye-ring and forecrown all the way to a largely white head (Graves 1980, Brumfield & Remsen 1996).

Juvenile Undescribed.

GEOGRAPHICAL VARIATION None; monotypic.

VOICE Song is a superb medley of clear whistles and rich trills, in some phrases reminiscent of the European Nightingale *Luscinia megarhynchos*, probably the result of duetting between the sexes. Call is a fast, gravelly chattering *ch-d-d-t*, often given as a group (Ridgely & Tudor 1989).

HABITAT Wet montane forest, including forest edge and second growth, 1,500–3,300m.

HABITS Gregarious, usually found in groups of a dozen or more, often in the company of other species. Groups frequently seem to consist of a pair, some immature birds and the most recent juveniles; it has been suggested that, as sub-adults may act as helpers at the nest, that the white feathering present in some adults may define social status (Graves 1980). Feeding birds keep fairly low or on the ground, rummaging around in thick vegetation. Will sometimes appear inquisitively near a quiet observer, but vanish into thick vegetation at the slightest provocation.

STATUS AND DISTRIBUTION Quite common in some locations; entirely within Andean Peru, from the slopes of the Marañón valley in the north to Ayacucho in the south.

BREEDING Only one nest found, on 23 September 1972 in Huanuco, Peru, a pouch, suspended from and partly penetrated by a curving bamboo stem, firmly tethered to it by fine rootlets, the entrance being a down-turned tunnel with a circular entrance-hole, about 3cm in diameter, encircled by green moss. The overall size of the nest was 20cm x 30cm x 15cm high, the main pouch being 10cm x 10cm x 15cm. Materials of construction were rootlets interwoven with green moss, the upper part of the pouch being made with dried bamboo leaflets. On that date there was one recently hatched chick and one egg, which was pale creamy-white sparsely

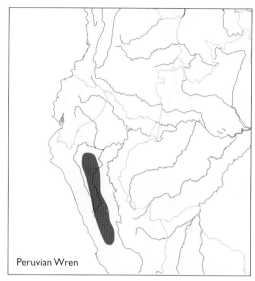

Peruvian Wren

speckled with reddish-brown (Gochfield 1979). Another egg date in Peru was 26 August; no description of the nest was given (Taczanowski 1887). Fledglings in August (Amazonas, Peru) and juveniles observed in February, June and November (La Libertad, Peru) (Fjeldså & Krabbe 1990). Incubation and fledgling periods unknown.

FOOD Not recorded; presumably largely or entirely invertebrate.

MOVEMENTS Presumably entirely sedentary.

MEASUREMENTS (Means) Wing of male 62.0, of female 60.2; tail 58.8 of male, of female 57.1; bill of male 13.3, of female 12.8; tarsus of male 23.1, of female 22.4 (Brumfield & Remsen 1996).

---

23 FULVOUS WREN
Cinnycerthia fulva

Plate 6

Thryophilus fulvus Sclater 1874 Huasampilla, Peru.

Alternative name: Superciliated Wren

The smallest and, in plumage, the most distinctive member of the Sepia-brown Wren complex.

IDENTIFICATION Length 14.5cm. Does not overlap in range with the Rufous Wren. Although the range limits of Peruvian Wren and Fulvous Wren in central Peru are not known with total precision, it appears likely that they are in fact fully allopatric. Fulvous Wren has a superficial resemblance in facial pattern to the Mountain Wren which is, however, much smaller and with a proportionately shorter tail.

DESCRIPTION *C. f. fulva*
Adult Crown reddish-brown, uniform with back; lower back and rump more rufescent. Rectrices red-brown with numerous (20+) narrow blackish transverse bars across entire tail. Supercilium and area immediately above bill buff-white, contrasting with crown and dull

brown lores. Ear-coverts cinnamon-buff, throat whitish-buff, darkening to cinnamon-buff on chest and darker reddish-brown on flanks and thighs. Remiges dull blackish-brown on innerweb, dull reddish-brown on outer, with numerous blackish-brown bars, giving on the closed wing about 20 narrow dark bars across all remiges. Shoulder with narrow dark bars. Underwing cinnamon-buff. Iris nut-brown, upper mandible blackish, lower mandible leaden, feet dark brown.

About one quarter of museum specimens (presumably fully adult birds) show some degree of white feathering on the face or forecrown, although never as extensive as that in some examples of Peruvian Wren (Brumfield & Remsen 1996).
Juvenile Similar to adult, eye-colour less reddish, cap greyish.

GEOGRAPHICAL VARIATION
   C. f. fulva (Central Peru [southern Cuzco]) Described above.

C. f. fitzpatricki (Cordillera de Vilcabamba, Peru) Crown dark, contrasting with back; supercilium whitish, not light brown (Remsen & Brumfield 1998).

C. f. gravesi (southern Peru [Puno] to Bolivia) Similar to *fulva*, but supercilium whitish contrasting with darker auriculars; paler below (Remsen & Brumfield 1998).

VOICE No information recorded; stated to be rather quiet in comparison to the Peruvian Wren (Brumfield & Remsen 1996). Given the fluidity of the taxonomy of this group, a comprehensive comparative study of the vocalisations of all populations would be most interesting.

HABITAT Wet mountain forest, usually 1,500–3,300m.

HABITS Little specific is recorded; much like other members of the genus.

STATUS AND DISTRIBUTION Fairly common in some locations. Andes of central Peru (Cordillera de Vilca- bamba, Cuzco), south to central Bolivia (La Paz, Cochabamba; Santa Cruz).

BREEDING Nest and eggs undescribed; birds in breeding condition collected in Bolivia (La Paz, Cochabamba) in January (Fjeldså & Krabbe 1990).

FOOD No data recorded.

Fulvous Wren

MOVEMENTS Presumably entirely sedentary.

MEASUREMENTS (Means) Wing of male 57.9, of female 55.3; tail of male 54.9, of female 53.3; bill of male 12.8, of female 12.6; tarsus of male 21.7, of female 20.7 (14 male and 17 female specimens) (Brumfield & Remsen 1996).

CISTOTHORUS

Very small wrens (wing typically less than 50mm) with short to medium-length bills, very rounded wings and short to medium-length tails (usually almost as long as wing). Plumage heavily barred or streaked, sexes identical except for size. All species that have been studied exhibit multiple nest-building, sometimes to an extreme degree, and polygyny. Habitat specialists, almost entirely restricted to grass, reed and sedge areas, often marshy. Four to seven species according to taxonomic opinion, ranging between them throughout the Americas from Canada discontinuously to Cape Horn.

24   SEDGE WREN
Cistothorus platensis

Plate 7

Sylvia platensis Latham 1790, Buenos Aires, Argentina.

Alternative names: Short-billed Marsh Wren, Grass Wren; French *Troglodyte à bec court*; Spanish *Soterrey Sabanero, Cucarachero de Ciénaga, Ratona Aperdizada, Chercan de las Vegas*; Portuguese, *Corriura-do-Campo*

After the House Wren, the most widely distributed wren in the Americas, ranging from central Manitoba and Saskatchewan disjunctly through Central and South America to Tierra del Fuego, although the separate populations may warrant specific status.

IDENTIFICATION Length 9–11.5cm. In North America, at least on the breeding-ground, only likely to be confused with the Marsh Wren, which differs by having a prominent eye-stripe and more well-marked longi- tudinal striations on the shoulders. During migration, it could conceivably coexist with the House Wren, which has a longer tail and unmarked back and crown; and with the Winter Wren, which is of similar shape, but is quite distinct in having brown underparts, barred flanks

and no streaks on the back. In South America the related Merida Wren and Apolinar's Wren (qq.v.) are similar but the area of possible sympatry is very restricted.

DESCRIPTION *C. p. stellaris*
Adult Forehead medium-brown, with diffuse darker streaks, contrasting with dark brown crown with buff-white streaks. Nape concolorous with forehead, giving a capped appearance, and contrasting with blackish-brown back, which is heavily streaked with off-white. Shoulders orange-buff with diffuse dark brown bars, becoming more sharply differentiated on closed primaries and secondaries. Innerwebs of remiges dark brownish-grey without markings; outerwebs with about four contrasting blackish-brown and buff bars, darker on secondaries than on primaries. Rump medium brown with darker markings, the uppertail-coverts having diffuse off-white tips. Rectrices mid buff-brown with 9–10 bars of dark blackish brown, becoming wider and more conspicuous distally. Throat and chin off-white, chest with a distinct band of orange-buff which continues on flanks; lower

flanks richer in colour with darker barring, contrasting with grey-white centre belly. Vent and thighs orange-buff. Underwing orange-grey. Iris brown, upper mandible dull blackish, lower mandible yellow with dusky tip, legs pinkish-brown with darker brown feet.

Juvenile Very similar to adult, but white streaking on crown and upperparts reduced, underparts paler.

GEOGRAPHICAL VARIATION Taxonomically a very complex species. The subspecies fall into three groups, separated geographically. These are the North and Central American races (*stellaris* to *lucidus*); northern and western South America (*alticola* to *graminicola*); and southern and south-eastern South America (*polyglottus* to *hornensis* and *falklandicus*). It seems likely that in fact three distinct species are involved (Ridgely & Tudor 1989); certainly the vocalisations differ widely over the 'species' huge range.

C. p. platensis 'La Plata Marsh Wren' (eastern Argentina to Córdoba and Mendoza) Crown, shoulders and back dark blackish-brown, conspicuously marked with lateral streaks of buff, the streaks becoming larger and longer on back. Upper rump, rump and tail-coverts buff-brown with few streaks. Wing-coverts buff-brown with some lateral buff streaks. Primaries and secondaries dark on innerwebs, outerwebs buff-brown with conspicuous dark-brown markings, forming conspicuous bars on closed wing. Supercilium bright buff, becoming somewhat darker on chest; flanks and lower belly orange-buff, the colour deeper and richer laterally. Bare parts as in *stellaris*.

C. p. hornensis 'Cape Horn Grass Wren' (South America from Cape Horn north to about 41°S) Similar to *platensis* but more profusely streaked above.

C. p. falklandicus (Falkland Islands) Like *hornensis* but with longer wings and proportionately shorter tail (Traylor 1988).

C. p. tucumanus 'Tucuman Grass Wren' (north-west Argentina [Jujuy to Catamarca and Tucumán]) Like *platensis* but bill longer, lower back and rump without spots or streaks.

C. p. polyglottus 'Brazilian Grass Wren' (Paraguay and south-eastern Brazil) The smallest race; similar to *platensis* but shorter, more slender bill, narrow buffy-white supercilium, unspotted rump, blackish innerweb of most rectrices.

C. p. alticola 'Roraima Grass Wren' (northern Colombia, northern Venezuela; isolated population in southern Guyana) Closest to *polyglottus* but supercilium much reduced, flanks darker brown and more rufescent.

C. p. aequatorialis 'Equatorial Grass Wren' (high altitudes in Ecuador and central Andes of Colombia) Similar to *alticola* but longer wings and legs; lores bright buff; supercilia broad and buff; bars on rectrices heavier.

C. p. tamae 'Paramo de Tama Grass Wren' (high altitudes of eastern Colombia and south-western Venezuela) Similar to *aequatorialis* but more rufescent.

C. p. graminicola 'Peruvian Grass Wren' (southern Peru [Junín and Cuzco] and north-western Bolivia) Much like *aequatorialis* but paler, and with pileum streaked with buff.

C. p. minimus (includes *boliviae*) (Puno, Peru) Similar to *polyglottus* but with crown streaked; smaller than *graminicola* and with black on innerwebs of rectrices.

C. p. tolimae (Tolima, Colombia) Crown and rump without streaks, tail barred throughout.

C. p. stellaris 'Short-billed Marsh Wren' (breeds from southern Quebec, Ontario north to Sault Ste Marie and Thunder Bay, central Manitoba and eastern Saskatchewan south to northern Mississippi, northern Kentucky and eastern Pennsylvania and New York; winters from Virginia through the coastal states to Texas and north-eastern Mexico) Described above.

C. p. tinnulus (northern Mexico from Nayarit to Michoacán to México and the Distrito Federal) Very pale and buffy with little streaking on crown.

C. p. potosinus (San Luis Potosí, north-central Mexico) Similar to *tinnulus* but paler and more sandy in colour.

C. p. jalapensis (Mexico, from central interior Veracruz [Jalapa] to Orizaba region) Darker brown than *tinnulus* or *potosinus*, black on crown and back more extensive.

C. p. warneri (lowlands of Veracruz, Tabasco and lowland Chiapas) Less ochraceous than *tinnulus*, paler than *jalapensis*, black on back and tail intermediate between *potosinus* and *jalapensis*.

C. p. russelli (Belize; specimens from highland Chiapas intermediate between *russelli* and *elegans*) Colour darker and richer than *jalapensis* or *elegans*, nape more reddish-brown.

C. p. elegans 'Guatemalan Grass Wren' (south-central Guatemala) Back strongly striped, crown heavily streaked. Resembles *lucidus* but less warmly coloured.

C. p. graberi (disjunct populations [which are inseparable in plumage but differ in size] in interior Honduras, and north-eastern Nicaragua and eastern Honduras) More grey than *elegans*, duller than *russelli*, little streaked on crown.

C. p. lucidus (central Costa Rica patchily to western Panama, at least formerly) (Ridgely 1976) In plumage closest to *aequatorialis* but more heavily streaked on crown, dorsal stripes whiter, supercilia less buffy and underparts less ochraceous.

VOICE The song of the North American race *stellaris* is a characteristic series of sharp, dry notes, accelerating and becoming a trill at the end *chip-chip-chip-chip-chipchipchip chrchrchrchr*, usually delivered from a concealed position. However, territorial males in dispute will climb to the top of vegetation and sing at each other. Night-time song is quite frequent. No evidence of song by the female (Walkinshaw 1935). Call a sharp *chip* or *chip-chip*; scolding notes *churrr, wrrrt*. The songs of the various Central American populations have not been studied in great detail but seem to be generally similar: that of *C .p. lucidus* is described as having a gurgling quality (Slud 1964) that is certainly absent from Canadian birds.

The songs of South American populations differ from each other and from the North and Central American races, leading to the speculation that the various groups are not conspecific. Andean birds (e.g. *aequatorialis*) tend to give short, discrete phrases, *sisisisi, trrr, chee-ee-ee-ee-ee*, followed by discrete, often lengthy pauses, whereas Argentinian birds (*platensis*) deliver a more or less continuous series of phrases, most of them either four or six of a single note or trill (Ridgely &

Tudor 1989). The Falkland Islands race (*falklandicus*) gives a pleasing series of ripples and warbles (Pettingill 1973).

HABITAT In North America, damp, sedgy meadows, sometimes with scattered small bushes such as alder or willow; sometimes the margins of sphagnum bogs with cotton-grass, rather than the bogs themselves. Generally avoids wetter marshes with actual standing water and cattails or rushes, and thus only rarely co-exists with Marsh Wren. However, in Arkansas it nests, sometimes abundantly, in rice-fields, especially weedy ones (Meanley 1952). In South America it is found in quite varied habitats, from dry cerrado grasslands in Brazil to the borders of tidal marshes and cornfields in Argentina (Wetmore 1926) in tussock grasses in the Falklands (Pettingill 1973), *páramo* grassland, partially flooded alder forest and bamboo bogs in Colombia, and open grassy savanna in Venezuela (Fjeldså & Krabbe 1990).

HABITS A furtive and skulking species, most usually detected when in song. Spends most of its time low in sedgy vegetation, although it may sometimes sing from the tops of clumps of sedge. Can be quite difficult to flush; when it does fly it keeps low over vegetation, into which it disappears and scurries away on foot. The flight is weak with rapidly beating wings. Cocks its tail over the back frequently and sometimes flirts it from side to side. Tends to occur in loose colonies in suitable habitat.

As in the Marsh Wren, destruction of eggs of other birds, both of their own species and others, seems quite common in the Sedge Wren (Picman & Picman 1980). Nests attacked include those of the Red-winged Blackbird *Agelaius phoeniceus*, Yellow-headed Blackbird *Xanthocephalus xanthocephalus*, Marsh Wren *Cistothorus palustris*, and Sedge Wren. Sedge Wrens have also been seen to attack the eggs of Cinnamon Teal *Anas cyanoptera*, but were not able to break the shell. The contents of eggs may be partially eaten, and the shells carried away from the predated nest. Egg-destruction by Sedge Wrens may have a significant effect on the overall nesting success of other species.

STATUS AND DISTRIBUTION In North America, breeds from southern Quebec, rarely southern New Brunswick (Squires 1952), Ontario to Manitoba and central Saskatchewan, sporadically to southern Alberta (Nordstrom 1978), south through eastern South Dakota, Nebraska, north-eastern Kansas to northern Mississippi, Kentucky and eastern Pennsylvania and New York; also Delaware and eastern Virginia. Winters from coastal Virginia through the Carolinas, Georgia and Florida to Texas, Nuevo León and Durango, Mexico. In Mexico, breeds from southern Nayarit at moderate altitudes across to Puebla, in Campeche, Tabasco and lowland Chiapas; Belize, Guatemala and discontinuously through Nicaragua, Honduras and Costa Rica. Formerly Panama. South America, from northern Venezuela in the mountains to central Bolivia, with an isolated population in the Guianian Highlands of Venezuela and Guyana; from southern Brazil (Goias, Minas Gerais) through most of Argentina, Chile south of about 30°S to Tierra del Fuego; Falkland Islands.

Over its North American range nowhere very common, tending to be spotty and sporadic (e.g. Gould 1987); breeding areas are frequently abandoned in an unpredictable and capricious manner (Brewer 1977). It is susceptible to habitat modification, and not very tolerant of, for example, changes following burning (Herkest 1994). Breeding bird surveys in Canada conducted in the

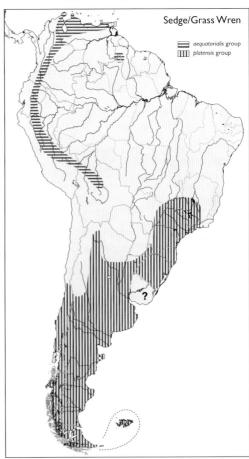

Sedge/Grass Wren

aequatorialis group
platensis group

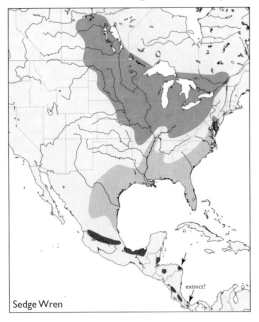

Sedge Wren

extinct?

years 1991 to 2000 seem to indicate a significant and substantial increase in population, although the erratic occupation of breeding habitat makes accurate population monitoring difficult for this species (Badzinski 2001).

BREEDING Most studies have concentrated on the North American race *C. p. stellaris*; the populations in South America would be a fertile area for study, especially given the taxonomic uncertainty surrounding them.

Sedge Wrens, in common with Marsh Wrens, build multiple nests and are frequently polygynous. Nests, built by the male, are globular constructions, about 10cm high, 8cm wide and 8cm deep, with a cavity about 6cm deep, 4cm long and 6cm wide. The entrance is about 2.5cm in diameter. Building materials are fine pieces of grass and sedge, interwoven with plant down, feathers, fur or other cottony materials (Walkinshaw 1935). Nests used for breeding are lined, by the female, with fine grass, feathers and down. Nests are located in vegetation such as grasses and sedges, usually 25–50cm from the ground, and are better concealed than those of the Marsh Wren. Multiple nest-building by the male is the rule; in a study in Minnesota each male averaged about nine nests per season (Burns 1982), which is about half the number frequently built by the Marsh Wren, in a typically much larger territory (1,800m² versus 300m² for the Marsh Wren). Polygyny is common, but not nearly as frequent as in the Marsh Wren, and trigamy has not been observed; in an Iowa study, 19% of males in the study area were bigamous. Nesting success of females is related to marital status; females mating with an already nested male tended to nest later, lay fewer eggs and rear fewer young than those in a one to one relationship, and their nestlings weigh significantly less (Crawford 1977). Double-brooding is common in females which do not share a male, whereas females mated to a bigamous male rear only single broods. Nesting success of the second brood, however, is lower than in the first, and similar to that of secondary females (i.e. those mated to a bigamous male).

Clutch-size four to eight, averaging seven (Bent 1948), but later broods average just under 6 (Burns 1982). Eggs are unmarked white. Incubation by female alone, about 14 days. Young are fed almost entirely by the female; in the Minnesota study only three out of nine males accounted for more than the 10% of feeding visits to the nest, and three made no visits at all. However, there was no correlation between male involvement in feeding and fledging success (Burns 1982). Fledging period 12–14 days.

The above information refers to North American populations. Very little is known about other races in Mexico, Central and most of South America; some brief studies have been done of the races *hornensis* in Tierra del Fuego, and *falklandicus* on the Falkland Islands. In the Falklands the species has been found nesting in October to December; one nest was described as a rough ball of grasses well lined with white feathers (Pettingill 1973). One nest with five eggs was found on 9 October, and an adult was seen feeding juveniles on 4 December. Presumably single-brooded. *Hornensis* is said to surround the entrance with thorns (Paessler 1928). One nest of *hornensis* has been described located in the bore of a small disused cannon (Castellanos 1935). The eggs of *hornensis*, in contrast to *stellaris*, are white with light reddish tones and the surface spotted with reddish or brown flecks which sometimes take the form of a wreath on the blunt end (Humphrey *et al.* 1970).

The nest and eggs of Sedge Wrens in northern South America appear to be undescribed; fledglings not long out of the nest have been seen in January and May in north-western Ecuador (race *aequatorialis*) and in April in Peru (*graminicola*) (Fjeldså & Krabbe 1990).

FOOD Almost entirely invertebrate; stomach contents of *stellaris* include ants, bugs, weevils, ladybird beetles, moths, caterpillars, locusts, crickets and grasshoppers (Howell 1932). A specimen of the race *hornensis*, taken in mid-winter in Tierra del Fuego when the ground was covered in snow and ice had been feeding on grass seeds as well as insects (Crawshay 1907).

MOVEMENTS The race *stellaris* is entirely migratory, usually arriving in southern Ontario in early to mid-May, in New York and Pennsylvania in late April, and in the Dakotas and Manitoba in early May. Northern parts of the breeding-range are vacated by early to mid-October. There are no long-distance banding recoveries of the species (Bird Banding Laboratory pers. comm.). All other populations seem to be sedentary, and the race *hornensis* spends winter in a more severe climate than any other species of wren, with the possible exception of Winter Wren; however, the type specimen of *hornensis* was 'taken at sea twenty leagues south-east of Cape Horn' (Lesson 1834), suggesting that this race may be somewhat migratory.

MEASUREMENTS (*C. p. stellaris*) Wing of male 43–47, of female 41–45.5; tail of male 36—41.5, of female 35–38; exposed culmen of male 10–11, of female 9.5–10.5; tarsus of male 15–17.5, of female 15.5–17 (Ridgway 1904).

25 MERIDA WREN
Cistothorus meridae

Plate 7

Cistothorus platensis meridae Hellmayr 1907, El Loro, Mérida, Venezuela. *Cistothorus meridae* Chapman 1921.

Alternative names: Paramo Wren; Spanish *Cucarachero Triguero*

Note: We have followed Ridgely & Tudor (1989) using Merida Wren (without an accent) rather than the more common name Paramo Wren, as the species is almost en-

tirely restricted to the state of Mérida, while several species of wren in central and South America inhabit *páramo*.

A Venezuelan endemic, with a very restricted distribution at high altitudes in the Cordillera de Mérida in the west of the country.

IDENTIFICATION Length 10cm. A very small, rather short-tailed wren, confusable only with the local race (*alticola*) of Sedge Wren, from which it differs by having a more pronounced and paler supercilium, more prominently streaked back, more heavily barred flanks and faintly barred pileum. The two species are usually separated, in any case, by altitude.

DESCRIPTION

Adult Crown and nape medium-brown with darker brown longitudinal streaking. Shoulders and upper back blackish-brown with many off-white longitudinal streaks, extending in centre down to upper rump. Rump and uppertail-coverts barred with rich brown and dull blackish. Rectrices medium-brown with about eight sharply demarcated bars of blackish-brown, extending across all feathers. Wing-coverts bright buffy-brown, with conspicuous bars of dark brown across all feathers. Primaries and secondaries blackish-brown, with outer-webs of buff-brown markings, giving a totally barred appearance on closed wing. Eye-stripe off-white, broader behind eye. Ear-coverts mottled brown. Throat and chin off-white, becoming buffy on chest and deeper buff on flanks which have several diffuse transverse bars of dull blackish-brown. Thighs with narrow transverse bars of the same colour. Underwing-coverts dull grey-white. Eyes brown, bill brown with pale pinkish or yellowish base, legs pale brownish.
Juvenile Undescribed.

GEOGRAPHICAL VARIATION None; monotypic.

VOICE Song is quite variable. Often, a series of high, clear, trilling notes interspersed with harsher buzzy scolding notes, introduced by a series of barely audible clicks. Song-types in two locations in Mérida state, only 6km apart, differed substantially from each other, whereas birds in one locality were more uniform (Kroodsma *et al.* in prep.). As with the Marsh Wren and Sedge Wren, singing males have an extensive repertoire of song types; however, that of the Merida Wren is less substantial than either species (and much less extensive than that of the western populations of the Marsh Wren, q.v.); some 25 song-types were recorded from one male, versus up to 200 from Marsh Wrens (Kroodsma *et al.* in prep.). Males also tend to repeat a song-type many times, rather than move through a repertoire as do other species. Females sing, or call, in duet with their mates; the female's contribution is a simple, dry rattle without the whistling notes of the male. Calls are mostly churring or buzzing scolds, also a high, almost cricket-like *jeet*.

HABITAT Found in wet areas of *páramo* with *freilejones*, a terrestrial bromeliad, *Espletia* and bushy areas, usually 3,000–4,100m above sea-level.

HABITS Typical of the genus in behaviour; actively moves

among low vegetation; not, in our experience, especially secretive. Frequently cocks tail over back, almost touching the head. Seems to require large territories. The duetting song-type is more typical of a monogamous species than one which is routinely polygamous (Kroodsma *et al.* in prep.). Some evidence to suggest that birds destroy the eggs of other species within their territory, in the same manner as Marsh Wren.

Merida Wren

STATUS AND DISTRIBUTION Geographically very restricted, to suitable habitat at 3,000–4,100m in the states of Mérida and Trujillo. Within this region fairly common; despite the small range (all sites would seem to fall within an area about 160km by 40km) there would seem to be no particular reason for anxiety as to its status. Readily found, for example, at Laguna Mucubají and Pico de Aguila near the city of Mérida (Wheatley 1994).

BREEDING No data published. Breeding nests have not been described. However, a number of dormitory nests were found near Mérida in May and June 1997. These were domed structures with a side-entrance, the outer shell consisting of woven grass stems, the inner lining made of fine hairs plucked from *Espeletia* leaves. One nest was situated in an *Espeletia* plant about 50 cm up; other nests were in clumps of sedge. Up to three birds were seen to roost together. At this time birds were not breeding; it is not known if roosting nests are also used for breeding (D.E. Kroodsma, pers. comm.). Eggs, incubation and fledging periods unknown.

FOOD Little information available; presumably mainly invertebrate.

MOVEMENTS There is some evidence of local, probably altitudinal, movement. After breeding, in the rainy season, some locations seem to be vacated (Kroodsma, *et al.* in prep.).

MEASUREMENTS Males, wing 49, exposed culmen 12–12.5, tarsus 21, tail 34–36 (2 specimens).

---

26 APOLINAR'S WREN
Cistothorus apolinari

Plate 7

Cistothorus apolinari Chapman 1914. Suba marshes, 4 miles east of Bogotá, Colombia.

Alternative names: Apolinar's Marsh-wren; Spanish *Cucarachero de Apolinar, Cucarachero de Pantano, Chirriador*

Etymology: Named after Brother Apolinar María,

director of the Instituto de la Salle in Bogotá, who was instrumental in helping F. M. Chapman obtain the first specimens.

A little-known species, endemic to a very restricted area of Colombia, where its status is a cause for some anxiety.

IDENTIFICATION Length 12cm. Not likely to be confused with any sympatric species. Differs from the local race of Sedge Wren (*C. p. tamae*) by its somewhat larger size, dingy grey underparts and more prominent grey, not buff, eye-stripe. The two species have different habitat requirements.

DESCRIPTION

Adult Crown dull chestnut-brown. Back and shoulders blackish-brown with conspicuous lateral streaks of whitish-buff extending down to mid-back. Upper rump, rump and uppertail-coverts bright rufescent-brown without streaks. Wing-coverts medium brown with bars of dark brown. Primaries dark brown with pale buff-brown edgings on outerwebs. Rectrices medium reddish-brown with blackish-brown transverse bars across all feathers giving about eight complete bars across whole tail. Facial pattern very obscure with inconspicuous eye-stripe posterior to eye. Ear-coverts unmarked, buff-brown. Throat pale buff-brown, becoming darker and more rufescent on flanks. Iris brown, upper mandible black, lower mandible clear grey, legs grey.

Juvenile Distinct from adult, head dark grey-brown (bluish in the field) without supercilium; lower nape buff; scapulars slightly paler than in adult and without dark blotches, giving the back a less streaked look; greater wing-coverts concentrically marked light and dark. Legs grey-brown (paler in adult) (Fjeldså & Krabbe 1990).

GEOGRAPHICAL VARIATION None; monotypic.

VOICE Song, a rapidly repeated sequence of up to six or seven harsh, sawing churring notes, usually starting with a low note and alternating up and down, or a series of rising and falling *churrs*, interspersed with harsher, gravelly notes. Call a harsh grating *chahh-chahh.*

HABITAT Largely confined to reed-beds surrounding lagoons and marshes, with tall vegetation, especially cat-tails *Typha* and bulrushes *Scirpus*, and in this sense more resembles Marsh Wren than Sedge or Merida Wren.

HABITS Rather secretive and not always easy to observe, although singing males may climb up onto vegetation. Forages by climbing some way up stems of reeds and dropping down to near water-level (Fjeldså & Krabbe 1990). In suitable habitat may form loose colonies. May have an antagonistic relationship with the local marsh icterid (in this instance Yellow-hooded Blackbird *Agelaius icterocephalus*) (Collar *et al.* 1992) as does the Marsh Wren.

STATUS AND DISTRIBUTION So far as is known, has always been restricted to the Colombian departments of Cundinamarca and Boyacá, at altitudes of 2,500–4,000m. The total range is encompassed in an area about 225km long and 200km wide, but even within this the number of known locations is quite small. In some locations may be quite numerous within the restricted suitable habitat, but overall is described as Rare (Collar *et al.* 1992) and requiring vigilance for the future. It has diminished substantially in recent years; the main threats to its continued survival are habitat destruction by drainage, agricultural pollution, and possibly decay of reed-beds. It has become extirpated in several

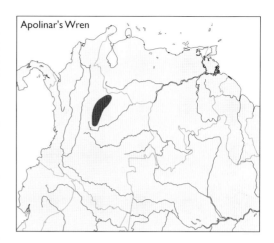

Apolinar's Wren

locations where it previously occurred. An important population, estimated at 30–50 pairs, exists at the Laguna de Tota, Boyacá (Varty *et al.* 1986); a second significant population, of unknown size, is found at the Laguna de Pedropalo in Cundinamarca; it still persists in some locations right around the city of Bogotá.

BREEDING Only one nest has been described, an unlined ball of *Typha* strips, 15cm across and 1.5m above water-level (Varty *et al.* 1986). This may well have been a non-breeding nest if Apolinar's Wren has similar nesting habits to those of its North American relatives. Not known whether multiple nest-building occurs, but this seems likely. Breeding season rather protracted (suggesting possible double broods); males with enlarged testes collected in March and August (Borrero 1953), eggs recorded in July (Fjeldså & Krabbe 1990), the nest mentioned above on 16 August and recently-fledged juveniles as late as October. A pair were seen feeding a fledgling Shiny Cowbird *Molothrus bonariensis* in early March (the only record so far of parasitism by this species on any member of the genus *Cistothorus*) (Velásquez-Tibatá *et al.* 2000).

FOOD Based upon faecal samples collected from live birds, entirely invertebrate. The largest single component was *Chironomus* midges (74% of individuals), followed by spiders, various dipterous flies, mosquitoes etc. The largest prey item was *Zygoptera* (damselflies) (Varty *et al.* 1986).

MOVEMENTS Apparently totally sedentary.

MEASUREMENTS Wing 56–58, exposed culmen10.5–13, tarsus 23-25, tail 46–48 (10 unsexed specimens).

Certhia palustris Wilson 1810, eastern Pennsylvania.

Alternative names: Long-billed Marsh Wren; French *Troglodyte de Marais*; Spanish *Saltapared Pantañero*

An abundant and conspicuous inhabitant of cattail and bulrush habitat around marshes throughout most of North America. Recent work suggests that the populations in eastern and western North America may well be two distinct species.

IDENTIFICATION Length 11.5–12.5cm. Usually the only wren in its habitat, but will sometimes be found with the Sedge Wren. It differs from that species by being somewhat larger, with a proportionately longer bill; by having a much more prominent eye-stripe, contrasting with a conspicuous brown or blackish cap without streaks; and by its pale undertail-coverts. On migration, or when in inappropriate habitat, other species of wren should be considered. Bewick's Wren is larger, with white corners on the tail, and House Wren has only a trace of an eye-stripe and is a less rich chestnut colour. Marsh Wrens differ from other North American wrens by having a prominent black bar across the shoulders and back with conspicuous white longitudinal streaks. Sedge Wrens also have this, but much less marked, and in all other sympatric species it is lacking. This feature also distinguishes Marsh Wren from all the Mexican species with overlapping ranges. In any case the habitat requirements of Marsh Wren on both breeding and wintering grounds prevent much confusion.

DESCRIPTION *C. p. palustris*
Adult Crown solid black-brown, darker at sides, forming a cap, contrasting with olive-brown sides of neck. Centre of back dull black with prominent off-white longitudinal streaks, continuing down centre of back to upper rump and contrasting with sides of back, shoulders and rump which are medium-brown. Primaries and secondaries darker blackish-grey, with very diffuse and not particularly obvious brown barring on outerwebs. Rectrices medium-brown with strong parallel bars of darker brown, wider and more prominent in lateral feathers. Prominent pale grey supercilium, contrasting obviously with dark crown and medium-brown of ear-coverts. Throat, chest and belly grey, becoming buffy at sides; lower belly buff, becoming richer and stronger on flanks and crissum. Underwing-coverts greyish. Eyes brown, bill dark brown above, yellowish-brown below (especially at base), legs pale brown.
Juvenile Generally duller than adult, white streaking on back much reduced or absent, supercilium much less obvious, barring on flight feathers more diffuse; tendency to a dull buff chestband.

GEOGRAPHICAL VARIATION Populations in eastern and western North America may be two good species, in which case they would be known as Eastern Marsh Wren *C. palustris* and Western Marsh Wren *C. paludicola*, with the status of the Mexican population in México, Hidalgo and Puebla states obscure (see below under Taxonomy). Even neglecting this complication the systematics of the species has been complex and volatile.

In 1957 the American Ornithologists' Union checklist recognised 10 races in North America; a review by Phillips (1986) increased this to 14, plus the isolated race in eastern Mexico.

C. p. palustris (breeds in salt or brackish marshes from Virginia to New York, possibly east to Rhode Island) Described above.
C. p. waynei 'Wayne's Marsh Wren' (Resident along coast of southern Virginia and North Carolina) Similar to *palustris* but darker and duller above, undertail-coverts usually barred with dusky. Chest with little wash of pale brownish.
C. p. griseus 'Worthington's Marsh Wren' (Coastal marshes from north-eastern South Carolina to central Atlantic coast of Florida) Very grey, devoid of rich brown tones. Crown brown or dusky. Sides and flanks pale, dull, usually barred with dusky.
C. p. marianae 'Marian's Marsh Wren' (resident on Gulf Coast from Florida to easternmost Texas) Sootier and less rufescent than *waynei*, with duller flanks. Browns darker than *griseus*, crown mostly black.
C. p. dissaeptus 'Common Long-billed Marsh Wren'. (Breeds from southern Ontario to northern Ohio, West Virginia and southern New England. Winters as far south as southern Florida and occasionally Veracruz state, eastern Mexico) Uppertail-coverts, sides and flanks dull brownish, not barred or spotted. Chest whitish, without any contrast to rest of median underparts.
C. p. iliacus 'Prairie Marsh Wren' (breeds from Manitoba and south-western Ontario to eastern Kansas and Missouri. Winters in southern USA west as far as south-eastern Texas and in interior Mexico as far south as Tlaxcala state) More reddish-brown than *dissaeptus* on flanks, lores usually buffy, light wing-markings more extensive.
C. p. laingi 'Alberta Marsh Wren' (breeds from northern Alberta and central Saskatchewan to south-east Manitoba south to Montana. Winters in Mexico south to eastern Jalisco, Oaxaca and central Veracruz states, north to southern Texas) Above palest brown, brightest, most rufescent or buffy. Black areas reduced, flanks pale, less rufescent than *iliacus* but brighter than *plesius*.
C. p. plesius 'Western Marsh Wren' (Breeds from south-eastern Idaho to central Colorado and New Mexico. Winters from central California, Nevada and Kansas to central Mexico) Flanks and upperparts paler and duller than *iliacus* or other southwestern races, crown duller, blackish usually restricted to sides, nape usually conspicuously brown.
C. p. pulverius (breeds from central British Columbia and central Idaho to north-eastern California and north-western Nevada. Winters from north-western Oregon and central Colorado to central Mexico (Baja California, north-eastern Jalisco and southern Guanajato) and southern Texas) Similar to *plesius* but still paler and duller; little or no trace of brownish chest-band.
C. p. tolucensis 'Mexican Marsh Wren' (resident in Mexico from Hidalgo and México to Puebla states)

Chest and sides darker than northern races; back of adult almost or totally black and white, extending to lower back.

C. p. browningi (resident in south-western British Columbia to central Washington; winters in south-western Washington) Darker than *pulverius* or *plesius*, greyer than other coastal races with little black on crown.

C. p. paludicola 'Tule Wren' (resident from south-western Washington to north-western Oregon) Similar to *browningi* but black on crown more extensive, underparts warmer brown.

C. p. aestuarinus 'Suisun Marsh Wren' (resident in central California [Sacramento and San Joaquin valleys to San Joaquin delta]. Winters also west to coast of California) Darker and dingier than *paludicola* but black on crown more intense and extensive. Tail and uppertail-coverts darker.

C. p. deserticola (interior southern Califonia) Similar to *aestuarinus* but white streaks on back more prominent, brown wash of chest and flanks brighter. In addition Phillips (1986) considered there to be a then undescribed race in southern coastal California south to San Diego county (*clarkae*).

SPECIES TAXONOMY Recent intensive study suggests that the 'Marsh Wren' is two distinct species, the names for which would be Eastern Marsh Wren *C. palustris* and Western Marsh Wren *C. paludicola* (Monroe & Sibley 1993). Although there are no very obvious plumage differences between the eastern and western groups of races, painstaking examination of song types, and the apparent isolation of song types in populations, has given support to this split.

The song of the 'western' group of Marsh Wrens tend to be much more varied, with a greater variety of sounds and a much larger repertoire, frequently sung without repetition. 'Eastern' type birds, by contrast, were much more limited in scope and variety, with slower singing rates but some more 'musical' notes. (Kroodsma 1988). Careful study in Nebraska showed that the 'eastern' type birds had, on an average, some 48 song repertoire types, whereas 'western' males averaged 211 types. In Nebraska there is an apparently clear-cut geographic division of the two types, with a corridor about 100km wide devoid of suitable habitat. Each type seems to be almost entirely restricted to one or other side of this dividing stripe of territory. In Canada, where suitable habitat occurs more or less continuously across the Prairie Provinces, there is a significant preference for assortative mating, with 'eastern' singing males selectively mated to genetically 'eastern-type' females (Kroodsma in press). Thus a taxonomic split of the two song types may well be justified. The status of the isolated breeding population in Mexico (race *tolucensis*) is presently obscure and would doubtless be a rewarding topic for future study.

VOICE The song of the Marsh Wren, loud and persistent, uttered throughout the day and frequently throughout the night as well, is one of the characteristic sounds of marshes across most of North America. Although not universally admired (Alexander Wilson opined that the species was 'deficient and contemptible in singing', while Audubon felt that the 'song, if song I may call it [was comparable to] the grating of a rusty hinge') (quoted in Kroodsma 1998), the song of the

Marsh Wren has been subject to a large amount of study; careful examination of the song itself and associated behaviours of different populations may lead to the Marsh Wren's split into two distinct species. The typical song of the eastern races, given by the male alone, is a sharp, rapid series of liquid rattling notes, half a dozen or more, compressed into about two seconds; it does to a considerable degree resemble the song of the Swamp Sparrow *Melospiza georgiana*, with which it shares habitat, but is much more liquid and metallic. In the western part of the range (races *plesius*, *pulverius*, *browningi*, *paludicola*, *clarkae*, *aestuarinus* and *deserticola*) the males have songs which are more varied and complicated, and individual birds have larger repertoires. In the Great Plains, western-type song includes 'harsh and grating broad-band sounds', while not far east the song is less harsh and more liquid (Kroodsma 1998). Careful analysis of songs shows about 50 different types in eastern populations but more than 200 in the west. Western birds are also more prone to countersinging, i.e. to matching and sometimes anticipating song types according to the patterns of adjacent males. Unlike many passerines, males actually increase their rates of singing after pairings, a strategy presumably related to the complex polygamous behaviour of the species. Wintering birds of the eastern populations sing on the wintering grounds, from January onwards, the songs being distinguishable, to a discerning ear, from those of resident birds. Young birds develop a subsong shortly after fledging, but full song is not employed until the subsequent year. Various other vocalisations are used; unfledged and recently fledged young make loud buzzing calls, western birds have a *click* or *cluck* call, foraging males call *tscheew tscheew* in flight, and adult at the nest greet each other by a melodious rolling warble (Kroodsma 1998). In sharp contrast to the Sedge wren, young Marsh Wrens learn song-types by listening, and their repertoire is strongly influenced by what songs they have heard (Colyer 2000).

HABITAT As a breeding bird usually confined to marshes with actual standing water of various depths (in contrast to the Sedge Wren *C. platensis* which is most common in damp sedgy meadows). Most northern populations nest in cattail *Typha latifolia* and *T. angustifolia* stands, bulrushes *Scirpus* spp. and phragmites *Phragmites australis*. Southern coastal populations, in brackish marshes, nest in various species of *Spartina* (cord grass), *Juncus* (sedge) and sawgrass. Wintering birds are usually found in whatever marsh habitat is available, both fresh and salt; northern birds, bred in fresh water marshes, may winter in brackish or salt-marshes. In suitable habitat the population density may reach extraordinarily high levels; a single linear territory in coastal *Spartina* in Georgia may be as small as 60m² (167 per hectare, or 75 per acre) (Kale 1965). In cattail marshes in southern Ontario density is very much less, rarely more than one or two per hectare (A.D. Brewer pers. obs.). The territory size may depend on the marital status, and hence presumably the requirements, of the male bird; in western Washington State bachelor birds dominated areas only about half as large as mated birds, whether monogamists or bigamists, and in eastern Washington the distinction was even greater (Kroodsma 1998). In Wisconsin, territory size was dependent very much on the dominant vegetation type, the most favoured (cattails in standing water) being able to support a three-fold higher density of breeding birds than dry cattail (Manci & Rusch 1988).

HABITS An active and acrobatic bird, constantly on the move. It is not excessively secretive, but may not be very easy to observe, especially in windy weather when it prefers to stay low in its reedy habitat. On calmer days birds will sing from the tops of cattails, the tail usually cocked sharply over the back. Especially during the breeding season and when involved in territorial disputes Marsh Wrens may become very conspicuous, making numerous short flights above the marsh vegetation. During migration it is much more furtive and difficult to observe.

A curious feature of Marsh Wrens, shared by several other wren species including some tropical ones, is their habit of destroying the eggs and, sometimes, the young, of other birds, both of their own species and of unrelated species. Allen (1914) in his classic study of Red-winged Blackbirds *Agelaius phoeniceus* was one of the first observers to document this; on occasion Marsh Wrens would not only destroy Red-wings' eggs but dine on the contents. Far from being the unusual behaviour of a criminally inclined minority of rogue birds (Welter 1935), egg-destruction by Marsh Wrens is so prevalent that the species may even be caught in traps baited with eggs (Picman 1980a). Interspecific hostility seems to be mutual. Red-wings frequently attack Marsh Wrens, and there is a negative association between the species (Jaeger 1980). Red-wings have a lower nesting success in nests near Marsh Wren courting centres (Bent 1970) and it has been estimated that more than half of Red-wing nests may be so destroyed (Picman 1980b,c). For their part Red-wings frequently attack Marsh Wrens. In western populations a similar state of cordial hostility exists between the Yellow-headed Blackbird *Xanthocephalus xanthocephalus* and Marsh Wrens (Verner 1980); the blackbirds may attempt to destroy wren nests or prevent a brooding female from returning. Other species known to suffer egg destruction by Marsh Wrens include birds as large as Least Bitterns *Ixobrychus exilis* (Chapman 1900). Perhaps easier to explain, since it would have the effect of eliminating competition for resources with neighbouring territories, is the Marsh Wren's well-documented habit of destroying the eggs, and on occasion the young, of its own species. Females have been observed to kill small chicks in the nests in adjacent territories and then throw the corpses out of the nest. (Kroodsma in press). Marsh Wren eggs are unusually thick-shelled and robust, presumably as a defence against such predation (Picman *et al.* 1996).

Marsh Wrens are night migrants and frequently figure in substantial numbers in counts of kills around radio towers and similar obstacles.

STATUS AND DISTRIBUTION Breeds across North America, from southern New Brunswick, central Ontario, Manitoba and Saskatchewan, northern Alberta and eastern and south-eastern British Columbia, south to central Virginia, southern Illinois, Nebraska, Colorado and most states westwards to the Pacific coast from southern Vancouver Island to central California and in the valley of the Colorado River; absent from some areas of the prairies and much of eastern

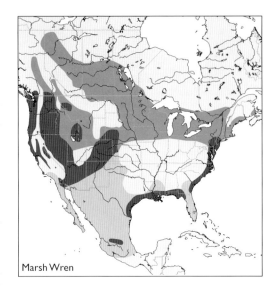

Marsh Wren

California. Isolated breeding in Nova Scotia, and on the shores of James Bay, Ontario (Weir 1983), stated to have nested in Greenland (Armstrong 1955). It also nests in coastal marshes from Cape Cod south to central Florida on both coasts, and east to central Texas. There is an isolated population in Mexico, at altitudes 1,000 to 2,500m, from Puebla east to Hidalgo and México. Northern and inland populations are mainly migratory, but coastal populations south of Massachusetts are largely sedentary, these frequently being augmented in winter by migrants of different races: also winters inland across the southern United States from the Carolinas, through Georgia, Texas, southern Colorado and Nevada south through most of Mexico, from Baja California south to Veracruz and Oaxaca. The Mexican breeding population is sedentary, as are the populations on the Pacific coast from British Columbia to California. Occasionally winters in New England and north to southern Ontario (James *et al.* 1976).

One record for Bermuda, in January 1996 (Kirwan 1996) and one for Cuba in August 1994 (Norton 1994).

Although there may be some evidence of a significant decline in some eastern populations (and local populations are vulnerable to habitat change), the species is reasonably common over much of its range where suitable habitat exists, at times attaining very high population densities. Populations may, on occasion, be augmented by human creation of suitable habitat, as in parts of southern Ontario (Brewer 1977) and in the Colorado River valley (Rosenberg *et al.* 1991). Recently breeding range extensions have occurred at both ends of the eastern range, north into the Maritimes and further south in Florida. In Ontario the overall range has not changed dramatically in fifty years (Cadman *et al.* 1987).

BREEDING The breeding of the Marsh Wren is notable for the strong development of two features, polygamy and multiple nest-building. Male Marsh Wrens devote an extraordinary amount of time to nest-building. In some populations the males may build more than twenty nests in a season. Females may inspect nests already built by the male, and having selected one, line it with fine leaves, feathers or down from cattail heads (Verner 1965): alternatively the male may construct yet another nest at her instigation (Welter 1935). Construction of a non-breeding nest can be accomplished in two days, but a complete breeding nest may take five to eight days (Welter 1935, Kale 1965).

Nests are domed structures, typically about a metre above water or tide level, although examples have been found from 30cm to 5m (Bent 1948). Construction material is usually thin strips of leaves and grasses, lined with vegetable down, occasionally feathers or snake skin (Low 1943). When the outer shell, typically made of coarser material, has been completed, building continues from the inside, using finer grasses and rootlets. The completed breeding nest is about 18cm high and 12cm wide, with the chamber between 7cm and 12cm in size. Breeding, but not dummy, nests have a sill or doorstep consisting of an extension of the lining, which prevents eggs from rolling out in high wind. The presence of this sill may be used to distinguish breeding from non-breeding nests.

Eggs 3–10, usually 4–6. Clutch size varies with race, averaging larger and with more variation in northern races, birds in Washington state and Manitoba averaging up to 6, in Florida as low as 3–4. There are no data for the Mexican race *tolucensis*. As the breeding season progresses average clutch size declines; in a study in salt marshes in Georgia (race *griseus*) late clutches averaged 3.8 eggs versus 4.7 early in the season (Kale 1965). Egg colour somewhat variable according to race, generally various shades of chocolate or dark brown with spots and dots of darker shades of brown (Bent 1948). White, or very pale, eggs occur, but apparently very rarely (Gross 1968). In one small colony of Marsh Wrens in Ohio numerous entire sets of white eggs were found, presumably from birds related to each other (Aldrich 1946). In 107 sets of Marsh Wren eggs in the US National Museum there are four white eggs, but since some of these may have been collected especially because they were white this number is probably not representative. Single white eggs in normal clutches also occur.

Incubation by female alone (who may evince considerable hostility to the male at this time, possibly because of his proclivity towards attacking eggs) for 13–16 days, varying somewhat with race and time in the season. Young are brooded by female alone. The degree to which males help in feeding the young varies, from almost nothing to substantial, and is related to the opportunities for bigamy and trigamy among males. When there exist opportunities for further multiple matings it seems that young from earlier liaisons tend to get short shrift. Young leave the nest at about 13–15 days although at this stage they are very weak flyers. Fledged broods may be fed by parents or a parent for some 12 days after fledging. Young may roost in a non-breeding nest, or in vegetation. Young do not, apparently, routinely help at the nest, although this has been observed in captivity (Skutch 1976).

Nest parasitism by Brown-headed Cowbirds *Molothorus ater* is very rare; out of 1,200 nests in British Columbia only one had Cowbird eggs (Picman 1986).

The sheer amount of effort devoted by male Marsh Wrens to the construction of multiple nests, the great majority of which are never put to any practical use, argues that this behaviour has strong selective advantage in enhancing gene propagation for males. However, precisely what that advantage is, and why it requires the construction of so many surplus nests, is more obscure and has long been the subject of debate. Certainly when a breeding nest is destroyed the availability of numerous alternatives which can quickly be refurbished to breeding condition would be advantageous. Many workers believe that the principal function of multiple nests is to act as decoys (Leonard & Picman 1987); the difficulty of concealing a nest in cattails (as opposed to, say, a species nesting in dense woodland) gives some weight to this view. Another suggestion is that the number of nests built may be an indication of a male's vigour; when nests are removed artificially from a territory a male has little success in attracting a mate (Verner 1964). However, other writers have concluded that 'none of the hypotheses proposed to date adequately explain the persistence' of multiple nest building (Metz 1991).

The degree of polygamy appears to vary with geographic location. The number of males with multiple mates was only 5% in Georgia, but up to 54% in Manitoba (Kale 1965, Leonard & Picman 1987). In the latter study, a total of ten bachelor males, 53 monogamists, 48 bigamists and nine trigamists suggests an overall sex ratio significantly skewed away from equality, in fact only about 0.65 males for each female.

FOOD Mostly invertebrate. A wide variety of insects, including ants, bees, wasps, dipterous flies, beetles, bugs (Hemiptera), dragonfly larvae and opluids; at times spiders form an important diet item (Welter 1935, Kale 1965).

MOVEMENTS Northern and interior populations are highly migratory; although occasional individuals may linger through mid-winter, the breeding range from Nova Scotia through central North America to Alberta and interior British Columbia is essentially vacated (races *iliacus, dissaeptus, laingi, pulverius* and *plesius*). Present throughout the year coastally from about Cape Cod to Florida and Texas, and southern British Columbia to California, although the northern most sections of these populations (races *palustris* and *waynei* in the east, and *paludicola* and *browningi* in the west) are partial migrants. Southern coastal populations, and the isolated race in Mexico (*tolucensis*) are sedentary. Sedentary populations in coastal marshes in the southern United States are augmented by winter visitors of different races, and interior marshes from the Carolinas through Texas and northern Mexico are wintering grounds. Vagrant to Bermuda (Kirwan 1996) and Cuba (Norton 1994).

There is only one long distance banding recovery; a bird marked as an adult male in Saskatchewan in May was recovered in Louisiana fourteen months later; however, since the method of recovery was 'caught by …raptors (including found in pellets)' the actual recovery date may have been well prior to July, by which month it would have been expected to be back on breeding territory (Bird Banding Laboratory data).

MEASUREMENTS Wing of male 48–54, of female 44.5–52.5; tail of 38.5–46.5, of female 37–41.5; exposed culmen of male 14–15.5, of female 13–15; tarsus of male 18.5–21, of female 18.5–20.

THRYOMANES

Small wrens (wing 45–60mm), with fine decurved bills with obvious rictal bristles and a relatively long, rounded tail. The separate existence of this genus has been a source of lively controversy, some authors (e.g. Phillips 1986) preferring to merge it with *Troglodytes*. Currently there are two species in the genus, Bewick's Wren and Socorro Wren; however, in the face of universal recent opinion that the latter is in fact a *Troglodytes*, we have anticipated changes in classification and left Bewick's Wren as the only member. Current DNA work does, however, strongly suggest that the Carolina Wren, currently the only North American representative of the genus *Thryothorus*, is much closer to *Thryomanes* than it is to other *Thryothorus* species (K. Barker pers. comm.). For the moment we have maintained its current accepted taxonomic position.

28 BEWICK'S WREN
Thryomanes bewickii   Plate 8

Troglodytes bewickii Audubon 1831, five miles from St Francesville, Louisiana.

Alternative names: French *Troglodyte de Bewick*; Spanish *Saltapared de Bewick*, *Chivirín cola oscura*

Etymology: Named by J. J. Audubon for his friend Thomas Bewick (1754-1828), English author and wood-engraver, 'a person too well-known for his admirable talents ...to need any eulogy of mine'.

A widespread and well-liked species over much of the western parts of the United states, frequently found in close association with man. Formerly also well-distributed in the eastern part of the continent.

IDENTIFICATION Length 12–13.5cm. Not easily mistaken for any other bird in its range. Most closely resembles Carolina Wren, both species having prominent white superciliaries, but immediately distinguished by its long, white-edged tail and grey, not buff, underparts. House Wrens do not have a prominent eye-stripe, and all sympatric Mexican species lack the light tips to the rectrices.

DESCRIPTION *T. b. bewickii*
Adult Crown, back and shoulders rich dark brown, becoming more rufous towards lower back and rump. Feathers of lower back with concealed white spots. Primaries and secondaries dull grey-brown, the outer-webs medium-brown with blackish-brown bars, giving eight to ten bars on the closed wing; barring extends across entire width of tertials. Central rectrices grey-brown with about 15 sharply-defined blackish bars; lateral rectrices blackish with extensive grey-white tips, largest on the outermost feathers. Lores greyish, conspicuous buffy-white postocular supercilium. Area behind eye rufous-brown, ear-coverts mottled grey and grey-brown. Chin and throat off-white, becoming greyish-white on chest and buffy-white on belly. Lower flanks dull brown. Eyes brown, bill blackish-brown with pale base to lower mandible, legs dark brown.
Juvenile Similar to adult but relatively paler plumage, often with dusky edgings to the feathers of the under-parts and loosely textured undertail-coverts (Pyle 1997).

GEOGRAPHICAL VARIATION Numerous subspecies, of which two have become extinct this century. There has been much debate about the validity of some races (Phillips 1986).
    T. b. bewickii (north-central USA to Kansas, Nebraska and Mississippi) Described above.

T. b. cryptus 'Texas Wren' (resident from south-central Kansas to northern Mexico (Nuevo León and Tamaulipas) Larger than *bewickii*, upperparts more grey, underparts whiter.
T. b. altus 'Appalachian Bewick's Wren' (formerly from southern Ontario to central Georgia, now much reduced) Similar to *bewickii*, but darker and more sooty.
T. b. eremophilus 'Desert Wren' (resident from eastern California through southern Utah and Nevada to western Texas, south to west-central Mexico) Similar to *cryptus*, but greyer above, whiter below. Bill larger.
T. b. calophonus 'Seattle Wren' (south-western British Columbia, western Washington and western Oregon; in winter may wander to northern California [Kennedy & White 1997]) Similar to *bewickii*, but upperparts rich brown, sides and flanks more strongly tinged with brown, bill longer.
T. b. spilurus 'Vigor's Wren' (central coastal California south to Monterey Bay) Similar to *calophonus*, but smaller and less brown, more grey, on upperparts.
T. b. marinensis 'Nicasio's Wren' (humid zone of north-western California from Del Norte to Marin counties) Similar to *spilurus*, but brighter brown on back and flanks.
T. b. drymoecus 'San Joaquin Wren' (central California including Sacramento Valley) Similar to *spilurus* but duller and paler, and somewhat larger.
T. b. atrestus (south-central Oregon, north-eastern California, west-central Nevada) Similar to *drymoecus* but larger, with upperparts darker and more greyish.
T. b. correctus 'San Diego Wren' (coastal California from San Benito county south to San Diego district) Similar to *drymoecus* but upperparts lighter brown, tail longer.
T. b. charienturus 'Sooty Wren' (northern Baja California south to about 30°N) Similar to *drymoecus* but upperparts less brown, tail longer, bill shorter.
T. b. magdalinensis (Baja California between latitudes 24° and 26°N) Smaller and more pale grey than *eremophilus* and *cerroensis*.
T. b. nesophilus 'Santa Cruz Island Wren' (Islands of Santa Cruz, Santa Rosa and Anacapa, California) Similar to *spilurus* but upperparts much lighter brown, flanks extensively tinged with pale brown.
T. b. catalinae 'Catalina Island Wren' (Santa Catalina Island, California) Similar to *charienturus* but darker dorsally and with heavier feet and bill.

T. b. cerroensis 'Cedros Island Wren' (Cedros island and adjacent mainland, central Baja California) Paler and more grey than *charienturus*, with smaller bill.

T. b. leucophrys 'San Clemente Island Wren' (San Clemente Island, California. Reportedly extinct [Phillips 1986]) Similar to *nesophilus*, but larger and more grey.

T. b. brevicauda 'Guadalupe Wren' (Guadalupe Island, off Baja California. Certainly extinct, probably about 1892, as a result of habitat degradation brought about by introduced goats and predation by feral cats) Very similar to *correctus* but much smaller, bill longer, tail shorter and less barred.

T. b. bairdii 'Baird's Wren' (south-eastern Mexico [Oaxaca, Veracruz and southern Puebla]) Similar to *eremophilus* but smaller, darker and browner.

T. b. murinus 'Hartlaub's Wren' (south-central Mexico [Hidalgo, México, Morelos, Tlaxcala, San Luis Potosí]) Similar to *bairdii* but larger, with darker and more brown upperparts.

T. b. percnus 'Jalisco Wren' (western Mexico [Jalisco, southern Zacatecas]) Similar to *murinus* but darker, with longer wings and tail.

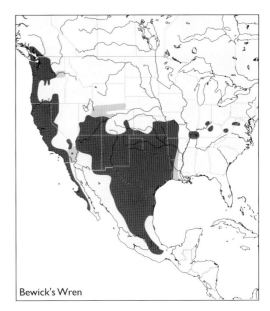

Bewick's Wren

VOICE Song is an attractive series of notes, the beginning phrases somewhat reminiscent of a Song Sparrow *Melospiza melodia*, usually ending with a fine trill. Much variation in song type throughout range, with individual birds having a varied repertoire (Kroodsma 1974, 1985). Song apparently entirely by male with no evidence of duetting or antiphonal song (Kennedy & White 1997). Alarm call *plit* and a scolding *dzz*.

HABITAT With such a large geographic range, very varied. Generally bushy areas, riparian woodland and brush. The populations east of the Mississippi are especially prone to associate with farmyards and suburban areas whereas in the west this is less frequently the case. In California frequently found in chaparral brushland, but also in a variety of other vegetation types including piñon juniper woodland, mesquite and cottonwood. In Mexico, in a wide variety of habitats, from arid prickly-pear and cactus-dominated scrub in Nuevo León to large trees in Mexico City (Kennedy & White 1997).

HABITS Not particularly shy, and in some parts of its range closely associated with man. Will sing from quite prominent posts; flights generally short in duration and low to the ground. Forages among litter on the ground, where it moves by hopping, and in vegetation.

STATUS AND DISTRIBUTION Over much of its range either resident or a short-distance migrant; south-western populations largely sedentary and island populations totally so. The eastern races (*bewickii* and *altus*) are migratory.

The range of Bewick's Wren has changed drastically during historic times and is changing again at the present time. Apparently expanded dramatically east of the Mississippi during the nineteenth century, doubtless due to the creation of suitable semi-open habitat by the clearing of forests for agriculture, and the provision of nest-sites around farmyards. First reported in West Virginia in 1834, Pennsylvania in 1843, Georgia in 1854, Ohio in 1879, to New Jersey in 1890 and southern

Ontario in 1898. At the maximum extent of its range extended as far east as south-eastern New York, Maryland and central Georgia. In winter it withdrew from the northern parts of the eastern range, wintering as far north as central Oklahoma and southwestern Ohio (Bent 1948). There are only two long distance banding recoveries, one from Vermont to Arkansas, the other from Arkansas to Kansas.

The present situation is quite different. Declines were first noticed as early as the 1920s, and became more serious in the 1960s and 1970s, when quantitative surveys allowed a numerical estimate of the situation. Bewick's Wrens were noted on 49% of routes covered by the Breeding Bird Survey in eastern North America in 1966; this had shrunk to 12% by 1979. In Kentucky, during the decade prior to 1979 the estimated decline was 75%, while it has been estimated that the decline from 1966 to 1994 was 14.4% per year (Kennedy & White 1997). In Ontario, formerly a rare summer resident north to Toronto (James *et al.* 1976), but not recorded as breeding anywhere in the province during the years 1981–1985 (Cadman *et al.* 1987). The race concerned, *T. b. altus*, has been proposed for listing as an Endangered population. Now only a sparse breeder anywhere east of the Mississippi, with very small populations in Kentucky, Tennessee, West Virginia, Virginia, Iowa and (prior to 1987) Ohio (Kennedy & White 1997).

In western North America, occurs in extreme southwestern British Columbia including southern Vancouver Island, Washington and Oregon, California and western Nevada, and from Utah east to western Missouri, south through Texas and Arizona to Oaxaca (Mexico) and through most of the central Mexican plateau (absent from humid tropical lowlands). Also on the Pacific shore of Baja California including some offshore islands. Populations on Guadalupe Island, Mexico and San Clemente Island, California now extinct (prior to 1903, and prior to 1986, respectively). Some western populations are partial or short-distant migrants, others are sedentary; for example it appears to withdraw from much of Utah, and in winter it may be found outside the breeding range in some parts of the western United States (e.g. parts of Washington, Oregon and Idaho, or in lowland parts of Arizona (Phillips *et al.* 1964) or Sonora (Russell & Monson 1998). Some western populations are also declining significantly, for example in British Columbia, although in New Mexico and Texas populations are increasing. The causes of the precipitous decline of the eastern populations of Bewick's Wren are not clearly understood; however, it seems likely that its disappearance is correlated with the invasion of its breeding range by the House Wren *Troglodytes aedon*, with its well-documented habit of entering nest-cavities of other species and destroying eggs. Ironically the spread of the House Wren has been aided by the provision of nestboxes.

BREEDING Nests are located in a variety of sites, closed, semi-open or open. Often in cavities such as nestboxes, woodpecker holes, in various crannies in sheds or barns, in crevices in rocks, abandoned motor vehicles, natural cavities in forest floors; also frequently on shelves or ledges in outbuildings etc. Nest is usually an open cup, more rarely domed, made of twigs, grasses, rootlets, leaf skeletons etc., with a cup of finer materials, feathers, etc., frequently lined with bits of snakeskin. Male may initiate building, and may start the foundation of a nest for the second brood before the first one has fledged; otherwise both sexes participate in building. Nest dimensions vary according to situation, but cup size averages 6.4cm in diameter and 4.5cm in depth (Kennedy & White 1997). Eggs three to eight, average clutch size 5.6, in colour white with variable amounts of brown, lilac or purplish spotting. Dates of first eggs vary from early March in Texas to late April in eastern populations; no data on southern Mexican birds. Incubation 14–16 days, apparently by female only, fed on nest by male. Young usually fed by both sexes, although sometimes one or the other may cease to participate, possibly to start another brood. Fledging period about 14–16 days, young are fed by parents for up to a further two weeks. In the more southerly parts of the United States range, frequently double-brooded, and occasionally triple-brooded; further north (e.g. in Oregon) second broods much more rare. No data on southern Mexican populations. A proportion of males (15% in a Kansas study, Kennedy & White 1997) are polygynous, the clutch from the second mate being laid after the fledging of the first brood. More rarely polyandrous; one female was observed to continue feeding her first brood while laying her second.

FOOD Mostly invertebrate. Stomach contents in California consisted of bugs (Hemiptera) 31%, beetles 21%, bees and wasps 17%, caterpillars and some butterflies and moths 12%, and smaller quantities of other orders; also some vegetable matter, especially in winter (Kennedy & White 1997).

MOVEMENTS Eastern populations migratory, western populations partially migratory or sedentary; no data on Mexican populations but doubtless sedentary (see above and map).

MEASUREMENTS (*T. b. bewickii*) Wing of male 52–58, of female 49–55; tail of male 46–56, of female 46–50; culmen of male 12.6–14.7, of female 11.9–13.7; tarsus of male 14.7–17.8, of female 12.9–16.6 (Kennedy & White 1997).

FERMINIA

An extraordinary and unique genus, of uncertain affinities, consisting of one species inhabiting a minute area of Cuba. Relatively large (15.5cm) and long-tailed, with short rounded wings. Rectrices broad and notably soft and fluffy. Bill medium in length, compressed, almost straight, slightly shorter than head. Legs one and a third times as long as the bill, feet rather weak. Feathers on the forehead coarse and bristly.

The relationships of *Ferminia* to other genera of wrens are obscure and well worthy of further study. It may represent some very extremely differentiated offshoot from the stock that gave rise to *Thryomanes* (Bewick's Wren) (Barbour 1926), although it should be noted that *Thryomanes* has twelve rectrices, *Ferminia* only ten; however, rectrix number may not be a very conservative character since it is known to vary within a genus (e.g. *Synallaxis*, *Phalacrocorax*). Further information about nesting and social behaviour, as well as comparative examination of DNA, would be highly informative.

29   ZAPATA WREN
Ferminia cerverai
Plate 16

Ferminia cerverai Barbour 1926, Santo Tomás, Península de Zapata, Cuba.

Alternative names: Cervera's Wren, Cuban Marsh Wren; Spanish *Fermina*

Etymology: Named after Sr. Fermin Z. Cervera, a soldier, on the Spanish side, in the Spanish-American war who was somehow not repatriated at the termination of hostilities. 'Although a somewhat peculiar person in several respects' he was 'nevertheless a born naturalist' who 'after real hardships and great difficulty and exposure' collected the first specimens (Barbour 1926, 1928).

A very aberrant wren of debatable affinities, confined to the Zapata Swamp of western Cuba.

IDENTIFICATION Length 15.5–16cm. Quite unlike any other wren, or any other species found in its limited and specialised range; the relatively large size, short wings and long tail and heavily barred plumage is diagnostic.

DESCRIPTION

Adult Crown blackish-brown, each feather edged finely with paler brown, giving an impression of dark speckles at close range. Nape, back and rump the same colours, the markings becoming fine lateral bars on the back and the tertials. Primaries and secondaries blackish-brown, the outerwebs with about ten buffy-brown spots, giving a series of fine narrow bars on closed wing. Tail blackish-brown with numerous fine lateral bars of greyish-brown; ends of rectrices notably diffuse and fluffy. Sides of face mottled brownish-buff, no very prominent eye-stripe. Chin pale whitish-buff, becoming browner on chest and darker on flanks; lower flanks with prominent transverse bars of blackish-brown. Vent and thighs brownish with diffuse darker barring. Iris clear brown, bill dark brown above, paler yellow-brown below, legs brownish.

Juvenile Similar to adult, but throat with very fine speckles of black, especially at sides, chest with a band of larger diffuse blackish-brown speckles, barring on flanks much less distinct.

GEOGRAPHICAL VARIATION None; monotypic.

VOICE Song is varied, typically a series of four to seven clear gurgling whistles, interspersed with harsher churring notes, frequently continuing for a minute or more. Currently there is some dispute as to whether both sexes sing; the song of the female is said to be shorter and higher-pitched than that of the male. Calls a low hoarse *chut chut*, *churr churr*, etc.

HABITAT Restricted to savanna-type swamp, where the dominant vegetation is a sawgrass *cortadero macho* (*Cladium jamaicense*) and a rush *Typha dominguensis*, with occasional bushes such as *arraigan* (*Myrica cerifera*), *yanilla blanca* (*Ilex cassine*), *yana* (*Conocarpus erecta*) and other bushes which may be used as song-posts. The water-level in the Zapata swamp is seasonally variable, but the Zapata Wren tends to occur in drier areas where it can forage on the ground (Garrido & García Montaña 1975).

HABITS Usually secretive, although it will climb into low bushes to sing for lengthy periods. A very poor flier (indeed, Barbour, its describer, originally thought it was flightless) (Barbour 1928), and rarely flies more than 15m at a time; it will, however, appear very rapidly from considerable distances when its song is played in a territory. The tail is frequently cocked over the back, except when during song when it is depressed. A notably quarrelsome bird, prone to drive off other species (such as Zapata Sparrow, *Torreornis inexpectata*, a substantially larger bird) if they trespass. It feeds quite frequently on the ground, scratching in search of insects and snail eggs.

STATUS AND DISTRIBUTION Confined entirely to the Ciénaga de Zapata on the southern coast of western Cuba. The status of the species has varied substantially since its discovery in 1926. In 1927 it seemed to be quite common around the original type-location, 5km north of Santo Tomás, and three specimens were acquired in short order, with others heard singing nearby (Bruner

1934). As late as 1962 it was common (Garrido 1980); however, by the late seventies it seemed to have declined catastrophically, and several expeditions failed to locate it, leading to fears of its extinction (Martínez García & Martínez García 1991). More recently it has been relocated and seems to be recovering (Gonzalez 1982). The known range (originally estimated at only 13km²) has been extended by observations at three new locations, respectively 20, 20 and 15km from Santo Tomás. Nevertheless the population is perilously small.

The population density appears to be quite low; although the defended territory was only 1ha, pairs were rarely within earshot of each other, and the overall density was 0.0008 pairs per hectare (1,250 ha/pair) (Martínez García & Martínez García 1991). The main threat to the species and the probable cause of its decline, was uncontrolled burning of the swamp vegetation by the local human population while hunting for edible terrapins. This is now controlled, although accidental fires still pose a threat. Other concerns centre on the introduced mongoose (*Herpestes*). A management plan has been proposed (Martínez García & Martínez García 1991), which should benefit two other Zapata endemics, the Zapata Rail *Cyanolimnus cerverai* and the nominate race of Zapata Sparrow *T. inexpectata*. Recently a new population, totalling about 24 birds in three adjacent sites, was found at a location several kilometres to the north of currently known locations (Kirkconnell *et al.* 1999). Best current (April 2000) estimates of the total population, based on opinions of local ornithologists who spend a lot of time in the Zapata Swamp, seem to be in the region of 80–100 pairs (R. Rolfe pers. comm.). Not all apparently suitable habitat is occupied.

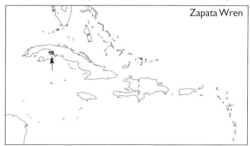

BREEDING The nest was not discovered until 1986. It is a near-spherical ball of sawgrass leaves, about 30cm in diameter with an entrance hole 5cm high. The interior is lined with small feathers. The four nests so far found were located in sawgrass, 50–70cm above the ground. Nest construction is by both sexes, but incubation by the female alone. The eggs are white, and all clutches so far observed were of two eggs only; the statement made by Bond (1971), based on comments from local people, that six eggs are laid, is obviously erroneous. The incubation period is unknown, although in one observed nest it had been proceeding for 23 days before the nest was predated by a snake. The breeding season seems to be quite protracted, from January to, at least, July. Two specimens in the Academy of Natural Sciences of Philadelphia, taken in January, had enlarged testes; nest construction has been observed on 20 February, a nest with eggs on 28 February, and a nest with well-feathered young on 12 June. Males sing vigorously in January, but song decreases in April, to increase again later, suggesting double-brooding. Nothing is known with regard to polygamy in the Zapata Wren.

FOOD The diet is surprisingly varied for a wren; stomach contents show mainly invertebrates (crickets, bugs, beetles, caterpillars, flies and spiders), but also snail eggs and slugs; small *Anolis* lizards seem to be quite frequent; including one estimated from the size of its bones to be not less than 10cm long. Vegetable matter includes lichen and seeds of *Chrystbalanus hicacus*.

MOVEMENTS None; totally sedentary.

MEASUREMENTS Wing of male 53–61, of female 51; tail of male 63–67.5, of female 57; exposed culmen of male 18–20.5, of female 17.5; tarsus of male 21–22, of female 20.

THRYOTHORUS

The largest genus of wrens, consisting of about twenty-five species (according to taxonomy). Medium-sized wrens (wing 52–70mm, length 12–16cm). Bill usually shorter than head, distinctly decurved, fairly stout, wings short and rounded, tail 80–100% as long as wing, with rounded tip. Rictal bristles short, but distinct. Legs and feet moderately sturdy, much less robust than *Campylorhynchus*, but stouter than *Troglodytes* or *Henicorhina*. Some species contrastingly marked with strong black or white markings on underparts; conspicuous supercilia and strongly-patterned ear-coverts frequent. Many species are superb songsters; antiphonal song, or duetting, frequent. Cooperative breeding not recorded. Nests (where known) domed with side-entrances, or in cavities.

Distribution is predominately tropical, with the greatest abundance of species in southern Central America and north-eastern South America; absent from the West Indies. One species (the Carolina Wren) only in the United States, marginally reaching southern Canada; however, recent DNA work suggests that this species is more closely allied to the genus *Thryomanes* (Bewick's Wren) than to the Central and South American members of *Thryothorus* (K. Barker pers. comm.).

30   CAROLINA WREN
Thryothorus ludovicianus   Plate 8

Motacilla troglodytes Gmelin 1788 (*Sylvia ludovicianus* Latham 1790).

Alternative names: Mocking Wren; Spanish *Saltapared de Carolina, Saltapared Carolinense*; French *Troglodyte de Carolina*

By far the best-studied member of the genus *Thryothorus*, and the only one to occur in the United States, the Carolina Wren is a familiar and conspicuous bird of both suburbs and rural areas over much of eastern North America. Possibly better placed in the genus *Thryomanes* (K. Barker pers. comm.).

IDENTIFICATION Length 12.5–14cm. Over most of its range not easily confusable with other wren species. Distinguished from the House Wren, with whose range it overlaps in the north-eastern United States and southern Ontario, by its larger size, prominent white superciliary and generally warmer chestnut colour; from Bewick's Wren by the lack of prominent white corners to the tail, and by its bright buff underparts; and from Marsh Wren, with which it overlaps geographically, but in quite different habitats, by the presence of buff underparts and the lack of strong lateral black-and-white streaking on the shoulders. In north-west Mexico, Spot-breasted Wren is immediately distinguished by the heavy black spots on the underparts; in the juvenile these are more muted, but still distinctive. White-bellied Wren is smaller, shorter-tailed and has paler underparts (see also under White-browed Wren).

DESCRIPTION *T. l. ludovicianus*
Adult Crown and back rich brown, becoming more chestnut on rump and uppertail-coverts. Shoulders and greater coverts rich brown, with a series of small white dots on tips of lesser primary coverts. Secondaries rich brown with darker brown barring on both webs; barring on primaries is on outerweb only, but darker and more conspicuous. Rectrices brown, less chestnut than rump, with about 18–20 narrow dark-brown bars extending across entire tail. Very conspicuous white superciliary streak, narrowly bordered with black above and below, and extending beyond head onto shoulders. Ear-coverts speckled grey and greyish-black. Chin and throat unmarked grey, becoming buff on chest and warm buff on flanks and lower belly. Underwing-coverts greyish-buff. Iris red-brown, upper mandible lemon-coloured, paler at base; lower mandible pale lemon. Legs flesh-coloured.
Juvenile Similar to adult, but generally paler, with wing-coverts with buff tips, and vent and crissum with fluffier feathers, usually without bars.

Partial albinism is rare, usually involving a few flight or body feathers; no records of complete albinism, although one juvenile bird in Massachusetts was pure white, but with brown, not pink, eyes (Seneca 1985).

GEOGRAPHICAL VARIATION
T. l. ludovicianus (North America from southern Ontario, southern Wisconsin and Massachusetts southwards, except where occupied by the following races) Described above.
T. l. berlandieri 'Berlandier's Wren' (north-eastern Mexico from Coahuila to Nuevo León and Tamaulipas) Similar to *ludovicianus*, but slightly smaller, bill larger, upperparts duller brown, underparts more deeply coloured, flanks frequently barred with brown or dusky (Hellmayr 1924–1949).

T. l. lomitensis 'Lomita Wren' (southern Texas and northern Tamaulipas state, Mexico) Differs from *berlandieri* by duller colour, dull white superciliary, underparts pale or almost white, sides and flanks frequently barred brown.

T. l. miamensis 'Florida Wren' (Florida from approximately latitude 30°N [Gainesville area] southwards) The largest race, upperparts darker rusty chestnut and more deeply coloured below. (Lowery 1940).

T. l. burleighi 'Burleigh's Carolina Wren' (offshore islands of the Mississippi coast; Cat Island, Ship Island, Horn Island) Duller and more sooty above than *ludovicianus*, with less distinct barring on tail.

T. l. nesophilus (confined to Dog Island, north-western Florida) Differs from *ludovicianus* by paler underparts and whiter supercilium (Stevenson 1973).

T. l. tropicalis (north-eastern Mexico [southern Tamaulipas and eastern San Luis Potosí] [Haggerty & Morton 1995]) Darker then all other races, especially on pileum, back and wings; tail more heavily barred than *berlandieri*.

Populations in the Yucatán Peninsula and in Nicaragua have frequently been considered two further races of the Carolina Wren (*T. l. albinucha* and *T. l. subfulvus* respectively). We have, however, followed Howell & Webb (1995) and treated them as races of the White-browed Wren *T. albinucha*.

VOICE Song is a series of loud chortling whistles, audible at a considerable distance, traditionally transcribed as *tea-kettle, tea-kettle*. In contrast to other members of the same genus, song in the Carolina Wren is almost exclusively by the male; however, notwithstanding statements to the contrary, duet song with the female has been reported, the female's part being to add a 'buzzy, rather high-pitched trill' to the end of the first phrase of the male's song (Shuler 1965). Some geographic variation in song; the song of *T. l. miamensis* is more rapid, with more notes than birds from further north (Borror 1956). Occasionally mimics other species, giving rise to a local name in Pennsylvania of 'Mocking Wren' (McAtee 1950). Calls are a variety of single and multiple-syllabled notes, described as *cheer, chirt, dit, pi-zeet*, etc.

HABITAT A generalist, adapting well to a variety of habitats including those much modified by human activity; in many parts of its range an abundant suburban bird. Natural habitats include oak hardwoods and mixed oak-pine woodlands, ash and elmwoods, hickory-oak woodlands and cottonwoods; tends to favour wetter bottomland woods rather than dry upland forest (McAtee 1950). Abundant in well-wooded farm-edges, suburbs and parks. The races *burleighi* and *nesophilus* inhabit slash pine and palmetto (Lowery 1940).

HABITS More often heard than seen. Feeds mostly on or near the ground, in tangles of vegetation and vines. May 'tree-creep'on lower levels of larger tree-trunks, probing in bark crevices. Leaf-litter is picked up or turned over for prey underneath. Larger items of prey such as Orthoptera may be dismembered by vigorous blows of the bill and eaten piecemeal. Flights are usually of short duration and low off the ground; frequently birds quietly disappear from the observer by quickly scurrying into thick cover. Roosts usually in cavities,

including a variety of artificial ones such as tin-cans, crevices in buildings, etc., as well as in abandoned hornets' nests, squirrel nests, etc.; several birds may roost together. Courting male hops around female with fanned, cocked tail, singing loudly; males may also feed females during courtship.

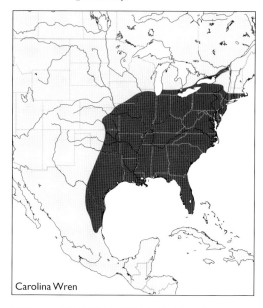

Carolina Wren

STATUS AND DISTRIBUTION Resident from southern Ontario, southern New York and Massachusetts throughout eastern North America to Florida; westwards to southern Iowa, eastern Nebraska and Oklahoma through eastern Texas to extreme north-western Mexico (eastern Coahuila, Nuevo León, Tamaulipas and eastern San Luis Potosí). Sea-level to 2,000m in Mexico, lower in northern parts of the range. Extralimital records west to eastern New Mexico, eastern Colorado, eastern Wyoming, southern Manitoba, South Dakota, and northern New Brunswick, Nova Scotia and Îles de la Madeleine (Gulf of St Lawrence).

Northern edge of range rather variable, shrinking substantially after severe winters. After a series of mild winters may breed sporadically as far north as Maine or southern Quebec (Townsend 1909, Godfrey 1986). In southern Ontario during the period 1981–1985, recorded in only forty 10km squares, with no more than one breeding pair per square (Cadman *et al.* 1987); ten years later it is a moderately common nesting bird in sheltered wooded areas in Ontario from Windsor to Niagara. There is strong correlation between Carolina Wren members as estimated by breeding bird surveys and the severity of preceding winters (Bystrak 1979).

FOOD Mainly invertebrate; insects including beetles, true bugs (Hemiptera), grasshoppers and katydids (Orthoptera), also spiders, ants, bees and wasps. Some small invertebrates (lizards, tree-frogs and rarely small snakes). Vegetable matter only a minority; fruit pulp, various seeds, etc. (Beal *et al.* 1916). In the northern part of its range routinely patronises bird-feeders, being especially fond of suet, but will also take seeds and peanuts. Has been seen to wedge hard-coated seeds in cracks and attempt to hammer them open in the manner of a nuthatch.

BREEDING Territories are maintained year-round, usually by a pair of birds; males defend winter territories and respond aggressively to taped songs even in mid-winter (Morton 1982). Females may or may not be able to maintain a winter territory in the absence of a mate (Morton & Shalter 1977). Territories range from 1ha to 8ha (Stevenson 1973). Apparently monogamous, with pairs remaining faithful over several years; one possible observation of polygamy (Haggerty & Morton 1995).

Nest is usually a substantial domed structure, with a side entrance, constructed of dried vegetation, grass, strips of bark, horsehair, various debris like string where available, wool and cast snake skins, lined with finer material. Male does the majority of work, sometimes delivering material to female who remains on site and does actual construction (Rosene 1954). Nests are usually in partial or complete cavities, such as bird-boxes, cavities in eaves of buildings, tin cans, mail-boxes, various natural cavities in trees and occasional odd sites such as pockets of a jacket hanging up in a shed. Nests are usually situated at heights of 1–3m from the ground, occasionally higher, rarely up to 10m; also, rarely, in holes in sloping banks and in the ground itself (Seeman 1946). Nests typically 8–23cm in length, 8–15cm wide (Ramsay 1987). Nests in totally enclosed situations may have reduced roofs or none at all (Laskey 1948). Multiple-brooded; usually new nests are built for each brood, though rarely a third brood may be raised in the relined nest used for the first. Occasional 'spare' nests may be built during breeding season, but not used. Eggs are white or creamy, with small spots of reddish-brown or brown, more heavily marked at blunt end.

Occasionally one egg is less heavily pigmented than the others (Haggerty & Morton 1995). Clutch size usually three to six eggs, five most common in Tennessee (Laskey 1948), four in Alabama (Haggerty & Morton 1995). Incubation by female alone, fed while on nest by male, 12–16 days, average 14.8 (Haggerty & Morton 1995). Female may carry eggshells away or eat parts of them (Laskey 1948). Young fed by both parents, entirely on invertebrates; fledge in 12–14 days. Parasitism by Brown-headed Cowbird *Molothrus ater* may be quite frequent, up to 25% of nests being affected (Haggerty & Morton 1995). Cowbirds may have a significant effect on reproductive success. Usually two and sometimes three broods a year in south-eastern United States. In Tennessee eggs of the first brood are laid from late March to April; late broods into early August.

MOVEMENTS Generally very sedentary, although some movement must occur to give the extralimital records noted above. Of 538 banding recoveries, only 31 showed any movement at all; of these, two involved movements of 75km and 150km, within the states of Michigan and Arkansas respectively. The furthest displacement from the point of banding, in coastal Massachusetts, to point of recovery, in interior New Hampshire (an area where Carolina Wren is not regularly found) was about 250km; the bird concerned was a juvenile, recovered six weeks after banding. All other banding recoveries showed zero or trivial movement (Data from Bird-banding Laboratory, Patuxent, Maryland).

MEASUREMENTS Wing of male 54.5–64, of female 55–59.5; tail 45.5–55.5, of female 45.5–50.5; exposed culmen of male 15–18, of female 14.5–17; tarsus of male 20–22.5, of female 20–21.5 (Ridgway 1904).

---

31   WHITE-BROWED WREN
Thryothorus albinucha   Plate 8

Thryothorus albinucha Cabot 1847, Yalahao, Yucatán, Mexico.

Alternative names: Cabot's Wren;. Spanish *Saltapared Nucablanca, Saltapared Chinchivirín, Chinchivirín cejiblanco*; Mayan *Yancotil*

An endemic wren of the Yucatán Peninsula, with outlying occurrences in Nicaragua. It may prove to be merely a well-marked, isolated race of the Carolina Wren.

IDENTIFICATION Length 11.5–13.5cm. Essentially similar to the Carolina Wren, by which it is isolated geographically by a gap of more than 800km; it differs from that species in having much paler underparts and lacking the barred flanks and warm rufous belly. Sympatric species are White-bellied Wren, which also has a white supercilium, but is smaller, shorter-tailed and with a very bland, featureless face-pattern; and, in Nicaragua, Plain Wren, which has a rufous tail with black bars, warmer rufous back and rump and warmer, cinnamon flanks and belly.

DESCRIPTION *T. a. albinucha*
Adult Crown, shoulders and back dark olive-brown,

becoming more rufous on lower back. Some concealed whitish spots on lower back and rump. Wing-coverts medium-brown, primaries and secondaries blackish-brown on innerwebs, rufescent-brown on outerwebs, giving a slightly rufous patch with diffuse darker barring on closed wing. Rectrices blackish-brown, the outer ones with conspicuous grey bars on outerwebs and on tips. Lores and eye-stripe brown, supercilium white, narrowly edged black at rear. Ear-coverts mottled blackish and grey. Chin and chest off-white, flanks buffy-brown, sometimes with a few obscure diffuse darker bars. Crissum barred blackish and white. Underwing greyish. Iris brownish-red, bill yellow-brown, paler at base. Legs flesh-coloured.

GEOGRAPHICAL VARIATION

T. a. albinucha (Yucatán Peninsula, including the states of Campeche, Yucatán and Quintana Roo; northern Guatemala [Petén], Belize [Howell & Webb 1995]) Described above.

T. a. subfulvus (known from one specimen in Nicaragua [Miller & Griscom 1925]; also apparently arid central Guatemala [Land 1970]). Breast and abdomen cinnamon rather than largely white, with indistinct bars on flanks. Recent specimens taken in Western Nicaragua (Martínez-Sánchez 1989) have not been assigned as to race.

VOICE The song is a series of loud, varied whistles and gurgles, much like that of the Carolina Wren. It will respond to taped songs of Carolina Wren, suggesting that its specific status may be dubious. Calls include a querulous, descending, buzzy trill, which may also be used in between phrases of song. Alarm calls churring and buzzing.

HABITAT Dry scrub and forest; in the southern part of its range, around Calakmul, Campeche and Tikal, Guatemala, in more humid forest. The type specimen of *subfulvus* in Nicaragua came from dry thorn scrub, but it is also found in semi-deciduous broad-leaved forest (Martínez-Sanchez 1989).

HABITS Not much recorded. Similar in general behaviour to Carolina Wren; not particularly furtive, but can be difficult to view clearly.

STATUS AND DISTRIBUTION Occurs over almost the whole Yucatán peninsula (states of Yucatán, Quintana Roo and most of Campeche except the extreme west; northern Guatemala (Petén) and northern Belize; also central Guatemala and sporadically in Western Nicaragua. Sea-level to 300m in Mexico, locally to 1,200m in Guatemala, and 400–750m in Nicaragua. Reasonably common in much of the Mexican part of its range; uncommon in the Petén and rare in central Guatemala (Land 1970), in Belize not recorded at all by Russell (1964), so presumably rare; in Nicaragua little known,

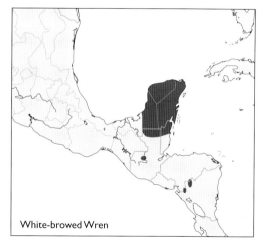

White-browed Wren

one specimen having been taken in 1925 (Miller & Griscom 1925) and three in 1984 (Martínez-Sánchez 1989).

BREEDING Nest and eggs presently undescribed; presumably similar to those of the Carolina Wren.

FOOD No data available; presumably predominately invertebrate.

MOVEMENTS Apparently entirely sedentary.

MEASUREMENTS Wing of male 54–59, of female 53.5–58; tail of male 44.5–55.5, of female 42–47; exposed culmen of male 18–19, of female 17.5–19.5; tarsus of male 20–22.5, of female 19–21.5.

32   BLACK-THROATED WREN
Thryothorus atrogularis

Plate 9

Thryothorus atrogularis Salvin 1864 Tucurriquí, Costa Rica.

Alternative name: Spanish *Soterrey Gorginegro*

A very dark-plumaged wren, more resembling some species of antbird, found on the humid Caribbean slope of Central America from Nicaragua to Panama.

IDENTIFICATION Length 14–15cm. The overall dark appearance, with chocolate body and extensive black throat, is unlike any sympatric wren; the Bay Wren has a white throat contrasting with black cap and chestnut underparts, while the Nightingale Wren, also very dark, is quite different in its almost tail-less form. More likely to be confused on a poor view with some of the antbirds, such as Dull-mantled Antbird *Myrmeciza laemosticta* or Chestnut-backed Antbird *M. exsul*; however, these typically have dots on shoulders, or bare blue skin around the eye, with a different bill shape, and lack light markings on ear-coverts.

DESCRIPTION
Adult Crown, back and rump unmarked uniform deep reddish-brown, becoming slightly more rufous on rump. Rectrices blackish-brown, with small inconspicuous buff

markings on outerwebs of outer feathers. Primaries and secondaries unmarked dark reddish-brown. Lores black with some white feathers; ear-coverts black with a small number of fine white streaks. Chin, throat and upper chest black, the black becoming interspersed then replaced by reddish-chestnut on lower chest and belly. Undertail-coverts dull black with fine white transverse bars. Underwing-coverts blackish-brown with paler streaks. Iris rufous or reddish-brown, upper mandible black, lower mandible black with blue-grey base; legs blackish or dark brown.
Juvenile Much duller and more uniform than adult. Throat dull blackish-brown with little contrast to chest or belly, crown and back uniform dull dark-brown, no white on ear-coverts, undertail-coverts uniform with belly and lacking white bars.

GEOGRAPHICAL VARIATION None; monotypic if *Thryothorus spadix* is separated specifically.

VOICE Song is a series of rich whistles, usually (in contrast to that of Sooty-headed Wren) ending in a distinct trill which may be higher or lower in pitch to the general motif. Sings antiphonally, the female adding notes at the end of a phrase. Call is a fast, nasal to wooden, rattling *praaaaaht* and a guttural rolling *beewrr* or *bweeurr* (Stiles & Skutch 1989).

HABITAT Lowland forest, especially second growth areas at forest edge and regenerated cleared areas, sea-level to 1,100m. Frequently in fairly wet areas, but less closely associated with water than is Bay Wren.

HABITS Very secretive; usually forages in pairs, mostly low down in tangles of vines and dead vegetation.

STATUS AND DISTRIBUTION In Costa Rica locally common. In Caribbean lowlands from eastern Nicaragua from San Juan del Norte (Greytown) and Río Escondido, throughout the Caribbean slope of Costa Rica to western Panama (western Bocas del Toro).

BREEDING Nest and eggs not described; in Costa Rica probably breeds in April or May to August (Stiles & Skutch 1989).

FOOD No information recorded; presumably wholly or largely invertebrate.

MOVEMENTS Presumably sedentary.

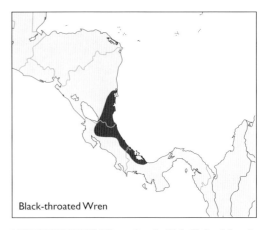

Black-throated Wren

MEASUREMENTS Wing of male 65.0–68.6, of female 60.0–63.7; tail of male 51.4–54.7, of female 45.6–50.5; bill of male 19.5–22.0, of female 19.0–20.9; tarsus of male 21.5–25.5, of female 22.9–24.5 (Wetmore *et al.* 1984).

---

33   SOOTY-HEADED WREN
Thryothorus spadix   Plate 9

Pheugopedius spadix Bangs 1910, Naranjito, Río Dagua, Colombia.

Alternative names: Southern Black-throated Wren; Spanish *Cucarachero cabeza fuliginosa*

A relatively little-known species, considered by some to be conspecific with the allopatric Black-throated Wren.

IDENTIFICATION Length 14.5cm. When seen well, cannot be confused with any other wren species in its range. The combination of black head and throat with unmarked chestnut chest is diagnostic. Sympatric races of the Bay Wren have a white throat and densely barred underparts. Chestnut-breasted Wren differs in form, having a short tail and peculiar arched bill; it also lacks the black throat and barred rectrices of the Sooty-headed Wren.

DESCRIPTION *T. s. spadix*
Adult Crown dull black, contrasting sharply with bright chestnut shoulders, back, rump and wing-coverts. Rectrices chestnut-brown with about twelve black bars across entire upper surface of tail. Lores black with some contrasting white feathers; ear-coverts black with conspicuous white streaking. Primaries dull blackish-brown on innerweb, bright chestnut on outerweb, giving the closed wing a bright chestnut colour. Throat black, with some white feathers below angle of bill. Lower throat and chest bright chestnut, sharply demarcated from black of upper throat. Colour becomes duller on lower chest and belly; centre of belly greyish-brown with inconspicuous dark mottles. Lower belly and thighs dull greyish-brown. Underwing-coverts dull greyish-brown. Iris brown or reddish-brown, upper mandible blackish-grey, lower mandible bluish-grey, legs dull grey.
Juvenile Much duller in all colours than adult, throat dull greyish-black, little white on ear-coverts, much less

contrast between crown and shoulders and between throat and chest.

GEOGRAPHICAL VARIATION
T. s. spadix 'Southern Black-throated Wren' (Colombia [various largely disjunct populations, from Chocó south to Nariño, east to the valley of the Río Magdalena]) Described above.
T. s. xerampelinus (Pacific slope of eastern Darién, Panama) Paler than nominate, less reddish-brown on flanks and with a paler belly.

VOICE Song is a loud series of clear gurgling whistles, about half a dozen in number, one motif frequently repeated; apparently pairs sing antiphonally. Differs markedly from the song of the Black-throated Wren, which usually starts as a series of whistles but usually terminates in a trill.

HABITAT Forest edge, especially humid forest and cloudforest with extensive moss growth; also heavy second growth, mostly 800–1,800m, but locally down to 400m in Colombia (Hilty & Brown 1986).

HABITS Little known. Extremely secretive. Usually found in pairs, but does not routinely associate in mixed flocks. Forages low down, often probing into dead leaves. In Colombia will follow the army ant *Laridus praedator* (Hilty 1994).

STATUS AND DISTRIBUTION In Colombia, uncommon to locally common; apparently disjunct populations in the Río Magdalena valley, northern end of central Andes south to Caldas, Pacific slope of Andes from southern Chocó to Nariño. To be expected in extreme north-western Ecuador but not apparently recorded so far (Ridgely & Greenfield 2001). In Panama restricted to foothills in eastern Darién (Cerro Tacarcuna, Cerro Quía); apparently uncommon.

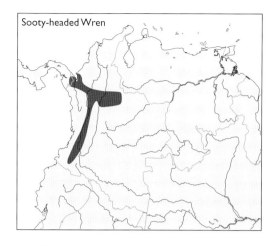
Sooty-headed Wren

BREEDING Breeding season apparently protracted; specimens in breeding condition taken in central Andes of Colombia from April to September, nest building observed in March and December, eggs in September. Nest is a bulky ball of leaves and coarse material, with a side entrance, about 1m up in a *Heliconia* thicket; eggs two, white, with small reddish spots around larger end (Hilty & Brown 1986). Incubation and fledging periods unknown.

FOOD Beetles, Hemiptera, ants, gryllids, caterpillars and spiders (stomach contents of specimens from Cana, Panama) (Wetmore *et al.* 1984).

MOVEMENTS Apparently sedentary.

MEASUREMENTS Wing of male 64.2–66.9, of female 58.2–61.8, tail of male 55.1–58.2, of female 50.3–54.6, bill of male 19.0–20.4, of female 17.8–20.4; tarsus of male 22.0–25.1, of female 20.7–22.8 (Wetmore *et al.* 1984).

34 BLACK-BELLIED WREN
Thryothorus fasciatoventris

Plate 9

Thriothorus [sic] *fasciato-ventris* Lafresnaye 1845, "Bogotá", Colombia.

Alternative names: Band-bellied Wren; Spanish *Soterrey Vientrinegro*

Probably the most strikingly-plumaged of all the wrens, with a superb song. Occurs in lowland areas from Costa Rica to Colombia.

IDENTIFICATION Length 15cm. Essentially unmistakable; the combination of white chest, black belly with white bars (the extent varying with the race) and black-and-white facial pattern, contrasting with the white throat, is diagnostic. The Bay Wren has a black nape and crown and lacks the striking white chest; no other wren has any resemblance. Juvenile Black-bellied Wrens are duller, with the white of the underparts replaced by grey and the belly brownish barred with dusky.

DESCRIPTION *T. f. fasciatoventris*
Adult Head and crown unmarked rich brown, becoming a richer chestnut-brown on back and rump. Primaries and secondaries less chestnut, with very obscure darker barring, not visible in field. Rectrices medium-brown, with about twelve strong parallel bars of blackish-brown, extending across entire tail and giving the tail a darker appearance than back. Prominent white supercilium, edged black above, contrasting strongly with crown and blackish-brown eye-stripe. Throat, chest and ear-coverts gleaming white. Lower chest abruptly contrasting, with black band across whole chest, further down on upper belly with narrow white parallel bars. These become more diffuse and more buff in colour on lower belly and flanks. Vent and undertail-coverts equally barred dull black and grey. Thighs dark brown with diffuse darker barring. Underwing-coverts dull buff-brown. Iris light brown or reddish-brown, upper mandible black, lower mandible bluish. Legs fuscous-black.
Juvenile Plumage very different from adult. Crown, back and rump dull chestnut, becoming brighter on rump.

Chin and throat dull whitish-grey, darkening laterally to dull grey-brown on chest; sides of chest and belly more brown and less grey, sometimes with very obscure barring. No sharp contrast between throat and chest and belly. Birds moulting into adult plumage will have white streaks on throat, contrasting with grey older feathers.

GEOGRAPHICAL VARIATION
T. f. fasciatoventris (Colombia, from the Valle de Cauca on the Pacific coast north to the Río San Juan, and eastwards to the foothills of the Santa Marta range and the valley of the Río Magdalena) Described above.
T. f. albigularis 'Panama Black-bellied Wren' (Colombia, from Chocó northwards, eastern Panama [Darién to the Canal Zone]) Similar to *fasciatoventris* but underparts with less conspicuous white bars, especially on upper belly, upperparts darker brown, auriculars more dusky.
T. f. melanogaster (Panama west of the Canal, and south-eastern Costa Rica to the mouth of the Golfo de Nicoya) Somewhat larger than *albigularis*, upperparts more richly chestnut, bars on rectrices broader and chestnut rather than light brown, forward part of belly more solid black with white barring much reduced or absent; undertail-coverts barred with light chestnut-brown rather than white.

VOICE Song is rich series of liquid gurgling notes of great variety and beauty, of three to eight or more notes, a set phrase being repeated many times before moving on to a different one (Chapman 1936). Both sexes sing, but not truly antiphonally; the songs of the two sexes overlap to a degree, that of the female being mostly at a rather higher frequency (Farabaugh 1982). Alarm call is a low rasping chatter or sputter (Stiles & Skutch 1989).

HABITAT Dense, humid, low-lying vegetation, especially near water and along the banks of streams; in Costa Rica especially fond of *Heliconia* and *Calathea* thickets (Stiles

& Skutch 1989). Sea-level to 500m in Costa Rica, but as high as 1,000m in Colombia.

HABITS Notoriously furtive and difficult to see, even though its song may be audible at a great distance. Forages from the canopy to ground-level but especially in low vine tangles; the pair do not routinely forage together. Defence of the pair territory by the female is only occasional. Allopreening by pairs frequent (Morton 1980). A somewhat solitary bird; probably does not form extended family groups.

STATUS AND DISTRIBUTION Density is low compared to some other *Thryothorus* species (Morton 1980). From the Pacific drainage of Costa Rica as far northwest as Carara (mouth of the Golfo de Nicoya), in Panama on the Pacific slope to the Canal and then in both drainages; Colombia on the Pacific coast as far south as the southern Valle de Cauca, east to the lower elevations of Santa Marta and south in the Río Magdalena valley to Tolima.

BREEDING Little-known. Nest in Costa Rica is a globular structure with a side entrance shielded by a visor, loosely woven wholly of dry strips of *Heliconia* leaves, 1–2m up in *Heliconia* thicket, usually when several petioles cross (Stiles & Skutch 1989). Breeding in Costa Rica probably May-July; in Panama possibly multiple-brooded (Chapman 1936). In Colombia nest-building in early February (Hilty 1994), birds in breeding condition March to July (Boggs 1961). Eggs not described; incubation and fledging periods unknown. Probably not a cooperative breeder (T. R. Robinson pers. comm.).

Black-bellied Wren

FOOD Little recorded; stomach contents 'insects' (August, Panama: FMNH). 'Usual variety of small insects and spiders' (Wetmore 1984).

MOVEMENTS Presumably sedentary.

MEASUREMENTS (*T. f. albigularis*) Wing of male 63.1–70.1, of female 59.7–63.6; tail of male 49.2–57.1, of female 45.0–50.2; bill of male 20.0–22.2, of female 19.0–21.0; tarsus of male 23.2–25.9, of female 20.1–24.7 (Wetmore *et al.* 1984).

35 PLAIN-TAILED WREN
Thryothorus euophrys
Plate 9

Thryothorus euophrys Sclater 1860. Lloa, near Quito, Ecuador.

Alternative names: Spotted-chested Wren; Spanish *Soterrey Colillano*

A common wren of bamboo thickets at moderate to high elevations in the northern Andes, more often seen than heard.

IDENTIFICATION Length 16cm. A large, brightly coloured wren with a tail diagnostically lacking in prominent transverse bars. Separated geographically and altitudinally from most other confusable species. Whiskered Wren *T. mystacalis*, which potentially overlaps in Ecuador, has a similar face pattern, but unspotted throat and chest and a barred tail. The closely related Inca Wren *T. eisenmanni* is allopatric. The northern and western populations of Plain-tailed Wren are much more heavily marked underneath than the southern races.

DESCRIPTION *T. e. euophrys*
Adult Crown brownish-black, contrasting with bright brown nape and shoulders; colour of back becomes richer and more chestnut on centre back and rump. Shoulders and wing-coverts chestnut-brown; innerweb of primaries and secondaries blackish-brown, but closed

wing appears bright red-brown. No barring on primaries or secondaries. Rectrices red-brown without barring. Supercilium greyish-white, eye-stripe dull black. Throat grey, prominent malar stripe black, upper chest speckled dull black and grey, merging into unmarked grey-brown lower chest. Underparts becomes browner posteriorly, with flanks, thighs and lower belly rich brown. Underwing-coverts dull brown. Iris light brown, bill dark grey, lower mandible bluish. Legs and feet bluish-grey.
Juvenile Crown more tinged with olive-grey, underparts below white, throat rufous without grey tinge or blackish spots (Fjeldså & Krabbe 1990).

GEOGRAPHICAL VARIATION
   T. e. euophrys 'Fraser's Wren' (western Andes of Ecuador and extreme southern Colombia [Nariño]) Described above.
   T. e. longipes 'Long-legged Wren' (eastern Andes of Ecuador) Similar to *euophrys* but markings on chest somewhat reduced and underparts more grey, with white largely confined to throat.
   T. e. atriceps 'Black-headed Wren' (northern Peru north of the Río Marañón) Spotting on underparts still further reduced, crown blackish.

T. e. schulenbergi (northern Peru south of the Río Marañón) The largest and dullest of the races, similar to *atriceps*, from which it differs from its greyish crown and nape, pale grey rather than white superciliaries, greyish-white rather than pure white throat, much less russet dorsum and wings, and greyer, less brown posterior underparts (Parker & O'Neill 1985).

VOICE Song consists of varied phrases of loud, gurgling whistles, *cheery-cheery-cheo*, etc., the phrases repeated rapidly many times over. Both sexes sing antiphonally so that in the dense cover inhabited by the species it is very difficult to determine which sex is responsible for what part of the song. Contact call is a loud, emphatic *choo-chip, choo-chip, choo-chip-chip*, quite unwrenlike; also a wheezy *zwee*.

HABITAT Dense undergrowth in mountain woodland, especially where there is a good density of *Chusquea* bamboo. Thus tends to colonise disturbed areas, for example where vegetation has been subject to landslides, and is frequently common in such areas.

HABITS Although the song is arresting and unmistakable, on quiet mornings audible for several hundred metres across the mountain valleys, Plain-tailed Wrens can be very difficult to observe clearly. Both members of a pair will, however, respond with great vigour to a playback of their song, prancing around the player while singing antiphonally, all caution forgotten. Pairs stay together throughout the year. Feeds low down for the most part, picking insects from the underside of leaves. Does not routinely join in mixed flocks. Holds body horizontal and tail slightly raised. Sings in an upright posture (Fjeldså & Krabbe 1990).

STATUS AND DISTRIBUTION Locally common in suitable habitat, from extreme southern Colombia (Nariño, central Ecuador on both slopes of the Andes

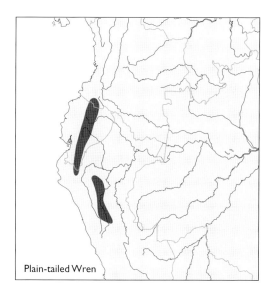

Plain-tailed Wren

and northern Peru (Cajamarca); disjunctly in north-central Peru (Amazonas and San Martín). 1,850–3,500m, mostly 2,000–3,300m.

BREEDING Nest and eggs not described. Juveniles July (north-western Ecuador), November, January (north-eastern Ecuador) (Fjeldså & Krabbe 1990).

FOOD Few details recorded; mostly invertebrate.

MOVEMENTS Appears to be entirely sedentary.

MEASUREMENTS (*T. e. euophrys*) Wing of male 64.0–71.2, of female 64.1–73.4; tail of male 62.4–69.0, of female 58.4–68.6; tarsus of male 27.2–29.2, of female 26.8–28.6; culmen of male 22.2–23.8, of female 21.1–22.5 (Parker & O'Neill 1985).

---

36   INCA WREN
Thryothorus eisenmanni

Plate 9

Thryothorus eisenmanni Parker & O'Neill 1985.

Etymology: Named after Eugene Eisenmann, a pioneer of neotropical ornithology.

The aptly named Inca Wren was only described to science in 1985, although it had been observed as early as 1965. It occurs in a very limited range in Peru, including the environs of the spectacular Inca city of Machu Picchu. Very little has been published about the Inca Wren; the account below is almost entirely taken from the original paper describing the species (Parker & O'Neill 1985).

IDENTIFICATION Length 16cm. Not likely to be confused with any other wren in its limited range; most closely resembles, and is probably most closely related to, the Plain-tailed Wren *T. euophrys*, but is clearly differentiated by its heavily spotted underparts and grey crown. The two species are geographically separated by 650km.

DESCRIPTION

Adult Crown, nape, lores, moustachial streak and upper half of ear-coverts dull black; broad superciliary white; lower half of ear-coverts white, finely streaked with black. Mantle, scapulars, back, rump and uppertail-coverts bright russet-brown; tail of the same general colour but slightly duller, and with obscure dusky barring crossing both webs of each rectrix. Throat white; breast and all but lowest portion of belly white, boldly streaked with black, these streaks formed by feathers that are white with two dark spots on each web and a white tip. Sides, flanks and undertail-coverts dull yellowish-brown. Tertials, secondaries and primaries, and greater primary coverts blackish-brown edged with russet-brown. Iris chestnut or reddish-chestnut, upper mandible, dark brown, lower mandible, silver-blue or blue-grey with blackish tip; feet and legs greyish-horn or grey-black.

Based on the relatively small amount of material available, there appears to be some sexual dimorphism.

139

In most females the belly is usually unstreaked, being instead a warm grey-brown spotted lightly with a mixture of dusky and dirty white. The crown in females is charcoal grey, not black; and the tail is usually unbarred, whereas some males have quite heavily barred rectrices. **Juvenile** Undescribed.

GEOGRAPHICAL VARIATION None; monotypic.

VOICE Both sexes sing well-synchronised antiphonal duets; these consist of sequences of rapidly repeated chortling whistles, rising and falling within a sequence of perhaps ten notes, continuously repeated for up to a minute. The female apparently sings a higher song, while the male provides a series of closely spaced notes on a lower pitch. Call, a sharp *chip-chip-chip*. Playback of Inca Wren song does not elicit obvious response from territorial Plain-tailed Wrens.

HABITAT Occurs in thickets of *Chusquea* bamboo, along road-edges and where natural landslides have cleared forest. Avoids dense, well-shaded forest. 1,830–3,350m.

HABITS Not excessively secretive; typically feeds at 0.5–1.5m above ground level, in pairs or groups of up to six individuals (family parties?). Does not routinely follow mixed flocks.

STATUS AND DISTRIBUTION So far has only been found in the Department of Cuzco, Peru, from the Cordillera de Vilcabamba south to the valleys of the Río Urubamba and the Río Santa Marta. Fairly common in suitable habitat. Despite its very limited range not apparently the cause of any concern; in fact as the *Chusquea* bamboo thrives on disturbed habitat the species may have increased in recent years.

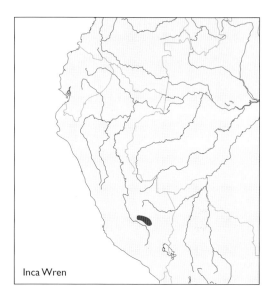

Inca Wren

BREEDING Nest and eggs not described.

FOOD Small beetles, caterpillars and cockroaches (based on stomach contents of specimens).

MOVEMENTS Sedentary, except that it will move out of areas of *Chusquea* subject to die-off.

MEASUREMENTS Male: wing 61.7–66.2, tail 55.4–61.8, tarsus 24.8–26.9, culmen to base 19.0–20.7 (six specimens) (Parker & O'Neill 1985). No female data available.

---

37   MOUSTACHED WREN
Thryothorus genibarbis
Plate 9

Thryothorus genibarbis Swainson 1837, Bahia, Brazil.

Alternative names: Portuguese *Garrinchao-pai-avo*, *Pio-vovo*

A widely distributed species, stretching from the foothills of the Andes all the way across South America to the easternmost point in Brazil. Formerly considered conspecific with the Whiskered Wren.

IDENTIFICATION Length 15.5cm. Allopatric from the Whiskered Wren. Distinguished from the Coraya Wren in their sympatry (i.e. south of the Amazon in eastern and western, but not central, Brazil) by the much greater extent of black on the sides of the face and ear-coverts of that species. Other sympatric *Thryothorus* species (in various parts of its range) are Buff-breasted, barred wings, no malar stripe, smaller, buff breast; Fawn-breasted, even smaller, buff throat, barred wings, less strongly marked on face and Long-billed, notably longer bill, barred wings and no malar stripe.

DESCRIPTION *T. g. genibarbis*
Adult Crown and nape olivaceous grey-brown, contrasting with bright chestnut of back, rump and wing-coverts. Primaries and secondaries dull blackish-brown

on innerwebs, chestnut on outer, giving a dull chestnut colour to closed wing except near tips of wing where duller and darker. Rectrices dull brown with about eight to ten blackish transverse bars extending across whole tail; less conspicuous on under-surface. Eye-ring and eye-stripe white, contrasting with grey-brown lores. Conspicuous white moustache-stripe, contrasting with black malar stripe. Ear-coverts greyish-black with conspicuous white streaking. Throat and upper chest off-white, becoming buffy on lower chest and deeper brown on belly and flanks. Undertail-coverts reddish-brown. Underwing-coverts whitish-buff. Iris reddish-brown, upper and lower mandibles black, legs and feet grey. **Juvenile** Crown browner and less dusky than adult, back duller and less chestnut, facial markings, especially malar stripe, less clearly defined, underparts more buff-brown, bars on rectrices less clearly defined.

GEOGRAPHICAL VARIATION

T. g. genibarbis (eastern Brazil from the Atlantic coast [Maranhão south to Espírito Santo], west to the Rio Madera) Described above.

T. g. juruanus 'Upper Amazonian Moustached Wren' (upper Amazonia, west of the Rio Madera to the

Rio Purus and possibly northern Bolivia) Not well defined; generally larger, with heavier bill and paler underparts than nominate race.

T. g. intercedens 'Central Brazilian Moustached Wren' (Central Brazil [Matto Grosso and Goias]) Similar to *genibarbis*, but bill more slender, back paler, no grey tinge on foreneck, underparts deeper buff.

T. g. bolivianus 'Bolivian Moustached Wren' (Amazonian Bolivia south to Santa Cruz) Similar to *intercedens* but sides of neck darker grey, foreneck tinged with ashy, underparts deeper ochraceous.

VOICE Song is a series of fast phrases, more like that of Coraya Wren than Whiskered Wren, and largely lacking the gurgling quality of the latter species; usually given antiphonally by the pair. Calls include a whining, querulous *jeeyr*, often incorporated into song (Ridgely & Tudor 1989).

HABITAT Forest and forest edge, including riverine forest and edges of lakes; often associated with bamboos *Bambusa*, sea-level to 1,500m on Andes foothills of Bolivia.

HABITS Usually found in pairs, foraging low down in vegetation. Somewhat furtive and difficult to see.

STATUS AND DISTRIBUTION Fairly common over much of its range. Brazil south of the Amazon from Pará and Maranhão east to Paraiba, south to Espirito Santo, Rio de Janeiro and Minas Gerais; westwards to central Bolivia (Santa Cruz and Beni); north to east-central Peru (Ucayali); western Brazil in Amazonas.

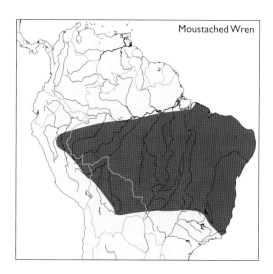
Moustached Wren

BREEDING Nest and eggs undescribed.

FOOD Undescribed; presumably largely or entirely invertebrate.

MOVEMENT Presumably sedentary.

MEASUREMENTS Wing of male 59–64, of female 60–64; tail of male 59, of female 53–59; exposed culmen of male 14.5–18, of female 14.5–17; tarsus of male 23–24, of female 22–24.

---

38 WHISKERED WREN
Thryothorus mystacalis

Plate 9

Thryothorus mystacalis Sclater 1860, Pallatanga, Chimborazo, Ecuador.

Alternative name: Spanish *Soterrey Bigotillo*

A large wren, very secretive but with a superb song, found in mountainous regions of Venezuela, Colombia and Ecuador. Sometimes considered conspecific with Moustached Wren, an allopatric lowland species with a quite different song.

IDENTIFICATION Length 16cm. Whiskered Wren is widely separated both geographically and altitudinally from Moustached Wren, and from Coraya Wren. The Plain-tailed Wren, which usually occurs at higher altitudes, has prominent spotting on the chest, and lacks barring on the tail (one race of the Whiskered Wren, *T. m. ruficaudatus*, has an unbarred tail, but this occurs only in northern Venezuela). Bay Wren, which overlaps in range in Colombia and Ecuador, is heavily barred on the underparts and on the wings, and has a prominent black crown.

DESCRIPTION *T. m. mystacalis*
Adult Crown grey-black, nape olivaceous grey, contrasting with bright chestnut back, shoulders and rump. Rectrices rufescent-brown with about 12 transverse bars of dull black. Supercilium, from bill to above central

ear-coverts grey-white; lores and ear-coverts dull blackish with some whitish speckling on ear-coverts. Crescent under eye whitish. Heavy blackish malar stripe edged with whitish above. Chin and throat off-whitish, contrasting with grey chest; belly more olivaceous-grey, flanks becoming rufescent. Remiges blackish-grey on innerweb, mostly rufescent on outerweb; closed wing rufescent on primaries, blackish-grey on tertials. Underwing dull greyish. Iris brown, upper mandible black, lower mandible silvery-grey or brown-grey. Legs and feet grey.
Juvenile Similar to adult, but generally duller; superciliary and marks on ear-coverts much less conspicuous, moustache stripe largely absent, throat much suffused with buff. Iris yellowish, bill dull black, paler at base of lower mandible, feet brown.

GEOGRAPHICAL VARIATION
T. m. mystacalis 'Sclater's Moustached (sic) Wren'. (western Ecuador and southern Colombia) Described above.
T. m. saltuensis 'West Colombian Moustached (sic) Wren' (western and central Andes of Colombia) Similar to *mystacalis* but crown clearer grey, chest more grey, barring on tail less distinct.
T. m. amaurogaster 'Tawny-breasted Wren' (subtropical zone of eastern Andes of Colombia) Much

141

darker than *mystacalis*, pileum dark sooty-brown, back and wings deep chestnut rufous, underparts strongly washed with ochraceous-tawny.

T. m. consobrinus 'Merida Moustached [sic] Wren' (western Venezuela [Lara and Mérida]) Similar to *mystacalis*, but bill more slender, supercilia tinged buff, foreneck and chest buffy rather than grey.

T. m. ruficaudatus 'Rufous-tailed Wren' (northern Venezuela [Carabobo and Distrito Federal]) Tail largely or entirely lacking in transverse bars, being strongly rufous, facial markings and throat strongly buff, primaries and secondaries with deep rufous edges.

T. m. macrurus 'Long-tailed Wren' (known from one specimen of unknown provenance taken in Colombia; possibly an aberrant example of *T. m. amaurogaster*) Similar to *saltuensis*, but tail fuscous rather than rufescent, with longitudinal barrings on outer rectrices.

T. m. yananchae (Yananchá, Nariño, Colombia) Similar to *mystacalis* but crown slaty-grey.

T. m. tachirensis (Páramo de Tama region, Táchira, Venezuela) No description available.

VOICE Song is a series of loud, gurgling whistles; sometimes two or three *whee-ha*, *whee-ha* or *too-whee*, etc., presumably sung by one bird only; frequently splendid duets from both members of a pair, consisting of a long sequence of rising and falling whistles with a strong gurgling quality. Calls are a deep, throaty *bong bong* (B. T. Thomas pers. comm.).

HABITAT Most common in dense undergrowth at humid forest edge and in clearings rather than the interior of unbroken forest, in Colombia, 1,000–2,800m (mostly 1,200m–2,400m), in Ecuador locally almost down to sea-level (Ridgely & Tudor 1989).

HABITS Very skulking and difficult to see, although the startling song is not easily overlooked. Usually found in pairs; forages from ground level to 10–12m up, often in *Heliconia* thickets (S. Farabaugh pers. comm.).

STATUS AND DISTRIBUTION Quite common over

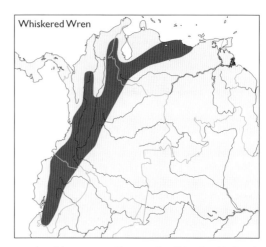

Whiskered Wren

much of its range. Venezuela (Distrito Federal, Carabobo through the Andes to Táchira), Colombia (Santander, Boyacá, southern Perijá mountains, south through the Andes to Huila and Nariño), Ecuador south almost to the Peruvian border.

BREEDING Nest is a large ball, with an outside diameter of about 20cm, made of roots and grass with entrance at side, at heights of 0.3m to 6.5m in ferns or in forks of small trees (Beebe 1949, B. T. Thomas pers. comm.). Egg colour and number, incubation and fledgling periods not known. Nest-building in northern Venezuela in March, April and May (B. T. Thomas pers. comm.). Not known whether any helpers at nest, nor whether single or multiple brooded.

FOOD No information recorded; presumably invertebrates.

MOVEMENTS Apparently sedentary.

MEASUREMENTS Wing of male 65–68, of female 64; tail of male 56–57, of female 56; exposed culmen of male 18.5–20, of female 18.5; tarsus of male 26–28, of female 25.

---

39   CORAYA WREN
Thryothorus coraya   Plate 10

Turdus coraya Gmelin, 1789, Cayenne, French Guiana.

Alternative names: Spanish *Cucarachero de Lluvias*; Portuguese *Garrinchao-coraia*; French, *Troglodyte coraya*; Suriname *Busigadofowru*

A common and widely distributed wren, found at lower altitudes over most of the northern Amazon basin.

IDENTIFICATION Length 14.5cm. The combination of white throat, unmarked chest, thick black malar stripe and heavy facial markings is unlike any other species. The plumage is not dissimilar from that of the sympatric White-breasted Wood Wren, but the much larger size, darker underparts and longer tail immediately distinguishes it from that species. Sympatric *Thryothorus* wrens are Buff-breasted, with which the Coraya Wren overlaps

in wide areas of northern South America; Moustached, with sympatry in parts of Brazil south of the Amazon and in eastern Peru; and marginally Rufous-and-White, with possible overlap in eastern Colombia. The first of these is immediately distinguished by its buffy underparts, barred wings, lack of heavy black facial markings and malar stripe.

DESCRIPTION *T. c. coraya*
Adult Crown and nape dull blackish-brown, contrasting with deep red-brown shoulders and back; lower back and rump somewhat paler and more rufous. Primaries and secondaries less rufous and greyer than back, unbarred. Rectrices dull brownish-black, contrasting with rufous of rump; seven to nine paler grey-brown bars on both webs. Lores, malar area and ear-coverts

black, with conspicuous white speckles on ear-coverts; white supercilium from eye to brown of shoulder. Chin and throat whiter, contrasting strongly with area underneath; white becomes buff on chest and deeper buff-brown on belly. Undertail-coverts reddish-brown with blackish transverse bars. Underwing reddish-brown. Iris brown or orange-brown, upper mandible black with grey base, lower mandible bluish-grey, legs bluish-grey. **Juvenile** Very distinct from adult. Black on sides of face replaced by dull blackish-grey with the white markings indistinct and suffused. White of throat and chest replaced by dull grey, warm colours on lower chest and belly much reduced, back and rump much less rufescent, iris greyish-brown.

GEOGRAPHICAL VARIATION

T. c. coraya (Guyana east of the Essequibo River, French Guiana, northern Brazil north of the Amazon and east of Manaus) Described above.

T. c. herberti 'Herbert's Wren' (northern Brazil south of the Amazon) Similar to *coraya* but black on sides of face more extensive, uppertail-coverts without bars and concolorous with back.

T. c. ridgwayi 'British Guiana Wren' (Guyana west of the Essequibo and south-eastern Venezuela [Roiraima]) Similar to *coraya* but underparts posterior to the foreneck deep ochraceous to bright brown.

T. c. barrowcloughiana (Cerro Cuquenam and Cerro Roraima, Bolívar, Venezuela) Similar to *ridgwayi* but chestnut on the upperparts brighter and more clear.

T. c. amazonicus 'Amazonian Wren' (Eastern Peru [Loreto and Huánuco]) Similar to *coraya* but upperparts lighter and less chestnut, flanks less rufescent.

T. c. albiventris 'Taczanowski's Wren' (eastern slopes of Peruvian Andes [San Martín]) Similar to *amazonicus* but bill shorter and less heavy, middle of breast and abdomen nearly white, flanks less brownish.

T. c. cantator 'Jelski's Wren' (Central Peru [Junín]) Similar to *amazonicus* but lacks white streaks on sides of head, ear-coverts almost solid black, bands on tail bright cinnamon brown rather than dull brownish-grey.

T. c. griseipectus 'Grey-breasted Wren' (north-eastern Peru north of the Río Marañón, eastern Ecuador and adjacent Brazil) Smaller than *amazonicus*, slighter bill, upperparts brighter rufous, chest pale grey with dark rufescent-brown flanks.

T. c. caurensis 'Caura Wren' (eastern Venezuela [Caura Valley]) Similar to *griseipectus* but rufescent-brown on flanks less extensive and paler.

T. c. obscurus (Cerro Auyan-tepuí, Bolívar, Venezuela) Underparts more rufous than in *caurensis*.

VOICE Song is a prolonged medley of varied bubbling trills and whistles, some phrases repeated many times before moving on to a new variation, interspersed with occasional high harsher notes; almost always given in duet by the pair. Calls include a characteristic *chidip chidip choopu* (Ridgely & Tudor 1989).

HABITAT Tends to occur in wetter locations, especially along riverbanks; humid forest both *terra firme* (unflooded) and *várzea* (periodically flooded). Also in second growth. Mostly fairly lowland (to 500m in Colombia) but as high as 2,400m in Venezuela.

HABITS Usually detected first by an explosive burst of song emanating from thick vegetation. It is not, however, as secretive or difficult to observe as other members of the genus as it often forages quite high up in bushes and low trees. Frequently associates with various antbirds and antwrens.

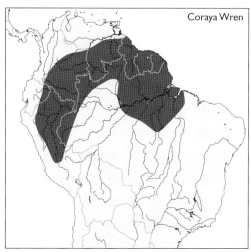

Coraya Wren

STATUS AND DISTRIBUTION Fairly common over much of its extensive range. Northern South America, including all three Guianas and north-eastern Brazil south to Goias; southern Venezuela in Bolívar and Amazonas; southern Colombia from Meta and Guaina southwards; eastern Ecuador and north-eastern Peru south to Cuzco. Sea-level to (mostly) below 1,000m, but recorded to 2,400m in Venezuela on tepuis (Meyer de Schauensee & Phelps 1978).

BREEDING Only two nests have so far been described, one in French Guiana (Tostain *et al.* 1992), the other in Suriname (Haverschmidt & Mees 1994). The former was an ovoid ball of dead leaves and twigs, built by both sexes, 30–40cm above the ground in a bush of the family Cyperaceae. Two eggs, rosy-white with fine dark speckles especially around the thick end. The Suriname nest was situated 30cm up on top of a mossy tree-stump. In Suriname, eggs on 25 February, newly-hatched young on 11 March, and juveniles out of the nest on 17 January to 21 April; in French Guiana, nest construction observed on 19 July and occupied nest 23 September. Not known whether breeding is cooperative.

FOOD Mostly invertebrate. Recorded food (from stomach contents of specimens); Arachnoidea (spiders), Coleoptera (beetles), Orthoptera (Locustidae) (Haverschmidt 1968). Stomach contents of the race *griseipectus* include seeds.

MOVEMENTS Apparently entirely sedentary.

MEASUREMENTS Wing of male 58–66, of female 53–59; tail of male 54–59, of female 48–54; exposed culmen of male 16.5–17, of female 14.5–17; tarsus of male 22–24, of female 21.5–24.

Thryothorus felix Sclater 1859 Juquila, Oaxaca, Mexico.

Alternative names: Spanish *Saltapared Reyezuelo*, *Saltapared Feliz*

A common endemic wren of western Mexico, where it has an interesting ecological relationship with the sympatric Sinaloa Wren.

IDENTIFICATION Length 12.5–14cm. Most closely resembles Sinaloa Wren, with which it frequently coexists; differs from that species by having a much more well-defined facial pattern and warm buff underparts. Other sympatric wrens are Banded Wren, immediately distinguished by its conspicuously barred flanks; Bewick's Wren, lacking the strong facial pattern and with a long-white-tipped tail; White-bellied Wren, totally different with a short tail and featureless face; and conceivably migrant Marsh Wren, with heavy stripes on the back and a different facial pattern.

DESCRIPTION *T. f. felix*
Adult Crown deep reddish-brown, back similar, becoming paler on lower back and rump. Shoulders, primaries and secondaries rufous-brown. Rectrices grey-brown with 9–11 bars formed by dull black and light brown edges to feathers. Lores dark; ear-coverts black with conspicuous white speckles. Sharp, thin, black malar stripe. Throat near-white, becoming buff on upper chest, than deeper brown on belly and flanks. Vent grey-brown with darker transverse bars. Underwing buff. Iris dark brown, upper mandible black, lower mandible dark grey, legs and feet dark grey.
Juvenile Similar to adult,but facial markings less distinct and underparts with a greyish-buff wash.

GEOGRAPHICAL VARIATION
T. f. felix (western Mexico from southern Jalisco through Colima, Michoacán, Guerrero to western Oaxaca) Described above.
T. f. pallidus 'Durango Wren' (western Mexico from central Sinaloa in mountains to north-western Michoacán and western Durango) Similar to *T. f. felix* but smaller, less rufescent on upperparts and paler and duller on underparts.
T. f. sonorae (north-western Mexico from southern Sonora to northern Sinaloa) Similar to *pallidus* but decidedly paler and more ashy; chin and throat pure white.
T. f. grandis 'Morelos Wren' (south-central Mexico [Morelos]) Intermediate in coloration between *T. f. felix* and *T. f. pallidus*, but larger than others.
T. f. lawrencii 'Lawrence's Wren' (María Madre Island, Tres Marías group, Nayarit, Mexico) Similar to *T. f. pallidus* but decidedly paler, cheeks much less strongly marked.
T. f. magdalenae 'Magdalena Island Wren' (María Magdalena Island, Tres Marías group) Similar to *T. f. lawrencii* in obscure markings on side of face but otherwise much darker.

VOICE Song is a rollicking series of gurgling whistles, *Chee wee chee chee cheery cheery* and variations. Both sexes

sing, alternating antiphonally; the contributions of each sex are distinct (Grant 1966a), in any song sequence, the males and females singing consistent but different phrases in sequence (Brown & Lennon 1979). Males also frequently sing solo. The song does differ from that of the sympatric Sinaloa Wren; nevertheless the two species seem to be mutually territorially exclusive, behaving to each other as if they were one species. Thus each species will respond to a playback of the other's song, and territories do not overlap between the two (Grant 1966b). The races on the Tres Marías Islands (when the Sinaloa Wren is absent) have less variation in their songs than those on the mainland (Grant 1996b). Calls include a dry gruff chattering and a springy, rising trill (Howell & Webb 1995).

HABITAT Fairly dry tropical deciduous forest, thorn scrub, oak-hornbeam forest and associated vegetation (Grant 1966a) including fairly disturbed habitat; from sea-level to 2,000m.

HABITS Although most often detected by song, not an excessively secretive bird. Forages mostly low down, on the ground and up to 2m from ground level; more rarely in trees up to 10m. The isolated island races appear to be more terrestrial than their mainland congeners.

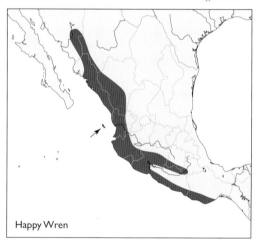

Happy Wren

STATUS AND DISTRIBUTION Quite common over most of its range. Western Mexico on the Pacific slope from southern Sonora to southern Oaxaca, and as far east as western Puebla, Morelos and Mexico. Isolated populations on the Tres Marías Islands (Nayarit).

BREEDING Builds a retort shaped nest of grass, fibres, fine twigs and bark shreds, built over a fine twig so that the nest cavity hangs over one side and the entrance passage over the other. The nests are approximately 10–12cm in width and height, and 22–25cm along the axis with the entrance passage. Nests are frequently built close to those of aggressive wasps, or in acacias defended by equally aggressive ants of the genus *Pseudomyrmicus*. Nests are also often built above water or a bromeliad. Nest height on the mainland of Mexico varies from ground level to 18m, averaging 3m; in a sample of eighteen nests only one was on the ground. On the Tres Marías Islands, presumably as a result of a lesser population of terrestrial predators, ground-nesting is more frequent (Grant 1966a). Eggs unmarked bluish-white, usual clutch size five. Breeding season in mainland Mexico late May and June, occasionally July; the populations on the Tres Marías Islands nest up to seven weeks later than on the mainland (Grant 1966b). Incubation and fledging periods not known. Very occasionally parasitised by the Bronzed Cowbird *Molothrus aeneus*.

FOOD Almost entirely invertebrate. In a study in the Mexican states of Jalisco and Nayarit (Grant 1966a) beetles predominated, followed by caterpillars, bugs, Hymenoptera and various other groups, and rarely, fruit.

MOVEMENTS Sedentary, except that there is some evidence of vertical movement in higher-altitude populations in Durango, Mexico (race *pallidus*).

MEASUREMENTS Wing of male 56.5–60, of female 53.5–55; tail of male 50.5–60, of female 50–56; exposed culmen of male 15–16.5, of female 14–16; tarsus of male 20.5–22.5, of female 19.5–21 (Ridgway 1904).

41   SPOT-BREASTED WREN
Thryothorus maculipectus   Plate 10

Thryothorus maculipectus Lafresnaye 1845 'Mexico' (probably Veracruz).

Alternative names: Spanish *Saltapared Pechimanchado, Chinchivirín Puito, Cluequita*; Mayan *Xan-coti*

A common and characteristic wren of lowlands, occurring from north-eastern Mexico to extreme northern Costa Rica. Formerly regarded as conspecific with Rufous-breasted Wren *T. rutilus* and Speckled Wren *T. sclateri*.

IDENTIFICATION Length 12.5–14cm. Essentially unmistakable. The combination of warm chestnut back and heavily spotted throat and chest is unique. Banded Wren is the only sympatric wren with any resemblance; it differs in having a clear white throat and chest, and white flanks heavily barred, not spotted, with black. The flanks of Spot-breasted Wren are chestnut brown without bars or spots. Juvenile Spot-breasted Wrens are less richly coloured and lack the strongly marked ear-coverts and chest of the adult, the chest being grey-brown with only a hint of dark spotting.

DESCRIPTION *T. m. maculipectus*
Adult Head and crown dull reddish-brown, becoming less rich on back but with rump and uppertail-coverts more chestnut. Rectrices dull brown, with about ten darker brownish-black bars extending across entire tail. Primaries and secondaries with obscure diffuse darker bars, barely discernable. Prominent white supercilium; ear-coverts strongly marked with black-and-white streaking. Throat whitish-grey, thickly marked with blackish speckles that extend over chest and down to centre of belly; flanks and lower belly unmarked orange-buff. Vent and crissum obscurely barred dull orange-buff and blackish-brown. Underwing-coverts dull grey. Iris brownish-red. Bill, both mandibles black, legs and feet blue-grey.
Juvenile Markings on throat, chest and upper belly much less prominent, more diffuse, and not extending so far down onto central belly. Ear-coverts obscurely marked with dull grey-brown and whitish grey.

GEOGRAPHICAL VARIATION
T. m. maculipectus (eastern Mexico, from Veracruz through Puebla and adjacent Oaxaca) Described above.

T. m. microstictus 'Small-spotted Wren' (north-eastern Mexico [Tamaulipas]) Similar to *maculipectus* but less rufescent above, bars on central rectrices narrower, spots on chest smaller and less profuse.
T. m. canobrunneus 'Yucatan Spotted-breasted Wren' (Yucatán Peninsula [Yucatán, Campeche, Quintana Roo and northern Belize (Russell 1964)], Petén, Guatemala) Paler than *maculipectus*, pileum light cinnamon brown.
T. m. umbrinus 'Guatemalan Spotted-breasted Wren' (southern Mexico [Tabasco, northern Chiapas] southern Belize) Larger and darker in colour than *maculipectus* with chestnut brown pileum.
T. m. varians 'Pacific Spotted-breasted Wren' (Pacific slopes of Chiapas, Mexico, Guatemala and El Salvador) Similar to *umbrinus* but slightly larger, and much paler and duller. Not certainly separable from *umbrinus* (Monroe 1968).
T. m. petersi 'Honduras Spotted-breasted Wren' (northern Honduras to northern Costa Rica) Upperparts more russet than all other races, bill thicker at base. Not certainly separable from *umbrinus* (Monroe 1968).

VOICE Song is a sprightly series of clear gurgled whistles *chee chee chee chewee* etc., verbalised as 'squeal, churl, squeal if you will!' (Sutton 1948), rather short in extent. Antiphonal singer; the male usually sings 5–7 notes, the female interpolating a shorter 2–4 phrase. Call note is a rising, buzzy trill, with a chattering scolding note (Stiles & Skutch 1989). The song is not dissimilar to that of the Happy Wren, which is allopatric; it differs markedly from that of the sympatric Banded Wren (Brown & Lennon 1979).

HABITAT Forest, including second growth, forest edge and citrus and cocoa plantations; from rather dry forest on limestone in northern Yucatán to more humid areas in Veracruz and Belize. Sea-level to 1,300m in Mexico (Howell & Webb 1995), to 1,050m in Guatemala (Land 1970), 1,300m in Honduras (Monroe 1968), but to only 200m in Costa Rica (Stiles & Skutch 1989).

HABITS Forages low in tangles of vines and vegetation, or at the edges of clearings; usually in pairs or family parties.

145

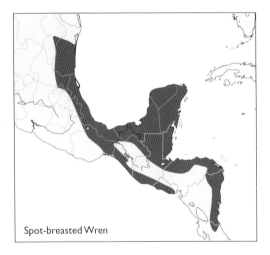

Spot-breasted Wren

of Mexico (Oaxaca and Chiapas), Guatemala and El Salvador to the Golfo de Fonseca.

BREEDING Nest is a dome shaped construction, 10cm x 15cm, with an entrance 4cm in diameter (Tashian 1952) with little or no entrance tunnel, usually in the crotch of trees or ferns 1–6m from the ground, one nest recorded as low as 13cm; one nest found in hanging baskets of plants suspended from a lattice roof (Skutch 1940). April–June and July in Costa Rica; in Oaxaca, Mexico, nest under construction, 22 March (Binford 1989) and well-incubated eggs on 4 May (Rowley 1984); young in nest in Chiapas, Mexico in late July (Tashian 1952). Eggs three or four, white with heavy blotches and streaks of reddish-brown. Incubation and fledging periods not recorded. Young fed by both sexes. Nests are also used as dormitories; it is not known if special nests are built for that purpose and whether they differ from breeding nests.

FOOD Not documented; probably entirely invertebrate.

MOVEMENTS Apparently entirely sedentary.

MEASUREMENTS Wing of male 54.5–60.5, of female 52.0–56.5; tail of male 42.5–50.5, of female 42.0–47.0; bill of male 9.3–12.8, of female 8.9–12.3; tarsus of male 20.9–23.2; of female 19.9–21.7 (Winker *et al.* 1996).

STATUS AND DISTRIBUTION Quite common over much of its range. Caribbean slope of Mexico from southern Tamaulipas and Nuevo León through the whole Yucatán peninsula including Belize and northern Guatemala, northern Honduras, northern Nicaragua and extreme northern Costa Rica; also the Pacific slopes

42   RUFOUS-BREASTED WREN
Thryothorus rutilus   Plate 10

Thryothorus rutilus Vieillot 1819 'L'Amerique septentrional' (in error for Trinidad).

Alternative names: Bush Wren, Speckled Wren, Jungle Wren (Trinidad); Spanish *Cucarachero pechicastano*, *Soterrey carimoteado*

A characteristically marked wren, with two disjunct populations in Central America and in northern South America. One of only two wren species found in Trinidad and Tobago.

IDENTIFICATION Length 14cm. The combination of densely-speckled throat, face and ear-coverts, differentiated sharply from a bright rufous chest and from a plain brown cap is diagnostic and does not resemble any other sympatric species, either in Central America or in South America. Stripe-throated Wren *T. leucopogon* has barred wings and no white on the belly; its range approaches, but does not overlap, that of *rutilus* in Panama and Colombia.

DESCRIPTION *T. r. rutilus*
Adult Crown, back and rump warm brown without streaks. Primaries and secondaries duller brown with very obscure barring on outerwebs, not visible in field. Rectrices grey-brown, with 10–12 heavy bars of blackish-brown extending across entire tail. Supercilium white, edged black on top. Throat and ear-coverts conspicuously patterned in black and white, tending to be white spots on a black ground in ear-coverts and white bars on a black ground on throat. Upper chest bright chestnut brown, sharply demarcated from throat. Centre belly

greyish-white; chestnut of underparts becomes duller and less rich on flanks and vent. Iris light reddish-brown, upper mandible and tip of lower mandible black, base of lower mandible bluish-grey, legs bluish-grey.
Juvenile Similar to adult but duller, especially on crown and posterior underparts; breast paler, more cinnamon; spots on throat and face larger, less well defined (Stiles & Skutch 1989).

GEOGRAPHICAL VARIATION Opinions differ as to the taxonomy of the group consisting of Spot-breasted Wren *Thryothorus maculipectus* of Mexico to northern Costa Rica, Speckle-breasted Wren *T. sclateri* of Colombia, Ecuador and Peru, and Rufous-breasted Wren *T. rutilus* of Costa Rica and Panama, and eastern Colombia to Tobago. Some authorities (e.g. Peters 1931–1986) merge all these as one superspecies; others join the two speckle-fronted plumage types as one species, despite their widely disjunct ranges (Meyer de Schauensee 1964), keeping *rutilus* as a separate species. We have followed the example of Ridgely & Tudor (1989) and maintained all these as separate species.
   T. r. rutilus (Trinidad; northern Venezuela from Sucre and Monagas to Lara) Described above.
   T. r. tobagensis 'Tobago Rufous-breasted Wren' (Tobago) Similar to *rutilus* but longer wings (male 64–66, female 61–63) and stronger bill, chest duller and whitish abdomen more restricted.
   T. r. intensus 'Maracaibo Wren' (State of Zulia, western Venezuela) Underparts more richly coloured than *rutilus* with some tendency to spotting.

146

T. r. hypospodius 'Grey-bellied Wren' (eastern Colombia and extreme western Venezuela [Táchira]). Similar to *rutilus* but tawny colour restricted to chest, flanks duller, upperparts more rufescent, pileum deeper rufous.

T. r. interior 'Lebrija River Wren' (Valley of the Río Lebrija, Santander, Colombia) Similar to *rutilus* but underparts paler, breast yellow-ochre, flanks very pale olive-brown.

T. r. laetus 'Santa Marta Wren' (Santa Marta region, northern Colombia) Similar to *rutilus* but breast paler and more ochraceous, chest with blackish subapical spots or bars.

T. r. hyperythrus 'Tawny-bellied Wren' (Costa Rica from Golfo de Nicoya sporadically to the Valle de Coto Brus; Panama [Chiriquí to Panamá provinces, absent from Darién]) Similar to *laetus* but underparts richer and warmer.

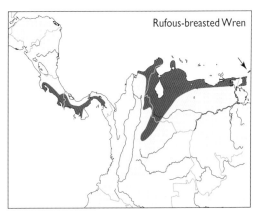

Rufous-breasted Wren

VOICE In Central America the usual song of the male is a series of four to seven pure, clear whistles, that of the female three or four slightly weaker notes. The sexes sing antiphonally, the blending of the two songs being so precise that a casual listener would not suspect that two birds were involved (Skutch 1960). Sometimes pairs sing in duets, and males may sing on their own. Young birds have an undeveloped, rambling song, which with age starts to include some of the clear notes of the adult. In Venezuela one song type consists of clear whistled notes interspersed with trills, a feature not found in Costa Rica (B. T. Thomas pers. comm.). Calls include a sharp *churr* and a rising *z'reeep*. Juvenile birds give a high-pitched double squeak (ffrench 1973).

HABITAT An active and restless bird, continuously on the move. Frequently forages higher up than other species of wren, making observation correspondingly easier. Spends most of its time searching for food in dense tangles of vegetation and on underside of canopy, usually in pairs or family parties. Pairs appear to remain together throughout the year. When foraging in dense vegetation pairs continuously call to each other with short, sharp notes. Birds sleep in a nest, usually on their own; frequently they will appropriate the nests of other species, such as Bananaquit *Coereba flaveola* or Riverside Wren *Thryothorus semibadius* for this purpose, even when the original owner has not relinquished possession. May also roost in crevices in thick vegetation. Fledglings may roost in the open. Allopreening seems to be quite frequent. There is one observation, unusual in wrens, of a distraction display of a female disturbed from an occupied nest (Skutch 1960).

STATUS AND DISTRIBUTION Common in suitable habitat. Costa Rica, from southern Guanacaste, sporadically through southern Puntarenas; Panama from Chiriquí eastwards to eastern Panamá province and the

Río Bayano. Absent from Darién and adjacent Colombia. Disjunct population from Santa Marta and western Guajira in Colombia south on Andean slopes to Casanare and Meta, eastwards through northen Venezuela to Pariá Peninsula; Trinidad and Tobago. From near sea-level on Tobago to 1,900m in Colombia (Hilty & Brown 1986).

BREEDING Nest is a bulky, domed structure built by both sexes, about 13cm high, 13cm long, and 15cm wide, with an entrance hole about 4cm in diameter. Made of grasses, bamboo leaves and dry stems, lined with finer materials and seed down. Located in tangled vegetation, in weeds or vines. Nest height variable, from 10cm above the ground to as much as 12m. Eggs two or three in Central America, two to four in Trinidad, white spotted with brown, the spots forming a wreath around the large end. Egg dates in Costa Rica January to July (mostly March to May) (Skutch 1960); in Trinidad, January to July (ffrench 1973); in Colombia, December to July (Hilty & Brown 1986). Incubation by female alone, probably for about 18 days; young are fed by both parents and fledge in about 16 days.

Builds multiple nests, but to a lesser extent than other species. Some nests are used exclusively as dormitories.

FOOD Largely invertebrate, insects and spiders, including occasionally large insects which have to be dismembered. Stomach contents of Suriname specimens include Coleoptera, Hemiptera, Diptera, Hymenoptera (Haverschmidt 1968); one stomach from Panama also contained a small seed (Wetmore 1984).

MOVEMENTS Appears to be totally sedentary; pairs remain together within a territory throughout the year.

MEASUREMENTS (*T. r. hyperythrus*) Wing of male 56.9–60.4, of female 50.6–54.7; tail of male 47.2–52.1, of female 40.4–46.5; bill of male 17.3–18.6, of female 16.6–18.0; tarsus of male 20.3–23.7, of female 19.1–20.5 (Wetmore *et al.* 1984).

---

43 SPECKLE-BREASTED WREN
Thryothorus sclateri

Plate 10

Thryothorus sclateri Taczanowski, Guajango, Río Marañón, Peru.

Alternative names: Maranon Wren; Spanish *Soterrey Pechijaspeado*

A relatively little-known species, although it is quite common in some locations in south-western Ecuador. Sometimes considered conspecific with the widely-distributed Rufous-breasted Wren.

IDENTIFICATION Length 13.5–14cm. The spotted underparts distinguish it from sympatric wren species. The Stripe-throated Wren (with a narrow area of overlap in Western Ecuador) has no breast spots and barred wings.

DESCRIPTION *T. s. sclateri*
Adult Crown reddish-brown, back and rump medium-brown without reddish tinge; rectrices with about eight alternate grey and dull black bars of about equal width. Lores grey-white, narrow supercilium white, bordered above by black, ear-coverts mottled black and white, eye-stripe dull blackish. Chin, throat, chest and upper belly covered in fine black and white bars; lower flanks grey-brown with diffuse blackish-grey bars. Remiges dull blackish-grey on innerweb, olivaceous-brown on outerweb with very ill-defined barring on closed wing. Underwing greyish. Iris reddish-brown or dark brown, upper mandible dark brown, lower mandible grey, legs black.
Juvenile Very similar to adult. Markings on underparts do not extend as far down onto belly, flanks essentially buff-brown without darker markings, iris brown without reddish tinge.

GEOGRAPHICAL VARIATION
T. s. sclateri (southern Ecuador [drainage of the Río Marañón] and adjacent Peru [Cajamarca]) Described above.
T. s. paucimaculatus 'Sharpe's Spotted Wren' (western Ecuador from Manabí to Loja) Somewhat smaller than *sclateri*, bill finer and shorter, centre of throat unmarked white, flank colour more olivaceous, markings on underparts broken into spots rather than bars and much reduced.
T. s. columbianus 'Colombian Band-billed Wren' (Colombia [two disjunct populations; western slope of central Andes in Valle and western slope of eastern Andes in Cundinamarca]) Similar to *sclateri*, but smaller and duller; back and, especially, the crown less warm brown, crown with olive tinge. Flanks more olive-brown and less rufescent than *sclateri*.

VOICE Song is a series a series of fast, repeated phrases which, while attractive, is not as musical as many of its congeners (Ridgely & Tudor 1989). Not known if the song is antiphonal, but this seems likely since both the Spot-breasted Wren and the Rufous-breasted Wren are antiphonal singers. Call is similar to the noise produced by rubbing one's fingers along a comb.

HABITAT Dense undergrowth and thickets in semi-humid forest and woodland; also in more arid woodland in southern Ecuador. In Colombia 1,300–2,000m (Hilty & Brown 1986), in Ecuador and Peru mostly below 1,100m, but also up to 1,600m (Ridgely & Greenfield 2001).

HABITS Forages mostly in forest understorey, usually in pairs. Sometimes in mixed flocks with other species. Not as secretive and retiring as some other members of the genus.

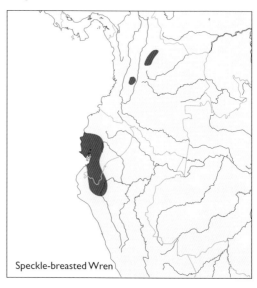

Speckle-breasted Wren

STATUS AND DISTRIBUTION Three disjunct populations. In Colombia, two very limited areas; the western slope of the central Andes above Palmira and Valle, and on the western slopes of the eastern Andes in Cundinamarca. Apparently uncommon in Colombia. In Ecuador and Peru, west of the Andes, from Manabí, Guayas, El Oro, Los Ríos and Loja, and in Peru in Tumbes and Piura and in the valley of the Río Marañón. In some locations in Ecuador (for example Machalilla National Park and the Chongón hills west of Guayaquil) quite common.

BREEDING Nest and eggs not described.

FOOD Stomach contents (Ecuador) 'insects'.

MOVEMENTS Apparently entirely sedentary.

MEASUREMENTS Wing of male 64–66.5, of female 59–61; tail of male 51–54, of female 49–52; exposed culmen of male 18–19, of female 17–17.5; tarsus of male 23–25.5, of female 22–22.5.

---

44   BAY WREN
Thryothorus nigricapillus   Plate 11

Thryothorus nigricapillus Sclater 1860 Nanegal, Pichincha, Ecuador.

Alternative names: Spanish *Cucarachero Cabecinegro*, *Soterrey Cabecipinto*, (Panama), *El Guerrero*

A spectacular and striking large wren with an extraordinary degree of plumage variation throughout its extensive geographic range.

IDENTIFICATION Length 14.5cm. The populations in

Central America and South America are very different in appearance and have sometimes been separated as two species *T. castaneus* (Bay Wren) and *T. nigricapillus* (Black-capped Wren). However, the distinction between the two is not clear-cut in eastern Panama (Wetmore 1984). In the race *costaricensis* (from Nicaragua to western Panama) and *castaneus* (central Panama), the combination of striking black-and-white facial pattern, white throat and unbarred chestnut underparts resembles no other species. In the South American races (starting in Darién in eastern Panama) the chest is heavily barred with black and white. Sympatric *Thryothorus* species include Black-bellied Wren (immaculate white chest and black belly), Stripe-throated Wren (no black cap, chest without barring), Sooty-headed Wren (black throat and unbarred chestnut chest) and Speckle-breasted Wren (brown cap and spots, rather than bars, on the chest).

DESCRIPTION *T. n. nigricapillus*
Adult Crown and nape black, contrasting sharply with rich unmarked chestnut-brown back, shoulders and rump. Rectrices rich brown with about eight or nine broad black bars across entire tail. Lores grey, area above and below eye white, narrow supercilium white. Ear-coverts black with well-defined white area posteriorly. Chin and throat unmarked white with narrow blackish bars beginning on upper chest, becoming broader and more sharply defined lower down and on sides. Lower chest and belly warm brown with well-defined blackish bars. Primaries and secondaries blackish on innerweb, warm chestnut with narrow black bars on outer, giving a strongly barred appearance to closed wing. Underwing-coverts mottled grey and dull black. Iris light mouse-brown, upper mandible black, tip of lower mandible dull pale olive-green, blackish on sides, changing at centre to light orange-yellow, legs fuscous-black.
Juvenile Very similar to adult; contrast between black cap and chestnut back less well-defined with less sharp border; brown colour on lower belly less rich; iris brown without reddish tinge.

GEOGRAPHICAL VARIATION The races of Bay Wren fall into two broad categories; those in South America, including the nominate race, with chest covered in sharply demarcated black-and-white bars, and those in Central America with largely unbarred underparts and white throat, with a degree of merging in central Panama. The description above is of the nominate race; a full description of one of the Central American races is given below.

    T. n. nigricapillus 'Black-capped Wren' (western Ecuador, from Esmeraldas to El Oro) Described above.

    T. n. connectens 'Intermediate Black-capped Wren' (north-eastern Ecuador [northern Esmeraldas] and south-western Colombia, [Nariño, southern Cauca]) Similar to *nigricapillus*, but barring on underparts more extensive.

    T. n. schotti 'Schott's Wren' (eastern Panama [Darién] and north-western Colombia [Antioquia, Chocó]) Differs from *nigricapillus* in that the barring on the underparts is narrower, and the throat is narrowly bound with black.

    T. n. castaneus (Panama, from the Canal west to Veraguas) Crown and nape dull black, contrasting sharp-ly with unmarked chestnut-brown back, shoulders and rump. Rectrices rich chestnut-brown with about eight broad black bars across entire tail. Primaries and secondaries with blackish-brown innerweb, outerweb rich brown with narrow blackish-brown bars, giving a sharply barred appearance to closed wing. Lores grey, semi-circular white area above and below eye, ear-coverts blackish with white speckles and with whitish patch posteriorly. Chin and throat white, contrasting with rich chestnut chest, belly and flanks, unmarked or with some blackish barring. Underwing-coverts deep brown. Iris rufous-brown, upper mandible blackish, lower mandible slaty-horn, feet dark slaty-grey. Differs from *nigricapillus* by lacking blackish bars on the chestnut-brown chest and belly. Juvenile has duller black crown, less bright chestnut back and strong dark barring on sides of chest and flanks, iris brown without reddish tinge.

    T. n. costaricensis 'Costa Rican Bay Wren' (western Panama [Bocas del Toro], Costa Rica [entire Caribbean drainage] and south-eastern Nicaragua [Río Escondido, area south of the Lago de Nicaragua, Greytown]) Underparts a richer chestnut than *castaneus*, and barring on lower underparts very much restricted.

    T. n. odicus (confined to the island of Escudo de Veraguas, Bocas del Toro, Panama) Larger than *costaricensis*, with larger bill, colour of back and undersurface paler.

    T. n. reditus (Caribbean slope of eastern Panama (eastern Colón, San Blas) Similar to *castaneus* but lighter coloured; white of breast more extensive; black barring on sides and abdomen more extensive.

VOICE Song is a varied series of loud ringing whistles, frequently repeated, then varied, and repeated again. Rendered as *sweety-it*, *sweet-whee-hee* etc. Call-note is a guttural *churr-r-sk* and a characteristic *heetowip*. Males may sing on their own but antiphonal song of a pair is frequent; the female sometimes imitates a bout of song, and inserts notes into the male's phrases. Song duets are invariably initiated by the female (Levin 1988).

HABITAT Humid forest edge and second growth rather than primary forest; in Colombia is replaced in interior forest by Sooty-headed Wren (Hilty & Brown 1986). Frequent near water; in Costa Rica especially fond of *Heliconia* thickets (Stiles & Skutch 1989), in Darién shows a marked preference for reed-beds on the banks of rivers (Griscom 1929). Also found, more sparsely, in drier habitat in southern Nicaragua. Sea-level to 1,100m.

HABITS Spends most of its time in thick vegetation where it is more often heard than seen. It will, however, reveal itself to a quiet observer, appearing briefly in the open to examine him curiously before disappearing again. The island race *odicus*, not accustomed to human beings, is notably more confiding. Pairs remain together throughout the year. Females are at least as aggressive as males in defending territory (Levin 1988). Females whether paired or unpaired respond strongly to record-ings of female song; in contrast, males respond to playbacks of both male and female songs, but paired males respond most strongly to male song, and unpaired males to female song (Levin 1988).

Bay Wren

Magdalena); Ecuador, the Pacific slope from Esmeraldas to El Oro, but absent from drier regions of the Guayas and Manabí.

BREEDING Nest is a loosely built elbow-shaped affair, made almost entirely of round-stemmed grass and lined with finer stems of the same, a few coarser stems and reddish-brown vine tendrils on the outside. Loosely placed in vines 1.2m up, by a stream (Stone 1912). Nests measure about 25cm long and 8–13cm in diameter. Both sexes build. Nests have been found at heights of between 1–5m, usually hung in an upright crotch of some small tree or shrub. In Panama the breeding season appears to be protracted; recently-hatched nestlings in March, and active nest construction in November (Wetmore 1984). In Colombia January through August (Hilty & Brown 1986). Eggs are three, white with cinnamon speckles, concentrated around larger end (Carriker 1910). Incubation and fledging periods unknown.

FOOD Probably entirely invertebrate; stomach contents of three specimens (race *reditus*) in Panama included beetles, earwigs, roach egg-cases and spiders (Wetmore 1984).

MOVEMENTS Highly sedentary.

MEASUREMENTS (*T. n. schotti*) Wing of male 64.0–66.9, of female 58.2–64.3; tail of male 48.0–52.3, of female 43.2–49.5; bill of male 19.5–22.1, of female 18.6–20.3; tarsus of male 24.3–26.8, of female 22.3–24.3 (Wetmore 1984).

STATUS AND DISTRIBUTION Fairly common in much of its range. Caribbean drainage of Central America (central Nicaragua, Costa Rica) in Panama, entire Caribbean slope, but also on Pacific slope in Veraguas, Coclé and Panamá, and on both slopes in eastern Panama (Darién and San Blas); Colombia, mostly on the Pacific slope (Chocó and Antioquia south to Nariño, but also eastwards into the valley of the Río

---

45   RIVERSIDE WREN
Thryothorus semibadius   Plate 11

Thryothorus semibadius Salvin 1870 Bugaba, 'Veraguas', (actually Chiriquí,) Panama.

Alternative names: Salvin's Wren; Spanish *Soterrey Pechibarreteado*

A strikingly-marked wren, geographically restricted to an area between central Costa Rica and western Panama.

The taxonomy of the *Thryothorus nigricapillus* group has been the subject of considerable debate. Some authorities (e.g. Hellmayr 1924–1938, Peters 1931–1970) have classified *nigricapillus*, *semibadius* and *castaneus* as races of one species, the Bay Wren *T. nigricapillus*; others have separated all three as distinct species. We have followed Stiles & Skutch (1989) and Ridgely (1989) and maintained *semibadius* as a separate monotypic species while merging *castaneus* into *nigricapillus*.

IDENTIFICATION Length 13–14cm. Within its limited range, the heavily-barred underparts are essentially unique. The Bay Wren *T. nigricapillus* at the southern end of its range is also heavily barred, but northern populations have almost unmarked underparts. Banded Wren *T. pleurostictus*, probably not sympatric, has the bars restricted to the flanks with a plain white chest. Stripe-breasted Wren *T. thoracicus*, mostly Caribbean slope, has laterally-streaked, not transversely-barred, underparts. Juvenile Riverside Wrens have underparts

more spotted rather than barred; however, Spot-breasted Wren *T. maculipectus* is allopatric.

DESCRIPTION
Adult Crown bright orange-brown, becoming deeper and more chestnut on nape, back and rump. Uppertail-coverts with inconspicuous darker bars. Shoulders and primary and secondary coverts blackish-grey, with narrow bars of greyish-white. Outerweb of primaries and secondaries, and both webs of tertials dull blackish-brown with narrow orange-brown markings, giving 10–12 narrow orange-brown bars on closed wing; innerwebs unmarked brownish-black. Rectrices dull black with eight or nine narrow buff-white bars across entire tail. Upper lores and narrow upper supercilium black; lower lores and lower part of supercilium white. Chin grey; sides of throat and ear-coverts dull black with conspicuous lateral spotting and streaking. Entire remainder of underparts grey with well marked, narrow, black bars, the barring becoming wider and the ground colour more buffy-white on the lower belly. Underwing-coverts grey with narrow blackish bars. Iris light reddish-brown, upper mandible black with grey cutting-edge, lower mandible grey, legs neutral grey.
Juvenile Similar to adult but duller; crown finely scaled blackish; below with black barring somewhat blurry; iris duller brown (Stiles & Skutch 1989).

150

GEOGRAPHICAL VARIATION None; monotypic.

VOICE Song, loud ringing phrases of one to four notes, repeated many times, then changing to a different, continuously repeated phrase; sometimes rather reminiscent of the song of the Ovenbird *Seiurus aurocapillus*. Both sexes sing, giving composite phrases of five to seven notes. Juvenile birds have a quite different song, a long-drawn medley of sweet low notes strung out in leisurely sequence and without definite phrasing (Skutch 1960). Calls, scolding, a harsh *churr*; also various clear tinkling notes.

HABITAT Dense vegetation, especially along watercourses (although it does not actually forage at water's edge) and in steep precipices; swampy edges of woodland. From near sea-level to 1,200m.

HABITS Forages low down in dense, tangled vegetation, often on the undersides of dead leaves. Usually found in pairs or family groups which remain together for much of the year. Not a routine follower of army ants, although it will join mixed flocks attending swarms for brief periods. Sleeps in dormitory nests, usually singly; the female will, however, sleep with the young in one nest for some time after fledging.

STATUS AND DISTRIBUTION Common, in suitable habitat, over much of its range. Costa Rica, mainly on the Pacific drainage, from the southern Gulf of Nicoya through the valley of El General to western Panama (Chiriquí), from near sea-level locally to 1,200m.

BREEDING The breeding nest is a complex structure, built probably by both sexes. In form it is roughly a globe with a deep indentation stretching across the lower side which fits over a single twig which supports the structure, which divides the nest into two nearly equal parts, the nesting chamber and an antechamber leading to the downward pointing entrance. In between the two chambers is a sill. Outside dimensions of the nest are about 15cm in length and 12.5cm in width and height. Nests are made of fine fibrous materials with a few bits of moss on the roof, which is insubstantial enough to admit light (Skutch 1960). Dormitory nests are more

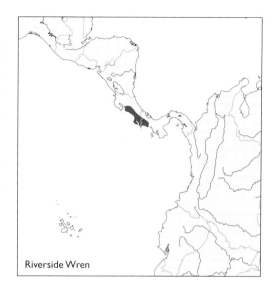

Riverside Wren

lightly constructed. Nests are low down, ranging from 1.5–2.2m above ground level, and are frequently sited above flowing water. The breeding season is very protracted; of six nests studied in Costa Rica, eggs were laid in February (one nest), July (three nests), August (one nest) and December (one nest) (Skutch, 1972). Eggs, two, white, finely speckled with cinnamon or pale brown, chiefly in a cap or wreath on the thicker end. Incubation by female alone for 18–19 days. Fledging period about 16 days.

FOOD Apparently entirely invertebrate (beetles, spiders, earwigs and roach eggs), including on occasion large insects which are dismembered piece by piece.

MOVEMENTS Sedentary.

MEASUREMENTS Wing of male 60.1–66.6, of female 60.5–64.7; tail of male 44.6–50.6, of female 41.7–47.5; bill of male 19.1–20.6, of female 19.2–20.8; tarsus of male 22.4–25.4, of female 22.4–24.5 (Wetmore *et al.* 1984).

---

46 STRIPE-BREASTED WREN
Thryothorus thoracicus   Plate 11

Thryothorus thoracicus Salvin 1864 Tucurriquí, Costa Rica.

Alternative names: Striped-breasted Wren; Spanish *Soterrey Pechirrayado*

A distinctively-marked wren found on the Caribbean slope of Central America from Nicaragua to Panama.

IDENTIFICATION Length 11.5–12.5cm. Not readily confused with any sympatric wren species; the peculiar teardrop patterned breast feathers are unlike any other species. The Riverside Wren, which occurs on the Pacific slope of Costa Rica and Panama and hence does not overlap, has barred rather than streaked underparts.

DESCRIPTION
Adult Crown grey-brown, becoming dark umber-brown

on back and rump. Some very diffuse and inconspicuous narrow blackish bars on mid-back. Shoulders and primary and secondary coverts dull umber-brown with narrow blackish bars. Outerwebs of primaries and secondaries, and both webs of tertials, dull buff-brown with greyish-black bars, giving 12–14 narrow bars on closed wing. Rectrices dull blackish, with dull buff-brown bars, giving 10–12 bars across entire tail. Lores and ear-coverts blackish-grey, the ear-coverts with conspicuous white streaking. Throat and chest with conspicuous broad, black, white and grey lateral streaks, stopping abruptly and contrasting with plain, unmarked dull olive-brown lower belly. Underwing grey-white with darker grey mottling. Iris red-brown, upper mandible greyish-black, lower mandible bluish-grey, legs grey-brown.

Juvenile Above brighter, more russet, crown scaled with black; throat and chest greyish-brown, irregularly striped with white, each stripe bordered with dusky; posterior underparts russet-brown to dull cinnamon. Iris dull brown (Stiles & Skutch 1989).

GEOGRAPHICAL VARIATION None; monotypic.

VOICE The Stripe-breasted Wren has two distinct styles of singing, so unlike that they seem to belong not merely to different species but to different families or even orders of birds (Skutch 1972). One song type, frequently heard at dawn, is a series of short whistles on the same pitch, repeated in a uniform series of perhaps a dozen notes, in some ways remarkably similar to the call of small owls such as the Ferruginous Pygmy Owl *Glaucidium brasilianum* or Northern Saw-whet Owl *Aegolius acadicus*. More rarely the notes will alternate between two different pitches. This song type, so far as can be determined, is uttered by one bird alone, presumably the male. The second song type is more typical of the genus, a series of tuneful liquid bubbling whistles of six to ten notes, originating from both sexes in an antiphonal performance. Juvenile birds also sing, a sweet rambling song quite different from the adult song. Call-note is a rolling *cherk* or *chrrhk*; scold a series of rather soft, guttural chatters and sputters (Stiles & Skutch 1989).

HABITAT Tangled vegetation along the edges of woodland, the more open parts of the forest, and the fringes of trees and bushes along streams. In cacao trees at low elevations in Costa Rica; at higher elevations in coffee bushes (Skutch 1972). Sea-level to 1,000 or 1,100m.

HABITS Forages in pairs, usually low down in dense tangled vegetation near ground, where it hunts for insects by poking into moss tufts, hanging trash, rolled leaves and gleans from branches and foliage. Less secretive than many *Thryothorus* wrens. Pairs seem to remain together throughout the year.

STATUS AND DISTRIBUTION Uncommon to quite common, from Caribbean slopes of eastern Nicaragua (San Juan del Norte, Río Escondido) through Costa Rica to western Panama (Bocas del Toro to Coclé, rarely into Canal Zone); also locally on the Pacific slope in northern Costa Rica and in Panama in Veraguas.

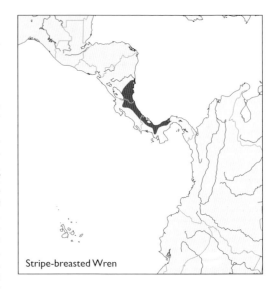

Stripe-breasted Wren

BREEDING Nest is a globular structures of fibres, leaf skeletons and the like, more or less covered in green moss, dangled over a thin branch, with the chamber portion on one side and the downward-pointing entrance and vestibule on the other, situated 1.5–6m up, in shrubs, cacao bushes or on top of palm fronds. Construction by both sexes over six to eight days. Eggs two or three, unmarked white or bluish-white; in Costa Rica from March to July. Incubation by female alone, period unknown. Young fed by both sexes, fledging period about sixteen days. Nests are used as dormitories as well as for breeding.

FOOD Apparently entirely invertebrate. Young are fed on caterpillars, moths, forest roaches, other insects and spiders (Skutch 1972).

MOVEMENTS Apparently entirely sedentary.

MEASUREMENTS Wing of male 55.0–62.5, of female 55.8–62.1; tail of male 37.1–40.4, of female 34.4–39.8; bill of male 18.1–20.0, of female 17.3–18.9; tarsus of male 20.6–22.3, of female 19.3–22.0 (Wetmore 1984).

47   STRIPE-THROATED WREN
Thryothorus leucopogon   Plate 11

Thryophilus leucopogon Salvadori & Festa 1899, Río Peripa, Pichincha, Ecuador.

Alternative names: Festa's Wren; Spanish *Soterrey Golirayado, Cucarachero Garganta Rayado*

An uncommon and relatively little studied species, found from eastern Panama to Ecuador. Sometimes considered conspecific with the allopatric Stripe-breasted Wren of Nicaragua to western Panama; however, the great differences in the songs of the two species would make this appear to be unlikely.

IDENTIFICATION Length 12cm. A rather nondescript

bird. Closest to the barely sympatric Rufous-breasted Wren, which is larger, with a warm buff-coloured chest contrasting with a white, unstreaked throat. Southern House Wrens lack the facial markings of the present species, while wood wrens have a shorter tail and grey or white underparts, not brown. All other sympatric wren species differ drastically.

DESCRIPTION *T. l. leucopogon*
Adult Crown and upper back dark brown, becoming slightly more rufescent on rump. Rectrices dull reddish-brown, with about ten narrow bars of dull blackish extending across entire tail. Lores greyish-brown, narrow

superthcilium of greyish-white. Ear-coverts with dull black and greyish-white streakings. Chin and throat with sharp longitudinal streaks of grey-white and dull black, extending below ear-coverts at sides and sharply demarcated from deep rufescent-buff upper-chest. Chest rufescent buff, becoming richer and darker on lower belly and vent. Wings dull brownish-black on innerwebs, finely and sharply barred with reddish-brown and blackish on outerwebs, giving 12–15 obvious fine bars on closed wing. Underwing-coverts greyish-brown. Iris light brown or reddish-brown, upper mandible black or dark grey, lower mandible paler grey with blackish tip, legs greyish-black or greyish-brown.

Juvenile Similar to adult; streaks on throat somewhat less well-defined, iris brown without reddish tinge.

GEOGRAPHICAL VARIATION

T. l. leucopogon (eastern Panama [Pacific slope of Darién]; Pacific slopes of Colombia and Ecuador) Described above.

T. l. grisescens (Caribbean slope of Panama and adjacent Colombia) Similar to *leucopogon*, but strikingly paler and greyer both above and below.

VOICE Song is a rather tuneless repetition of two or three notes, *chu-chi-chu chu-chi-chu* or *chu-chip-chu-chip*, etc., very distinct from songs of Stripe-breasted Wren. No data on duetting or antiphonal song. Calls resemble elements of song.

HABITAT Borders of secondary forest, *várzea* forest, sea-level to 900m.

HABITS Little known. Unlike most wren species routinely participates in mixed flocks with antwrens and other species; forages 3–10m above ground level. Pairs apparently remain together throughout year.

STATUS AND DISTRIBUTION Scarce and local throughout most of its range. Eastern Panama, both slopes in Darién and San Blas; recently a population was found well to the west of the known range, near Nusagandi in western San Blas (P. Burke pers. comm.); Colombia, Pacific slope from Chocó to Nariño, eastward

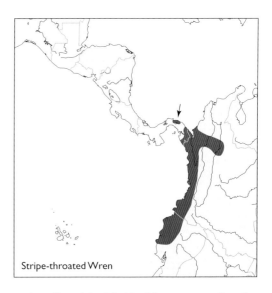

Stripe-throated Wren

to the valley of the Río Magdalena; western Ecuador (Esmeraldas, south to Manabí).

BREEDING Nest is an untidy ball, irregular in form, placed near the end of small branches with no attempt at concealment (Wetmore *et al.* 1984). Eggs undescribed, incubation and fledging periods unknown. Nest-building in Panama at the beginning of March; birds in breeding condition in north-western Colombia in April (Hilty & Brown 1986).

FOOD Museum specimen stomach contents 'insects' (ANSP). No other data.

MOVEMENTS Apparently entirely sedentary.

MEASUREMENTS (*T. l. grisescens*) Wing of male 55.4–58.0, of female 51.6–56.2; tail of male 34.3–39.7, of female 34.4–36.2; bill of male 17.5–19.3, of female 17.3–19.3; tarsus of male 18.0–21.7, of female 18.6–20.2 (Wetmore *et al.* 1984).

48   BANDED WREN
Thryothorus pleurostictus   Plate 11

Thryothorus pleurostictus Sclater 1860 La Paz, Guatemala.

Alternative names: Spanish *Chinchivirín Rayado, Saltapared Vientre-barrado, Soterrey de Costillas Barretedeas, Saltapared arañero*

A common and diagnostically plumaged wren of the Pacific slope of Central America, from central Mexico to northern Costa Rica.

IDENTIFICATION Length 14–15cm. Not easily confused with any other species of wren in its range. The combination of whitish underparts, unmarked throat and chest, heavily barred, not spotted, throat and white eye-stripe is unique in most of its range. For distinctions from Spot-breasted Wren see under that species. Riverside Wren (doubtfully sympatric in a

limited area of Costa Rica) is finely barred over most of the underparts including the chest.

DESCRIPTION *T. p. pleurostictus*
Adult Crown and nape reddish-brown, becoming more rufescent on shoulders, back and rump. Rectrices cinnamon-brown with 8–10 transverse bars of dull blackish, extending across entire tail. Lores dull blackish-brown; supercilium from bill to posterior ear-coverts off-white. Ear-coverts finely speckled with black and off-white, the markings becoming sharper and coalescing into black and off-white streaks posteriorly. Chin, throat and chest unmarked off-white; sides of chest with prominent black bars which become wider on sides of lower chest and extend across lower belly. Undertail-coverts with sharp black and white bars.

Primaries and secondaries with dark brown innerwebs, outerwebs reddish-brown with numerous blackish bars, giving about 10–15 narrow bars on closed wing. Underwing-coverts whitish-grey. Iris dark brown; upper mandible dark brown, lower mandible flesh-colour with bluish tinge; legs and feet light brown to horn.

Juvenile Facial markings almost absent. Chin and throat off-white with brownish mottling. Bars on sides of chest and belly totally absent, being replaced with dull pale buff with darker brown mottling. Bars on remiges much more obscure.

GEOGRAPHICAL VARIATION

T. p. pleurostictus (eastern Guatemala [Zacapa]) Described above.

T. p. nisorius 'Deppe's Banded Wren' (southern Mexico in Morelos, Puebla and Michoacán) Similar to *pleurostictus* but larger, barring on underparts more extensive, black streaks on throat and chest.

T. p. ravus 'Nicaraguan Banded Wren' (western Nicaragua to western Costa Rica) Smaller than *pleurostictus*, upperparts more brightly rufescent, barring on primaries and secondaries less prominent.

T. p. lateralis 'El Salvador Banded Wren' (western Honduras, eastern and central El Salvador) Smaller than *oblitus*, generally brighter and more rufescent.

T. p. oblitus 'Sclater's Banded Wren' (western El Salvador, coastal Guatemala and eastern Mexico) Larger, browner and less warmly coloured on upperparts than *lateralis*.

T. p. acaciarum (Chiapas, Mexico) Lower belly more buff than nominate, flank barring somewhat heavier.

T. p. oaxacae (Mexico from Guerrero to Oaxaca) Very similar to nominate; no whitish on primary webs.

VOICE One of the most accomplished vocalists in the genus. The song is an arresting, varied series of whistles, gurgles and trills, with some phrases strongly reminiscent of the European Nightingale *Luscinia megarhynchos*. Calls include short trills and a harsh nasal churr, *jerr-jerr-jerr*.

HABITAT Scrub forest, including second growth, arid tropical scrub or tropical deciduous forest; in western El Salvador in swamp forest; in Honduras and Costa Rica, sometimes in mangrove swamps. In Mexico, commonest at lower elevations but locally up to 1,600m; in Honduras to 1,100m and in Costa Rica to 800m.

HABITS Active and busy, not excessively secretive. Feeds at lower elevations or on ground, pushing over dead leaves and probing into crevices in bark. Will also forage higher up in trees in habitats where there is little understorey. Usually in pairs or family parties; will associate in mixed flocks of warblers and vireos (Dickey & Van Rossem 1938). Wags tail from side to side when excited (Stiles & Skutch 1989).

STATUS AND DISTRIBUTION Reasonably common to abundant over much of its range. Mexico, on Pacific

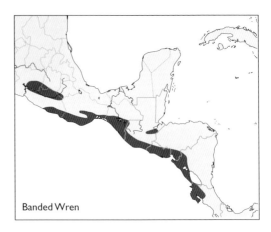

Banded Wren

drainage from Guerrero through Oaxaca and Chiapas, with a disjunct population in Michoacán, northern Guerrero and Puebla; coastal Guatemala, also with a population in the eastern interior; El Salvador, Pacific drainage but absent from much of central part of country; southern Honduras; Pacific coast of Nicaragua and north-western Costa Rica south to the Golfo de Nicoya.

BREEDING Nest is a retort-shaped or elbow-shaped roofed construction, hung in the crotch of a small tree, with the chamber on one side of the support and the entrance tube, which slopes downward at about 45°, on the other, built of rootlets, weed-stems and the like, and lined with fine grasses (Skutch 1940), or fine yellow grass inflorescences (Stiles & Skutch 1989). Height 1–3m, frequently located close to hornets' nests, or in bull's horn acacias which are inhabited by aggressive and defensive ants, or sometimes in irritating nettle-bushes *Cnidoscolus* (Rowley 1966). In El Salvador apparently uses the nests of the Yellow-olive Flycatcher *Tolmomyias sulphurescens* after the original owner has raised its brood; these nests were 2–10m from the ground and pendant from the tips of slender branches (Dickey & Van Rossem 1938). Breeding season May to July in central Mexico (Friedmann *et al.* 1957), and May to August in southern Mexico and El Salvador, possibly to take advantage of the availability of second-hand nests. Eggs three to five, occasionally white, more often pale blue to a rich 'Robin's egg' blue, unmarked. Incubation and fledging periods unknown.

FOOD Little recorded; apparently entirely invertebrate, insects and spiders.

MOVEMENTS Appears to be entirely sedentary.

MEASUREMENTS Wing of male 63–69.5, of female 59.5–65.5; tail of male 49–58.5, of female 46.5–54.5; exposed culmen of male 17–19, of female 15–18; tarsus of male 20.5-24, of female 20.5–22.5 (Ridgway 1904).

---

49   RUFOUS-AND-WHITE WREN
Thryothorus rufalbus

Plate 11

Thryothorus rufalbus Lafresnaye 1845, 'Mexico' (in error, Guatemala).

Alternative names: Spanish *Saltapared Rufiblanco, Cucarachero curtido, Cucarachero Rozijo, Soterrey Rufo y Blanco*

A widely distributed and reasonably common wren which is found in natural and lightly disturbed habitat from Mexico to Venezuela.

IDENTIFICATION Length 14.5–16.5cm. A strikingly rufous, rather large wren with a conspicuous face pattern and whitish underparts. Sympatric species in its range are Plain Wren (Mexico and Central America), smaller, duller brown on back, no distinct facial markings. In Venezuela and Colombia, Buff-Breasted Wren, much duller above, more buffy below; Niceforo's Wren, iron grey-brown, rather than rufous above, with greyish flanks and Whiskered Wren, no bars on wing feathers, conspicuous, thicker malar stripe.

DESCRIPTION *T. r. rufalbus*
Adult Crown dark ochraceous-brown, becoming more rufescent on back and shoulders and fox-brown on rump and uppertail-coverts. Rectrices rufous-brown with sharp, narrow blackish bars across entire tail. Supercilium narrow, grey-white, behind eye finely bordered by blackish above and below. Area behind eye and lores brown. Ear-coverts mottled whitish-buff and blackish. Throat off-white with obscure greyish mottling on chest. Flanks dull ochraceous-brown. Primaries and secondaries dull blackish-brown on innerwebs, reddish-brown on outer, with fine blackish-brown markings forming numerous fine bars across flight-feathers of closed wing. Undertail-coverts with transverse blackish bars. Iris hazel or reddish-brown, upper mandible black, lower mandible bluish-flesh colour, legs pale leaden blue.
Juvenile Facial markings more obscure; chest with indistinct grey and grey-brown mottlings; barring on undertail-coverts very diffuse and obscure.

GEOGRAPHICAL VARIATION
    T. r. rufalbus (Highlands of Guatemala and El Salvador) Described above.
    T. r. transfinis (extreme south-western Chiapas, Mexico) Similar to *rufalbus* but tail longer.
    T. r. castanonotus 'Chestnut-backed Wren' (Pacific slopes of Nicaragua and Costa Rica and Panama east to the Canal Zone) Similar to *rufalbus* but lighter rufous on upperparts and with grey flanks lacking rufous suffusion.
    T. r. cumanensis 'Cumana Wren' (northern Venezuela and northern Colombia from Sucre [Pariá Peninsula] westwards to Cartagena) Similar to *castanonotus* but upperparts paler, breast almost as white as throat, bill more slender.
    T. r. minlosi 'Minlos's Wren' (eastern Colombia from Uleta northwards, north-western Venezuela [Zulia, Apure and Cojedes]) Similar to *cumanensis* but darker rufous above with an ill-defined darker cap, auricular streaking heavier and darker, flanks deeper tawny-brown.

VOICE Song is characteristic, and unlike other members of the genus, consisting of four to five slow, low-pitched 'hooting' whistles, often preceded by and ending with a higher note; one recurring phrase is a *whee-hoo-hoo-hoo-hoo-whit* (Ridgeley & Tudor 1989). 'One's instant thought on first hearing it is "owl"' (Dickey & Van Rossem 1938). Alarm note is a harsh scolding; also a castanet-like chattering, in El Salvador heard only during the winter.

HABITAT Mostly in rather dry deciduous forest and forest edge, including plantations; more locally in semi-humid forest. In the *llanos* in gallery forest. In El Salvador in winter (but not in summer) in *huiscoyol*. Mostly 300–1,500m, down to sea-level in winter in El Salvador.

HABITS Exceptionally shy and furtive. Forages low, especially in leaf-litter and in low vine tangles. In contrast to Buff-breasted Wren, a rather solitary bird; frequently forages singly, family association after fledging very short, and allopreening not observed (S. M. Farabaugh pers. comm.). During periods of food shortages has been observed to seek out and kill nestlings of the House Wren, not for food, or for nest-sites (since the two species nest in different situations), but apparently to remove competition for food resources. This infanticide seems to be triggered by periods of scarcity, and is quite general in occurrence (Freed 1987).

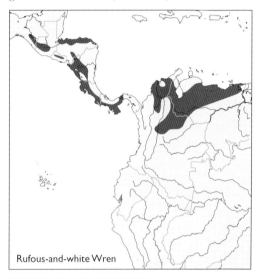
Rufous-and-white Wren

STATUS AND DISTRIBUTION Low to moderate abundance in suitable areas. Southern Mexico (south-western Chiapas) into southern Guatemala; central Guatemala (uncommon); Honduras (wooded interior highlands and on Pacific slope, 900–1,400m, rather uncommon); also disjunctly on Caribbean slope in more open rainforest, down to sea-level; central El Salvador, but also on coast in winter; Pacific slopes of Nicaragua and Costa Rica (reports in the Caribbean slope of Costa Rica in the Río Reventazón drainage apparently in error); Panama, mainly on Pacific slope to the Río Bayano, but also on the Caribbean slope near the Canal Zone; disjunctly in Colombia from Bolívar eastward to Cesar and the Sierra de Perijá, south in the Magdalena Valley, eastward across northern Venezuela to the Pariá peninsula and south to Amazonas; central Colombia (Vicheda, Mata, Arauca).

BREEDING Nest is a globular structure of grass and fibres, with an entrance tube pointing downwards at 45°. Nests are frequently situated in bull-horn acacias whose aggressive symbiotic ants provide protection against climbing predators (S. M. Farabaugh pers. comm.). Eggs two or three, rarely four, blue-green or sky-blue without markings. Incubation and fledging periods not known; young fed by female alone, in contrast to Buff-breasted Wren where both sexes feed the young. Nesting period May to July in Venezuela (Phelps & Schaffer 1954), late March to early June in El Salvador (Dickey & Van Rossem 1938) and up to late July in Panama (Wetmore 1984). In Costa Rica fresh eggs on 11 May and 6 June (Carriker 1910). Frequently parasitised by Striped Cuckoo *Tapera naevia* whose nestlings will kill the wren nestlings (Morton & Farabaugh 1979).

FOOD Little data: stomach contents 'insects' (*T. r. rufalbus* El Salvador) (FMNH). Has been seen to feed

'red berries' to a fledged Striped Cuckoo *T. naevia* (Loetscher 1952).

MOVEMENTS Probably largely sedentary; however, in El Salvador (and presumably in other areas of northern Central America) there may be some altitudinal movement, since it is found in coastal forest at sea-level in winter but not in summer (Dickey & Van Rossem 1938).

MEASUREMENTS (*T. r. castanonotus*) Wing of male 67.2–72.1, of female 61.2–67.8; tail of male 48.2–54.7, of female 46.2–51.5; bill of male 19.7–23.6, of female 19.5–21.5; tarsus of male 24.2–25.7, of female 23.8–25.0 (Wetmore *et al.* 1984).

50   NICEFORO'S WREN
Thryothorus nicefori   Plate 11

Thryothorus nicefori Meyer de Schauensee 1946, San Gil, Santander, Colombia.

Alternative name: Spanish *Cucarachero de Nicéforo*

Etymology: Named for Brother Nicéforo María of Bogotá (for whom the Yellow-billed Pintail *Anas georgica niceforoi* is also named), who collected the first specimen (Meyer de Schauensee 1946).

A highly localised, little-known and undoubtedly endangered wren, found only in a very restricted area of Colombia. It may only be a well-marked race of the Rufous-and-white Wren *T. rufalbus*.

IDENTIFICATION Length 14.5cm. Most resembles Rufous-and-white Wren, but much less rufous on back.

DESCRIPTION
Adult Crown, nape and back greyish-brown, with diffuse and obscure darker barring, becoming warmer and more rufescent on back and upper rump; some semi-concealed whitish spots on lower back and upper rump. Wing-coverts dull rufescent-brown with darker spots. Rectrices medium brown with darker bars. Primaries and secondaries blackish-brown on innerweb, barred rufescent-brown and blackish on outerweb giving a strongly barred appearance on closed wing. Conspicuous white supercilium before and behind eye; eye-stripe greyish-brown, ear-coverts mottled whitish-grey and dark grey-brown. Blackish malar stripe. Chin, throat and chest white. Sides of chest grey, becoming buffy-grey on flanks. Iris reddish-brown, legs dull blue-grey. Bill horn-colour, lower mandible paler at base.
Juvenile Undescribed.

GEOGRAPHICAL VARIATION None; monotypic. The taxonomic status of Niceforo's Wren is a source of debate; several authorities have suggested that it is merely a well-marked race of the widespread Rufous-and-white Wren *T. rufalbus* (e.g. Ridgely & Tudor 1989). This viewpoint is supported by observations that the songs of the two forms are identical, and that Niceforo's Wren responds to a play-back of the song of the Rufous-and-white Wren (Collar *et al.* 1992).

VOICE No recordings available (Hardy & Coffey 1991); however, it is stated to be 'exactly like Rufous-and-white

Wren' (q.v.) (Collar *et al.* 1992).

HABITAT Recently found in thick xeric acacia scrub above sea-level at 1,095m; does not appear to be able to adapt to coffee plantations.

HABITS Unknown; presumably similar to those of the Rufous-and-white Wren.

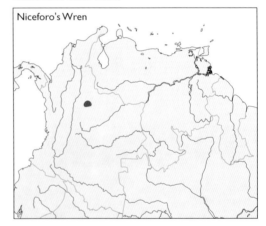
Niceforo's Wren

STATUS AND DISTRIBUTION Apparently restricted to a small area of acacia scrub near San Gil on the Río Fonce, south of Bucaramanga, Colombia (6°33'N, 73°08'W). Seven specimens were taken in 1945 (Meyer de Schauensee 1946); not apparently again observed until 1989, when a pair was located about 1km east of San Gil. Seems to be dependent on acacia scrub, which is highly disturbed by clearing for agriculture; the status of the species, or race, is clearly endangered (Collar *et al.* 1992).

BREEDING Nest and eggs undescribed; presumably similar to those of close relatives.

FOOD Undescribed.

MOVEMENTS Apparently totally sedentary.

MEASUREMENTS Male: wing 71, exposed culmen 19, tarsus 23, tail 49 (Meyer de Schauensee 1946). No female measurements available.

Thryophilus sinaloa Baird 1864. Mazatlán, Sinaloa, Mexico.

Alternative names: Bar-vented Wren; Spanish *Saltapared sinaloense*

A very common wren of western Mexico, generally sympatric with the related Happy Wren.

IDENTIFICATION Length 12.5–14cm. Most closely resembles Happy Wren, from which it differs in having much less well-defined facial markings, greyish chest and pale-brownish, not warm rufous-brown, flanks. The races of Happy Wren (*lawrencii* and *magdalenae*) on the Tres Marías Islands have less prominent facial markings, but the Sinaloa Wren does not occur on the islands. In the southern part of its range overlaps with Banded Wren *T. pleurostictus* which is immediately distinguished by its prominently barred flanks. Cannot be confused with any other sympatric wren species.

DESCRIPTION *T. s. sinaloa*
Adult Crown dull-brown, becoming slightly rufous on back and more rufous on rump. Shoulders and wing-coverts medium-brown. Primaries and secondaries dull blackish-brown with rufous-brown outerwebs, the closed wing having about ten dark bars on a rufous-brown background. Rectrices rufous-brown with seven or eight dark transverse bars. Supercilium whitish, lores and eye-stripe medium-brown, ear-coverts and sides of face speckled blackish and grey-white, sides of chest grey; sides of belly and flanks ochraceous-brown. Crissum whitish with strong transverse black bars. Underwing grey-brown. Iris hazel-brown, upper mandible medium horn, lower mandible almost white, darkest at tip. Legs pale reddish-brown.
Juvenile Similar to adult but face less distinctly marked, sides washed dusky, undertail-coverts dusky pale cinnamon (Howell & Webb 1995).

GEOGRAPHICAL VARIATION
T. s. sinaloa (western Mexico, from central Sinaloa south to Colima and Michoacán, and east to western Durango) Described above.
T. s. cinereus 'Ashy Wren' (north-western Mexico, from south-eastern Sonora to northern Sinaloa and western Chihuahua) Similar to *T. s. sinaloa* but decidedly paler and greyer.
T. s. russeus 'Russet Wren' (central Guerrero, México) Similar to *T. s. sinaloa* but darker and richer in colour, back deep russet-brown, uppertail-coverts cinnamon-rufous.

VOICE Song is a cheerful series of clear, gurgling whistled notes, often interspersed with a rapid series of short trills, reminiscent of some parts of the song of the European Nightingale *Luscinia megarhynchos*; in spite of some published statements to the contrary, not particularly similar to the song of Happy Wren. For a very thorough comparative analysis of the song types of the two species see Brown & Lennon (1979). Female Sinaloa Wrens also sing; the song resembles that of the male but is shorter and simpler. In contrast to the Happy Wren, pairs of the Sinaloa Wren do not sing in syncopated duets. Calls include a harsh chatter and dry churring notes.

HABITAT Quite varied; tropical deciduous forest, thorn scrub, and oak-hornbeam forest, including areas quite heavily disturbed (Grant 1996b). Coexists with Happy Wren, and may occupy the same territory in successive years; perhaps tends on average to inhabit sparser woodland than the Happy Wren. Sea-level to 2,000m.

HABITS Typical of the genus, very active, not excessively secretive. Spends most of its time foraging on or near the ground, up to 2m or so, more rarely in the canopy.

Sinaloa Wren

STATUS AND DISTRIBUTION Common over much of its range. Restricted to western Mexico, from south-eastern Sonora, western Chihuahua, coastally Sinaloa, extreme western Durango and Nayarit to Guerrero and western Oaxaca; inland in the Balsas drainage as far as western Puebla. Mostly tropical zone, sea-level to 2,000m in Jalisco and Michoacán.

BREEDING Nest is very similar to that of the Happy Wren, a retort-shaped construction built over a branch with the chamber on one side and the downward-pointing entrance on the other, made of grass stems, fibres, rootlets, etc.; typically about 25cm long and 10–12cm in width and height. Frequently situated near the nests of hornets, or in acacias protected by the ant *Pseudomyrmicus*. Situated at heights of 1.3–3.5m above the ground (Grant 1996b). Eggs usually five, bluish-white, unmarked. Incubation and fledging periods not recorded. In Nayarit nest-building started in the second week of May, first eggs observed in the third week and five fledged young in the first week of June (Grant 1996b). At higher altitudes in Jalisco egg laying as late as 24 July (Pacific Coast Avifauna 1957). Birds in Nayarit were still in breeding condition in August, suggesting a second brood.

FOOD Almost entirely invertebrate; actual composition not recorded.

MOVEMENTS Appears to be entirely sedentary; not

known if vertical movements of higher-altitude populations occur.

MEASUREMENTS Wing of male 57.5–63, of female 54–56; tail of male 43.5–51, of female 40.5–45; exposed culmen of male 15.5–18, of female 15.5–16; tarsus of male 21–23, of female 20–21.

52 PLAIN WREN
Thryothorus modestus
Plate 12

Thryothorus modestus Cabanis 1860, San José, Costa Rica.

Alternative names: Cabanis' Wren, Modest Wren; Spanish *Saltapared Sencillo, Chinchirigüí*

A common wren of much of Central America, lacking in striking plumage features, but with an arresting song.

IDENTIFICATION Length 12.5–14cm. As its name suggests, the Plain Wren has no very obvious plumage markings, being largely unmarked russet-brown above and whitish and buffy below; the most striking feature is a conspicuous pale supercilium. Distinguished from the White-browed Wren, which is probably not sympatric, by the lack of strong markings on the ear-coverts and the warm rufous tail. From White-bellied Wren, also barely sympatric, by its larger size, more rufous tail and rump, and buffy flanks; and (in Panama) from Buff-breasted Wren by having less well-marked barring on wings and tail and whitish, not buffy, chest. For distinctions from Canebrake Wren see under that species.

DESCRIPTION *T. m. modestus*
Adult Crown unmarked dark grey-brown. Back more rufous, becoming orange-rufous on rump and uppertail-coverts. Rectrices rufescent-brown with about nine transverse dark bars extending across width of tail. Primaries and secondaries warm brown with very obscure barring. Supercilium white, broader and more conspicuous behind eye. Lores and eye-stripe greyish-brown. Cheeks mottled grey-white and dark greyish-brown. Throat white, chest pale greyish-buff, centre belly buffy-white, sides of belly, flanks, thighs and undertail-coverts warm orange-buff, the colour becoming more intense posteriorly. Underwing-coverts whitish-grey. Iris bright reddish-brown, legs and feet slaty-lilac or bluish-slate, upper mandible dark-brown, lower mandible pale plumbeous-blue.
Juvenile Iris dark brown, legs and feet pale plumbeous, lower mandible flesh coloured (Dickey & Van Rossem 1938).

GEOGRAPHICAL VARIATION
T. m. modestus 'Cabanis' Wren' (southern Mexico [extreme western Oaxaca, Chiapas]; central and southern Guatemala; a disjunct population in southern Belize, Nicaragua, Honduras, El Salvador, Costa Rica [except on Caribbean slopes]) Includes *T. m. pullus* ('Chiapas Wren'), which is not a justifiable race (Russell 1964, Monroe 1968). Described above.
T. m. elutus 'Panama Wren' (Pacific drainage of Panama, from about the Costa Rican border to just east of the Canal Zone) Similar to *T. m. modestus* but duller and paler, very buffy on lower flanks, wing and bill averaging longer, tail shorter, iris yellow.

VOICE The song is a loud, three or four syllabled whistle, with the emphasis on the first note, giving the onomatopoeic local name in Costa Rica, *chin-cheer-gwee* or *chin-cheery-gwee*. Sometimes the entire song is given by one bird, but frequently the pair sing antiphonally, the male providing the first two or three notes, the female the last one, so perfectly co-ordinated that the whole appears to be one song from one individual. Recently fledged birds will sometimes produce a quite different song, a low diffuse rambling reminiscent of a Grey Catbird *Dumetella carolinensis* (Skutch 1960) and unpaired males appear to have a softer, less strident song. Calls, a sharp loud *churr*, other harsh rasping notes and a rippling tinkling *chi-chi-chik* (Howell & Webb 1995).

HABITAT Edges of forests, roadsides, overgrown gardens and farmland and other similar disturbed habitats in both humid and dry areas; avoids dense wet forest. Sea-level to 2,000m.

HABITS Secretive and furtive; would be much overlooked but for the song. Forages low down in dense vegetation, rarely coming to the tops of bushes, although sometimes it will feed quite high up in trees. Flight is weak and always low down. Lives in mated pairs throughout the year, the birds constantly maintaining contact vocally; apparently territorial throughout the year. Roosts singly, in nests built specially for this purpose. Juvenile birds may roost in the open or in the nests of other species until a dormitory nest is constructed.

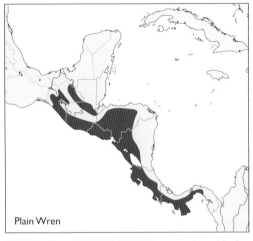

Plain Wren

STATUS AND DISTRIBUTION From southern Mexico (extreme eastern Oaxaca, Chiapas), coastal and central Guatemala (avoiding wet lowland forest areas), El

Salvador (except extreme western area), Honduras and Nicaragua (mostly on drier Pacific drainage, absent from humid Caribbean lowlands), Pacific sides of Costa Rica and Panama to Río Bayano. Quite common in suitable habitat over most of its range.

BREEDING Builds two types of nests. Dormitory nests are an extremely thin-walled and flimsy cylindrical constructions, about 7cm in diameter and 10–15cm in length, made of grasses and fine plant fibres with no lining, at a height of 0.3–2m above the ground. The construction is so flimsy that the bird may make an emergency exit by simply forcing its way out through the back (Skutch 1960). The breeding nest is much more substantial, made of grasses and fibres and lined with plant down. In form it is elliptical with the short axis horizontal, with a circular slightly downward-facing entrance, protected above by an extension of the roof forming something of a lintel. Concealed usually in dense vegetation, 0.5–3m above the ground. Breeding season in Costa Rica very protracted, from January through to

September; in El Salvador nesting recorded July to September. Eggs two, rarely three, white without markings. Incubation by female alone, 18 days; fledgling period probably 14 days or more.

FOOD Mainly invertebrate, insects and spiders; however, an adult was seen to feed a fledgling with a berry (Skutch 1960). In El Salvador it has been caught in mousetraps baited with cornmeal, although it is possible that the birds were in fact after insects feeding on the bait (Dickey & Van Rossem 1938). Has been seen to attack the eggs of the Dusky Antbird, though more probably as an attempt to reduce competition (as in the Marsh Wren) than as a source of food (Fleischer & Tarr 1995).

MOVEMENTS Appears to be totally sedentary.

MEASUREMENTS (*T. m. elutus*) Wing of male 58.1–60.9, of female 53.4–56.7; tail 45.6–51.2, of female 42.0–49.5; bill of female 18.1–18.9, of female 17.1–18.9; tarsus of male 23.0–24.8, of female 21.6–23.0 (Wetmore *et al.* 1984).

---

53   CANEBRAKE WREN
Thryothorus zeledoni

Plate 12

Thryothorus zeledoni Ridgway 1878 Talamanca, Costa Rica.

Alternative names: Zeledon's Wren

The taxonomy of this wren, found on the Caribbean coast from Nicaragua to Panama, is presently unresolved; it may simply be a well-marked race of the Plain Wren.

IDENTIFICATION Length 14cm. Very similar to the Plain Wren, but substantially larger, and much more grey, with little rufous on tail and rump, the flanks light olive-brown instead of fulvous. Bill and feet more robust than in the Plain Wren.

DESCRIPTION
Adult Crown, back and rump grey, becoming olivaceous on rump and uppertail-coverts. Wing-coverts brownish-grey. Rectrices olivaceous-brown with conspicuous blackish bars, 10–12, becoming broader and more prominent near tip of tail. Primaries dull greyish-brown, the outerwebs with darker markings giving about ten diffuse, inconspicuous darker bars on closed wing. Conspicuous white supercilium, contrasting with darker eye-stripe. Ear-coverts mottled grey and off-white. Chin, throat and underparts off-white, with chest becoming greyer, especially at sides; belly pale greyish-buff, lower flanks darker grey. Vent and undertail-coverts with buffy tinge. Iris grey-brown, upper mandible black, lower mandible grey, legs dark olive.
Juvenile Very similar to adult; facial markings less distinct, barring on wings even more obscure, underparts duller.

GEOGRAPHICAL VARIATION None, monotypic.

VOICE Song different from Plain Wren; lower-pitched and more throaty, also gives a series of rich or harsh slurred whistles (Stiles & Skutch 1989). Given the uncertainty of the taxonomy of the Canebrake Wren,

vocalisations and interspecific response to playback would obviously be a fertile field of study.

HABITAT Scrubby second growth, overgrown farmlands and roadsides and wild cane-brakes, avoiding virgin forest. To lower altitudes than the Plain Wren.

HABITS Much as Plain Wren; spends most of its time in dense cover. Relatively little studied.

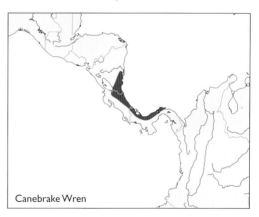

Canebrake Wren

STATUS AND DISTRIBUTION Quite common in the Caribbean drainage of Central America, from eastern and southern Nicaragua (Greytown; Los Sabalos) through Costa Rica to Panama (Bocas del Toro and Colón).

BREEDING One nest in Panama was an elliptical ball of long slender plant fibres (apparently aerial rootlets, mixed with fine grass stems and a lesser amount of broad-bladed grass) measuring 12 x 16cm. The entrance hole in the end was underneath so that it was sheltered

159

(Wetmore 1984). Eggs undescribed, incubation and fledging periods unknown.

FOOD Undescribed.

MOVEMENTS Apparently totally sedentary.

MEASUREMENTS Wing of male 62.3–65.0, of female 60.0–63.3; tail of male 49.4–53.9, of female 48.5–51.5; bill of male 17.4–21.5, of female 17.4–21.5; tarsus of male 24.2–25.8, of female 24.2–25.8 (Wetmore *et al.* 1984).

Taxonomy of the *Thryothorus leucotis* superspecies

Currently four closely related species are recognised. These are *Thryothorus leucotis* (Buff-breasted Wren), *T. guarayanus* (Fawn-breasted Wren), *T. longirostris* (Long-billed Wren) and *T. superciliaris* (Superciliated Wren).

All are lowland species, with some differences in habitat preference; for example *leucotis* is usually closely associated with water and *superciliaris* is a relatively arid-country species. There is by no means a consensus regarding the taxonomy of the group.

Leucotis and *guarayanus* may be conspecific; however, there is no evidence of intergradation between the two forms. Alternatively the race *T. leucotis rufiventris* has been raised to full specific rank (Carriker 1935) while merging *leucotis* and *guarayanus*. In eastern South America intermediate specimens between *T. leucotis rufiventris* and *T. longirostris bahiae* exist, raising questions as to the validity of *longirostris* as a good species. *T. superciliaris* is, uniquely, geographically isolated from other members of the superspecies by the Andes.

54 BUFF-BREASTED WREN
Thryothorus leucotis   Plate 12

Thryothorus leucotis Lafresnaye 1845 'In Colombia aut Mexico' (probably Río Magdalena, Colombia).

Alternative names: Spanish *Cucarachero Flanquileonado, Soterrey Pechanteado*; Portuguese *Garrinchao-de-barriga-vermelha, Marido-e-dia*; French *Troglodyte à Face Pale*; Creole *Rossignol*; Suriname *Busigadofowru*

The most widely distributed and by far the best-known species of the *leucotis* superspecies group, found from Central Panama to south-eastern Brazil.

IDENTIFICATION Length 14–14.5cm. In various parts of its range overlaps with a number of other *Thryothorus* species. In Panama there is a limited area of sympatry (in the general area of the Canal) with Plain Wren, which has less distinct barring on wings and tail and is largely white, not buff, below; in South America, there is wide sympatry with Coraya Wren (heavy black markings on side of face and no barring on wings) and Moustached Wren (strong malar stripe, grey nape and unbarred wings). Stripe-throated Wren (some overlap in Colombia and Panama) and Rufous-breasted Wren (sympatric in Venezuela and eastern Colombia) both have heavy markings on throat. Most closely resembles Fawn-breasted, Long-billed and Superciliated Wrens (qq.v for distinctions). Other *Thryothorus* wrens in its range are totally distinct. Southern House Wren is substantially smaller with less conspicuous supercilia and plain cheeks.

DESCRIPTION *T. l. leucotis*
Adult Crown, nape, shoulders and upper back uniform greyish-brown, becoming warmer laterally; warm orange-brown on rump and uppertail-coverts. Rectrices dull reddish-brown with 10–12 blackish bars, extending across whole width of tail and becoming wider and more conspicuous near tip. Wing-coverts greyish-brown with narrow blackish bars; primaries and secondaries conspicuously barred with buff-brown and blackish, giving an overall barred appearance to the closed wing. Lores greyish, supercilium white, eye-stripe grey-brown. Ear-

coverts mottled grey-brown and off-white. Chin and throat off-white, becoming buffy on chest and cinnamon on belly. Lower flanks and undertail-coverts deeper cinnamon-buff. Iris dusky-brown, upper mandible black, lower mandible whitish or bluish-flesh colour, legs grey or leaden blue.

Juenile Facial markings more diffuse than in adult.

GEOGRAPHICAL VARIATION
T. l. leucotis 'White-eared Wren' (Colombia, from Santa Marta westwards to the Río Sinu and south into the Magdalena valley) Described above.

T. l. venezuelanus 'Venezuelan Wren' (northern Colombia east of Santa Marta and western Venezuela east to Cojedes) Similar to *leucotis* but less rufescent and underparts paler.

T. l. albipectus 'White-breasted Wren' (eastern Venezuela, the Guianas, north-eastern Brazil east to Maranhão and south to Mato Grosso) Very variable in tone; generally similar to *venezuelanus* but upperparts less deeply rufous.

T. l. zuliensis 'Zulia Wren' (Venezuela [Zulia, Táchira and Mérida] and adjacent parts of Colombia) Similar to *venezuelanus* but colours, especially of upperparts, more intense.

T. l. hypoleucus 'White-bellied Wren' (north-central Venezuela [Guárico, Apure to Cojedes and Bolívar]) Similar to *albipectus* but underparts paler, upperparts less rufescent and more olivaceous.

T. l. rufiventis 'Rufous-bellied Wren' (central and east-central Brazil [southern Maranhão, Piauí, western Minas Gerais and São Paulo, Goias]) Similar to *albipectus* but bill longer, underparts except throat deep ochraceous.

T. l. bogotensis 'Villavicencio Wren' (central Venezuela and eastern Colombia) Similar to *venezuelanus* but upperparts more rufescent and underparts darker.

T. l. peruanus 'Peruvian Wren' (eastern Peru south to Junín, western Brazil [Amazonas, south of the Amazon]; eastern Ecuador and south-eastern

Colombia) Similar to *albipectus* but smaller with shorter tail; underparts darker, upperparts duller. Duller than *bogotensis* with underparts less ochraceous.

T. l. collinus (restricted to Serrania de Macuira, Guajira, Colombia)

T. l. conditus 'San Miguel Wren' (Islands of Rey, San Miguel and Viveros [Pearl Islands] and Coiba Island [Panama]) Similar to *leucotis* but slightly larger and deeper in colour. Underparts much deeper buff, colour much deeper and more extensive.

T. l. galbraithii 'Galbraith's Wren' (eastern Panama, from about the Canal eastwards into north-western Colombia) Similar to *conditus* but smaller and more pale.

VOICE Song is a complex series of abrupt sharp notes with numerous short clear whistles, up to a dozen notes per motif, repeated numerous times. Phrases tend to end in a downward slur, in contrast to the somewhat similar song of the Plain Wren, which frequently rises at the end. This song is made up of closely interwoven antiphonal synchronised elements from the male and the female, each sex singing its specific phrase, clearly distinct from that of its mate. The phrases from each sex are within the same frequency range, in contrast to species (such as Rufous-and-white Wren) when male and female sing simultaneously, where the song of the female is at a higher pitch (Farabaugh 1987). Fledged young, which remain with their parents for a prolonged time, also sing; juvenile males acquire a male song-type and antiphonate with their mothers, juvenile females correspondingly with their fathers (Farabaugh 1987). It is hypothesised that this cooperative song behaviour is a result of a high population density (in comparison to such related species as Rufous-and-white Wren which is less densely spaced), giving a more effective territorial defence (Morton 1980). Call is a distinctive rapid incisive *chit-cho* or *chit-cho-cho* (Hilty & Brown 1986); also *chunk*.

HABITAT Thickets and brush in forests and forest edge. Frequently associated with water, more so than Coraya Wren. In northern Venezuela largely confined to gallery forest (Morton 1980) and flooded areas (Schafer & Phelps 1954); in Amazonia, largely confined to *várzea* (seasonally flooded) forest; in Panama, where it is sympatric with Plain Wren, it is largely separated from that species by its preference for wetter habitat (Eisenmann 1950). Sea-level to 950m in Venezuela, but only to 300m in Ecuador (Ridgely & Greenfield 2001).

HABITS Skulks in vegetation and is not easy to see. Usually found in pairs or frequently in family parties, all members of which will physically participate in territorial defence (Morton 1980). Rarely in association with other species. Forages especially in subcanopy vines, in contrast to the sympatric Rufous-and-white Wren

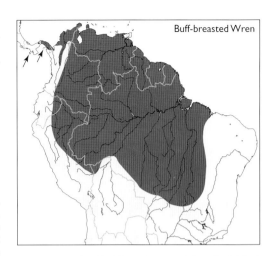
Buff-breasted Wren

which is mainly a leaf-litter forager, giving diminished competition in the same habitat. Allopreening frequent.

STATUS AND DISTRIBUTION Over much of its range fairly common within its preferred habitat, which may be quite restricted to wetter areas. Panama, from about the Canal Zone eastwards, including some offshore islands on the Pacific side; northern Colombia including the Magdalena valley, north of Venezuela except the region around the Paría peninsula, the Guianas, northeastern Brazil to Maranhão, south Minas Gerais, west to Amazonian Peru (Junín), eastern Ecuador, lowland Colombia and northern Bolivia to east of the Andes.

BREEDING Builds multiple nests. Nest height 1m or more, built by both sexes, a globular structure of dead leaves and grasses with a short access tunnel, located frequently in palms (S. Farabaugh, B. T. Thomas pers. comm.). Eggs white with small brown spots. Incubation by both sexes, period not known; fledging period also unknown. Nesting recorded in Suriname from January through September (Haverschmidt 1968); in Venezuela January, May and June (Schafer & Phelps 1954, B. T. Thomas pers. comm). Frequently parasitised by the Striped Cuckoo *Tapera naevia*.

FOOD In Suriname, insects of the order Coleoptera; Hymenoptera, Hemiptera, Lepidoptera and Diptera (Haverschmidt 1968); in Panama, caterpillars, spiders and pseudoscorpions (Wetmore 1984).

MOVEMENTS Apparently sedentary.

MEASUREMENTS (*T. l. galbraithii*) Wing of male 62.0–65.4, of female 58.0–60.9; tail of male 41.0–44.3, of female 37.6–41.1; bill of male 18.5–20.6, of female 17.0–19.6; tarsus of male 23.2–24.9, of female 22.3–24.3 (Wetmore *et al.* 1984).

55   SUPERCILIATED WREN
Thryothorus superciliaris   Plate 12

Thryothorus superciliaris Lawrence 1869, Piura Island, Ecuador.

Alternative name: Spanish *Soterrey Cejón*

The western representative of the superspecies, restricted to the Pacific slopes of Ecuador and Peru.

IDENTIFICATION Length 14.5cm. Most closely

resembles Buff-breasted Wren, from which it differs by its white chest and lack of markings on ear-coverts; the two birds are not sympatric, being both lowland species on opposite sides of the Andes. Speckle-breasted Wren occurs in lowland western Ecuador, but is immediately distinguished by its heavily-marked underparts and cheeks and lack of prominent white supercilia.

DESCRIPTION *T. s. superciliaris*
Adult Crown dark greyish-brown, contrasting with more rufous-brown back and shoulders; rump more rufescent. Rectrices reddish-brown with about nine sharply demarcated black transverse bars across whole tail. Lores grey; prominent white supercilium extending beyond ear-coverts. Eye-stripe dark brown. Ear-coverts buffy-white. Chin and throat pale buffy-white, becoming slightly darker on lower chest and buff-grey on flanks. Primaries brownish-black on innerwebs; outerwebs warm brown with black markings, giving narrow sharply demarcated black bars across closed wings and tertials. Underwing-coverts greyish. Iris brown, upper mandible black, lower mandible grey with dark tip, legs grey.
Juvenile Very similar to adult: crown duller and paler, colour of back somewhat less warm.

GEOGRAPHICAL VARIATION
T. s. superciliaris (western Ecuador, from Manabí south to Guayas) Described above.
T. s. baroni 'Baron's Wren' [south-eastern Ecuador [El Oro, Loja], south through western Peru to Ancash] More rufescent than *superciliaris*, back and rump brighter tawny, flanks and undertail-coverts darker.

VOICE Song is a series of short phrases of two or three notes, repeated frequently, sometimes extending into longer phrases, with some trilling notes; not as rich or musical as that of the Buff-breasted Wren. No data as to whether it duets or sings antiphonally, but this seems at least likely (K. Barker pers. comm.).

HABITAT Much less wedded to humid habitats than the other three members of the superspecies; dry woodland, arid scrub, hedgerows and brushy areas in farmland, less commonly in more humid woodland undergrowth. Sea-level to 1,500m, locally to 1,850m (Ridgely & Greenfield 2001).

HABITS Generally skulking, feeding low down or actually on the ground, usually in pairs; more easily observed than some other members of the genus, mainly because of the sparser nature of its habitat.

STATUS AND DISTRIBUTION Uncommon to fairly

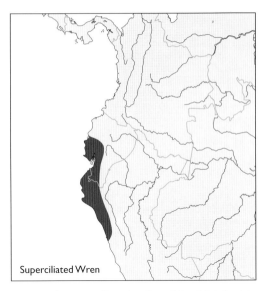

Superciliated Wren

common in range; Ecuador, from Manabí, inland to Pichincha, south to the Peruvian border in El Oro and Loja; Peru from Tumbes and Piura south to Ancash.

BREEDING Nest is a somewhat flimsy retort-shaped construction with a lateral entrance covered by a long frayed porch, sited in a variety of trees and bushes, from 1.6–3.2m above the ground. Numerous nests are built. Occupied nests are lined with fine material and feathers. Frequently located in proximity to wasps' nests; occasionally sited under roofs of old buildings. Eggs two or three, white with a slightly greenish tinge. Two nests with eggs in western Peru, 29 January and 20 February (Taczanowski 1884). Incubation period unknown, fledging period probably 10–13 days (in a nest shared by a young Shiny Cowbird *Molothrus bonariensis*). Cowbird parasitism was very common in a study area in Ecuador, five out of five nests in one year, and one or two of three in another, being so affected (Marchant 1960). May be double-brooded.

FOOD Nothing recorded; presumably mainly or entirely invertebrate. Stomach contents insects.

MOVEMENTS Apparently sedentary.

MEASUREMENTS Wing of male 63–67, of female 63–65; tail of male 42–49, of female 42–46; exposed culmen of male 18–22, of female 21; tarsus of male 24–26, of female 24.5.

---

56   FAWN-BREASTED WREN
Thryothorus guarayanus   **Plate 12**

Troglodytes guarayana Lafresnaye and d'Orbigny 1837, Guarayos, Santa Cruz, Bolivia.

A little-known species largely confined to lowland Bolivia. Although it is not uncommon in parts of its range, virtually nothing has been published about its life-history and habits. Possibly conspecific with the

widely-distributed Buff-breasted Wren *T. leucotis*.

IDENTIFICATION Length 13.5cm. A typical *Thryothorus* wren in shape and form. Extremely similar to the Buff-breasted Wren. Differs from the Peruvian race (*peruanus*) of Buff-breasted by having a more buff, less whitish, throat with upperparts less rufescent and more grey, and with stronger markings on the cheeks. The race of Buff-breasted Wren in south-western Brazil (*rufiventris*) is even more similar, but somewhat larger than Fawn-breasted. The ranges of the two species overlap little, if at all. The taxonomy of the wrens of this group in western-central South America is by no means universally agreed upon (Ridgely & Tudor 1989). Moustached Wren is larger, with greyer nape, black malar stripe, whiter belly and no barring on remiges. Southern House Wren is smaller, without prominent cheek markings.

DESCRIPTION

Adult Crown, nape and back unmarked medium brown, lower back more rufescent and rump and uppertail-coverts reddish-brown. Rectrices reddish-brown with about 10–12 sharply demarcated transverse black bars. Wing-coverts somewhat rufescent-brown with narrow dark blackish bars. Primaries and secondaries reddish-brown with sharp blackish bars, giving about 12–15 conspicuous but narrow bars on closed wing. Narrow white supercilium behind eye. Ear-coverts mottled grey-white and blackish-grey. Narrow blackish malar stripe with white moustache stripe. Chin whitish, becoming orange-buff on throat and warm orange-buff on chest; belly and undertail-coverts deep orange-buff. Obscure dark mottling on throat and upper chest. Underwing-coverts pale orange-buff. Iris hazel, upper mandible black, lower mandible leaden blue, legs leaden blue.
Juvenile Facial pattern less sharply demarcated.

GEOGRAPHICAL VARIATION None: monotypic.

VOICE The song is quite distinct from that of the Buff-breasted Wren, usually being of simple form; two or three clear notes *whiew whiew chuwoh* or *dee-da-deee* repeated numerous times. Not known whether pairs sing antiphonally. Call is a prolonged scolding chatter.

HABITAT Thickets near water and undergrowth in woodland and forest borders (Ridgely & Tudor 1989).

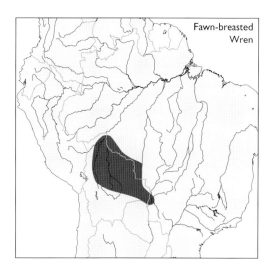

Fawn-breasted Wren

HABITS Little-known, presumably similar to the Buff-breasted Wren.

STATUS AND DISTRIBUTION Within its limited geographic range it appears to be fairly common; since human habitation is fairly sparse over much of its range not, apparently, a cause for concern. Most readily and accessibly seen in the Pantanal of south-western Brazil between Cuiaba and Porto Joffre (Wheatley 1994).

BREEDING Nest and eggs undescribed. Not known whether it breeds cooperatively.

FOOD No information recorded.

MOVEMENTS Presumably sedentary.

MEASUREMENTS Wing of male 60–62, of female 59; tail of male 42–43, of female 39; exposed culmen of male 15–16.5, of female 14; tarsus of male 23–24, of female 21.

57   LONG-BILLED WREN
Thryothorus longirostris
Plate 12

Thryothorus longirostris Vieillot 1818 'Brazil'

Alternative names: Portuguese *Cambaxiera grande*, *garrinchao-de-bico-grande*, *Rouxinol*, *Curruirucu*, *Framato*

A common species in coastal Brazil, the dominant wren species in some habitats.

IDENTIFICATION Length 15cm. Most closely resembles Buff-breasted Wren *T. leucotis* from which it is usually distinguished by its noticeably longer bill and by the more rufescent tone of its underparts. However, the bill length in *longirostris* seems to be a variable character and intermediates between it and *leucotis* occur (see note on taxonomy prior to the account of Buff-breasted Wren). Others sympatric wrens are Moustached, immediately distinguished by its heavily marked cheeks, black malar stripe, grey nape and unmarked wings, and Southern House Wren, much smaller, shorter bill and less prominent supercilium.

DESCRIPTION *T. l. longirostris*
Adult Crown and nape rich dark brown, becoming more rufescent on back and reddish-brown on rump. Very indeterminate narrow dark bars across central back. Rectrices reddish-brown with about 12 black bars, broader toward tip, extending across entire tail. Supercilium off-white. Eye-stripe medium dark brown, lores greyish. Ear-coverts and under eye mottled off-white and dark grey. Narrow black malar stripe. Chin off-white, throat pale buff, chest reddish-buff, belly deep rich buff, the colour stronger on flanks and vent. Primaries and secondaries blackish-brown on innerweb, deep reddish-brown on outerweb with blackish markings, giving sharp narrow black bars on closed wing, strongest and most broad on tertials. Underwing-coverts warm buff. Iris brown or reddish, bill grey-blue, legs dull grey.
Juvenile Very similar to adult; markings on ear-coverts and malar stripe may be less well defined.

163

GEOGRAPHICAL VARIATION

T. l. longirostris (coastal south-eastern Brazil, from extreme eastern Minas Gerais to southern Bahia and northern Paraná) Described above.

T. l. bahiae 'Bahia Long-billed Wren' (north-eastern Brazil [Ceara and eastern Piaui south to northern Bahia and Alagoas]) Paler than *longirostris*, with markings on cheeks less prominent.

VOICE Song loud and varied; a loud *choop-chip-chip, chee-wah-lii*, etc., many times repeated. Males and females sing loud, slightly different phrases, superimposing them in a duet; phrases not as loud as territorial song are repeated by both sexes without synchronisation; warning call *cha-cha-cha-charr*. The phrases of an individual bird may change in the course of a day; according to popular Brazilian belief, in response to the weather (Sick 1993).

HABITAT Forest edge, dense secondary forest, *caatinga*; also mangroves, but less closely associated with water than Buff-breasted Wren. Sea-level to 900m.

STATUS AND DISTRIBUTION In some locations common. Two disjunct populations, north-eastern Brazil (*bahiae*, range above) and coastal southern Brazil (*longirostris*). Status in central Bahia, in between these two ranges, obscure.

BREEDING Nest is a domed construction with a downward sloping entrance port; dormitory nests of a simpler design, with a shallower basket and lacking the entrance

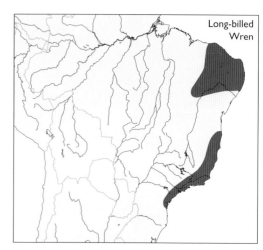

Long-billed Wren

port, are also built (Sick 1993). Eggs undescribed; incubation and fledging periods unknown.

FOOD No data; presumably mainly or entirely invertebrate.

MOVEMENTS Presumably sedentary.

MEASUREMENTS Wing of male 63–66, of female 59–64; tail of male 52–57, of female 51–55; exposed culmen of male 24–27, of female 21.5–24; tarsus of male 24–26.5, of female 23–25.5.

58   GREY WREN
Thryothorus griseus   Plate 12

Thryophilus griseus Todd, 1925, Hiutanaa, Rio Purus, Amazonas, Brazil.

Alternative name: Amazon Wren

An unusual and aberrant wren found only in a limited area of western Brazil. Although currently placed in the genus *Thryothurus*, its many divergent features – the overall grey plumage, short tail and lack of striking facial markings – suggest that it may merit a genus of its own. Virtually nothing is known about the life-history of this species; information about the nest and breeding strategy for example, would be extremely interesting and might give some clues as to the correct taxonomic position of this wren.

IDENTIFICATION Length 11.5cm. Not likely to be confused with any other wren. Although the plumage is superficially similar to that of the Tooth-billed Wren, which is barely sympatric, the two species are totally different in form, the Grey Wren being plump and short-tailed, the Tooth-billed waif-like and more like a Gnatcatcher than a wren. Grey Wren, on superficial sighting, is more likely to be confused with some of the antbirds than with any other wren. Some sympatric antshrikes (e.g. Bluish-slate Antshrike *Thamnomenes schistogynus* and Plain-winged Antshrike *T. schistaceus*) have basically grey plumage but are larger and without bars on the tail; and some antwrens (e.g. Plain-throated Antwren

Myrmotherula hauxwelli and Leaden Antwren *M. assimilis*) are similar in size, but usually have wing-bars formed by covert-tips, and again, no transverse dark tail-bars. However, all antbirds are simply unwrenlike to the discerning observer, with characteristically-shaped bills and generally different 'jizz'.

DESCRIPTION
Adult Crown, nape, back and rump uniform unmarked dull leaden grey. Rectrices dull grey, with three or four broad, dull, blackish bars. Primaries and secondaries blackish-grey on innerwebs, dull lead-grey on outer, with very obscure bars of darker grey-black. Throat whitish-grey, becoming somewhat darker on chest and slightly buffy on lower belly. Face pattern very featureless; inconspicuous white eye-stripe and obscure mottling on ear-coverts. Underwing-coverts dull grey-white. Iris brown, bill blackish on top, dull horn on lower mandible. Legs dull blue-grey. **Juvenile** Undescribed.

GEOGRAPHICAL VARIATION None; monotypic.

VOICE Song is simpler in form than that of most *Thryothorus* wrens; typically a two or three note phrase, *chu-choww, chu-choww* or *chippit, chippit* repeated numerous times without variation, getting louder as it progresses. Not known whether antiphonal or duet song occurs, an interesting question which might shed light on the correct taxonomic position of the species.

Grey Wren

HABITAT Locally common in tangled undergrowth at edge of *várzea* (periodically flooded) forest and woodland and in overgrown clearings (Ridgely & Tudor 1989).

HABITS Not well known. Usually found in pairs or family parties, foraging in viney tangles. No information about association with other species.

STATUS AND DISTRIBUTION Restricted to western Brazil (Amazonas along Rio Javari, upper Rio Jurna and upper Rio Purus) (Ridgely & Tudor 1989, Sick 1993). Apparently locally common.

BREEDING Nest and eggs not described.

FOOD Presumably mainly or entirely invertebrate.

MOVEMENTS Apparently sedentary.

MEASUREMENTS Wing of male, 57, of female, 53-54; tail of male, 36, of female, 31-34; exposed culmen of male, 14, of female, 14-15; tarsus of male, 21, of female, 20-21.

TROGLODYTES

Very small wrens, wing 45–60mm, bill varying from slightly shorter to slightly longer than the head, straight with decurved tip, rictal bristles obsolete, wing very rounded (seventh and sixth (or eighth to fifth) primaries the longest). Tail fairly short to short, rounded. Legs quite sturdy and long. Plumage rufous-brown to grey-brown, frequently barred but without striking black or white areas. Anywhere from four to more than 13 species, depending on which taxonomy is adopted.

It has been recently suggested on the basis of DNA analysis that the Winter Wren, *Troglodytes troglodytes*, is sufficiently distinct from the purely New World species to warrant its own genus (Rice 1999).

59   WINTER WREN
Troglodytes troglodytes   Plate 13

Motacilla Troglodytes Linnaeus 1758, Sweden.

Alternative names: Wren, Northern Wren, Holarctic Wren; Welsh *dryw*, French *Troglodytes mignon*; German *Zaunkönig*; Dutch *Winterkonig*; Swedish *Gardsmyg*; Russian *Krapivnik*

Note: there is considerable difficulty in choosing an appropriate name for a bird which, to a large section of the English-speaking ornithological world, has always simply been 'the' Wren. None of the possible alternatives is truly satisfactory for all locations where the species occurs, if we exclude the pedantic 'Holarctic Wren'. For the purpose of this work we have settled for the usual name in North America, Winter Wren.

The original 'wren', and the only one to overflow from the ancestral heartland of the family, now found breeding on four continents and three zoogeographic regions with a confusing plethora of subspecies.

IDENTIFICATION Length 9–10cm. In the Old World, unmistakable. In North America it must be distinguished from several other wren species. Confusion is most likely with the House Wren, which is larger and longer-tailed and lacks the heavily-barred warm brown flanks and belly; and with the Sedge and Marsh Wrens which have obvious markings on the back and shoulders and again lack heavily-barred underparts. Other wrens in

North America are obviously distinct in plumage, size and form.

DESCRIPTION *T. t. troglodytes*
Adult Crown dark brown, becoming warmer brown on back and rufous-brown on rump. Obscure narrow dark barring on back, becoming better-defined on rump. Shoulders and wing-coverts rufous-brown with darker barring. Primaries and secondaries dull dark grey-brown, the outerwebs with alternating dark brown and pale buff-brown areas, giving about seven or eight conspicuous bars on closed wing. Rectrices warm rufous-brown with about eight blackish transverse bars. Lores and ear-coverts brown, with a paler supercilium. Chin and throat grey-brown, becoming warmer rufous-brown on belly, and dark rufous-brown, strongly barred with blackish, on lower flanks. Underwing grey-brown. Iris brown, bill and legs light brown.
Juvenile Breast indistinctly mottled, barring on flanks more obscure.

Partial albinism, or leucism, rather rare; one example of a bird with bright yellow legs (Sage 1956).

GEOGRAPHICAL VARIATION A taxonomically very complex species.

   T. t. troglodytes (much of mainland Europe, from Scandinavia and the Urals south to Spain, Portugal, Italy and Greece) Described above.

T. t. indigenus (British Isles except for the areas occupied by the four races below) Darker and duller above and less brightly rufous than *troglodytes*.

T. t. hirtensis (St Kilda, Outer Hebrides, Scotland) Substantially bigger than *indigenus*, more grey-brown above and paler below. Length 10.5–11.5cm.

T. t. zetlandicus (Shetland Islands, Scotland) Darker above and below than *indigenus*.

T. t. fridariensis (Fair Isle, between Orkney and Shetland, Scotland) Paler than *zetlandicus*, less greyish than *hirtensis*.

T. t. hebridensis (Outer Hebrides, Scotland) Similar to *zetlandicus* but more buffy, less heavily barred, bill somewhat weaker and shorter.

T. t. borealis (Faroe Islands) Paler than *zetlandicus*, not as richly coloured above and below, more heavily barred.

T. t. islandicus (Iceland) Large and dark brown, heavily barred, with strong bill.

T. t. koenigi (Corsica and Sardinia) Darker and more earth-brown, less rufous, than *troglodytes*, with heavier barring above and below.

T. t. kabylorum (North Africa from Morocco to Tunisia, Balearic Islands, perhaps southern Spain) Paler above and below than *troglodytes*.

T. t. juniperi (north-western Cyrenaica from the Tocra Pass east to Derna, Libya) Similar to *kabylorum* but bill longer, feet darker-coloured.

T. t. cypriotes (Crete, Rhodes, Cyprus and Near East; recently expanded into Israel [Paz 1987]) More extensively barred below than *juniperi*.

T. t. hyrcanus (Crimea, Caucasus and Iran) Similar to *troglodytes* but more greyish-brown above, paler on throat and more extensively barred below.

T. t. tianschianicus (north-eastern Iran through central Asia to Chinese Turkestan) Distinctly paler and greyer than *hyrcanus*, with fainter barring.

T. t. magrathi (borders of Afghanistan and Pakistan) Densely banded with bars extending over the mantle and breast.

T. t. neglectus (western Himalayas [Gilgit to western Nepal]) Darker than *magrathi* with smoky-brown throat.

T. t. nipalensis (Nepal to Assam and southern Tibet) Similar to *neglectus* but darker.

T. t. talifuensis (Central Sikang to northern Yunnan, north-eastern Burma) Paler than *nipalensis* with reduced barring.

T. t. szetschuanus (southern Shensi and Szechwan, east to Hupeh) More olivaceous than *talifuensis* with heavier barring.

T. t. idius (northern China from southern Jehol to Shantung) Paler and greyer than *szetschuanus*.

T. t. dauricus (eastern Siberia [Buryatia to Amurland], Sakhalin, Manchuria and Korea) Darker than *idius*.

T. t. pallescens (Kommandorskii Islands and Kamchatka) Dull and grey with very long bill.

T. t. kurilensis (northern Kurile Islands [Shasukotan and Ushichi Islands]) Long-billed, but darker than *pallescens*.

T. t. fumigatus (southern Kuriles, Japan) Darker than *idius* or *dauricus* with short bill.

T. t. mosukei (seven islands of Izu, possibly Borodinos) Darker and more reddish-brown than *fumigatus*.

T. t. ogawae (Tanegashima and Yakushima Islands) Darker, duller and more sooty than *fumigatus*.

The above are extracted from Vaurie (1959).

T. t. taivanus (Taiwan [Hartert 1910]) Greyer and less rufous then *mosukei* or *ogawae*.

North American races. Opinions concerning the taxonomy of the North American populations are fluid and varied; for an account of the general confusion in this area, see Hejl & Holmes (2000). Subspecies in the New World fall into three broad groups; larger, longer-billed and paler birds in Alaska and islands, smallest, shortest-billed and uniformly dark-coloured western races and medium, reddish-brown birds with white throats in the east (Pyle 1997).

T. t. hiemalis 'Eastern Winter Wren' (eastern North America from southern Alberta to Newfoundland, south to Minnesota and Massachusetts and in the mountains south to southern Georgia) Differs from *T. t. troglodytes* in being more reddish-buff, less greyish-brown, and with more intensely barred flanks.

T. t. pullus (West Virginia to northern Georgia, in mountains) Shorter bill than *hiemalis*, upperparts more reddish.

T. t. pacificus 'Western Winter Wren' (coastal south-western Alaska to California) Bill short, upperparts dark rufous-brown, throat rufous-brown.

T. t. salebrosus (interior British Columbia to western Montana and eastern Oregon) Upperparts medium-brown with a rufous wash.

T. t. helleri 'Kodiak Wren' (Kodiak Island, Alaska) Bill longer than in *pacificus*, upperparts medium-dark brown.

T. t. meligerus 'Aleutian Wren' (Attu and Buldir Islands, Alaska) Large, bill medium-long, upperparts dull dark dusky brown.

T. t. kiskensis 'Kiska Wren' (Kiska and Little Kiska Islands, Alaska) Similar to *meligerus* but upperparts lighter and less rufescent.

T. t. tanagensis 'Tanaga Wren' (islands of Tanaga, Adak and Atka, Alaska) Similar to *kiskensis*, but wing longer, lower back and rump more rufescent and lighter.

T. t. alascensis 'Alaska Wren' (St George and St Paul, Pribilof Islands) Large, bill medium length, upperparts medium brown, throat and breast medium pale brown.

T. t. petrophilus 'Unalaska Wren' (islands of Unalaska, Amaknak and Akutan, Alaska) Similar to *alascensis* but wing shorter, upperparts more sooty greyish.

T. t. stevensoni 'Stevenson's Wren' (islands of Amuk and Amagat and probably neighbouring islands and western end of Alaska Peninsula) Similar to *petrophilus* but upperparts more greyish and sooty.

T. t. semidiensis 'Semidi Wren' (Semidi Islands, Alaska) Similar to *petrophilus* but upperparts more greyish and somewhat darker.

Numerous other races have been postulated, from Newfoundland to the Aleutian chain.

VOICE Song is a remarkably loud, vehement and prolonged succession of clear notes and trills, usually delivered from low cover, occasionally on the wing and sometimes at night. The song of the race *hiemalis* has been described by Brackenbury as copious, rapid, prolonged and penetrating, having a great variety of the sweetest tones, and uttered in a rising and falling or finely undulating melody. The power output of Winter Wren song, weight for weight, is ten times that of a cockerel (Brackenbury 1982, in Kroodsma & Miller 1982).

Song types vary across North America, western birds having a more complex song type and a more varied repertoire (Kroodsma 1980). Songs from the Aleutian islands and the Kommandorskii Islands are distinctively harsher in tone. By contrast, there is more homogeneity of song type in the Old World (Kroodsma & Momose 1991).

Calls include a variety of hard, sharp *tic-tic* type notes, loud churrings, chitter calls, etc. Sometimes makes an audible snap with the bill. The significance of different calls is fully explored by Armstrong (1955).

HABITAT Very varied. In Britain it is very general, being found in habitats ranging from deciduous woodland, suburban gardens, moorland scrub and offshore islands with very scanty vegetation; the most favourable habitats, however, are damp deciduous or mixed woodlands with much undergrowth. In other parts of the Old World the habitat requirements are more restrictive; for example, in the Atlas Mountains most breed in stream valleys or forests at 1,200–1,800m (Cramp 1988). In North America, primarily breeds in moist coniferous forests with extensive undergrowth, but also in hardwood or mixed hardwood-conifer stands; also on treeless offshore islands (Hejl & Holmes 2000).

HABITS Not especially shy, particularly in suburban situations where birds are habituated to human presence. Spends most of time in dense vegetation close to the ground, frequently disappearing into masses of closely-tangled branches or crevices in decaying logs. Rarely climbs to more than 15m. Usual movement is an incessant series of short hops, the tail usually carried cocked over the back. Flights are usually short and whirring, low to the ground and usually only between adjacent patches of vegetation; speed estimated at about 20kph (Armstrong 1955). Roosts communally in winter,

usually in cavities, sometimes in surprising quantity; while roosts are usually of not more than ten birds (Armstrong & Whitehouse 1977), up to 96 have been found in one roost (Cramp 1988). Roosting birds form layers sitting on each other's backs, heads inwards (Armstrong 1955). Communal roosts also occur in North America, with 31 birds found in one small nestbox during severe weather in Washington state (Bent 1948). Some nests may be built specifically as roosting sites.

For a detailed account of social behaviour and display, see Cramp (1988).

STATUS AND DISTRIBUTION Occurs in Iceland (excluding central lava deserts), Faroes, British Isles, most of continental Europe (except for the northern parts of Norway, Sweden and Finland), North Africa (Morocco, Algeria, northern Tunisia, disjunctly in Libya), most Mediterranean Islands, Turkey and the Levant, Caucasus republics; central Asian republics, northern Iran and Afghanistan, southern Himalayas, eastern Siberia, Japan, China and Taiwan. Populations in north-eastern Europe migratory; less information on Asian populations. North America from Newfoundland, Maritimes and Maine, south in mountains to Georgia, westwards across Quebec and Ontario to British Columbia and Alaska; Aleutian and Pribilof Islands; western United States to central California, Idaho and western Montana. Winters south to Arizona, northern Mexico (Nuevo León) and Florida.

Vagrant in Kuwait, Ustica (Liparian Islands), Madeira; a record of an apparent family party in the Azores (Van Vegten & Schipper 1968) was deemed unacceptable (Cramp 1988). Scarce winter visitor to Malta.

Population is highly variable, suffering catastrophic declines after severe winters, followed by spectacular increases in subsequent years; the total estimated British population has oscillated between one million and ten million (Sharrock 1976). The Winter Wren at normal unreduced population levels is one of the three most widespread species of bird in Britain. Recently colonised Israel (Paz 1987).

Generally abundant and in no danger. Some island races have very small populations, notably *fridariensis* which is confined to the 7.6km² of Fair Isle; censuses have shown the numbers of singing males to vary from a high of about 50 to a low of 10 in 1981. By 1987 this

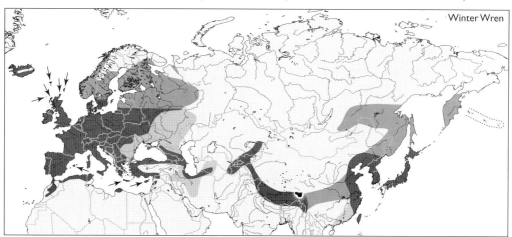

Winter Wren

167

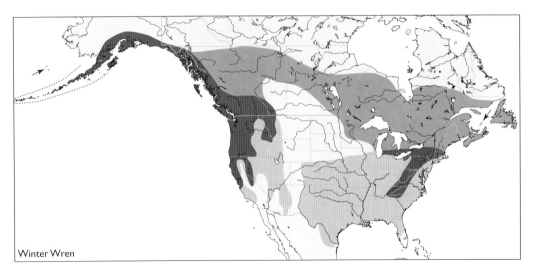

Winter Wren

had increased to over 30 (Aspinall & Aspinall 1987). The designation of the St Kilda Wren as a separate species in 1884 led to a frenzy of collection with skins fetching up to one guinea each, prompting gloomy prognostications of its impending extinction which were probably unfounded (Williamson 1958). Estimated populations have varied, from 68 pairs in 1931, less than 100 in 1927 and 1928, and 233 counted singing males in 1957. Early, very low, estimates were probably inaccurately small, but the population is clearly highly variable. The race *borealis* (Faroe Islands) is estimated 250–500 pairs.

It is generally agreed that the Old World population arose from colonists crossing the Bering Strait. Based on an analysis of song, Kroodsma & Momose (1991) hypothesised that it was an eastern population, not the isolated western one, which colonised Asia; based on a study of ectoparasites, Armstrong (1953) reached precisely the opposite conclusion. Other theories hypothesise two separate invasions of the Old World, giving rise to the European and Asian populations (Hejl & Holmes 2000).

BREEDING Nest is a domed structure of grass, fine leaves, moss etc., lined with feathers and hair, with a side entrance, built primarily by the male with the lining completed by the female. Average dimensions; height 11.3cm, width 13.0cm, depth 14.5cm; internal dimensions height 5.6cm, diameter 6.2cm. Nesting material is often wet when used – as in the dippers – and contracts on drying, giving a compact construction (Armstrong 1955). Nest sites are very variable, in dense vegetation, hollows, crevices, cavities of various kinds including nestboxes and a variety of bizarre locations such as pockets of hanging coats etc. Island races, such as *hirtensis*, very frequently nest in crevices in ruins. Eggs three to nine, usually five to eight, clear white, with small spots of reddish-brown or pale brown concentrated more thickly around larger end; more rarely, nearly immaculate. Eggs of the race *meligerus* of the Aleutians are pure white (Bent 1948). Clutches of up to 17 in one nest may result from two females in a polygamous relationship. Island races tend to lay smaller clutches (Hejl & Holmes 2000). Incubation about 16 days, by

female alone. Young fed by both parents, but brooded only by female. Fledging period 14–19 days, usually about 17; young are cared for for a further 9–18 days after fledging. In Britain, usually double-brooded; in western North America double, perhaps sometimes triple, brooded; in Israel, double-brooded (Paz 1987). Polygyny is frequent in some western European populations – about half the males are polygynous in western races (Cramp 1988) – but apparently less so in most North American populations (Hejl & Holmes 2000).

Males build surplus nests, the numbers of which are variable. In England and Holland the number of nests built per season averaged six to seven; in western North America, one to four. Island races apparently build fewer nests (Armstrong 1955). Female selects nests from those partially built and herself adds lining; only rarely are females involved in construction of main body of nest. Nests may be reused in subsequent years, sometimes by birds other than the builders.

Rather rarely the victim of nest parasites: Brown-headed Cowbird, *Molothrus ater*, in North America and Cuckoos *Cuculus* in the Old World.

FOOD Primarily invertebrates and very varied. Many types of arthropods, especially beetles and spiders, but also grasshoppers, earwigs, moths, woodlice etc. Some small vertebrates such as tadpoles, young frogs and small fish; may immerse head or wade in search of such prey. Sometimes flycatches. Some vegetable matter, e.g. elderberries, raspberries, blueberries and some seeds; also fragments of seaweed. Has been seen to associate with badgers *Meles meles*, opportunistically seizing disturbed prey (Cramp 1988).

MOVEMENTS In the different parts of its range varies from totally sedentary, partial migrant and long-distance migrant. Island races are generally sedentary (although there is one record of a bird of the Shetland race in Aberdeenshire [King 1969] and Iceland and Hebridean birds show local movements). In mainland Britain, most ringing recoveries showing movement of less than 50km are of random orientation, but longer movements show a south-north movement with the seasons. Three birds ringed at Dungeness have been recovered in France,

168

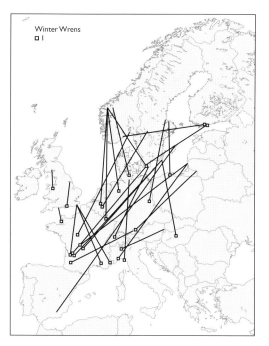

Winter Wrens
□ 1

France, and Lithuania to Bordeaux. Nocturnal movements have been noted at lighthouses in March in Denmark. There is less information about populations further east; wrens are winter visitors to much of the Ukraine and parts of central Asia, and in the coastal strip of China from Shandong to Guandong. North African populations apparently show only altitudinal movement.

In North America, highly migratory: there are only two long-distance banding recoveries, both involving south-westerly displacements, from Massachusetts to Maryland and from Maryland to Alabama. Neither bird was banded on the breeding-ground and both were obviously on migration at the time of capture. Coastal populations in Alaska, British Columbia and the Aleutians are sedentary so far as can be seen, but the remainder of the Canadian population in winter leaves the breeding area entirely, with the exception of a small part of southern Ontario where some birds linger in winter. A winter visitor to Arizona, Nevada and Utah, presumably originating from interior British Columbia and Alberta; and to the south-eastern United States from Florida to Texas (and, very sparsely, to north-eastern Mexico), originating, presumably, from eastern Canadian breeding populations.

MEASUREMENTS (*T. t. troglodytes*) Wing of male 47–52, of female 45–50; tail of male 29–34, of female 28–32; exposed culmen of male 10.1–13.6, of female 9.1–11.1; tarsus of male 17.0–18.3, of female 16.2–17.6.

The northern island races are significantly larger; for *T. t. islandicus* wing of male 56–61, of female 53–59 (Cramp 1988).

one as far south as Marseilles (Hawthorn & Mead 1975). On the continent of Europe some birds make very substantial journeys, generally with a south-westerly orientation in autumn, with ringing recoveries from Sweden to southern Spain, Germany to south-western

Taxonomy of the House Wren group

Apart from the artificially introduced House Sparrow *Passer domesticus*, the House Wren group has the greatest latitudinal breeding range of any passerine, from about 58°N in western Canada to about 55°S in Tierra del Fuego. Within this vast range it occupies a great diversity of habitat, and shows a considerable variation of plumage type. Predictably, opinions as to its taxonomy show an equally wide variation; at one extreme, some authorities have lumped all forms into one species, *Troglodytes aedon*, including in this all mainland and island forms, while others have recognised up to ten distinct species.

On the mainland of North and South America, three forms, the Northern House Wren *T. aedon*, the Brown-throated Wren *T. brunneicollis* and the Southern House Wren *T. musculus* were originally described as separate species (e.g. Oberholser 1904), then later 'lumped' under the one name *T. aedon* (e.g. Paynter 1957). A study of populations of the House Wren and Brown-throated Wren in southern Arizona and northern Mexico (Lanyon 1960) strongly suggested that they were conspecific, apparent differences in song and eggs being inconsistent. However, more recent biochemical analysis (Brumfield & Capparella 1996) suggests that all three species should be resurrected, a course which we have followed in this book. The populations of House Wren in the Lesser Antilles (Guadeloupe to Grenada) known as the '*martinicus*' group may well deserve specific status (AOU 1998). However, in the absence of a comprehensive biochemical study we have followed the practice of Hellmayr (1924–1938) in treating these as races of *T. musculus*, while fully realising that this is very much subject to change. The island forms – *T. beani* on Cozumel, *T. tanneri* on Clarión in the Revillagigedo group and *T. cobbi* in the Falklands have been given full specific status, in accordance with most recent opinion (e.g. Woods 1993, Howell & Webb 1995).

60 NORTHERN HOUSE WREN
Troglodytes aedon   Plate 14

Sylvia domestica, Wilson 1808; suppressed in favour of *Troglodytes aedon* Viellot 1809.

Alternative names: House Wren; Spanish *Saltapared-*

continental Norteño, Saltapared Cucarachero. French *Troglodyte familier*

The most widely distributed and by far the most familiar

of the North American wrens. Since it occurs so frequently in association with Man, and readily uses artificial sites for nesting, it is also one of the best-studied North American passerines.

IDENTIFICATION Length 11.5–12.5cm. Probably only likely to be confused with the Winter Wren, which is a smaller bird with a notably shorter tail and much darker, more brown barred underparts. For distinctions from the Brown-throated Wren and Southern House Wren see under those species.

DESCRIPTION *T. a. aedon*
Adult Crown and nape medium brown, colour becoming warmer and more rufescent on back and rump. Obscure transverse darker barring on back and wing-coverts. Primaries and secondaries grey-brown with alternating buff and dark brown sections on outerweb giving barred appearance to closed wing; barring (of light and dark brown) more prominent on both webs of tertials. Rectrices rufescent-brown with transverse darker markings giving 12–14 bars on closed tail. Sides of face grey-brown with obscure greyish-buff supercilium. Throat, chin and chest buffy-white, becoming rufous-buff on lower belly and flanks. Undertail-coverts barred off-white and dark brown. Underwing-coverts greyish-white. Iris brown, upper mandible dusky-brown, lower mandible pale horn, legs dark brown.
Juvenile Dusky mottling on breast and less distinct barring on the flanks (Pyle 1997).

GEOGRAPHICAL VARIATION
T. a. aedon 'Eastern House Wren' (includes the poorly differentiated *T. a. baldwinii*) (breeds eastern North America, from New Brunswick and Maine westwards through southern Ontario to Lake Superior, south to Tennessee and the Carolinas; winters eastern USA and the Gulf of Mexico lowlands, possibly to Veracruz, Mexico) Described above.
T. a. parkmanii 'Western House Wren' (western Ontario to British Columbia, south to northern Baja California, east to western Kentucky; winters across southern US and Mexico) Rather larger, and more pale and more grey than *aedon*.

VOICE The song is a sharp series of extremely rapid, loud notes, 15–20 in number, initially almost on one pitch then falling at the end, the whole sequence taking two to three seconds. Lacks the sweetness and variety of the song of the Winter Wren. Both sexes sing, at least in some populations (Johnson 1998), the songs of the females generally being shorter, although a small proportion of females produce songs which are identical to that of the male. Call notes harsh churring and rattling, also various high-pitched squeaks. Rarely mimics; one record of a House Wren giving mixed songs of its own species and that of Carolina Wren.

HABITAT Semi-open country with bushes and brushy areas; farmland, provided there are major areas of thick hedgerow, abandoned agricultural areas which are partially grown over. Adapts well to modified habitat, including suburban areas which have substantial quantities of bush and low trees. Generally absent from the interiors of dense woodland, though frequent in wood-edge. In western North America found in open deciduous and coniferous woodland. Sea-level to 3,000m.

HABITS Not particularly secretive. Feeds generally low down, and flights are usually short and low. Moves rapidly among tangled vegetation, the tail frequently cocked. Singing males are particularly bold, often singing from conspicuous perches; males frequently choose a song-perch within a few metres of an occupied nest. The tendency of House Wrens to destroy the eggs and young of other species, both cavity and open nesters, has been well-known for many years, occasioning vituperative attack in the literature (e.g. Sherman 1925). Numerous species have been known to be the subject of this predation; experimentally, House Wrens have destroyed quail eggs in artificial open nests placed near their own. Eggs so attacked are not eaten. Circumstantial evidence suggests that the decline of Bewick's Wren in eastern North America may be linked to House Wren predation; at least, in several areas, the disappearance of the one and the appearance of the other have occurred simultaneously (Kennedy & White 1997, Johnson 1998). In some areas, destruction or usurpation of nest-sites by House Wrens may be the primary source of nesting failure for some cavity-nesting species, such as Prothonotary Warbler *Prothonotaria citrea* (Johnson 1998). Adult House Wrens have also been suspected of killing other adults of their own species, perhaps to steal their nest-sites (Belles-Isles & Picman 1987). Numerous reports of House Wrens feeding the young of other species, especially, but not exclusively, those in cavity nests.

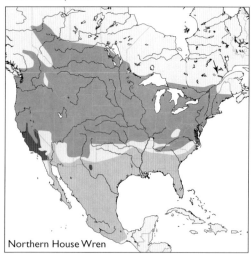
Northern House Wren

STATUS AND DISTRIBUTION Over much of its range, common or abundant in suitable habitat; for example, estimated at greater than 1,000 breeding pairs per 10km^2 in parts of Ontario (Cadman *et al.* 1987). Territories may be less than 1ha in extent (Bent 1948). Eastern North America, breeds from western New Brunswick (at least formerly) and Maine across southern Ontario, Manitoba and Saskatchewan, Alberta east of the Rockies north to about 58°N, interior British Columbia, southern Vancouver Island; south to South Carolina, Kentucky, northern Texas and New Mexico, coastal California and northern Baja California to about 30°N. Winters almost entirely south of the breeding range (save in California and Baja California); from the Carolinas across the southern United States to Arizona and California; and over most of Mexico as far south as Oaxaca. Vagrant in western Cuba, the Bahamas, Newfoundland and as far north as Churchill, Manitoba.

The range of the species has increased substantially with the clearing of dense forest for agriculture and settlement; for example, colonised western West Virginia by late 1800s, North Carolina by the 1920s, South Carolina by the 1940s. Range expansion has continued until recently, perhaps aided by the provision of nestboxes. Breeding Bird Survey data show a significant increase in numbers (e.g. an estimated annual increase over 30 years of 1.6% per annum [Johnson 1998]).

BREEDING A cavity nester; natural cavities include old woodpecker holes and other tree cavities, but readily takes to nestboxes and other artificial sites. Has also been recorded as using the nests of paper-wasps as nest-sites (after removing some of the interior structure), disused pendant nests of Northern Orioles *Icterus galbula*, mud nests of Cliff Swallows *Hirundo pyrrhonota*, the riverbank burrows of Belted Kingfishers *Megaceryle alcyon*, and in the bases of Osprey *Pandion haliaetus* nests. In many areas artificial sites now house the great majority of nests. Cavities are always filled with a base of coarse twigs until the hole is largely filled; nestboxes are always filled to within 2–3cm of the top. Sometimes other material such as rusted wire, old nails etc. may be used as well as twigs. Males may stake a claim to unoccupied nest sites by dropping a few twigs in through the hole. The foundations of the nest are built by the male, but after pairing, the female finishes the stick platform and builds a nest cup lined with feathers, hair or wool. Eggs four to eight, rarely three to ten, white or pinkish or greyish-white, with small spots or blotches of reddish-brown or lavender. Incubation by female only, 12–14 days. Males feed the sitting females only rarely. Young fed by both sexes; fledging period 16–18 days. Fledged young are fed by parents up to a further 13 days after leaving the nest. Double-brooded over much of the United States range; single-brooded at higher altitudes and in north of range. Occasionally triple-brooded in south. Males may build multiple nests that are not used.

Although the majority of males are monogamous, in some populations at least substantial levels of polygyny do occur, especially if surplus nest-sites are available. Mated males may advertise for secondary females by song. Generally secondary females are not as successful in rearing young as the primary female, who enjoys the assistance of the male in feeding the young (Johnson *et al.* 1993); nevertheless some females seem to choose as a mate an already mated bird, notwithstanding the availability of unmated males (Johnson *et al.* 1994). Experimental removal of males from normally mated pairs does not normally result in lower success rate,

suggesting that the absence of male help is only crucial during the first few days of the nestling period (Bart & Tornes 1989).

FOOD Predominantly invertebrate; caterpillars, grasshoppers, beetles, leafhoppers, bugs (Hemiptera) and spiders. Only 2% vegetable matter (Bent 1948).

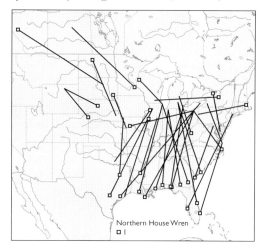

Northern House Wren

MOVEMENTS Highly migratory; only present throughout the year in southern California. Winter grounds are deserted by late April or early May in southeastern United States, earlier in Mexico. Arrives at northern end of breeding-range (e.g. in southern Ontario) in mid-May. Data from building and tower kills indicate that it is a nocturnal migrant.

Data from banding encounters show that birds nesting in the coastal areas of eastern North America (from New York to Delaware) winter in Florida. Birds from east of the Appalachian chain winter in a broader area, from Florida and Georgia as far west as eastern Texas, birds from the western end of this area tending to winter further west with a greater westerly longitudinal displacement than those from further east; there are, however, a couple of recoveries showing major westerly displacements of more eastern birds, for example from southern Ontario to Texas. Birds from the Prairie Provinces and Great Plains have, by contrast, a strongly south-easterly displacement in winter. There are no significant long-distance recoveries from western North America (data from Bird-banding Laboratory and Canadian Wildlife Service).

MEASUREMENTS Wing of male 49–53, of female 47–53; tail of male 40–44, of female 39–43; exposed culmen of male 11–13, of female 12–13; tarsus of male 16.5–18.5, of female 17–18 (Ridgway 1904).

---

61 BROWN-THROATED WREN
Troglodytes brunneicollis

Plate 14

Troglodytes brunneicollis Sclater 1858. La Parada, six leagues from Oaxaca, Mexico.

Alternative names: Spanish *Saltapared-continental Goricafé*, *Sonajita*

The 'House Wren' of highland areas of most of Mexico, marginally occurring in southern Arizona.

IDENTIFICATION Length 11.5–12.5cm. In the breeding season allopatric from Northern House Wren. However, that species occurs over much of Mexico in winter. Brown-throated Wren differs by having a distinctly buff eye-stripe, a more rusty, less grey, back, buffier underparts and small dark spots on sides of breast.

DESCRIPTION *T. b. brunneicollis*
Adult Crown dark greyish-brown, becoming warmer brownish on back and rufous-brown on rump; back and upper rump with obscure darker transverse bars. Primaries and secondaries grey-brown, the outerwebs with alternating blackish-brown and medium-brown sections, giving 8–10 conspicuous bars on closed wing, the barring extending across both webs of the tertials. Ear-coverts mottled grey-brown. Chin and throat greyish-brown, becoming warmer brown on chest, with rufous-brown flanks. Rectrices warm brown, with 15–17 darker transverse bars. Underwing greyish-brown. Iris dark brown, bill and legs brown.
Juvenile Feathers on crissum loosely textured; underparts with some darker mottling.

GEOGRAPHICAL VARIATION
T. b. brunneicollis (central and southern Mexico, from San Luis Potosí and Hidalgo south to Oaxaca) Described above.
T. b. cahooni 'Cahoon's Wren' (southern Arizona to the central part of the Mexican plateau) Similar to *brunneicollis* but paler below, greyer above, and with flanks less heavily barred. Includes *T. b. vorheisi*.
T. b. nitidus 'Zempoaltepec Wren' (humid forests of Mount Zempoaltepec, Oaxaca) Similar to *brunneicollis* but deeper in colour.

VOICE Song is very similar to that of the Northern House Wren, sometimes with an additional high trill at the beginning. Also a bright springy trill, suggesting Rock Wren (Howell & Webb 1995).

HABITAT Mountain forests of Ponderosa and other species of pine, mixed pine-oak woodlands, and mountain oak forests and forest edge, 1,600–3,000m.

HABITS Do not differ substantially from those of the Northern House Wren.

STATUS AND DISTRIBUTION Over much of its range

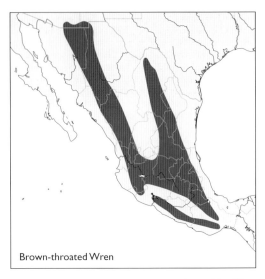

Brown-throated Wren

common in suitable habitat. Arizona: Santa Rita, Huachuca and possibly other ranges (with much controversy over taxonomy [Phillips *et al.* 1964]); south at suitable altitudes through the Sierra Madre Occidental and Oriental to the central Mexican plateau and northern Oaxaca; disjunctly, Sierra Madre del Sur in the states of Guerrero and Oaxaca.

BREEDING Nests in cavities. Nest and eggs of the nominate race apparently not described. Nests of the race *cahooni* (*vorheisi*) in southern Arizona have been located in holes in oaks and sycamores, 5–10m above the ground. In spite of numerous statements to the contrary, the nest and eggs do not differ in any consistent way from those of admitted House Wrens further north in Arizona (Marshall 1956, Lanyon 1960).

FOOD Little specific information; presumably similar to that of Arizona populations of House Wren.

MOVEMENTS No information; may show altitudinal movements.

MEASUREMENTS Wing of male 50–53, of female 49–52; tail of male 40–44, of female 41–44; exposed culmen of male 11.5–14, of female 12–13; tarsus of male 18.5–20, of female 18–20.

---

62 SOUTHERN HOUSE WREN
Troglodytes musculus

Plate 14

Troglodytes musculus Naumann 1823, Bahia, Brazil.

Alternative names: (West Indies) God-bird; French *Oiseau Bon Dieu*; Spanish *Ratonera*, *Cucarachero común*; Portuguese *Cambaxirra*; (Suriname) *Gadofowroe*

A species with a huge geographic distribution, from southern Mexico and the West Indies all the way through South America to Cape Horn, with a bewildering variety of subspecies occurring in the most diverse habitats. Over most of the West Indies, it is known in dialect as

'God-bird' in several languages; conversely, in Brazil, it is regarded as an omen of ill-luck.

IDENTIFICATION Length 11.5–12.5cm. A rather plain, featureless wren, smaller than most members of the genus *Thryothorus* and lacking the facial patterns found in most members of that genus and in the wood wrens. Mountain Wren may overlap in some habitats in northeastern South America; Northern House Wren is less warmly rufous, and lacks an obvious buffy eye-stripe.

DESCRIPTION *T. m. musculus*

Adult Crown greyish-brown, becoming warm brown on back and rufous-brown on rump. Shoulders and wing-coverts rufous-brown with darker transverse bars. Primaries and secondaries dull grey-brown, the outer-webs alternately warm buff-brown and dark brown, giving 8–10 conspicuous bars on closed wing; bars extend across both webs of tertials. Rectrices rufous-brown with about 15 darker transverse bars. Lores and ear-coverts grey-brown, very obscure paler postocular supercilium. Chin, throat and chest pale buffy-brown, becoming warmer buff on flanks. Underwing buffy-grey. Iris brown, bill dark-brown with paler base, legs brown or pinkish-brown.

Juvenile Conspicuous darker scalloping on underparts from chin to belly.

GEOGRAPHICAL VARIATION

T. m. musculus (most of Brazil, from Ceara south to Matto Grosso; Paraguay: northern Argentina [Missiones]) Described above.

T. m. puna 'Puna House Wren' (Peru, from Cajamarca and San Martín southwards; north-western Bolivia) Larger than *musculus*, underparts deeper cinnamon buff, belly rufous and dorsal surface less rufescent.

T. m. clarus 'Pale-bellied House Wren' (Trinidad, the Guianas, Venezuela, eastern and northern Peru, eastern Colombia, Brazil east of the coast region south to Matto Grosso) Differs from *musculus* by paler underparts.

T. m. tobagensis 'Tobago House Wren' (Tobago) Similar to *clarus* but wings longer, bill heavier, underparts whiter.

T. m. carabayae 'Carabaya House Wren' (central and southern Peru [Junín, Cuzco, Puno]) Similar to *clarus* but underparts more buff, upperparts darker with distinct narrow dusky bars on back.

T. m. striatulus 'Cauca House Wren' (Colombia, from the western slope of the Andes westwards, excluding the Santa Marta area and south-western Colombia) Large size, greyish-brown upperparts, underparts whitish or pale buffy.

T. m. atopus 'Santa Marta House Wren' (Santa Marta region, Colombia) Intermediate between *clarus* and *striatulus* but more deeply ochraceous below than either.

T. m. albicans 'White-bellied House Wren' (south-western Colombia and western Ecuador) Smaller than *striatulus*, upperparts warmer rufous, underparts sandy-coloured.

T. m. columbae 'Colombian House Wren' (eastern Colombia and western Venezuela) Similar to *striatulus* but upperparts darker greyish-brown with fine dusky bars, underparts darker.

T. m. audax 'West Peruvian House Wren' (arid west coast of Peru from Trujillo south to Pisco) Similar to *albicans*, but tail longer and underparts more uniformly ochraceous.

T. m. tecellatus 'Barred-backed House Wren' (extreme south-western Peru and northern Chile) Similar to *audax*, but more greyish above and with distinct broad blackish bars on back.

T. m. chilensis 'Chilean House Wren' (Chile north to Aconcagua Province, south to Tierra del Fuego, and, Argentina south of the Río Colorado. Migrates north in winter as far north as Entre Ríos and Atacama) Similar to *bonariae* but upperparts paler.

T. m. atacamensis 'Atacama House Wren' (northern Chile) Similar to *chilensis*, but bill longer and more slender, with paler upperparts without bars.

T. m. rex 'Bolivian House Wren' (central and eastern Bolivia) Similar to *chilensis* but bill longer and heavier, and underparts a brighter isabelline.

T. m. intermedius 'Costa Rica House Wren' (includes *peninsularis* 'Mangrove Wren' and *oreopolus* 'Nicaraguan House Wren') (Mexico from southern Veracruz to central Costa Rica) Ventral surface uniform deep cinnamon buff.

T. m. inquietus 'Panama House Wren' (Panama as far east as Darién and adjacent Costa Rica [Río Térraba]) Larger than *intermedius*, more grey above and less buff below.

T. m. carychrous (Isla Coiba, Panama) Similar to *inquietus* but much brighter brown throughout.

T. m. mesoleucus 'St Lucia House Wren' (St Lucia, West Indies) Differs from *tobagensis* in being much more rufescent above and white below.

T. m. musicus 'St Vincent House Wren' (St Vincent, West Indies) Larger than *mesoleucus*, more rust-coloured above, the back with obscure darker bars.

T. m. martinicensis 'Martinique House Wren' (Martinique, West Indies; probably extinct) Upperparts dark brown, narrowly lined with black.

T. m. guadeloupensis 'Guadeloupe House Wren' (Guadeloupe, West Indies; present status uncertain) Smaller and more rufescent than *martinicensis*.

T. m. grenadensis 'Grenada House Wren' (Grenada, West Indies) Closest to *guadeloupensis* but larger, paler, no bars on back.

T. m. rufescens 'Dominica House Wren' (Dominica, West Indies) Closest to *grenadensis* but much darker overall; crissum with black bars.

VOICE Song is much like that of Northern House Wren, a rather variable series of rapid notes, the sequence lasting two to three seconds; sometimes preceded by a more leisurely warbling. Populations in southern South America tend to conclude their song with a series of harsh, rising notes (A. Jaramillo pers. comm.). Both sexes sing, but the female song is quite different; a low, rapid *twitting*, followed at times by a slight clear trill (Skutch 1953). Female song usually antiphonal or duetting with male. Call (in Ecuador) is a nasal *jeeyah*, quite different from that of Northern House Wren (Ridgely & Tudor 1989). Alarm call a harsh grating *cloudy-ditch, cloudy-ditch* (Chapman 1929), again quite different from the corresponding call of *aedon*.

HABITAT Extremely varied. In general, all open or semi-open areas, often associated with man; this includes humid lowland areas, quite heavily urbanised situations, montane habitat and arid areas, from sea-level to 4,000m. Generally absent from unbroken forest, but will rapidly colonise clearings and forest edge.

HABITS Active and nervous, but not excessively furtive; although it will disappear very effectively when startled, usually remains nearby, calling harshly. Forages mostly on or near the ground, in tangles of vegetation, but will examine the lower areas of tree-trunks in the manner of a woodcreeper. Males will frequently sing from high exposed perches, though when disturbed they will plummet into cover. Roosts in holes, disused nests and in other protected sites such as inside clumps of bananas.

Southern House Wren

STATUS AND DISTRIBUTION Over most of its wide range common or abundant in suitable habitat; however, since it is not found in unbroken forest the actual overall density in, for example, much of Amazonia may be quite small. Readily adapts to modified habitat and has hence probably increased in recent times. Over most of its range sedentary; however, the extreme southern populations are highly migratory. The winter range of the race *chilensis*, from Tierra del Fuego, extends at least 800km north of the breeding range.

The situation of the endemic populations in the West Indies is, however, quite different. On Dominica it is common, in Grenada common in some areas, on St Vincent uncommon. On Martinique it probably became extinct about 1900; on Guadeloupe it was believed to be extinct since about 1914, but small populations were rediscovered in 1969 and 1973 (Barlow 1978), but it has not been seen since (Raffaele *et al.* 1998). On St Lucia a tiny population remained in 1984 (Graves 1985). In all of these locations the cause of decline or extinction seems to be the usual ones of habitat destruction and introduced predators, especially mongooses.

BREEDING The nest is essentially similar to that of the Northern House Wren; situated in a cavity, frequently an artificial one such as niches in outbuildings. Takes very readily to nestboxes. The base of the nest is a mass of coarse twigs, gradually becoming finer further up. The base is largely made by the male while most of the finishing is done by the female; the male may continue to drop larger twigs into the cavity during this stage, which are then removed by the female. In Colombia, nest sites from 0.5–11m above the ground have been

recorded, but the majority are about 2–3m up (Alvarez-López *et al.* 1984). For a tropical wren, the Southern House Wren is unusually fecund; clutches in Colombia are two to four, most commonly three, with an average of 3.2; one female laid seven clutches, to a total of 20 eggs, in 17 months (in contrast to, for example, the wood wrens whose clutches seem invariably to consist of two eggs only); in Costa Rica, clutches usually four eggs, very rarely five, questionably two (Skutch 1953); in Trinidad four or five (Belcher & Smooker 1937). Eggs whitish, densely flecked all over with fine markings of brown, reddish-brown or cinnamon (Skutch 1953); rarely white (Kattan 1993). Incubation by female only, 14.5–15.5 days, rarely 17. Young fed by both sexes, but as the fledging period progresses, increasingly by the female; young fledge in 18–19 days, rarely 17–20. Pairs appear to remain faithful through several broods, in contrast to the situation in Northern House Wren, where mate switching is rampant in some populations (Drilling & Thompson 1991). Again in contrast to the Northern House Wren, polygamy in Southern House Wrens is rare. It was not noted in a detailed study in Colombia (Alvarez-Lopéz *et al.* 1984), although in Panama several instances were observed (Freed 1986). In this instance both active displacement of the male of a mated pair, and opportunistic taking-over of an apparently bereaved female by a vigorous male from an adjacent territory was noted. Prospective infanticide (i.e. the killing of young or destruction of eggs of different paternity by an incoming male) has also been observed (Freed 1987).

Assistance in feeding young by the young of previous broods has been observed in Costa Rica but not in Colombia and is apparently a rare occurrence. Breeding territories in Colombia can be as small as 0.12ha.

In the tropical parts of its range the Southern House Wren has a very extended breeding season. In Costa Rica, every month of the year except October and November (Skutch 1953); in Trinidad, year-round with a peak in May (Belcher & Smooker 1937); and in Suriname, year-round with peaks in January and July (Haverschmidt 1952). Populations in temperate South America have a definite breeding season; in Uruguay October and November, in northern Chile from August onwards and further south in Chile from September (Johnson 1967).

Parasitism by the Shiny Cowbird *Molothrus bonariensis* is frequent.

FOOD Apparently entirely invertebrate. Seen to take spiders, caterpillars, grasshoppers, crickets, cockroaches and doubtless many other orders of arthropods.

MOVEMENTS Over the tropical parts of its range very sedentary; in Colombia there was a high degree of permanent faithfulness to sites (Alvarez-Lopéz *et al.* 1984). Southern populations are strongly migratory; the southern edge of the wintering range is, however, imperfectly known. Apparently leaves Isla Grande, Tierra del Fuego, entirely in winter, but is found year-round in the Torres del Paine area in Chile (A. Jaramillo pers. comm.).

MEASUREMENTS Wing of male 48–53, of female 45–49.5; tail of male 32–38.5, of female 31–36; exposed culmen of male 12–14, of female 13–14; tarsus of male 17–19.5, of female 17.5–18 (Ridgway 1904).

63   CLARION WREN
Troglodytes tanneri   Plate 16

Troglodytes tanneri Townsend 1890, Clarión Island, Revillagigedo group, Mexico.

Alternative name: Spanish *Saltapared Clarión*

A large insular member of the House Wren group, treated by some authorities as a race of the House Wren, confined to the 8km long Isla Clarión.

IDENTIFICATION Length 12.5–14cm. The only wren on Isla Clarión.

DESCRIPTION
Adult Crown and nape dull blackish-brown, becoming dull grey-brown on back and more rufescent on rump. Primaries and secondaries dull grey-brown with alternating light and dark brown areas on outerweb giving obscurely barred appearance to closed wing; tertials with similar but more prominent bars. Rectrices alternately barred with dark brown and greyish-brown, giving about 20 transverse bars across closed tail. Supercilium buffy-white, lores grey-brown, ear-coverts grey-brown with obscure lighter mottling. Throat and chest buffy-white, becoming deeper on lower belly and flanks. Underwing-coverts greyish-white. Iris brown, bill dark brown with paler horn-brown at base, legs brownish.
Juvenile Underparts flecked dusky, forming faint scallops (Howell & Webb 1995).

GEOGRAPHICAL VARIATION None; monotypic.

VOICE Song resembles House Wren, typically begins with two or more gruff *chut* notes then runs into warbling, lower and with more gruff chattering than Socorro Wren song. Also a prolonged scratchy warbling (post-breeding) (Howell & Webb 1995). Calls an insect-like, dry, churring rattle.

HABITAT Scrub and arid cactus bush.

HABITS Little information recorded.

STATUS AND DISTRIBUTION In 1897 not uncommon (Anthony 1898). Most recent populations estimates 170–200 pairs (Howell & Webb 1989). The vegetation of the

Clarion Wren

island seems to have changed drastically in the 100 years since Anthony's visit (Everett 1988), due to burning and the introduction of pigs, hares and goats, but the wren's survival does not appear to be in danger. Highest density of birds was in fact adjacent to buildings (Howell & Webb 1989).

BREEDING Probably breeds in January; numerous flying young in May. One nest was described as 'composed of material such as might have been selected by *Troglodytes aedon*, but the shape of the nest as well as its location might have been the design of a Song Sparrow' (Anthony 1898). Eggs not described, incubation and fledging periods unknown.

FOOD No information.

MOVEMENTS Sedentary.

MEASUREMENTS Wing of male 58–60, of female 56–59; tail of male 45–49, of female 46–48; exposed culmen of male 16–17, of female 16; tarsus of male 20.5–22, of female 21–21.5 (Ridgway 1904).

---

64   COZUMEL WREN
Troglodytes beani   Plate 16

Troglodytes beani Ridgway 1885. Cozumel Island, Quintana Roo, Mexico.

Alternative name: Spanish *Saltapared de Cozumel*

The endemic wren of Cozumel Island, off the Yucatán Peninsula. Frequently 'lumped' with the Southern House Wren, but perhaps closer to the West Indian forms of the House Wren superspecies.

IDENTIFICATION Length 12–12.5cm. Not confusable with any other species on Cozumel Island.

DESCRIPTION
Adult Crown warm grey-brown; back more rufescent,

and rump warm rufous-brown. Wing-coverts rufescent-brown. Primaries and secondaries grey-brown with prominent dark-brown and rufous-brown bars on outerweb, extending across both webs in tertials. Tail deep rufous-brown with 15–18 narrow darker bars across all feathers. Chin, throat and chest buffy-white, with grey-buff flanks and rufous-buff lower flanks. Underwing-coverts greyish-buff. Iris brown, bill dark brown with pale base, legs brown or pinkish-brown.
Juvenile Not described.

GEOGRAPHICAL VARIATION None; monotypic.

VOICE Song is somewhat similar to that of the Southern

House Wren, but has some distinctive features; it is fuller and richer without trills, typically begins with a slight scolding *chih-chih*, breaks into a short rich warble which ends with a bright *wheet wheet wheet wheet*, or with longer series of bright notes which may suggest White-throated Wren (Howell & Webb 1995); often interspersed with a persistent *wha-wha* note. Calls a scolding *sheh-sheh* and a rolled *jirr-rr-rr-rr-rr*.

HABITAT Brush, scrublands, bushy areas around habitation.

HABITS Not shy; forages at all levels in bushes, with frequent calls. Flights tend to be low and short. Frequently sings from exposed and obvious sites.

STATUS AND DISTRIBUTION Restricted to Cozumel Island, where it is frequently common or abundant in suitable locations. Despite its very restricted distribution not apparently in any danger; provided some scattered bushes are left, adapts well to low-density human settlement.

BREEDING Nest and eggs undescribed.

FOOD Little data; predominantly or entirely invertebrate.

Cozumel Wren

MOVEMENTS Entirely sedentary.

MEASUREMENTS Wing of male 50–55.5, of female 50–57; tail of male 40–48, of female 42–45; exposed culmen of male 16–18, of female 15.5–17; tarsus of male 20–21, of female 19–20.5 (Ridgway 1904).

65 COBB'S WREN
Troglodytes cobbi

Plate 16

Troglodytes cobbi Chubb 1909, Falkland Islands.

Alternative names: Falkland Wren, 'Rock Wren' (local name)

Etymology: Named after A. F. Cobb who was born in the Falklands in 1877. In 1908 he collected the first specimen on Carcass Island, north-west of West Falkland.

A very large insular form, obviously closely related to the Southern House Wren, but clearly much modified to an existence at or below ground level in boulder piles and tussock grass. Its tide-line foraging habits are probably unique in the Troglodytidae.

IDENTIFICATION Length 13–14cm. The only other wren on the Falkland Islands is the local race of the Sedge Wren, which is paler, with obvious black and buff striations on the shoulders.

DESCRIPTION
Adult Crown and nape grey-brown, becoming somewhat warmer on back and shoulders and brighter rusty-brown on rump. Primaries and secondaries blackish-grey on innerwebs, the outerwebs with warm brown transverse bars, giving about 12–15 alternating blackish-grey and brown bars on the closed wing. Rectrices warm brown with narrow blackish-grey bars, giving about 9–10 bars extending across entire tail. Lores, cheeks and ear-coverts unmarked grey-brown with no obvious eye-stripe; chin and throat slightly lighter grey-brown. Chest and belly unmarked grey-brown, the flanks and undertail-coverts much richer and warmer in colour. Underwing grey-brown. Iris brown, bill blackish above and below,

legs dark brown. Birds in worn plumage are substantially less rich in colour.
Partial albinism is quite common, doubtless resulting from inbreeding in small island populations.
Juvenile Not described.

GEOGRAPHICAL VARIATION None; monotypic,

VOICE The usual song is loud and consists of a mixed phrase of quick trills and whistles with harsh notes, rapidly delivered, and lasting about two seconds with regular intervals of three or four seconds. Song varies greatly between individuals. One bird sang only a slow trill repeated at the second intervals; another elaborated the normal song into a continuous warbling lasting about twenty seconds. It sings mainly from late August to February, but snatches of song have been heard in mid-April. The call-notes are all harsh and buzzing, commonly *chiz* or a higher *cheez* (Woods 1975).

HABITAT Generally associated with tussac grass *Paradiochloa flabellata*, a very tall characteristic Falkland plant which is highly susceptible to burning and trampling; however, it can also occur away from tussac, provided introduced predators are also absent (Woods 1993).

HABITS Generally tame and confiding. Feeds in tussac grass but also in crevices on boulders and on beaches where kelp is washed up (R. W. Woods pers. comm.).

STATUS AND DISTRIBUTION Now confined to small islands scattered around the Falkland archipelago, including the isolated Beauchêne Island some 50km south of East Falkland. It seems to be very susceptible

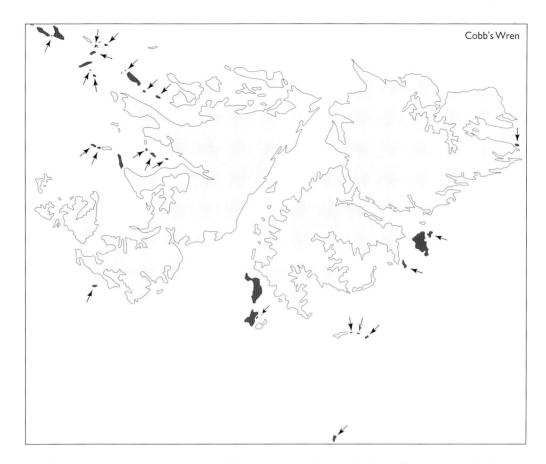

to habitat destruction, and especially to predation by feral cats and black rats, and is essentially absent from any island where these species occur, or where the tussac grass has been destroyed by unwise grazing practices. It is possible that prior to human settlement the species was found all over the archipelago; in 1771 Pernety noticed 'great numbers of wrens like those in France' in the area of Port Louis, not far from present-day Stanley on East Falkland. About this time large numbers of cattle were introduced and allowed to run wild, along with cats and rats. Charles Darwin during his visit in 1833–1834 did not note any wrens, although the native fox (now extinct) was abundant at that time. In prime habitat (tussac grass adjacent to beaches with rotting kelp) population density is high, with territories varying from 40–205m of shoreline (Woods 1993). Recent surveys show the presence of Cobb's Wren on more than thirty offshore islands, varying in size from 5–3,000ha. Current total population estimates are 4,000–8,000 pairs (R. W. Woods pers. comm.). The future survival of Cobb's Wren depends on keeping its present habitat free of alien predators, as well as preserving the tussac habitat.

BREEDING Nest is the shape of a coconut, but some-what larger, with an aperture pointing slightly upwards, made of tussac grass and seal hairs and densely lined with feathers (Bennett 1935). Most of the few nests so far found have been at or close (maximum 90cm) to ground level, in the bases of tussac clumps; also beneath large boulders, and in one case in a sheepskin hanging on a fence (Woods 1993). Eggs three or four, pinkish, thickly spotted with red or light brown (Woods 1975). No details of incubation or fledging periods. Nests in September and October; eggs (fully incubated), 20 October (Bennett 1935), small chicks October (Woods 1993).

FOOD No published details.

MOVEMENTS Appears to be sedentary; no evidence of inter-island movement, except possibly between two closely adjacent islands.

MEASUREMENTS Wing of male 58, of female 58; tail of male 39.5, of female 40; exposed culmen of male 16.5, of female 16; tarsus of male 20.5, of female 19.5.

Thryothorus sissonii Grayson 1868, Socorro Island, Revilla-gigedo Group, Mexico.

Alternative names: Spanish *Saltapared de Socorro*
Etymology: The species was originally described by Col. A. J. Grayson, based on specimens sent to the Smithsonian Institute in 1867, and named 'for my esteemed friend, the U.S. Consul at Mazatlán'. However, since Grayson chose to describe the new species in *The California Farmer and Journal of Useful Sciences*, a publication of somewhat less than global circulation, his description initially went unnoticed, and the species was redescribed as *Troglodytes insularis* (Lawrence 1871). Grayson's eventful zoological career included being shipwrecked on Socorro; he died prematurely in 1869 from a fever contracted on another collecting expedition to Isla Isabela, off the coast of Na-yarit in western Mexico and thus was never able to claim the priority that was correctly his (Taylor 1951).

An endemic wren of the Revillagigedo group, found only on Socorro Island. Traditionally placed in the genus *Thryomanes*; however, there is common agreement among ornithologists who have field experience of the species that it is in all ways a typical *Troglodytes* (J. C. Barlow pers. comm.).

IDENTIFICATION Length 11–12cm. The only wren on Socorro Island.

DESCRIPTION
Adult Crown grey-brown, with darker centres to some feathers. Shoulders and back grey-brown, with very obscure fine barring. Rump warmer brown. Primaries and secondaries blackish-grey, with grey or greyish-white patches on outerweb, giving prominent barring on closed wing; bars extend across both webs of tertials. Rectrices grey-brown with contrasting dark greyish-black bars, giving about 12 bars across entire tail. Lores buffy, supercilium pale buff, giving an obscure pale postocular stripe. Ear-coverts mottled grey-buff. Chin and throat buffy-white, chest somewhat more buff, belly whitish-buff, colour stronger on flanks, thighs and vent. Underwing grey-buff. Iris dark brown. Bill dark brown above, paler below. Legs and feet brown.
Juvenile Conspicuous dark scalloping on underparts.

GEOGRAPHICAL VARIATION None; monotypic.

VOICE Calls, a dry scolding *chuk chuk chuk-chuk* and a rapid scolding *jihr-jihr*. Song type is clearly reminiscent of a *Troglodytes* rather than Bewick's Wren; typically begins with two or more low, gruff *chuk* notes, breaks

into a short, rich, slightly scratchy warble, and often ends with a rich chortle or clear *sweet-weet-weet-weet*; female may countersing with male, contributing gruff chatters (Howell & Webb 1995).

HABITAT Woodlands and brushy hillsides (Jehl & Parkes 1982).

HABITS Forages low down or on the ground, turning over leaves, or climbs over old logs or, creeper-like, the trunks of trees (Grayson 1868).

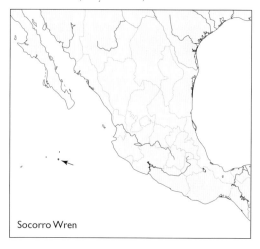

Socorro Wren

STATUS AND DISTRIBUTION Confined to Socorro Island in the Revillagigedo group. Socorro is about 15km long and wide. Fairly common in suitable habitat, though greatly outnumbered by the endemic form of the Tropical Parula Warbler *Parula pitiayumi* (Jehl & Parkes 1982).

BREEDING Nest itself undescribed; one nest was sited in a knot-hole of a decayed tree (Grayson 1868). Apparently breeds early; families with fledged young in early April (Jehl & Parkes 1982).

MOVEMENTS Sedentary.

FOOD No information.

MEASUREMENTS Wing of male 46.5–49, of female 47–48; tail of male 40–46.5, of female 43–45; exposed culmen of male 14–15.5, of female 14–15.5, tarsus of male 19.5–21, of female 21–22.

Taxonomy of the endemic *Troglodytes* wrens of Central America and north-eastern South America

The taxonomy of the *Troglodytes rufociliatus* group has been very fluid and subject to frequent revisions. Recent biochemical work (Rice *et al.* 1999) supports the viewpoint of earlier authors (e.g. Ridgely & Tudor 1989) in maintaining *T. rufociliatus* (Rufous-browed Wren), *T. ochraceus* (Ochraceous Wren), *T. solstitialis* (Mountain Wren) and *T. rufulus* (Tepui Wren) as separate species. Rice *et al.* did not examine *T. monticola* (Santa Marta Wren) but we have followed Ridgely & Tudor in giving it full specific status. Rice *et al.* suggest that *T. rufociliatus* is closer to the House Wren group than it is to the other species.

Plate 15

Troglodytes solstitialis Sclater 1858. Near Riobamba, Ecuador.

Alternative names: Equatorial Wren; Spanish *Cucarachero Paramero*

A common and (by virtue of its persistent call) rather conspicuous bird of the northern Andes.

IDENTIFICATION Length 10.5–11cm. Allopatric with Tepui Wren and Ochraceous Wren; only likely confusion is with Southern House Wren, from which it is distinguished by its warm buff supercilium, shorter tail and generally more rufescent underparts. The two species tend to have different habitats. The Sepia-brown Wren is much larger; Grey-breasted Wood Wren has a conspicuous pattern on the face.

DESCRIPTION *T. s. solstitialis*
Adult Crown and forehead rufous-brown, becoming a less rufescent-brown on nape, shoulders, back and rump. Primaries and secondaries dark chocolate-brown on innerweb, with light rufescent-brown bars on outerwebs, giving about twelve prominent bars on closed wing. Rectrices rufous-brown with about ten blackish bars extending across entire tail. Lores reddish-brown, with a buff-brown eye-stripe before and behind the eye, becoming more prominent posteriorly. Area behind eye darker brown contrasting with eye-stripe and warm buff-brown ear-coverts. Throat and chest warm buff, becoming paler on belly. Flanks buff-brown with indistinct transverse darker bars. Undertail-coverts greyish-white with indistinct darker bars. Underwing dull buffy-brown. Iris dark brown, bill black, feet greyish to greyish-brown.
Juvenile Quite distinct. Warm buff colour of underparts replaced by dull grey-brown with diffuse dark grey-brown speckling from chin to upper belly, upperparts less warm in colour, eye-stripe colder buff.

GEOGRAPHICAL VARIATION
   T. s. solstitialis (extreme southern Colombia, Ecuador and north-western Peru) Described above.
   T. s. solitarius 'Pale-breasted Wren' (western Venezuela and Colombia except where occupied by *solstitialis*) Similar to *solstitialis* but upperparts darker, auricular patch deeper brown, throat and foreneck much paler buff, flanks less rufescent, tail longer.
   T. s. macrourus 'Long-tailed Equatorial Wren' (eastern Peru, from Urubamba valley north to Junín) Similar to *solstitialis* but larger and longer-tailed; middle of breast white.
   T. s. frater 'White-browed Equatorial Wren' (extreme southern Peru [Puno] and Bolivia) Closest to *macrourus* but superciliaries white or buffy-white.
   T. s. auricularis 'Argentinian Equatorial Wren' (north-western Argentina [Tucumán and Jujuy]) Very similar to *frater*, but tail shorter and upperparts less rufescent.

VOICE Song is a rather quiet and understated series of high notes, *treee-treeee-tititiki*. Call, constantly given, is a characteristic *dzz* or *di-di*.

HABITAT Humid forest, cloudforest and forest edge up to tree line, sometimes in bamboo. Mostly 1,700–3,500m but down to 700m in northern Argentina.

HABITS Not particularly shy; usually located by persistent call-notes. Forages mostly low down, occasionally climbing up into moss-covered trees. Usually occurs in pairs or family groups; sometimes joins other species in mixed flocks. Tail is not usually held cocked over the back.

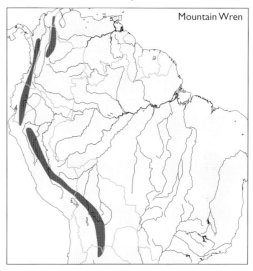
Mountain Wren

STATUS AND DISTRIBUTION Resident, Andes from western Venezuela (western Zulia, Táchira, Mérida, Trujillo and Lara) and Colombia (Sierra de Perijá, Santa Marta), disjunctly in western Andes south through Ecuador to northern Peru (Cajamarca); disjunctly from north-central Peru (San Martín, Huánuco) south through highlands of Bolivia to northern Argentina (Salta, Jujuy, Tucumán). In suitable habitat at times common or abundant.

BREEDING Not well-known. Two nests in Ecuador were located respectively in a pile of brush in the crotch of a tree, about 2m up, and in a natural cavity in the trunk of a tree nearly 10m above the ground; the nest was described as a bulky structure made chiefly of fibrous roots, lined with narrow dry leaves, with a side entrance but no roof, being situated under trash (Skutch 1960). In Colombia, one adult observed bringing nesting material (fine rootlets) to a cluster of dead *Cecropia* leaves situated at a height of about 7m (Ridgely & Gaulin 1980). Eggs are two, white (Sclater & Salvin 1879). Incubation and fledging periods not recorded. Time of breeding apparently protracted, and varies greatly within the range of the species; in Colombia, eggs August and November, November in northern Argentina; nest-building in Colombia in March, fledglings in virtually in all months of the year in Colombia, October in Ecuador, February to December in Peru, November and February in Bolivia (Fjeldså & Krabbe 1990).

FOOD No information recorded; presumably invertebrate.

MOVEMENTS Apparently sedentary.

MEASUREMENTS Wing of male 45–52, of female 47–49; tail of male 28–31, of female 29–32; exposed culmen of male 12–14, of female 12.5–13.5; tarsus of male 18.5–19.5, of female 18–19.5.

68   SANTA MARTA WREN
Troglodytes monticola
Plate 15

Troglodytes monticola Bangs 1899. Parámo de Chiruqua, Santa Marta Mountains, Colombia.

Alternative names: Paramo Wren; Spanish *Cucarachero de Santa Marta*

A very little-known species, found only at high elevations on the mountain range which gives it its name, an area now little visited. Frequently regarded as conspecific with the Mountain Wren.

IDENTIFICATION Length 11.5cm. In its range, probably separated altitudinally from other wren species. Differs from House Wren by having a prominent, warm buff supercilium, deeper, more rufescent colour overall and barred flanks and crissum. Grey-breasted Wood Wren has prominent facial markings and white eyestripe. Mountain Wren is allopatric.

DESCRIPTION
Adult Crown, back and shoulders rufous-brown, the primaries, secondaries and lower back barred blackish. Rectrices brown with darker transverse bars. Supercilium buff, eye-ring buffy-white, chin pale buff, throat and chest buffy-brown, vent white with blackish bars, flanks buffy-white with obvious dark brown bars. Iris brown, bill dark brown above, paler base, legs brownish.
Juvenile Similar to adult but back and underparts with dark tips to feathers.

GEOGRAPHICAL VARIATION None; monotypic.

VOICE Little information recorded; stated to be rather silent (Todd & Carriker 1922).

HABITAT Found in low, thick shrubbery at timberline and in sheltered spots higher up in the *páramo* zone 3,200–4,800m (Ridgely & Tudor 1989).

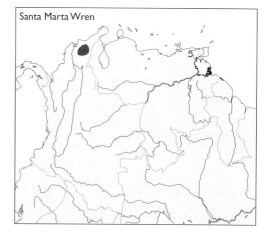

HABITS Little known; reported to be shy and easily overlooked (Todd & Carriker 1922).

STATUS AND DISTRIBUTION Confined to the upper levels of the Santa Marta range. No recent information about abundance, since its range is now rarely visited by ornithologists.

BREEDING Nest and eggs unknown.

FOOD No information recorded.

MOVEMENTS Presumably sedentary; not known if altitudinal movements occur.

MEASUREMENTS Wing of male 57, of female 54–55; tail of male 54–55, of female 42–45; exposed culmen of male 14, of female 13.5 (Hellmayr 1918–1938).

69   OCHRACEOUS WREN
Troglodytes ochraceus
Plate 15

Troglodytes ochraceus Ridgway 1882 Volcán de Irazú, Costa Rica.

Alternative name: Spanish *Soterrey Ocroso*

A very small, brightly coloured *Troglodytes*, endemic to high altitudes of Costa Rica and Panama. Relatively little is known of its life-history.

IDENTIFICATION Length 9.5–10cm. Among sympatric, or near sympatric species, most resembles the Southern House Wren, from which it differs in its richly-coloured face and broad ochraceous supercilium. The Timberline

Wren has a white supercilium and throat, and much paler underparts; the Plain Wren is larger, longer-tailed and again with a whitish supercilium; and the short-tailed Grey-breasted Wood Wren has prominent markings on the side of the face, dark cap and grey underparts.

DESCRIPTION *T. o. ochraceus*
Adult Crown, nape and back rich medium-brown, slightly more orange on forehead; rump slightly more rufous. Shoulders and coverts concolor with back. Primaries and secondaries dark dull brown, the outerwebs with orange-brown markings giving 9–10 light and dark

bars on closed wing; tertials deep brown with blackish-brown bars on both webs. Rectrices dull brown with 10–12 blackish-brown bars. Lores buff-brown, prominent supercilium buffy-orange, starting behind eye and widening onto shoulder; ear-coverts contrastingly darker with dark area reaching forward to eye. Chin, throat and chest buffy-brown, becoming darker on flanks and lower belly. Underwing buffy-grey. Iris brown, upper mandible dark brown, lower mandible dark brown with pale base, legs brown.

Juvenile Similar, but underparts with extensive darker scales and obscure mottling; supercilium less rich in colour.

GEOGRAPHICAL VARIATION

T. o. ochraceus 'Irazú Wren' (Costa Rica [Cordilleras de Tilarán and Talamanca and highlands in between]) Described above.

T. o. ligea 'Chiriqui Wren' (western Panama) Very similar to *ochraceus* but heavier bill and duller upperparts.

T. o. festinus 'Mount Pirre Wren' (eastern Panama [Darién]; possibly adjacent Colombia [Ridgely & Tudor 1989]) Similar to *ochraceus* but smaller, longer-billed and with lighter underparts.

VOICE Song is a varied medley of high, thin, slurred whistles and liquid trills in a subdued tone. Call is a rolling, thin, high-pitched *peeew* or *peeer*; a low, weak, dragging *churr* (Stiles & Skutch 1989).

HABITAT Humid montane forest with extensive epiphytic growth, mostly 900–2,450m, rarely 600–3,000m. Will venture out into pasture-land provided enough trees remain.

HABITS Rather retiring, though not difficult to observe with care and patience. Forages mostly on mossy trunks and branches, up which it climbs easily. Families (probably one parent and two young) will roost in a nest previously used for breeding.

STATUS AND DISTRIBUTION Fairly common in suitable habitat. Costa Rica from the Cordillera de Tilarán discontinuously at suitable altitude to western Panama (Chiriquí and Veraguas); one record from just west of the Canal Zone, then absent until eastern Panama (Cerro Pirre, Darién) (Ridgely 1976).

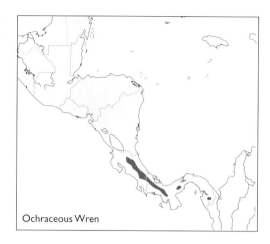

Ochraceous Wren

BREEDING So far only three nests described, all in Costa Rica, and none closely examined. All three were in the same (very unusual for a *Troglodytes* wren) situation; in free-swinging bunches of epiphytes, arising from the breaking-off of the end of a heavily overgrown branch, the broken-off part being prevented from falling by aerial roots. All three nests were thus suspended at a height of about 15m above the ground. The situation of the nests precluded close examination, but they appeared to be located in cavities of dead branches or in niches between epiphytes. Construction apparently mostly by the female. Eggs undescribed. Incubation and fledging periods unknown. Clutch size not known, but family groups of two young and one adult seen. Nesting period in Costa Rica April to July; young being fed in nest in early May, and nest construction seen in late May (Skutch 1960).

FOOD No information; presumably largely or entirely invertebrate.

MOVEMENTS Presumably entirely sedentary.

MEASUREMENTS Wing of male 46–47.5, of female 46; tail of male 30–33.5, of female 31.5; exposed culmen of male 13.5–14, of female 13.5; tarsus of male 17.5–18, of female 17.5 (Ridgway 1907).

---

70   RUFOUS-BROWED WREN
Troglodytes rufociliatus

Plate 15

Troglodytes rufociliatus Sharpe, 1881. Volcán de Fuego, Guatemala.

Alternative names: Spanish *Saltapared Cejirufo*

A highland species, widely distributed in mountainous regions from southern Mexico to (sparsely) Nicaragua. Formerly regarded as conspecific with the Ochraceous Wren of Costa Rica and Panama.

IDENTIFICATION Length 10–11.5cm. In form a typical *Troglodytes* wren, rather short-tailed. Distinguished from sympatric races of the House Wren by its barred flanks, shorter tail and warm rufous supercilium. All *Thryothorus*

wrens are larger and longer-tailed, usually with markings on the ear-coverts or face, or, in the case of Plain Wren, a whitish supercilium. Grey-breasted Wood Wren has a very short tail and prominent markings on the face and ear-coverts.

DESCRIPTION *T. r. rufociliatus*
Adult Crown and back warm brown with very obscure darker barring on back, becoming better defined on rump. Primaries and secondaries greyish-black, with pale buff-brown markings on outerwebs, giving obvious dark bars on closed wing. Shoulders warm brown with pale greyish-white central streaks on some feathers. Rectrices

warm brown with darker blackish-brown bars. Lores buff with darker brown markings, supercilium pale buff, contrasting with crown and with dark brown postocular area. Lower eyelid pale buff, area below eye dark brown, ear-coverts and sides of throat orange-brown. Chin buffy, throat and chest orange-brown, becoming washed-out on belly. Sides of chest warm brown with obscure darker barring, flanks barred, the bars made up of alternating grey, warm brown and dark brown bars. Centre of belly sometimes with small obscure spotting, sometimes without, becoming barring on lower belly and undertail-coverts. Underwing buffy. Iris brown, bill dark horn, legs dark grey-brown.

Juvenile Similar to adult but barring on sides more obscure, chest with fine dusky edgings on feathers.

GEOGRAPHICAL VARIATION

T. r. rufociliatus (eastern Guatemala and northern El Salvador) Described above.

T. r. chiapensis (high mountains of Chiapas, Mexico) Similar to *rufociliatus* but darker brown above, throat a richer rufous, belly almost pure white and crissum greyish.

T. r. nannoides 'Santa Ana Wren' (Volcán Santa Ana, El Salvador) Similar to *rufociliatus* but darker on back, barring on flanks heavier.

T. r. rehni (Honduras and [presumably] Nicaragua) Similar to *rufociliatus* but reddish-brown above, throat ochraceous, belly buffy.

VOICE Song is a varied, scratchy warble run into a tinkling trill (Howell & Webb 1995). Call is a loud nasal *zhreeet*.

HABITAT Humid epiphytic montane forest; in El Salvador only in the darkest, and dampest sections of the cloudforest (Dickey & Van Rossem 1938). In Guatemala, more catholic in tastes, being found in mixed pine-oak forest as well as epiphytic cypress forest (Skutch 1960). Temperate zone, 1,700–3,500m. Recently found in Nicaragua at 1,250m (Martínez-Sánchez 1989).

HABITS Spends most of its time foraging in thick epiphytes and undergrowth low down, creeping below fallen logs and into piles of brush; also in epiphytes on tree-branches. Often very difficult to observe. Remains in pairs throughout year, often roosting together in nests.

STATUS AND DISTRIBUTION Exists in disjunct populations in the mountains of Central America, separated by lowland areas. Mexico, northern Chiapas,

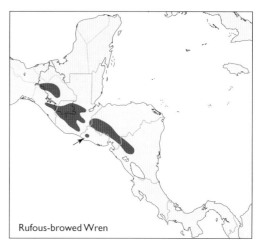

Rufous-browed Wren

central Chiapas; central Guatemala, southern Honduras. In El Salvador, Volcán Santa Ana, other populations apparently no longer extant. Nicaragua, one specimen at an unusually low altitude disjunctly from Honduran populations, present status not known. In many locations quite common.

BREEDING Not well-known. Three nests from the Sierra de Tecpán, Guatemala, have been described (Skutch 1960). All were well-made cups, built out of pine needles and dry grass leaves, lined with feathers, located in crevices or crannies in dead tree stumps or in a hole in a bank, the highest 1m from the ground. Eggs three, white, speckled all over with cinnamon. Incubation by female alone, sometimes fed by male (unusual for a wren). Young fed by both parents. Nesting in Guatemala from the third week of April until early July; in El Salvador, birds of the race *nannoides* in breeding condition in May, and gravid females on 8 May (Dickey & Van Rossem 1938).

MOVEMENTS Presumably sedentary.

FOOD Little information; presumably predominantly or entirely invertebrate. Has been seen to take caterpillars.

MEASUREMENTS Wing of male 50, of female 47; tail of male 35, of female 33; exposed culmen of male 11.5, of female 13; tarsus of male 18.5, of female 16 (Ridgway 1904).

---

71 TEPUI WREN
Troglodytes rufulus

Plate 15

Troglodytes rufulus Cabanis 1848 (1849), Roraima, British Guiana.

Alternative name: Spanish *Cucarachero de Pantepui*

The Tepui Wren is appropriately named, since it is found in the tepuis, an extraordinary series of flat-topped mountain ranges rising like islands from a sea of dense tropical forest. Due to the inaccessibility of much of its range, a little-known species.

IDENTIFICATION Length 12cm. Allopatric from the similar Mountain Wren. Much more rufous than the Southern House Wren. The Flutist Wren has a much shorter tail and no conspicuous supercilium.

DESCRIPTION *T. r. wetmorei*
Adult Entire crown, nape, shoulders, back and rump unmarked chestnut-brown, becoming slightly more rufescent on lower back and rump. Primaries and

secondaries dull blackish-grey on innerwebs, rufous-brown with narrow and not particularly obvious bars on outerwebs, the bars extending across entire width of tertials. Rectrices dark rufous-brown, with narrow dull black bars (about 16–18 in number) extending across entire tail. Lores grey; supercilium whitish-buff, contrasting with crown and with dark brown postocular region. Chin, throat and chest clear grey, becoming grey-brown on lower belly and warm brown on flanks. Vent and undertail-coverts buffy-brown with dark brown bars. Underwing grey-buff. Iris dark brown, upper mandible black, lower mandible black with silver base, legs medium grey.

Juvenile Much darker with scaled underparts.

GEOGRAPHICAL VARIATION

T. r. wetmorei (Cerro de la Neblina, Amazonas, Venezuela) Described above.

T. r. rufulus 'Roraima Wren' (Subtropical zones of Mount Roraima and Vei-Tepui on the borders of Venezuela and Guyana) Similar to *wetmorei*, but belly warmer rufous.

T. r. duidae 'Duida Wren' (Amazonas and Bolívar, Venezuela, on about six tepui mountains) Similar to *rufulus* but underparts whitish, dusky bars on tail and inner secondaries more pronounced.

T. r. yavii (three mountains in northern Amazonas, Venezuela) Similar to *rufulus* but underparts whitish.

T. r. fulvigularis (south-eastern Bolívar, Venezuela) Much darker and less rufous then nominate.

VOICE Song is a series of thin, high, whistled twitters, sometimes in a series lasting several seconds, sometimes in short discrete phrases in the manner of a Red-eyed Vireo *Vireo olivaceus.*

HABITAT Humid forest on slopes of tepuis; forest edge and shrubbery, 1,000–2,800m.

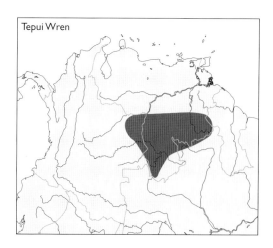

Tepui Wren

HABITS Little information recorded; apparently forages low down or actually on the ground (Meyer de Schauensee & Phelps 1978).

STATUS AND DISTRIBUTION Confined to disjunct forested areas on the slopes of tepuis in southern Venezuela, immediately adjacent Brazil, and extreme western Guyana. Little information about abundance.

BREEDING Nest and eggs undescribed.

FOOD No information recorded; presumably mainly invertebrate.

MOVEMENTS Apparently sedentary.

MEASUREMENTS (*T. r. wetmorei*) Wing of male 53, of female 55; tail of male 38, of female 37; exposed culmen of male 15, of female 14; tarsus of male 24.5, of female 24.5.

THRYORCHILUS

An ill-defined genus, perhaps not deserving of a separate identity; by some authors regarded as an aberrant *Troglodytes*, but in many ways (song, plumage, behaviour and nest-style) perhaps closer to *Henicorhina* (Stiles & Skutch 1989). Recent biochemical work (Rice *et al.* 1999) suggests a distant relationship to *Troglodytes*, but closer to that genus than to *Henicorhina*. Small, very short-tailed but long-legged; only ten rectrices. Wings short and very rounded. Bill shorter than head, with narrowly ovate nostrils and obsolete rictal bristles (Ridgway 1904).

72 TIMBERLINE WREN
Thryorchilus browni   Plate 17

Troglodytes browni Bangs 1902. Volcán de Chiriquí, Colombia (i.e. Panama).

Alternative name: Spanish *Soterrey de Bambú*

A reasonably common inhabitant of high altitudes of Costa Rica and adjacent Panama.

IDENTIFICATION Length 10cm. Generally occurs at higher altitudes than Ochraceous Wren, from which it is distinguished by its white, not buff, supercilium, much whiter underparts, a whitish patch on the primaries of the closed wing and more prominent facial markings.

The Southern House Wren, which again occurs at lower altitudes, has a longer tail, no white eye-stripe and is generally more grey.

DESCRIPTION *T. b. browni*

Adult Crown, nape, back, shoulders and rump rich chestnut-brown, with some feathers in centre of upper back with concealed white centres. Primaries and secondaries dark greyish-black on innerwebs; first approximately five primaries edged off-white on outerwebs, remainder with rufous markings, giving a whitish patch on outer part of closed wing and a series of dark bars on inner primaries, secondaries and tertials. Rectrices rufous-brown with about 12 obscure dark transverse bars. Lores and supercilium grey-white giving a prominent white eye-stripe which broadens above rich chocolate-brown ear-coverts. Area immediately in front of eye dark brown. Cheeks and area between ear-coverts and shoulder grey-white with some narrow black edgings. Throat, chest and belly grey-white, with some mottling on chest, becoming dull brown on lower belly, and more rufous on lower flanks. Vent rufous-brown. Underwing grey-buff. Iris brown, lower mandible dull black, upper mandible flesh-horn, legs dull pale brown. **Juvenile** Similar to adult but underparts more grey, less white, with narrow dark grey-black edgings to feathers giving a scalloped appearance, especially on chest and belly. Markings on head and (especially) in front of shoulders much duller and more diffuse. Flanks duller and less rufescent.

GEOGRAPHICAL VARIATION
T. b. browni 'Brown's Wren' (western Panama [Volcán de Chiriquí, Volcán Barú]) Described above.
T. b. ridgwayi 'Ridgway's Wren' (highlands of Central Costa Rica [Turrialba and Irazú]) Similar to *browni* but larger, upperparts deeper rufous-brown.
T. b. basultoi 'Basulto's Wren' (Cordillera de Dota, Costa Rica) Differs from other races by stouter bill, whiter underparts and dusky pileum.

VOICE Song is unlike that of any *Troglodytes* wren; a series of six or so very rapid scratchy warbling notes, lasting from two to three seconds, usually repeated numerous times without breaks or intermissions between the sets of phrases. Call is a harsh scolding *churr*, repeated.

HABITAT Bamboo thickets in *páramo* and *subpáramo*, forest edges at timberline and in patches of bushes above timberline. 2,800–3,600m, but locally to 2,200m.

HABITS Active, inquisitive, often cocks and pumps tail; gleans in foliage tangles, probes rolled leaves and crevices; creeps along branches, sometimes hops on

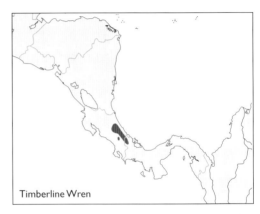

Timberline Wren

ground; flutters to pluck prey from underside of leaf or twig; probably paired year-round (Stiles & Skutch 1989).

STATUS AND DISTRIBUTION Costa Rica, at high altitudes from the Central Cordillera (Volcán Irazú) through the Cordillera de Talamanca to Chiriquí, Panama (Volcán Barú and Cerro Copete). Quite common in many locations; a considerable portion of its range is in national parks, especially in Costa Rica.

BREEDING Nest is a hollow ball with a side entrance, woven entirely of bamboo leaves, with a sparse lining of fine fibres, 1–3m up in shrub or bamboo. Eggs two, white, finely speckled all over with pale brown. Breeding season April–June (Stiles & Skutch 1989). Incubation and fledging periods not recorded.

FOOD Small insects, caterpillars and spiders.

MOVEMENTS Apparently entirely sedentary; no details of altitudinal movements.

MEASUREMENTS Wing of male 45–51.5, of female 48; tail of male 28–35.5, of female 31.5; exposed culmen of male 13–14.5, of female 13.5; tarsus of male 22.5–24.5, of female 22.5 (Ridgway 1904).

UROPSILA

Very small wrens, wing 45–54mm. Basically very similar in form to *Troglodytes*, differing in having a bill distinctly notched, nostril small, roundish or broadly oval, nonoperculate, opening in the lower anterior portion of nasal fossa (Ridgway 1904). The nesting habits are also quite distinct from *Troglodytes*, the nest being somewhat similar in construction to several species of *Thryothorus*. Several authors (e.g. Peters, 1931–1986) suggest that the genus is invalid, and merges with either *Henicorhina* or *Thryothorus* has been suggested (Sutton 1948), but in the absence of a convincing argument it still stands.

73   WHITE-BELLIED WREN
Uropsila leucogastra   Plate 16

Troglodytes leucogastra Gould 1836. Tamaulipas, Mexico.

Alternative names: Gould's Wren (nominate race). Spanish *Saltapared Vientre-blanco, Saltapared Saltón*

A small somewhat featureless wren, locally quite common, occurring from north-eastern Mexico to northern Guatemala, with isolated populations in Honduras and Nicaragua.

IDENTIFICATION Length 9.5–10cm. A very small wren lacking in striking identification features. Almost entirely pale below, brown above without prominent markings; conspicuous pale supercilium and lores. In form most closely resembles Southern House Wren, but differs from all races by its pale underparts and obvious supercilium. Bewick's Wren, almost entirely allopatric, has a much longer white-tipped tail; Plain Wren, again almost entirely allopatric, is larger and warm buff on the belly. Confusion is most likely with White-browed Wren, with a coincident range in the Yucatán Peninsula; it differs from White-bellied Wren in its larger size, longer, more heavily barred tail and in having much more sharply defined face-markings with prominent speckling on the ear-coverts.

DESCRIPTION *U. l. leucogastra*

Adult Crown, nape and back medium brown, becoming slightly more rufescent on rump. Rectrices medium brown with about 12–13 fine darker bars extending across whole tail. Supercilium behind eye greyish-white; lores and area in front of eyes medium brown. Eye-stripe behind eye mid-brown. Ear-coverts mottled brown on greyish base. Throat, chest and upper belly grey; flanks, thighs and vent buff. Underwing-coverts greyish. Iris brown, bill blackish-grey with paler base, legs dull brown. **Immature** Very similar to adult; supercilium less well-defined, mottling on ear-coverts more diffuse.

GEOGRAPHICAL VARIATION

U. l. leucogastra 'Gould's Wren' (Atlantic lowlands of Mexico from southern Tamaulipas to northern Oaxaca) Described above.

U. l. musica 'Palenque Wren' (southern Mexico, in Chiapas and Tabasco, and adjacent Guatemala) Darker than *U. l. leucogastra*, the upperparts being deep russet-brown, the flanks almond brown.

U. l. brachyurus 'Temax Wren' (Yucatán Peninsula and Belize) Differs from *U. l. leucogastra* in having much more well-defined bars on tail, undertail-coverts barred with dusky. (Russell 1964).

U. l. pacificus 'Colima Wren' (Disjunct population in western Mexico [Colima, Michoacán, Guerrero]) Similar to *U. l. leucogastra*, but upperparts paler, wing and tail longer, legs shorter.

U. l. hawkinsi (Department of Yoro, Honduras [Monroe 1963]) Like *brachyurus* in having rectrices and undertail-coverts barred, but darker and greyer-brown above, sometimes with dark crown contrasting with back.

VOICE Song, a short series of six rapid, loud up-and-down notes, the whole with a gurgling, liquid quality, the last note longer and descending. The song of the western race *pacificus* apparently lacks the bubbly quality of the other races. Both sexes sing, the songs of each being essentially identical. May sing in duet, but not, apparently, antiphonally. Calls include a hard, dry crackling rattle, a gruff scolding chatter and a mellow, fairly low *chek* or *whek* (Howell & Webb 1995).

HABITAT Thick woodland, including both semi-xeric forest with scattered cacti in the northern part of the range, and humid rainforest in southern Yucatán and Honduras. In north-eastern Mexico frequently in thickets of wild pineapple *Bromelia pinguin*, sea-level to 500m.

HABITS Not excessively secretive; forages in vegetation from ground level to a considerable height. In *Bromelia* thickets feeds on the bases of leaf-rosettes. In the southern part of its range will follow ant-armies. Described as not having particularly wren-like mannerisms in that they rarely cock their tails over the back (Sutton 1948).

STATUS AND DISTRIBUTION Reasonably common over much of its range; on the Caribbean slope, from

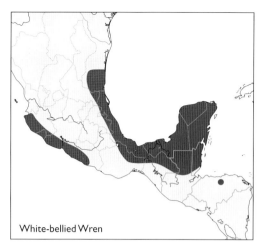

White-bellied Wren

southern Tamaulipas through Veracruz, all of the Yucatán Peninsula including northern Guatemala (Petén), and northern Belize; an isolated population in north-central Honduras. Disjunctly in western Mexico, in coastal lowlands from Jalisco to Guerrero. Sea-level to 500m.

BREEDING The nest is a peculiar structure reminiscent of an old-fashioned chemical retort. Nests used for breeding are beautifully woven from fine grasses, the outside decorated with lichens, Spanish moss, small seed-pods, spider egg-cases and mosses. They are oval in shape, about 20cm long and 12.5cm wide, with a downward-pointing entrance tunnel on the long end, about 5cm in length and 2.5cm in diameter. The lining does not apparently contain fur or feathers (Sutton 1948). Smaller nests, with thinner walls, also occur, which may be dormitory or non-breeding nests as with other species of wren; it is not known how many nests may be built. Nests are frequently sited protectively; in *Bromelia* thickets, usually directly above the sharp spiky rosettes of the plant. Over much of the range there is a commensal relationship between White-bellied Wrens and *Pseudomyrmex* ants, which are obligate symbionts with various species of swollen-thorn acacias. The ants live in the hollow acacia thorns and protect the tree against herbivores, being provided in return with protein, lipids and carbohydrates. Wrens and other species nesting in acacia trees are afforded vicarious protection by the aggressive ants but do not seem to contribute anything in return. In a study in Tikal, Guatemala, 55 out of 59 nests were in such acacias (Gilardi & von Kugelgen 1991). White-bellied Wrens will also nest in apparently deliberate proximity to the nests of aggressive hornets. Possibly because of this protection, little effort seems to be made to conceal nests, which are obvious and readily found. Nests are usually about 3–4m above the ground, but have been found from 1.5–15m.

The eggs are four in number, glossy pale blue without markings of any kind. Incubation apparently by both sexes, (Sutton 1948), period unknown; young fed by both sexes, fledging period unknown. Birds in breeding condition in late March in Tamaulipas and a nest with partially-incubated eggs on 2 June; in Oaxaca, nest under construction on 20 April and a fledgling on May (Binford 1989). Not known whether multiple-brooded.

FOOD Insects and spiders; sometimes feeds from spider-webs. Where its range overlaps with that of army ants will follow swarms.

MOVEMENTS Apparently totally sedentary.

MEASUREMENTS Wing of male 48.5–52, of female 45–48.5; tail of male 28.5–32, of female 26.5–28.5; exposed culmen of male 12.5–14.5, of female 12.5–13.5, tarsus of male 18–20, of female 18–19.5 (Ridgway 1904).

HENICORHINA

Very small short-tailed wrens with small, highly rounded wings (fifth to seventh primaries longest), sturdy powerful legs (tarsus about half as long as the wing) and bills only slightly decurved, quite strong and thick, and shorter than the head. Resemble many members of the genus *Thryothorus* in having sharply marked cheeks and ear-coverts, but differ by having a stubby rounded tail, usually held cocked over the back. In form and manner most closely resemble *Troglodytes*. Inconspicuous, foraging low down or on the ground in dense vegetation, but with arresting, rollicking songs with a volume out of all proportion to the size of the singer. Three species, two widely distributed from Mexico to northern South America, the third, only recently discovered, from a few montane locations in northern Peru and southern Ecuador.

74 GREY-BREASTED WOOD WREN
Henicorhina leucophrys   Plate 17

Troglodytes leucophrys Tschudi 1844, Montaña del Vitoc, Junín, Peru.

Alternative names: Highland Wood Wren; Spanish *Saltapared-selvatico Pechigris, Saltabrena, Soterrey de Selva Pechigris*

An abundant and widely spread species, far more often heard than seen. Found in forested, mountainous regions from central Mexico south to northern Bolivia.

IDENTIFICATION Length 10–11.5cm. Very similar in form to the White-Breasted Wood Wren *H. leucosticta*, from which it is usually separated by altitude; however, at some locations at medium elevations the two species may occur together. Distinguished from that species by its much greyer underparts and richer coloured, more rufous-brown flanks. Additionally, in the Amazon Basin and north-western Colombia *leucosticta* has a blackish, not brown, crown. In north-western Ecuador and western Colombia the local race (*inornata*) of White-breasted Wood Wren has a dingy grey-white chest, but the sympatric Grey-breasted (*brunneiceps*) is especially dark. Juvenile examples of White-breasted do in fact have greyish chests, but in this plumage the throat of the Grey-breasted is streaked. Several species of *Thryothorus* wrens (e.g. Rufous-and-white wren, *T. rufalbus*) have similar patterns of brown upperparts, and pale underparts and crisply marked black-and-white ear-coverts, but all are immediately distinguished by their much longer tails. Grey-breasted is sympatric with several *Troglodytes* species, (e.g. Ochraceous Wren, *T. ochraceus*) but these are brown below and lack the ear-covert pattern. In Costa Rica and Panama, at high elevations, occurs with Timberline Wren *Thryorchilus browni*, which has much less prominent markings on the ear-coverts, and a narrow line of white spots on the wing-coverts.

DESCRIPTION *H. l. leucophrys*
Adult Crown dull black, the feathers broadly tipped with dark brown. Nape and shoulders dark olive brown, becoming more chestnut on lower back and rump. Primaries dull chestnut-brown on outerweb with 8–10 darker bars on closed wing due to dark marks on outerweb; innerweb dull grey-black. Tertials dull red-brown with narrow darker bars. Tail short, rectrices dull chestnut-brown with seven to eight parallel bars of dull blackish-brown across entire tail. Lores and supercilium grey-white; ear-coverts black with prominent grey-white streaking. Chin and throat whitish-grey, becoming greyer across chest. Belly dull grey in centre, becoming brownish-buff on lower belly and undertail-coverts, especially on flanks. Underwing greyish-brown. Iris reddish-brown, bill black on both mandibles with dark-grey base to lower mandible, legs and feet dingy brownish-black.
Juvenile Facial markings much less sharply demarcated, throat greyish.

GEOGRAPHICAL VARIATION
H. l. leucophrys 'White-browed Wood Wren' (Subtropical zone of Peru, western Colombia, Ecuador except south-western and north-western sections) Described above.
H. l. boliviana 'Bolivian Wood Wren' (Bolivia, Departments of La Paz and Cochabamba) Very similar to *leucophrys*, throat more streaked, flanks less rufescent-brown.
H. l. hilaris 'Berlepsch's Wood Wren' (Subtropical zone of south-western Ecuador) Similar to *leucophrys*, but foreneck and breast much paler, fulvous colour of flanks more extensive.
H. l. brunneiceps 'Brown-headed Wood Wren' (south-western Colombia and north-western Ecuador) Similar to *leucophrys* but bill heavier, upperparts brighter ferruginous, throat distinctly streaked blackish, grey of breast darker, flanks and pileum deeper brown. Apparently has a different song-type (Ridgely & Tudor 1989).
H. l. meridana 'Merida Wood Wren' (western Venezuela [Cordillera de Mérida] and eastern slope of eastern Andes of Colombia) Differs from *leucophrys* in more profusely streaked throat, breast slate-grey, flanks and pileum more rufescent brown.

H. l. bangsi 'Bang's Wood Wren' (Santa Marta mountain, Colombia, below 2,000m altitude) Similar to *hilaris* but throat and breast pale grey-white, this colour extending down to the middle of the abdomen, only the flanks and undertail-coverts being strong yellowish-brown.

H. l. anachoreta 'Santa Marta Wood Wren' (Santa Marta mountain, Colombia, from 2,000m up to 4,000m) Substantially different from *bangsi*, having dusty streaking on the throat, grey forehead and breast and less rufescent flanks; also, apparently, structurally, with a shorter bill. It has been suggested that, notwithstanding some evidence of intermediate forms in the contact zone, that *bangsi* and *anachoreta* may be specifically distinct (Ridgely & Tudor 1989).

H. l. venezuelensis 'Venezuelan Wood Wren' (northern Venezuela from near Caracas to Lara) Similar to *bangsi* but sides of breast darker grey, middle of abdomen undulated with greyish, flanks much less rufescent.

H. l. castanea 'Chestnut Wood Wren' (Atlantic slope of Guatemala) Darker than neighbouring races, with smaller bill and throat streakings more diffuse. Includes *H. l. composita* (Griscom 1932, Monroe 1968).

H. l. collina 'Chiriqui Wood Wren' (central Costa Rica to western Panama) Paler on the back than *castanea*.

H. l. capitalis 'Grey-crowned Wood Wren' (Pacific slopes of southern Mexico and Guatemala) Similar to *collina* but less chestnut above, throat-streakings less demarcated, centre of pileum greyish-sooty.

H. l. mexicana 'Mexican Wood Wren' (Mexico, from Veracruz and Puebla to northern Oaxaca) Similar to *capitalis* but brown of flanks deeper and more rufescent.

H. l. festiva 'Guerrero Wood Wren' (south-western Mexico from Guerrero to Michoacán) Similar to *mexicana* but upperparts duller brown, pileum and nape greyish-brown.

VOICE Call, an emphatic *tek-tek-tek* in Mexico and Guatemala; the race *collina* in Costa Rica has a softer call. The song is a superb series of rich, loud ringing musical phrases, repeated numerous times, sometimes interspersed between phrases by the *tek* call. There seems to be some geographical variation in song; in Costa Rica it is described as a long-continued series of clear, sweet, tinkling notes which might run on almost indefinitely (Skutch 1960). As the breeding season approaches the song of the Costa Rican race becomes less rambling and more precisely phrased. Both sexes engage in spirited duets. Sings throughout much of the year, in all weathers. Alarm calls are harsh churrs and scoldings.

HABITAT Humid mountain forests, usually above 1,500m, but on the Pacific slope of Colombia as low as 400m, and in Mexico occasionally down to 600m. As high as 3,800m in Costa Rica. Found in several different forest types within this altitudinal range, including mixed pine and oak forests and in cypresses in Guatemala, bamboo thickets and second growth in Costa Rica. Extends to fringes of *páramo* in central Costa Rica in areas of mostly tussock-grass with scattered bushes.

HABITS A busy, active bird, usually found in pairs or family groups, foraging in the lower levels of dense vegetation. Difficult to observe (and almost always more often heard than seen); however, with care it will come out into the open. Tail is typically held acutely cocked over the back; flights are very short and low and the bird spends much time on or very near the ground. Roosts in pairs or in family groups in dormitory nests which are not distinguishable in form from the breeding nests.

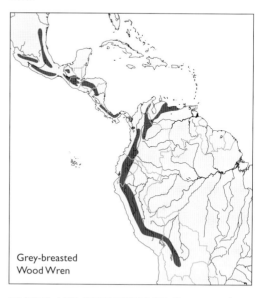

Grey-breasted Wood Wren

STATUS AND DISTRIBUTION Common where suitable habitat remains. Mexico, from San Luis Potosí and Jalisco southwards with disjunct populations separated by lowland areas throughout Central America; again disjunctly in eastern Darién and the Andes from Venezuela to north-eastern Colombia and the western Andes from Colombia through Ecuador and Peru to central Bolivia (north-western Santa Cruz).

BREEDING The nest, built by both sexes, is a globular structure, consisting of a rounded chamber, the roof of which projects forward and downward, giving a downward-pointing ante-chamber in the front, necessitating an almost vertical mode of entry by the bird (Skutch 1960). It is made of fibrous rootlets with moss attached to roof and walls, and is of lighter, less dense construction than the nest of the White-breasted Wood Wren. Situated in low vegetation and shrubs, including bamboo thickets, frequently over a bank or ravine. Eggs two, totally white without markings; in Costa Rica late March to early June, in Andean Colombia December through June. Incubation by female alone, 19–20 days. Young fed by both sexes, fledging period 17–18 days. Possibly multiple-brooded. In addition to breeding nests, nests are built as roosting sites; these do not differ substantially from those used for breeding (and indeed may be used for this purpose), in contrast to the situation in the White-Breasted Wood Wren where the nests are clearly different in siting and construction. Single birds, pairs or entire families (of four) may roost together (Skutch 1960).

FOOD Apparently entirely invertebrate; no evidence of vegetable matter (Skutch 1960).

MOVEMENT Largely sedentary. In Guatemala, it is stated to frequent densely vegetated ravines during the dry season, but after rains to spread out from this habitat into thickets further up the mountains (Skutch 1960).

MEASUREMENTS (*H. l. mexicana*) Wing of male 51.5–55, of female 51–54; tail of male 27–30, of female 25–28.5; exposed culmen of male 13–14, of female 12–14; tarsus of male 23.5–24, of female 20–22.5 (Ridgway 1904).

75   WHITE-BREASTED WOOD WREN
Henicorhina leucosticta   Plate 17

Cyphorhinus leucosticta Cabanis 1847, Guiana

Alternative names: Lowland Wood Wren; Spanish *Soterrey de Selva Pechiblanco, Saltapared Gallinita*; Portuguese *Uirapuru-de-Peito-Branco*

The lowland congener of the Grey-breasted Wood Wren, found in lower altitude forest from eastern Mexico to the Guianas and Peru.

IDENTIFICATION Length 10–11.5cm. Distinguished from most other wrens by its small size and short tail. For distinctions from the Grey-breasted Wood Wren in the limited areas where the two species coexist, see under that species. Differs from the White-billed Wren *Uropsila leucogastra*, which is sympatric in Mexico, by its richer chestnut colour and strikingly marked face and cheeks; from various members of the genus *Thryothorus*, which have prominent facial markings, by its stubby tail and general form; and from the Southern Nightingale Wren *Microcerculus marginatus*, which has both a white belly and a short tail, by its facial pattern.

DESCRIPTION *H. l. leucosticta*
Adult Crown black, nape black with tips of feathers deep brown, back rich deep brown becoming more rufescent on rump. Rectrices deep reddish-brown with about eight narrow blackish bars extending across entire tail. Supercilium in front of eye greyish, behind eye white. Lores blackish-grey, area behind eye blackish with a border of small white spots at neck; ear-coverts conspicuously marked with grey-white spots and streaks on a black base. Throat, chin and chest white; sides of chest grey. Belly and flanks warm ochraceous-brown. Primaries and secondaries dull dark brown on innerwebs; outerwebs warm brown with darker brown markings forming indistinct wing-bars on closed wing. Underwing-coverts grey-brown. Iris brown, upper mandible black, lower mandible black with horn-coloured base, legs dark grey. Juvenile Crown brown, not black, with little contrast with colour of back; throat and chest much duller, either greyish or dull buff; chest and belly grey, sometimes with indistinct transverse barring.

GEOGRAPHICAL VARIATION
H. l. leucosticta 'Black-capped Wood Wren' (northeastern South America; eastern Venezuela, Guyana, Suriname, French Guiana [one record, Tostain 1980], northern Brazil) Described above.
H. l. hauxwelli 'Hauxwell's Wood Wren' (Tropical zone of upper Amazonia east of the Andes from southern Colombia, eastern Ecuador and northeastern Peru) Similar to *leucosticta* but wings, back and tail deeper, more rufous, chestnut, flanks somewhat darker rufous brown.

H. l. prostheleuca 'Sclater's Wood Wren' (southern and eastern Mexico, from Veracruz and Campeche to Northern Guatemala and Belize) Pileum reddish-brown, upperparts less rufescent than *tropea*.
H. l. smithei (central Petén of Guatemala, southern Yucatán, integrating with *prostheleuca* in Belize) Paler dorsally and on flanks of Central American forms; less rufous than *tropaea*, greyer dorsally than *pittieri*, and greyish-brown rather than rich reddish on crown (Dickerman 1973).
H. l. tropaea 'Central American Wood Wren' (Honduras and Nicaragua) Similar to *prostheleuca* but central crown-stripe more reddish-brown, back and flanks more rufescent (Hellmayr 1924-1949).
H. l. costaricensis (Costa Rica in the provinces of Cartago and Limón) Generally uniformly dark chocolate-brown dorsally, but always darker and usually less rufescent than other Central American populations (Dickerman 1973).
H. l. pittieri 'Pittier's Wood Wren' (south-western Costa Rica and Pacific slope of Panama east to the Canal Zone) Similar to *tropaea*, but upperparts bright chestnut, flanks more russet, median crown-stripe more rufescent (Hellmayr 1924-1949).
H. l. darienensis 'Darien Wood Wren' (Panama from Canal Zone eastwards to north-western Colombia) Similar to *tropaea*, but pileum black.
H. l. eucharis 'West Andean Wood Wren' (Subtropical zone of western Colombia) Similar to *prostheleuca* and *tropaea* but larger, upperparts duller, blackish barring on primaries and secondaries less prominent, malar streak absent, less black on cheeks.
H. l. albilateralis 'White-sided Wood Wren' (Tropical and subtropical zones of northern and north-western Colombia) Similar to *eucharis* but duller, with cinnamon-brown back and little grey on sides of flanks; differs from *hauxwelli* by having a brownish, not blackish, pileum and more distinctly barred wing-feathers.
H. l. inornata 'Lita Wood Wren' (Tropical zone of western Colombia south of the Río San Juan and extreme north-western Ecuador [Esmeraldas province]) Similar to *pittieri* but brighter upperparts, rufous pileum, white supercilium narrower, flanks deeper rufous-brown, bill thicker (Hellmayr 1924-1949).

The taxonomy of the White-breasted Wood Wren is somewhat fluid and debatable. It is possible that the Middle American races are specifically distinct from the disjunct South American population, and even that birds in Mexico may be separate from populations in Costa Rica and Panama (Winker *et al.* 1996).

VOICE The song, loud and with a power out of all proportion to the size of the bird, consists of three to five loud, clear whistles, forming a phrase constantly repeated. The phraseology of the song varies widely, sometimes with an ascending series of pure whistles, or a short trill followed by a few clear notes, with much variation between individuals and locations. A bird may repeat a particular phrase continuously, then after a short pause switch to a different phrase. Both sexes sing, frequently in response to each other. In a pair in Guatemala, the male's song consisted of three full rich whistles ascending in pitch; his mate answered with a pretty verse of five notes which were not quite so full and mellow as the song of the male (Skutch 1960). The female may sing while incubating. Calls vary within the species' extensive range; in Veracruz, Mexico, a bright, almost metallic *tink*; in Costa Rica, a hoarse *eerp* and in Panama, *bweer* (Winker 1996).

HABITAT Wet lowland forest, from sea-level to 1,300m in Mexico; in Costa Rica mostly between 300–1,850m, occasionally to 2,000m where the forest has been somewhat opened up (Carriker 1910, Skutch 1979). In South America usually below 1,100m but up to 1,800m in west Colombia and south Venezuela (Ridgely & Tudor 1989).

HABITS An intensely busy little bird, constantly foraging from ground level to 2–3m up, rarely higher; especially fond of tangles surrounding fallen trees and in ravines. Not excessively wary and will on occasion briefly come out into the open to inspect the quiet observer, but the dense nature of its habitat makes prolonged study difficult. Holds tail cocked over the back; when singing the whole bird throbs and vibrates. It will sometimes briefly join in flocks of other species following ant swarms but is not really a habitual swarm follower. Usually in pairs or family groups. Roosts in nests constructed for that specific purpose (see below); in contrast to the Grey-breasted Wood Wren, which is found at colder altitudes, White-breasted roost singly when adult. Young will roost with an adult, probably the female. When roosting the bird invariably faces outwards, so the white chest is visible through the nest entrance.

STATUS AND DISTRIBUTION Common or abundant in many parts of its range where habitat remains; however, the lowland terrain favoured by this species is especially attractive for agricultural development and it no longer occurs in parts of its former range. Mexico, from south-eastern San Luis Potosí through lowland areas throughout Central America, appearing on the Pacific coast from central Costa Rica southwards to northern Ecuador; disjunctly (separated by the Andes) in Amazonian Colombia, Ecuador, Peru and Venezuela (including the Orinoco drainage), the Guianas and Brazil south to Pará.

BREEDING In contrast to the Grey-breasted Wood Wren, the breeding nest of the White-breasted is quite distinct in construction and siting from that used for roosting. Five nests observed in Costa Rica (Skutch 1960) were all well concealed, either on the ground or very close (25cm) to it, built among tangles, roots and ferns or in one case in a tree-stump. A nest in Peru (race *hauxwelli*) was much higher (60cm) off the ground, and placed in vegetation on the trunk of a tree fern. The nest is a substantial construction, ovoid in shape and rather taller than wide, with a thick bottom, firm walls and roofs and a round, sidewards-facing entrance, the lower edge of which is well above the bottom and which is protected above by a visor-like projection of the roof (Skutch *loc.cit*). Nests are made of fibrous vegetable material, rootlets, etc., the outside camouflaged with moss. Interior is lined with feathers. Dimensions of Costa Rican nests are; height about 15cm; width 9–10cm, entrance about 5cm in diameter, depth of interior from entrance 5cm. Nest is built by both sexes. Eggs are two, usually immaculate glossy white, occasionally with a few brown speckles; in Costa Rica February to May, rarely January; in Suriname freshly-fledged young on 14 March and 26 May, and a female about to lay collected on 5 July (Haverschmidt 1968); in French Guiana, flying young on 3 December (Tostain *et al.* 1992); in Colombia, birds in breeding condition from January to July (Hilty & Brown 1986). Incubation probably by female alone, who may sing occasionally while sitting on eggs. Incubation period about 18 days. Young fed by both sexes, apparently entirely on animal matter, especially grubs and larvae and pupae. Adult birds do not fly direct to the nest, but walk the last few metres. Fledging period not known but presumably similar to the Grey-breasted Wood Wren (17–18 days).

The dormitory nest is quite different from the breeding nest, being much more flimsy in construction, longer than it is high and usually located higher up (1–2m, occasionally 0.6–3m). The doorway is level with the interior floor with no sill. No great effort seems to be made to conceal the nest. Dimensions of roosting nests about 12.5cm long and 10cm high. A number of dormitory nests may be built in a territory and each used only occasionally. In contrast to breeding nests which are usually located in dense tangles of vegetation, for better concealment, roosting nests are usually sited in the forks of slender saplings which cannot be climbed by a predator without alarming the occupant. After fledging the young leave the breeding nest and roost in a dormitory nest with the female until no longer dependent on the adults.

FOOD Mostly or entirely invertebrate.

MOVEMENTS Apparently entirely sedentary.

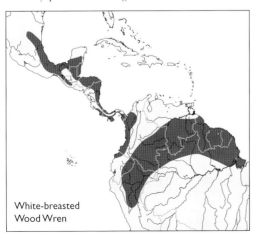

White-breasted
Wood Wren

MEASUREMENTS Wing of male 57–58, of female 49.5–54; tail of male 22.5–30.5, of female 21.5–27.5; exposed culmen of male 14.5–16.5 of female 14–16; tarsus of male 20–23.5, of female 19–24 (Ridgway 1904).

76 BAR-WINGED WOOD WREN
Henicorhina leucoptera   **Plate 17**

Henicorhina leucoptera Fitzpatrick, Terborgh and Willard 1977, Department of Cajamarca, Peru.

A newly described species, closely related to the Grey-breasted Wood Wren, so far only encountered in a few remote mountain areas of northern Peru and southern Ecuador.

IDENTIFICATION Length 11cm. It occurs frequently sympatrically with the Grey-breasted Wood Wren, from which it is immediately distinguished by the double white wing-bar on wings which are nearly black, by the narrow white edgings on the outer three primaries, by the paler underparts (intermediate between White-breasted and Grey-breasted Wood Wrens), and by the darker tail, faintly barred with dusky-brown.

DESCRIPTION
Adult Crown, centre light brown, greyish at front; fore-crown and narrow border over eyebrow neutral grey; mantle dark reddish-brown, warm reddish cast on lower back becoming amber on rump and uppertail-coverts. Lores grizzled white, purest white at base of bill and continuous with broad white supercilium stripe; conspicuous white eye-ring broken with black behind eye. Broad postocular patch black, a few feathers tinged fuscous; cheek, suboculars and malar region boldly streaked black and white; four white streaks extending to mantle and anterior sides. Broad black malar streak. Chin, throat and upper breast nearly white, becoming darker lower down and at sides; medial flank feathers tinged brown. Lower breast white to grey, becoming pale cinnamon on lower belly, crissum and undertail-coverts cinnamon-brown. Greater and median secondary coverts largely black, all broadly tipped white forming two solid white wing-bars; outermost greater secondary covert white on entire outerweb; primary coverts black, tipped white. Primaries almost entirely black, faintly barred burnt umber, outermost three edged white on outerweb, forming a bold white border. Secondaries largely black, narrowly barred dark reddish-brown on outerwebs. Rectrices black, finely barred fuscous on outerwebs and distal part of central pair. Tail partially graduated, outermost rectrices about 11mm shorter than central pair. Legs are heavier and longer than in the Grey-Breasted Wood Wren and the bill is larger and finer. Iris dark reddish-brown, upper mandible black, lower mandible black at base, paler grey to whitish at tip, legs dark grey (Fitzpatrick *et al.* 1977).
Juvenile (Only one specimen known.) Lacks crisp black and white on facial regions. White of belly less clear and extensive than adult, with some brown feathers scattered throughout. Lores grey, not white, eye-stripe does not extend in front of eye, without black border above. On wings only alula and a few primary coverts are tipped white.

GEOGRAPHICAL VARIATION No discernible differences between specimens taken from any of the presently known locations (Davis 1986).

VOICE Alarm call is a rapid, high-pitched chatter. The song is of two types, as in other species of *Henicorhina*. The first resembles the song of the Grey-breasted Wood Wren, a rich warbled phrase repeated in rapid succession, with a great variety of individual motifs. Compared to Grey-breasted Wood Wren the song is faster, higher, and has a more ringing quality, with more frequent trills. The second song type consists of longer phrases, beginning and ending with a trill, uttered singly or in pairs. Duetting is frequent, each sex singing its own motif in syncopation with its partner.

HABITAT Restricted to somewhat impoverished forest types, based upon a quartz sand, with a sparse canopy of stunted trees, of height mostly 6–9m. Due to rapid leaching the forest is very xeric and poor in variety of species, with a heavy understorey of ericaceous shrubs and bromeliads, the ground being carpeted with moss and lichens. In this habitat type it sometimes coexists with the Grey-breasted Wood Wren, but is frequently much more common, or may be the only species of *Henicorhina* present (Davis 1986). Recently also recorded in a variety of habitats, from tall, moist, hill forest to fern-covered slopes in savanna woodland (Barnett & Kirwan 1999).

HABITS Similar to the other species of the genus. Forages singly or in pairs, close to the ground in thick understorey. Flights are frequent, short and low to the ground. Tail is held cocked above the back as in the other species.
  When two similar species occupy the same area it is frequently found that each tends to specialise to a degree in food-gathering techniques, with a reduction in competition. It has been suggested (Fitzpatrick *et al.* 1977) that, with its heavier legs and longer, finer bill, the Bar-winged Wood Wren is differentiated from the Grey-breasted Wood Wren in foraging speciality, tending to spend more time on vertical perches or foraging near the ground. Presumably this degree of specialisation has allowed it, as a relict species, to persist in a few areas of isolated, impoverished habitat in the face of competition from the successful and widespread Grey-breasted Wood Wren.

STATUS AND DISTRIBUTION Originally described from two locations in remote mountain regions of northern Peru, near the Ecuadorian border. One was in the Cordillera del Condor, Department of Cajamarca, at elevations of 1,950–2,450m and the other above the headwaters of the Río Neva, Department of San Martín, at an elevation of 1,900m. Has since been found in two further Peruvian locations in the Department of San

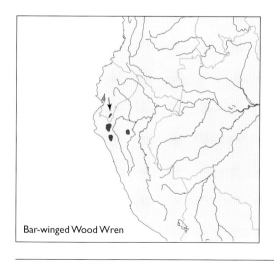

Bar-winged Wood Wren

Martín and La Libertad (Davis 1986) and more recently on the Ecuadorian side of the border, also in the Sierra de Condor (Krabbe & Sornoza 1994). Given the very limited range, will always be vulnerable to any habitat destruction in the future. Presently it seems to be common or abundant in its known locations.

BREEDING Nests and eggs unknown, but presumably similar to those of the Grey-breasted Wood Wren. One bird in juvenile plumage taken 19 July.

FOOD Insects (Davis 1986).

MOVEMENTS Presumably totally sedentary.

MEASUREMENTS Wing of male 54.4–58.2, of female 57.0–55.2; tail of male 35.0–37.0, of female 32.2–34.8; exposed culmen of male 10.6–12.0, of female 10.5–11.8; bill to skull of male 18.2–19.0, of female 18.0–20.0; tarsus of male 25.0–26.2, of female 24.8–26.0 (Fitzpatrick *et al.* 1977).

MICROCERCULUS

A small group of wrens adapted to life in the lower levels of dense rainforest. Typically very dark plumage, short rounded wings, extremely short tail and heavy legs, with a bill quite thick and as long as the head. Probably most closely related to *Henicorhina*, but much more terrestrial in behaviour; share, by convergent evolution, many features of the smaller Antpittas such as *Grallaricula* which occupy similar ecological niches. Extremely secretive and difficult to observe, but superb singers, whose haunting, beautiful whistled songs are a characteristic sound of lower altitude humid forests from Mexico to Bolivia.

The taxonomy of the genus is disputed, fluid, confusing and liable to change. We have followed what appears to be the contemporary majority opinion and treated the group as four species, while recognising that this is unlikely to be the last word on the subject.

In Brazil, birds of this genus are considered hunting-charms, ensuring success in the pursuit of deer; however, to be efficacious for this purpose the bird must be caught on a Thursday or a Friday with a waxing moon (Sick 1993).

77   SOUTHERN NIGHTINGALE WREN
Microcerculus marginatus   **Plate 18**

Heterocnemis marginata Sclater 1855 'Bogotá' Colombia.

Alternative names: Scaly-breasted Wren; Spanish *Cucarachero Ruiseñor, Cucarachero Silbador*; Portuguese *Uirapupu-Veado*

The most widely distributed member of its genus, a secretive skulker in the lower levels of dense humid forest, frequently only detected by its superb song. More than one species may be involved.

IDENTIFICATION Length 11cm. Usually detected by song, which is completely diagnostic. There are major variations in plumage throughout the species' range, with corresponding complications in identification. In all cases the extremely short tail separates this wren from all other genera except the wood wrens, *Henicorhina*, which are immediately distinguishable by their strongly-marked ear-coverts and white or grey underparts. The Central American race *luscinia* (sometimes regarded as a separate species [Stiles 1983]) has a pale throat and rich brown back. In form it closely resembles the Northern Nightingale Wren which is a much darker, scaled bird, but the two species do not appear to overlap

although they closely approach sympatry in Costa Rica (Stiles *loc. cit.*). In South American populations the adults have mostly white underparts, while in the juvenile the underparts are dark brown. Populations in western Ecuador, northern Colombia and western Venezuela have heavily scaled underparts. In all cases the species' behaviour, walking on the forest floor with a mincing, rail-like gait with constant teeterings in the manner of a Spotted Sandpiper *Actitis macularia*, distinguishes it from all sympatric wrens and confusion is in fact more likely with some of the smaller antbirds, although the absence of wing-bars or spots eliminates these species. It does not overlap in range with the structurally-similar Flutist Wren. In central Colombia the Speckle-breasted Wren is superficially similar to the local race of Southern Nightingale Wren, but differs totally in habits and structure, being a typical long-tailed *Thryothorus*.

DESCRIPTION *M. m. marginatus*
Adult Crown, nape, shoulders and back deep chocolate-brown, becoming slightly more rufescent on rump. Rectrices dark chocolate-brown. Lores and ear-coverts

dull grey-brown. Chin, throat and chest white; feathers of sides of chest and upper belly have dark tips giving a scalloped appearance. Lower belly, flanks and thighs deep chocolate-brown. Primaries and secondaries dark chocolate-brown on outerwebs; tertials the same colour with very obscure darker barring. Underwing-coverts dark chocolate. Iris dark-brown, upper mandible black, lower mandible black at tip, cream at base. Legs greyish-black.

Juvenile Crown and back with obscure darker barring. White of chin, throat and upper chest with dark brown tips to each feather, giving a scalloped appearance. Dull black barring of flanks more pronounced.

GEOGRAPHICAL VARIATION

M. m. marginatus (western Amazonia, including southern Venezuela, eastern Colombia, eastern Ecuador and Peru south to north-eastern Bolivia and north-western Brazil) Described above.

M. m. squamulatus 'Squamulated Wren' (includes *M. m. antioquensis*) (north-western Venezuela and north-eastern Colombia) Underparts with conspicuous scaly markings.

M. m. taeniatus 'Illingworth's Wren' (Tropical zone of western Ecuador) Similar to *squamulatus* but deeper rufous brown on upperparts, blackish barring on underparts wider and more sharply defined.

M. m. luscinia 'Whistling Wren' (central Costa Rica to eastern Darién, Panama) Pale throat, back rich brown.

M. m. corrasus 'Santa Marta Squamulated Wren' (Santa Marta region, Colombia) Very similar to *squamulatus* but bill finer, ground colour of underparts purer white, bars on foreneck, breast and middle of abdomen narrower.

M. m. occidentalis 'Western Scaly-breasted Wren' (western Colombia and north-western Ecuador) Similar to *marginatus* but bill longer and more slender, upperparts darker, sides of body darker chocolate-brown, broad blackish bars on abdomen.

Recent studies of the DNA of populations of *marginatus* north and south of the Amazon suggest a major difference, even though there is no obvious external plumage distinction between the populations (J. Bates pers. comm.).

VOICE All populations have spectacular, arresting songs, although there are major differences in the songs throughout the range, differences which may ultimately be best reflected in specific status. The song of the Central American population opens with a series of about 10–15 short notes that decelerate, lengthen, increase in loudness and rise in pitch, followed by two loud, upslurred notes. There follows a series of pure, long-drawn-out high-pitched whistles, which gradually become longer, then begins a series of double whistles (Stiles 1984). The complete song sequence takes about $2^{1}/_{2}$ minutes. This song type extends through Panama into western Amazonia, with minor differences in eastern Amazonia. In eastern Peru and northern Bolivia the song consists of pure, clear notes given almost at random, with changes in length, pitch and loudness (Ridgely & Tudor 1989). Calls, an antbird-like chatter and a strong *stchep* (Slud 1958).

HABITAT Lower levels of humid tropical and subtropical forest from sea-level up to 1,800m in Venezuela, 1,200m in Colombia and 1,700m on the Pacific coast of Costa Rica; one record at 3,100m in Chiriquí, Panama (Ridgely 1976).

HABITS Intensely secretive and almost always detected by song or call-notes; however, with patience it may be decoyed into view by a whistled imitation of its song or with a tape-recorder. Spends most of its time on or very near the ground, walking in the manner of a miniature rail or antpitta; it has a habit of constantly teetering its tail, much in the manner of an Ovenbird *Seiurus aurocapillus*. Solitary; does not associate with other species and, except for the population in southern Central America, does not appear to follow ant swarms.

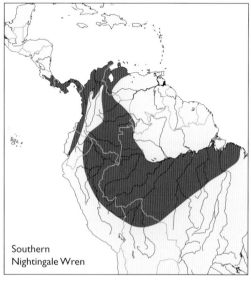

Southern Nightingale Wren

STATUS AND DISTRIBUTION Costa Rica south and east from the Río Barranca on the Pacific drainage and the Río Reventazón on the Caribbean, Panama (absent from lowlands on Pacific slope in west of country), northern Venezuela, most of Colombia except for the higher Andes and drier areas, Amazonian drainage of eastern Ecuador, eastern Peru and north-eastern Bolivia, western Brazil extending eastwards south of the River Amazon to the Atlantic coast (Pará and Maranhão). While population density never appears to be very high, it is reasonably common in suitable habitat over much of its range.

BREEDING Nest and eggs only recently discovered (Christian & Roberts 2000). Two nests have now been described, both in Panama, one in the Canal Zone at an altitude of 90m, the other in Chiriquí province at 1,600m. Both were located in burrows in earthen banks, originally made in all probability by Scaly-throated Leaftosser *Sclerurus guatemalensis* and Blue-crowned Motmot *Momotus momota* respectively. The nest is made of dead leaves placed at the end of the burrows. The two clutches so far observed were of three and two eggs. Eggs are stated to be white (Schönwetter 1963–1974), but without confirmatory detail. Incubation period of one clutch 16–17 days; fledging period 19–20 days, young fed by both sexes. The eggs in the Canal Zone nest were probably laid about 1 July, and in the Chiriquí nest about 21 May. However, adults have been seen feeding recently-fledged young in Costa Rica in mid-February; a female in breeding condition was taken in the Canal Zone in November (Wetmore 1984).

FOOD Little information; adults in Panama were seen to carry spiders and Orthoptera to nestlings (Christian & Roberts 2000).

MOVEMENTS Appears to be totally sedentary, with no evidence of seasonal altitudinal movement.

MEASUREMENTS (*M. m. luscinia*) Wing of male 52.4–58.6, of female 52.5–59.2; tail of male 23.5–24.5, of female 16.5; exposed culmen of male 16.9–20.0, of female 15.9–19.4; tarsus of male 21.3–23.7, of female 20.6–23.3 (Ridgway 1904, Stiles 1983).

---

78   NORTHERN NIGHTINGALE WREN
Microcerculus philomela

Plate 18

Cyphorhinus philomela Salvin 1861, Alta Vera Paz, Guatemala.

Alternative names: Spanish *Soterrey Ruiseñor, Saltapared Ruiseñor, 'Pito real'* (Costa Rica), *Chinchivirín Cholincillo*

The northernmost representative of the *Microcerculus* complex, resident in humid forest from Mexico to northern Costa Rica. Formerly lumped specifically with populations in southern Central America and South America.

IDENTIFICATION Length 10–11.5cm. A small, terrestrial, very dark wren, which when properly seen is not readily confused with any other wren in its range. The very dark plumage, almost non-existent tail, and rail-like behaviour is diagnostic. The Song Wren, which is sympatric from Honduras to Costa Rica, has a rufous chest, obvious bare orbital ring and behaves rather differently. The female Silver-fronted Tapaculo *Scytalopus argentifrons* is superficially somewhat similar, but has a greyish chest and throat, with bars, rather than scallops, on the lower underparts only; the range of geographic and altitudinal overlap is very limited.

DESCRIPTION
Adult Crown, nape, shoulders, back and rump deep chocolate-brown, each feather tipped with blackish, giving a scalloped appearance at close range. Rectrices dull brownish-black. Sides of face and lores dark greyish-brown. Throat dark grey, each feather with a dark blackish-brown tip giving a mottled appearance. Chest and belly dull blackish-brown with scattered paler greyish speckling; lower belly and flanks with a more rufescent tinge with obscure darker barring on flanks. Primaries and secondaries dull blackish-brown. Underwing-coverts dull blackish-brown. Iris dark brown, bill and legs black.
Juvenile Similar to adult, darker and less rufescent above, the feathers of the crown and back obscurely edged with black; below darker and duskier, with little grey and no white, the feathers distinctly edged, and squamate in appearance (Blake 1953).

GEOGRAPHICAL VARIATION None; monotypic.

VOICE The song is 'amazing' (Stiles & Skutch 1989) 'marvelous' (Griscom 1932a) and 'unmistakable and haunting' (Howell & Webb 1995). It consists of a long series of clear whistled notes, at the rate of about two per second, each changing in pitch unpredictably, either higher or lower than the one preceding; the whole

sequence, which can go on for half a minute, famously described by Stiles (1983) as giving the impression of a 'slightly tone-deaf person whistling a hymn-tune', usually preceded by a softer, more rapid series of ascending notes. Call, a harsh *thuk*; juvenile begging call, a soft, sad *peew* (Stiles & Skutch 1989).

HABITAT Humid forest, especially undisturbed virgin forest, from near sea-level to 1,200m, occasionally as high as 1,800m.

HABITS A very retiring, secretive inhabitant of dark forest floors; spends most of its time walking, with a constant teeter of the tail, on the ground or on fallen logs; rarely more than a metre above the ground. Sings from perches on or near the ground. Very difficult to observe, and prone to vanish surreptitiously at the slightest disturbance.

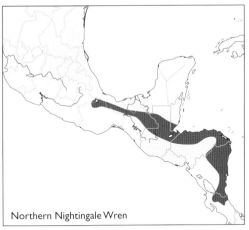
Northern Nightingale Wren

STATUS AND DISTRIBUTION In suitable habitat where it remains, from southern Mexico (eastern Chiapas), central Guatemala, extreme southern Belize, the Caribbean slopes of Honduras and Nicaragua to Costa Rica, mostly on the Caribbean drainage, south to the Río Reventazón, beyond which it is replaced by the Southern Nightingale Wren. Sea-level to 1,400m in Honduras, locally common in Costa Rica; uncommon in Guatemala (Land 1970).

BREEDING Nest and eggs undescribed; in Costa Rica breeds from May or June through to at least September (Stiles & Skutch 1989).

FOOD Little information, presumably largely invertebrate. In Costa Rica, insects, spiders, centipedes and sow-bugs (woodlice) (Stiles & Skutch 1989).

MOVEMENTS Apparently entirely sedentary.

MEASUREMENTS Wing of male 52.4–58.6, of female 57.7–58.3; exposed culmen of male 15.9–18.2, of female 16.0–18.1; tarsus of male 19.9–21.5, of female 19.8–21.6 (Stiles 1983).

79   FLUTIST WREN
Microcerculus ustulatus   Plate 18

Microcerculus ustulatus Salvin & Godman 1883, Cerro Roraima, British Guiana.

Alternative names: Spanish *Cucarachero flautista*

A secretive terrestrial species of the forest floor, most often detected by its superb song, with a fairly limited distribution in (mostly) inaccessible areas of Venezuela, Guyana and Brazil.

IDENTIFICATION Length 11.5cm. A very dark, uniform species. It overlaps in range with the Tepui Wren, which differs in its conspicuous eye-stripe and longer tail; the behaviour of the two species is also dissimilar, since the Flutist Wren is a typical ground-walking *Microcerculus* while the Tepui Wren is a typical *Troglodytes*. From Southern Nightingale Wren, in the limited area of overlap, by the absence of a whitish throat. Superficially similar to some female *Scytalopus* Tapaculos, but allopatric with all confusable species.

DESCRIPTION *M. u. obscurus*
Adult Crown rich chocolate-brown, back, shoulders and rump slightly more rufescent. Rectrices dark chocolate-brown. Lores, sides of face and ear-coverts dark rufescent-brown. Chin lighter than crown, light chocolate-brown with obscure narrow dark edgings to feathers; colour becomes richer, and edgings broader and more prominent, on chest and upper belly. Lower belly, flanks, thighs and vent darker rufescent chocolate-brown. Primaries and secondaries dull blackish-brown. Iris brown, upper mandible black, lower mandible cream at the bottom with darker tip, legs black.
Juvenile Undescribed.

GEOGRAPHICAL VARIATION
M. u. obscurus (Mts Ptari-Tepui and Sororopán-Tepui, Bolívar, Venezuela) Described above.
M. u. ustulatus 'Roraima Nightingale Wren' (Sub-tropical zone of southern Guyana and adjacent south-eastern Venezuela) Paler on back than *obscurus*, and less rufous below.
M. u. duidae 'Duida Nightingale Wren' (Cerro Duida, Amazonas, Venezuela) Similar to *ustulatus* but paler throughout; upperparts lighter and less rufous, underparts less umber.
M. u. lunatipectus (Mt Guaiquinima, Bolívar, Venezuela) Differs from other races by having more prominent squamulations below, which extend forward over the breast and invade the throat.

VOICE Truly remarkable. The song is a beautiful glissando; after one or two brief introductory notes, it gradually and slowly slides upwards, the whole song often taking 10–20 or even more seconds. A variant is similar but

the notes are more clipped and gradually drop in pitch (Ridgely & Tudor 1989).

HABITAT Dense wet montane forest, including the summits of some of the tepuis, 860–2,100m.

HABITS Much like other members of the genus; terrestrial, spending most of its time walking with teetering gait on or close to the ground. Secretive and not easy to observe; will respond to tape-recordings of its song.

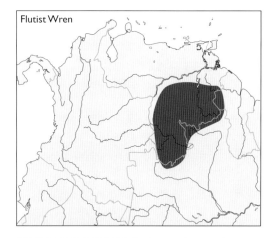
Flutist Wren

STATUS AND DISTRIBUTION Southern and eastern Venezuela (Amazonas and Bolívar), north-western Brazil (Roraima) and extreme western Guyana. Quite common. Most locations are extremely inaccessible, but the species is readily found by the El Dorado-Santa Elena road in eastern Bolívar, Venezuela (Wheatley 1994).

BREEDING Nest and eggs undescribed.

FOOD Little information; presumably principally invertebrate.

MOVEMENTS Apparently totally sedentary.

MEASUREMENTS Wing of male 49–59, of female 54–56; tail of male 28–33, of female 28–29; exposed culmen of male 15.9–17.6, of female 13.7–16.8; tarsus of male 20.4–24.6, of female 22.0–24.2.

Formicerius bambla Boddaert 1783. Cayenne.

Alternative names: White-banded Wren; Spanish *Cucachero bandeado*, French *Troglodyte bambla*; Portuguese *Uirapuru-de-asa branca*

A very distinctively marked, highly terrestrial wren with an arresting and beautiful song.

IDENTIFICATION Length 11.5cm. Unlike any other wren except the Bar-winged Wood Wren, which overlaps it neither geographically nor in habitat. The prominent white bar on the greater coverts is diagnostic; a less conspicuous bar is formed by white edgings to the median coverts. More likely to be confused with some antbirds than any wren; the Banded Antbird *Dichrozona cincta*, which is sympatric in a limited area of Venezuela, is superficially similar, but is immediately distinguished by its white underparts and spotted chest. Most other antbirds with wing-bars are grey rather than brown.

DESCRIPTION *M. b. bambla*
Adult Crown, back, shoulders and rump dark chocolate-brown, each feather obscurely tipped darker. Rectrices dull blackish-brown with very obscure darker barring. Lores and ear-coverts dark brown. Chin dull greyish, throat somewhat darker, chest greyish-brown with narrow dark bars on each feather. Belly and flanks browner and less grey than chest, with darker and lighter barring. Wing-coverts dark chocolate-brown, the greater primary and secondary coverts with broad white tips forming a complete white bar across the entire closed wing; primaries and secondaries dark chocolate-brown. Underwing-coverts dull chocolate. Iris brown, upper mandible black, lower mandible yellowish with dusky tip, legs brownish-grey.
Juvenile Lacks the white edgings to the greater coverts; scaling on chest possibly more pronounced.

GEOGRAPHICAL VARIATION
  M. b. bambla (south-eastern Venezuela [Bolívar], the Guianas, north-eastern Brazil [Roraima]) Described above.
  M. b. caurensis 'Venezuelan Banded Wren' (eastern Venezuela [western Bolívar]) Similar to *bambla* but upperparts brighter rufous, lacks dusky markings on back, breast and flanks.
  M. b. albigularis 'Western Banded Wren' (eastern Ecuador, western Brazil) Resembles *caurensis* but throat markedly paler.

VOICE The song, one of the most beautiful sounds of the Amazonian rainforest, starts with three to six long, clear and high-pitched notes separated by relatively short pauses. It may end after this prologue, but more frequently the last whistle is followed by several notes becoming faster and merging into a long sustained glissando of shorter and slightly lower notes (Huguet & Tostain 1990). Song occurs at dawn and dusk, or during the day after heavy rain; the song is delivered from a log or branch, the singer with head and bill pointed upwards and wings quivered (Jullien & Cariveau in press). Call, a sharp metallic *chek*.

HABITAT Lowland rainforest, including forests with both a dense understorey and more open types, provided that the understorey is wet and rich in rotting logs. Absent from drier parts of forest that do not meet those requirements (Jullien & Cariveau in press). Usually at lower elevations than Flutist Wren *M. ustulatus*, mostly sea-level to 1,100m, but recorded to 1,500m in Venezuela (Ridgely & Tudor 1989).

HABITS Furtive and retiring. Very terrestrial; frequently not caught in mist-nets because it routinely walks underneath them. Seems to be rather specialised in its feeding habits. In contrast to other species of *Microcerculus*, rarely explores leaf-litter; instead, spends most of its time exploring rotten logs and the detritus resulting from rotting trees, frequently disappearing for a few seconds into cavities in rotten stumps.

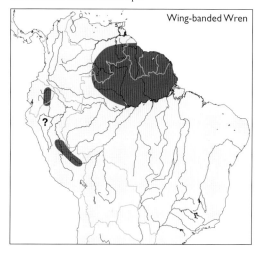

Wing-banded Wren

STATUS AND DISTRIBUTION North-eastern South America, from French Guiana through Suriname and Guyana to eastern and southern Venezuela (Bolívar and Amazonas) and adjacent Brazil. In French Guiana not common, but widely spread in the forested interior massif. In Suriname not recorded until 1968 (Mees 1968) and probably not common. Apparently more abundant in Guyana (e.g. Iwokrama Reserve) (D. Agro pers. comm.). Isolated populations in eastern Ecuador (Napo and Pastaza) and south-eastern Peru (Terborgh *et al.* 1984).

BREEDING To date, only two nests have been described, both at the Nouragues biological research station, French Guiana. They were found on 21 and 22 March 1999 respectively. Each was located in an old termite nest, situated on a rotten buttress of a fallen dead tree, about 2m above the ground. Both termitaries were highly concealed by vegetation. Wren nests were located in cavities in the termite nests, previously excavated by another species of bird, most probably the Yellow-billed Jacamar *Galbula albirostris*. When discovered, each nest held one well-developed nestling. Adults visited the nests with food about four to six times an hour. Prey items brought to the nest included moths, tiny frogs, worms, orthoptera and spiders. Both young fledged by 26 and 28 March respectively (Jullien & Cariveau in press). Apart from this, the only information relating to breeding is of a bird in French Guiana carrying food on 21 January (Tostain *et al.* 1992). Colour of eggs, incubation period, etc. not known.

FOOD No recorded data, apart from that mentioned above.

MOVEMENTS Apparently entirely sedentary.

MEASUREMENTS Wing 58–64, bill length 13.3–16.0, tarsus 23.2–27.4 (six individuals, not sexed) (M. Jullien, field measurements).

CYPHORHINUS

Small to medium-sized wrens, extensively adapted to a terrestrial existence on the forest floor and showing many features converging on the characteristics of ground-dwelling antbirds. Bill compressed laterally with a peculiar and unique sharp arched upper surface, usually about the same length as the head. Wings short and very rounded; tail very short, the individual rectrices rounded. Legs and feet quite sturdy. Plumage typically uniform brown or rufous, with barring on flight feathers and coloured bare skin around the eye.

81 CHESTNUT-BREASTED WREN
Cyphorhinus thoracicus   Plate 19

Cyphorhinus thoracicus Tschudi 1844, mountains of Uchubamba, near Vitoc, Junín, Peru.

Alternative names: Spanish *Soterrey Pechicastaño*

A little-known species, found in mountain forests discontinuously from the Colombian to the Peruvian Andes.

IDENTIFICATION Length 15cm. Perhaps just as likely to be confused with an antbird or even a tapaculo as with other wren species. The very different Plain-Tailed Wren aside, Chestnut-breasted Wren is unique in its lack of barring on wings and tail. A number of antbirds have a similar altitudinal range, and females are superficially similar. Uniform Antshrike *Thamnophilus unicolor* has grey cheeks, pale eyes and lacks the capped appearance of the northern race of Chestnut-backed Wren. The Immaculate Antbird *Myrmeciza immaculata* is substantially larger and has a much more extensive area of bare blue skin round the eye. The bill shape of *Cyphorhinus* wrens and antbirds differ quite markedly, the high-ridged but pointed shape of the wrens bills being unique and diagnostic. Sympatric Tapaculos, though similar to wrens in shape and in their retiring terrestrial habits, always lack the bright chestnut throat of the present species. From Song Wren by lack of barring on flight feathers and absence of obvious bare blue skin around and behind eye and from Musician Wren by absence of obvious supercilium, unbarred wings and lack of blue skin around eye.

DESCRIPTION *C. t. thoracicus*
Adult Crown sooty brown-black, back and rump rich dark brown, rectrices dark brown. Lores concolor with crown. Bare skin around eye blue. Area behind eye and ear-coverts deep orange-brown. Chin brownish-grey, throat and chest deep orange-brown, upper belly buffy-orange, lower belly, flanks, thighs and vent dark-brown. Shoulders, coverts and remiges dark brown, primaries slightly paler than secondaries. Underwing-coverts dark brown. Iris brown, bill and legs black.
Juvenile Very similar to adult; lower belly paler.

GEOGRAPHICAL VARIATION
C. t. thoracicus 'Ferruginous-breasted Wren' (Peru, from northern Pumo through Cuzco, Junín, Ayacucho to Huánuco) Described above.
C. t. dichrous 'Chestnut-breasted Wren' (northern Peru [San Martín] disjunctly in Ecuador [eastern Andes] and in Colombia from northern Nariño to Antioquia) Similar to *thoracicus* but darker on head, wings and abdomen.

VOICE Song is quite different from that of either the Song or Musician Wrens. It lacks the harsh notes of the Song Wren, but consists of a series of unearthly, ethereal clear whistles, usually three or four in number, in a repeated cadence, often one note rising, one on a constant pitch and one falling, or variations of this, repeated many times over. Calls, a harsh *churr*.

HABITAT Wet, montane forest including cloudforest with moss and epiphytes. 1,300–2,300m in western Colombia, down to 700m on Pacific slope.

HABITS Little known. Very difficult to observe, mostly terrestrial. Nothing recorded about feeding techniques or social organisation. Far more often heard than seen.

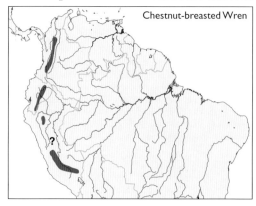
Chestnut-breasted Wren

STATUS AND DISTRIBUTION Four disjunct populations. In Colombia quite common, elsewhere uncommon to locally common (Ridgely & Tudor 1989), from Antioquia through western Andes (both slopes) and central Andes, south to Cauca and Tolima; in central Ecuador south to Zamora-Chinchipe; in northern Peru (San Martín); and in central and southern Peru (Huánuco to Puno). Status in north-central Peru (northern Huánuco and southern San Martín) obscure.

BREEDING Nest and eggs undescribed; presumably similar to other members of the genus. Birds in breeding condition in June, central Andes of Colombia; grown juvenile in April above Cali; and nest-building in September, with two juveniles accompanying adults in December (Hilty & Brown 1986).

FOOD Not recorded; presumably mainly or entirely invertebrate.

MOVEMENTS Probably entirely sedentary.

MEASUREMENTS Wing of male 73.5–74.5, of female 68–71; tail of male 43–49, of female 45–47; exposed culmen of male 20.5–21, of female 17.5–19; tarsus of male 28–30, of female 26.5–28.

---

82   SONG WREN
Cyphorhinus phaeocephalus   Plate 19

Cyphorhinus phaeocephalus Sclater 1860, Esmeraldas, Ecuador.

Alternative names: Spanish *Violinero, Soterrey Canoro*

A dark, ground-dwelling wren of humid woodland, elusive but frequently heard.

IDENTIFICATION Length 13cm. Its dark plumage, bare orbital ring and terrestrial habits result in the Song Wren being frequently mistaken for an antbird. The female Bare-crowned Antbird *Gymnocichla nudiceps* is superficially similar, but is substantially larger, longer-tailed and lacks barring on the wings and rectrices. The Chestnut-backed Antbird *Myrmeciza exsul* is more similar in shape, but has whitish spots on the shoulders and coverts and again lacks barring on the flight feathers. The Tawny-throated Leaftosser *Sclerurus mexicanus* has unbarred wings and tail and lacks the bare orbital ring. In Colombia, Chestnut-breasted Wren has a reduced area of bare skin around the eye, and flight feathers without prominent bars; it is also altitudinally separated.

DESCRIPTION *C. p. phaeocephalus*
Adult Crown blackish-brown, becoming rich dark brown on back, shoulders and rump; upper and middle back with very obscure, narrow transverse darker bars, barely discernible. Rectrices blackish-brown. Lores blackish-brown, ear-coverts and area behind eye warm orange-brown, chin, throat and chest warm orange-brown becoming medium brown on sides and on belly. Occasionally some white feathers on lower belly. Primaries and secondaries dark brown on innerweb; outerwebs with orange-brown markings, forming narrow bars across closed wing. Underwing-coverts warm brown. Bare skin around eye flesh-coloured or greyish-white except for area behind eye which is pale blue. Iris brown, bill black, legs brown.
Juvenile No apparent differences from adult. Some individuals, possibly juvenile birds, have a variable amount of white on the throat, ranging from a small patch on the chin to a completely white throat.

GEOGRAPHICAL VARIATIONS
   C. p. phaeocephalus 'Dusky-headed Song Wren' (north-western South America, from the Río Sucio in western Colombia south to El Oro province in southern Ecuador) Described above.

   C. p. propinqua 'Jaraquiel Song Wren' (north-western Colombia [Bolívar and Santander]) Paler than the nominate race on both upper and lower parts, throat more contrasting with chest.
   C. p. lawrencii 'Lawrence's Song Wren' (north-western Colombia and most of Panama except the north-west [western Bocas del Toro]) Rufous throat contrasts with paler chest.
   C. p. infuscata 'Costa Rican Song Wren' (north-western Panama [Almirante Bay] and Caribbean lowlands of Costa Rica) Darker than *lawrencii* with crown often distinctly blackish.
   C. p. richardsoni 'Richardson's Song Wren' (eastern Nicaragua and south-eastern Honduras) Very similar to *lawrencii* but rump more brightly rufescent and blackish on malar region reduced.

VOICE Song is a truly remarkable medley of harsh *chowk chowk-a-chowk chuck* noises interspersed with clear, flute-like whistles, rising or falling. Pairs sing antiphonally, each bird leaving its own motif of pure whistled notes, usually three or four, rising or falling in pitch, the combination giving a complex pattern of notes, repeated many times, mixed with harsher *chowk-chowk* notes; 'a musician who strives for bizarre effects' (Skutch 1960). Calls are harsh and frog-like, resembling parts of the song; alarm call a series of harsh *churrs*.

HABITAT Understorey of humid forest and in second growth woodland, from sea-level to 1,000m.

HABITS Feeds on or close to the ground or on fallen logs, poking around under fallen leaf-litter. Wary and not easily observed. Lives in family groups throughout most of the year. Male offspring delay dispersal and may remain associated with their parents for 4–18 months after fledging; they do not, however, care for younger siblings. Mature females actively initiate divorce and frequently leave a mate after several successful breeding seasons, even when an alternative male is not immediately available (T. Richardson pers. comm.). Will sometimes follow ant swarms, often in the company of various antbirds. Roosts communally in nests, sometimes up to six birds.

STATUS AND DISTRIBUTION Reasonably common over much of its range. A few records from eastern

Song Wren

penetrating only slightly east of the Río Magdalena in Santander; Ecuador, west of the Andes and lower slopes, from Esmeraldas to El Oro. Not so far encountered in Peru. Sea-level to 700m, more rarely to 1,050m.

BREEDING Builds a bulky, untidy nest shaped like an elbow, built over a thin branch with nesting-chamber on one side and the downward-pointed entrance on the other; about 25cm in overall length, 15cm high and 12.5cm wide, made of coarse fibrous roots, leaf skeletons and decayed fragments of vine; nesting-chamber thickly lined with leaf skeletons. 0.6–2.5m above ground level (Skutch 1960). Eggs two, white with a variable amount of brown speckles around the thick end. Incubation and fledging periods not known. Nesting season in Costa Rica January to May, rarely October (Stiles & Skutch 1989), in Colombia, birds in breeding-condition March to May (Hilty & Brown 1986).

FOOD Apparently entirely invertebrate; small insects and spiders, mostly captured on or near the ground.

MOVEMENTS Completely sedentary.

MEASUREMENTS Wing of male 59–71, of female 58–62; tail of male 28–35, of female 26–29; exposed culmen of male 18–21.5, of female 19–21; tarsus of male 24.5—7.5, of female 24–24.5.

Honduras (Río Segovia, Olancho), Caribbean slope of Nicaragua and Costa Rica (reaching the Pacific slope in Guanacaste province); Panama, on entire Caribbean slope and on Pacific slope from eastern Coclé through Darién; Colombia, mostly close to the Pacific coast,

---

83   MUSICIAN WREN
Cyphorhinus aradus

Plate 19

Mymornis arada Hermann 1783, Cayenne.

Alternative names: Musical Wren, Quadrille Wren, Organ Bird, Carillon Bird, Necklaced Jungle Wren; French *Troglodyte arada*; Spanish *Soterrey Virtuoso Violinero*; Portuguese *Musico, Uirapuru-verdadeiro*; Suriname *Baskupu, Kaptenkupu*

As its various names suggest, the Musician wren has one of the most arresting songs of any South American bird; curiously, in Suriname, the song is considered to be a bad omen for hunters. Sometimes 'lumped' with Song Wren.

IDENTIFICATION Length 12.5cm. Resembles Song Wren (from which it is geographically separated), but has a brighter orange chest and throat, with front of crown and supercilium more orange, with less dark on the crown; pale blue skin around edge less extensive than in Song Wren. On a poor look more likely to be confused with an antbird, which differ in bill shape, lack of barring on wings and general deportment.

DESCRIPTION *C. a. aradus*
Adult Crown and nape deep reddish-chestnut. Shoulders and upper back with a broad collar of brownish-black, conspicuously marked with broad longitudinal buff-white streaks, contrasting with both the nape and the lower back. Lower back and rump less deep warm brown. Rectrices similar in base colour to rump, but with four to six inconspicuous bars of darker brown. Supercilium pale orange-white, contrasting with cap and with orange-brown eye-stripe and ear-coverts. Chin, throat and upper chest bright orange-brown, darker

below, sharply demarcated from paler orange-buff lower chest and belly; flanks and lower belly medium ochraceous-brown. Underwing-coverts dull brownish-grey. Iris brown, upper mandible greyish-black, lower mandible greyish with whitish at base, legs brown or greyish-black.
Juvenile Very similar to adult; indistinct barring on lower belly may be a consistent feature.

GEOGRAPHICAL VARIATION
   C. a. aradus (north-eastern South America [Guianas, adjacent Venezuela and Brazil]) Described above.
   C. a. faroensis (northern Brazil) Similar to *aradus* in having conspicuous streaks on shoulders.
   C. a. griseolateralis 'Grey-flanked Musician Wren' (Brazil in drainage of Rio Tapajos) Collar reduced in extent when compared to *aradus* or *faroensis*, generally more grey above and below.
   C. a. urbanoi (region of Faro and Obidos, Pará, Brazil) Similar to *aradus* in having a black and white collar, but distinctly paler above and below.
   C. a. interposita 'Todd's Musician Wren' (Brazil, west of the Rio Tapajos to northern Matto Grosso) Collar absent, auriculars brownish-grey, not rufous.
   C. a. salvini 'Salvin's Musician Wren' (south-eastern Colombia, eastern Ecuador, possibly north-western Brazil) Collar absent, cheeks and auriculars uniform dark brown.
   C. a. modulator (Amazonia, from northern Bolivia to eastern Peru) Similar to *salvini* but upperparts lighter, superciliary extends further.
   C. a. transpluvialis (eastern Amazonas, Brazil and

southern Colombia [Caqueta]) Small and generally pale.

VOICE Song is a series of pure, clear, haunting whistles, varying all over the scale, the same phrase repeated with minor variations many times over before switching to another, usually interspersed with lower gurgling sounds. Both sexes sing antiphonally. Call is a harsh *churk*.

HABITAT Lower levels of humid forests; in Amazonia also in seasonally flooded *várzea* forest. Sea-level to 500m in Colombia; sometimes up to 1,000m in Venezuela.

HABITS Keeps low down, foraging on the ground in leaf-litter or lower down in forest understorey. Generally secretive, although frequently located by call-note. Usually in pairs or small parties, occasionally joining mixed flocks at ant swarms, but for the most part not in association with other species.

STATUS AND DISTRIBUTION Uncommon to fairly common. Eastern Venezuela (eastern Bolívar), the Guianas, north-eastern Brazil south to Amapa on the coast, Pará and Matto Grosso, north-eastern Bolivia (Santa Cruz and Beni), eastern Peru (Loreto), eastern Ecuador (Napo, Pastaza), south-eastern Colombia (Amazonas, Caqueta).

BREEDING Only a few nests have been described. Nest is a roughly spherical construction 'like a leafy vase held by a twist of the funnel-shaped neck over a supporting branch', made of leaf skeletons, bound together with fine fibres and coarse grass. Entrance cavity quite large, opening into a small inner cavity near the top; lined with a few large feathers (Beebe 1917). The two nests so far described were about 1.5m from the ground in small bushes. Eggs two, pure white with little gloss (Beebe 1917). In Guyana, eggs in July, in Suriname a

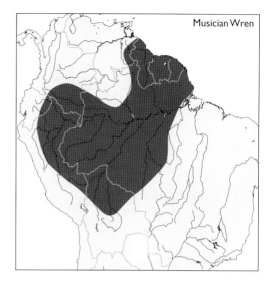

Musician Wren

nest with two small nestlings on 6 September and adults seen attending a fledgling on 26 July (Haverschmidt & Mees 1994). Incubation and fledging periods not recorded. Possibly double-brooded (Beebe 1917).

FOOD Mostly invertebrate; Crustacea (Decapoda: Natantia); Arachnoidea and lepidopteran larvae; beetles, millipedes. Also stated to take berries (Chubb 1921).

MOVEMENTS Probably entirely sedentary.

MEASUREMENTS Wing of male 55–59, of female 53–59; tail of male 29–34, of female 30–32; exposed culmen of male 15.4–17.5, of female 15.7–18.1; tarsus of male 20.3–22.0, of female 17.7–21.4.

CINCLUS

Aquatic ten-primaried Oscines, with plump body, short tail and rounded wings. Bill shorter than head, slender, much compressed. Rictal bristles absent. Wing short, very concave below, ninth to seventh (or eighth to sixth) primaries the longest. Tail short, rounded, rectrices broad with rounded tips. Tarsus sturdy and quite long. Plumage very dense but soft. Preen gland unusually large.

84   EURASIAN DIPPER
Cinclus cinclus   Plate 20

Sturnus cinclus Linnaeus 1758.

Alternative names: 'Dipper', White-throated Dipper, White-breasted Dipper, Water Ousel; numerous dialect English and Scottish names (see Tyler & Ormerod 1994); Welsh *Mwyalchen Ddwr, Trochwr*; French *Cincle plongeur*; German *Wasseramsel*; Dutch *Waterspreeuw*; Swedish *Strömstare*; Polish *Pluszcz*; Russian *Obyknovennaya Olyapka*

The most widely distributed of the Dippers, occurring in three continents, and to European observers the most familiar, a distinctive and most attractive bird found typically in wild and beautiful locations.

IDENTIFICATION Length 17–20cm. Unmistakable and highly distinctive; resembles no other species in its habitat and over most of its range. For distinctions from Brown Dipper see under that species.

DESCRIPTION *C. c. gularis*
Adult Crown dark chocolate-brown, back darker. Lower back and rump feathers dark grey-black with blackish edgings. Shoulders similar to lower back. Primaries and secondaries dull, dark blackish-brown. Rectrices dark blackish-brown. Lores and ear-coverts concolor with crown. Chin, throat and chest and upper surface of eyelid white. Upper belly with broad band of rufous merging into dark chocolate-brown lower belly, the

lower flanks having a greyish tinge. Underwing chocolate-brown. Iris brown, bill black, legs dark brown. **Juvenile** Quite distinct. Mottled dark grey and black above. Tertials and wing-coverts with narrow whitish edgings. Underparts down to lower belly dirty white with fine blackish-brown speckles, especially on chest.

GEOGRAPHICAL VARIATION

C. c. gularis 'British Dipper' (England, Wales, Scotland except west and Hebrides) Described above.

C. c. cinclus 'Black-bellied Dipper' (Scandinavia, western France, north-western Spain, Corsica, Sardinia. Migrant and sparse visitor, British Isles from Shetland to Kent) Belly largely or completely lacking rufous tinge.

C. c. hibernicus 'Irish Dipper' (Ireland, western Scotland including Hebrides) Similar to *gularis* but darker.

C. c. aquaticus (central and southern Europe, from Belgium, eastern France and eastern Spain across to Greece and Poland; Sicily) Belly-band bright rufous, upperparts paler than *cinclus*.

C. c. minor (North Africa [Morocco to Tunisia]) Similar to *aquaticus* but larger (despite the name).

C. c. caucasicus (Turkey, Iran, Iraq, Caucasus) Upperparts grey-brown, rump distinctly greyish.

C. c. persicus (south-western Iran [Zagros Mountains]) Similar to *caucasicus* but larger and paler.

C. c. rufiventris (western Syria and Lebanon) Similar to *persicus*, but smaller, with a darker rufous breast- and belly-band.

C. c. olympicus (Troodos Mountains, Cyprus) Extinct; last recorded in 1945 (Flint & Stewart 1983). Almost certainly absent by 1958 (Bannerman & Bannerman 1958). Very similar to, and possibly not distinguishable from, *caucasicus*.

C. c. uralensis (Ural Mountains) Upperparts intermediate in colour between *cinclus* and *aquaticus*.

C. c. leucogaster 'White-bellied Dipper' (northern Afghanistan through central Asia to eastern Siberia) Very distinct; entire underparts, apart from lower flanks, white.

C. c. cashmeriensis (Himalayas and Nepal) Chocolate-brown upperparts and lower belly; pale shading on upper belly.

C. c. przewalski (mountains of western China, south-eastern Tibet and northern Bhutan [Tyler & Ormerod 1994]) Similar to *cashmeriensis* but belly wholly dark; in some parts of western China a dark-chested morph occurs (Meyer de Schauensee 1984).

VOICE Song is a very sweet rippling warble, somewhat Wren-like in general pattern, uttered equally freely by both sexes (Hollom 1952). Female song is, in fact, less sweet, less melodious and more scratchy, and can usually be distinguished from that of the male (Cramp 1988). Song is usually given from a perch, occasionally in flight, and sometimes at night. Call is a loud, penetrating *zit-zit* and variations thereof, given repeatedly, perched or in flight.

HABITAT Fast-flowing, rather shallow, streams and rivers, especially with gravel or rocky bottoms; the presence of rocky cliffs at waterside (for nesting) or artificial sites such as bridges is also important. May tolerate substantial streamside development, even occurring in rivers running through towns, provided water quality is not impaired. Also occurs on lakes, provided the edges are relatively clear of aquatic vegetation, and sometimes even on seashore, especially in winter.

HABITS Unique, resembling only other members of the genus. Intimately associated with fast-running water, in which it wades, swims and dives. Most frequently seen perched on boulders in mid-stream, or flying with rapid whirring wing-beats low over the surface. When perched, characteristically 'dips', a rapid bowing movement made more conspicuous by the gleaming white chest. Dipping is more frequent and rapid at times of agitation or during territorial disputes. A second characteristic display is a rapid blinking, where the white surface of the eyelid (as opposed to the nictitating membrane) is repeatedly flashed. Blinking may occur more rapidly when the bird is disturbed or stressed, sometimes at a rate of one blink a second.

Feeds mostly in rapidly moving water. It may wade in shallow water, occasionally submerging its head to locate prey. In deeper water it will swim down to the bottom, using powerful wing movements. Much controversy has existed on the subject of whether dippers actually walk on the bottom of streams, in defiance of their buoyancy, by grasping stones. Most recent observation suggests that, while the bird may, briefly, grasp pebbles to stop itself floating to the surface, the wings are the main source of locomotion underwater; indeed Tyler & Ormerod (1994) quote an example of a one-legged dipper which apparently maintained a normal body-weight. Dippers also dive head-first into turbulent water, either from a perch, a wading position or in flight. Birds pursued by hawks may escape by diving directly into the water from mid-flight.

STATUS AND DISTRIBUTION Breeds from British Isles, Scandinavia, central and southern Europe, Spain, Morocco, Algeria, Italy, Corsica, possibly Sardinia, Greece, Turkey, Syria, Lebanon, Northern Iran, Caucasus republics, Central Asian republics, northern Afghanistan, Kashmir, Tibet, western China, Russia (Urals and Siberia east to Lake Baikal and Buryatia). Extinct, Cyprus. Vagrant to Faeroes, Malta and Iraq.

In Britain, breeds in Cornwall, Devon, Somerset, Dorset, Worcestershire, and Herefordshire, most of Wales, Derbyshire, Yorkshire and Lancashire north through most of Scotland. Formerly Orkney but not Shetland. Occasional breeder elsewhere in England, e.g. in Middlesex in 1876 and 1877 (Mitford 1882). Formerly (to about 1950), Isle of Man; again in 1988-1991 (Gibbons *et al.* 1993). Ireland, over most of Ulster and Donegal and in south and west, but absent from large areas of central Eire.

In France, formerly Brittany and Normandy, now in eastern and south-eastern areas and Pyrenees only. Occasional breeder in Holland and Baltic republics.

Estimated populations (breeding pairs) (Tyler & Ormerod 1994). Britain and Ireland, 26,000–30,000; Norway, 10,000–15,000; Sweden, 10,000; Finland, 300–400; Denmark, 6–8; Belgium, 740–1,200; Holland, bred 1910 to 1915 and 1933, but not since; France, 1,000–10,000; Austria, numbers not known but common;

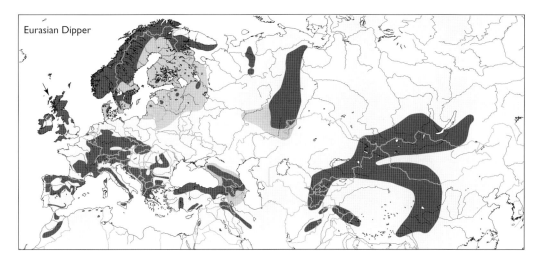

Eurasian Dipper

Switzerland, not uncommon; Czech Republic and Slovakia, not uncommon; Germany, 5,700–32,200 (west), scarce and declining in east; Poland, now scarce, declining in some areas; Hungary, 10–15 declining; Baltic Republics, breeds occasionally; former Soviet Union, common in west and Caucasus, not uncommon in east; Bulgaria, common in upland areas, former Yugoslavia, unknown; Iran, unknown but frequent near Tehran and Alborz; Turkey, estimate 500–5,000; Greece, less than 50; Cyprus, extinct; Syria, not known; Lebanon, locally common breeding resident on streams and rivers of the western slopes, 600–1,800m (Ramadan-Jaradi & Ramadan-Jaradi 1999); Italy and Sicily, not known but declining in Sicily; Spain, Portugal, Corsica and Sardinia, unknown but probably declining; Morocco, probably 500–1,000; Algeria, only known from five locations, less than 100 pairs; Afghanistan, apparently common; India, Pakistan and Nepal, frequent in the Himalayas but scarce in Nepal, some concern over habitat degradation.

Over much of the range the populations seem to be fairly stable; however, the species is vulnerable when water quality is impaired, due to such causes as acidification due to mining, silting due to deforestation or poor agricultural practices, or eutrophication from fertiliser run-off. Planting of conifers close to streamside also results in poor Dipper habitat. Comparison of breeding locations in Britain and Ireland for 1968–1972 and 1988–1991 shows more instances of Dippers disappearing from sites than appearing in new ones (Gibbons *et al.* 1993). However, in some cases the decline of the mining industry in Britain has resulted in recolonisation of previously abandoned rivers (Tyler & Ormerod 1994). Populations in southern Norway increased between 1978 and 1997, due apparently to climatic warming resulting in more ice-free streams in mountainous regions (Saether *et al.* 2000).

BREEDING The nest is a domed structure with a wide, downward-pointing side-entrance, actual size dependent on the site; depth 17–26cm, width 13–22cm, height 16–23cm, entrance 5–7cm in diameter. Internal cup diameter 10cm, depth 4.5–7cm. Outer shell made of mosses, grass, stems and leaves, cup of finer rootlets, hair and leaves. Both sexes build, but the female completes the cup. Moss is moistened by immersion in the stream before being used in building. Nests are built in a variety of situations, both natural and artificial; in crevices in rock-faces, ledges behind waterfalls, cavities in tree-stumps, etc., and under bridges, in pipes or culverts, holes in walls, etc.; also nestboxes if properly sited. Nests are usually directly above flowing water. Nests rather early; egg dates in Britain vary from late February to mid-June, mostly in late March or early April; later in more northern latitudes or greater altitudes. Eggs glossy white, unmarked, one to seven, usually four or five. Incubation by female alone, very rarely with male help, 12–18 days, usually about 16 days. Young fed by both sexes, fledging period 20–24 days, usually about 22. Some pairs rear two broods, more rarely three (Cramp 1988). Generally monogamous, but instances of polygyny not uncommon.

FOOD Mostly invertebrate, taken under water. Great variety of prey, but larval forms of aquatic insects such as mayflies and caddis flies are a major proportion. Caddis fly larvae, which build a substantial protective tube of small stones around themselves, may be removed from the water and hammered open on a rock, although small ones may be swallowed case and all. Also small fish such as minnows, and salmon eggs; rarely, vegetable matter (Cramp 1988).

MOVEMENTS Some populations largely sedentary. In Britain, movements tend to be short and involve post-breeding dispersal of young birds, especially young females. No information about populations in south-western Europe or North Africa but movements apparently small and altitudinal in nature. By contrast Scandinavian and Russian populations are migratory. Norwegian and Swedish birds move mainly in a south-easterly direction, into southern Finland and the Baltic republics, or into Denmark; more rarely westwards to Britain. There is one ringing recovery from Sweden to Fife, Scotland (Mead & Clark 1988). There is one remarkable occurrence involving ringing recoveries of birds of two races; a male, ringed as a nestling in Switzerland in June 1992, and observed overwintering in the same area until the following March, was retrapped near Gdansk, Poland in November 1993,

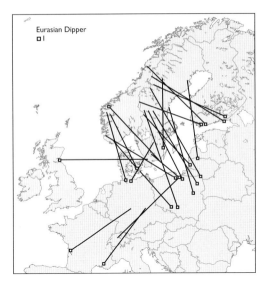

Eurasian Dipper
□ l

overwintering there. Meantime a female, ringed as a nestling in central Sweden in June 1992, was retrapped near Gdansk in December 1993. In April 1994 this mixed race pair (the male *C. c. aquaticus*, the female *C. c. cinclus*) successfully nested in the same area of Poland, where the Swiss-hatched male spent the subsequent winter. The female, however, was retrapped in Sweden in early November 1994, then reappeared in Poland three weeks later, overwintering in the same area (Jenni 1998). The Ural population is at least partially migratory, although birds are able to withstand winter temperatures of -40°C provided streams are still open (Dementiev & Gladkov 1966). Central Asiatic populations may move altitudinally.

MEASUREMENTS (*C. c. gularis*) Wing of male 92–99, of female 82–91; tail of male 48–56, of female 46–54; bill to skull of male 21.1–23.4, of female 19.6–22.4; bill to nostril (distal corner) of male 11.8–13.5, of female 11.0–12.5; tarsus of male 29.4–31.1, of female 27.3–29.3. Wing-length can thus be used as a sexing criterion (Cramp 1988).

85   BROWN DIPPER
Cinclus pallasii

Plate 20

Cinclus pallasii Temminck 1820 'Crimea' (actually Okhota River, eastern Siberia).

Alternative names: Pallas's Dipper, Asian Dipper; Russian *Buraya Olyapka*; Japanese *Kawagarasu*; Chinese *Xie He Ngiao*

A characteristic bird of the mountain-ranges of Central Asia, China and Japan; in some parts of its range sympatric with the Eurasian Dipper.

IDENTIFICATION Length 21–23cm. Unmistakable. The Eurasian Dipper has a white chest or totally white underparts; juvenile Brown Dippers have uniform mottled grey-brown plumage, while juvenile Eurasian Dippers are extensively whitish below.

DESCRIPTION *C. p. pallasii*
Adult Entire bird dark chocolate-brown, the back and chest being slightly warmer and more rufous than the head or rump. Remiges and rectrices dark chocolate-brown, underwing dark greyish-brown. Iris brown, bill blackish, legs dark blackish-brown.
Juvenile Very distinct from adult; plumage basically dull blackish-brown, conspicuously spotted (on head and throat) or scalloped (chest, belly and back) with greyish-white. Tertials, secondaries and rectrices with contrasting grey-white edgings.

GEOGRAPHICAL VARIATION
   C. p. pallasii (Japan, north-eastern Asia, western China, northern Thailand, north Vietnam) Described above.
   C. p. tenuirostris (Central Asia [Kazakhstan, Kirgizistan, Uzbekistan, Tibet]) Paler chocolate-brown than *pallasii*.
   C. p. dorjei (south-eastern Tibet, northern Burma, northern Thailand, Assam) Darker chocolate-brown

than *tenuirostris*; juveniles more rufous than other races.
   C. p. marila (Khasia Hills [Meghalaya], India) Very similar to *dorjei*.

VOICE Call is a sharp *zit zit* or *dzchit dzchit* similar to Eurasian Dipper. Song is a loud bubbling warble, possibly given by both sexes.

HABITAT Rushing mountain streams. In Kazakhstan prefers streams with wooded banks, or, in the absence of woods, with rocky banks. Also occurs on the shores of mountain lakes (Dolgushin *et al.* 1970). In Kazakhstan, 1,500–2,700m; in Tadzhikistan, 1,000–2,100m (Abdusalyamov 1973); in Nepal, up to 4,575m (Fleming *et al.* 1976), but in far-eastern Russia and Japan, much lower.

HABITS Very similar to Eurasian Dipper; forages by diving into rushing water; swims on surface. Flight rapid and direct. Bobs and bounces on rocks in a similar manner to Eurasian species.

STATUS AND DISTRIBUTION Central Asia from Afghanistan and the Tien-Shan Mountains (Kazakhstan, Kirgizistan, Uzbekistan, Tadzhikistan), Tibet, Nepal, Assam, northern Burma; disjunctly in Meghalaya, India; north-western Thailand, northern Annam, northern Burma, China, Taiwan, Japan from Kyushu northwards; eastern Siberia (Primorskiye Krai), Kamchatka and the Kurile Islands. Generally resident, but evidence of altitudinal migration in Uzbekistan (Kashkarov *et al.* 1995) and doubtless elsewhere. Migrant in northern China. Population declines noted in Nepal due to water diversions and deforestation of adjacent slopes (Tyler & Ormerod 1994), but over much of its range still common. In extreme parts of its range in Central Asia it is sympatric with Eurasian Dipper. It has been stated

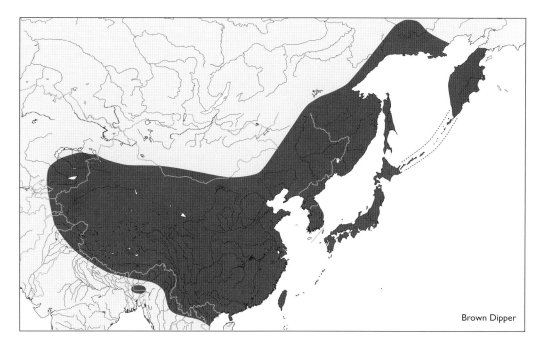

Brown Dipper

(Meyer de Schauensee 1984) that there is an altitudinal separation between the species, the Brown Dipper occurring lower down. However, this is certainly not invariable; in one stream in Uzbekistan the nests of the two species alternated along a length of stream (Kashkarov *et al.* 1995).

BREEDING Nest is a spherical or elliptical construction; in the Tien-Shan mountains, 22.5–28cm in diameter, the walls being 3.5–5cm thick, the entrance-hole on the side, 8–8.5cm in diameter. Double-layered, the outside being largely of moss, the inner layer of finer material, small rootlets and leaf ribs (Kashkarov *et al.* 1995). In far-eastern Russia, 75% of nests were located directly above flowing water, 90% in crevices on rock-faces, the remainder in caves or in rocks among falling water (Voloshina 1977). Sometimes nests under bridges or behind waterfalls, but possibly more rarely than Eurasian Dipper. Nest-sites may be semi-permanent, used for several years by successive birds. Nest-building by both sexes, taking about 7–10 days. In northern India and Nepal nesting occurs (depending on altitude) in December to August (Baker 1932); in Kazakhstan nesting begins in late March or April (Dolgushin *et al.* 1970); in

Kirgizistan fledged young in mid-May (Yanushevich 1960); in Japan, nest construction in mid-April (Asami & Haga 1983). Eggs three to six, most commonly five, glossy white without markings. Incubation period 19–20 days, fledging period 23–24 days (Voloshina & Myslenkov 1980) in eastern Russia; 21 days in Japan. In Japan single-brooded; probably single-brooded also in Central Asian republics, situation unclear in other parts of the range. No evidence of polygyny (Sunquist 1976).

FOOD Aquatic insects, larvae of caddis flies, mayflies, etc.

MOVEMENTS Over much of its range apparently largely sedentary; altitudinal movements, at least in Central Asian Republics and in Nepal. Birds from the northern edge of the range in China migrate southwards (Meyer de Schauensee 1984). Vagrant in Hong Kong (two records, April and August) (Webster 1976).

MEASUREMENTS (*C. p. tenuirostris*) Wing of male 93–105, of female 89–103; tail of male 56–59, of female 52–59; tarsus of male 26–30.5, of female 27.5–30; bill of male 19.5–21, of female 18.5–21 (Dolgushin 1970: ANRK, MGUZM).

---

86 AMERICAN DIPPER
Cinclus mexicanus
Plate 21

Cinclus mexicanus Swainson 1827, Temescaltepec, Mexico.

Alternative names: Water Ouzel, Waterthrush; Spanish *Cinclo Norte americano*, *Mirlo-acuático Americano*; French *Cincle d'Amerique*

The best-known of all the New World dippers, and by far the most widely distributed, occurring from north

of the Arctic Circle in Alaska to well south of the Tropic of Cancer in Central and probably South America.

IDENTIFICATION Length 15–17.5cm. Resembles no other species in its range and habitat.

DESCRIPTION *C. m. unicolor*
Adult Entire bird dark grey, slightly paler on chin and

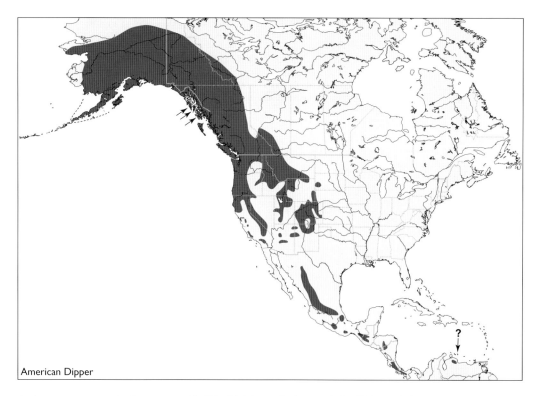

American Dipper

darker on crown and wing-coverts. Eyelid whitish. Remiges slightly browner in tinge. Iris raw umber, bill plumbeous black or drab, legs light pink.

Juvenile Similar to adult but underparts from chin to vent extensively mottled or scalloped with greyish-white, in some cases with throat and chin largely greyish-white. Greater and lesser coverts and tertials with narrow off-white edgings.

GEOGRAPHICAL VARIATION

C. m. unicolor (western North America from Alaska and the Aleutian Islands south through Canada to California, Arizona and New Mexico) Described above.

C. m. mexicanus 'Mexican Dipper' (Mountains of northern Mexico [Chihuahua] south to México and western Puebla; one record in southern Arizona [Phillips *et al.* 1964]) Head and neck darker, and more brownish, than in *unicolor*. Juvenile plumage with dark throat and underparts mottled with pale rust.

C. m. dickermani (southern Mexico (Guerrero, Veracruz, southern Oaxaca, north-eastern Puebla) Similar to *mexicanus* but crown, lores and throat darker, sides of head sootier (Phillips 1986).

C. m. anthonyi 'Guatemalan Dipper' (Mexico east of the Isthmus of Tehuantepec [Chiapas], Guatemala, Honduras, Nicaragua) Paler above than *dickermani*.

C. m. ardesiacus 'Costa Rican Dipper' (Costa Rica and western Panama) Much paler than other races, the underparts ash-grey. Juvenile with white throat and largely white belly.

There have been intriguing site records of dippers further south. In 1965 C. R. Schneider saw a dipper near Cana, Darién, Panama; unfortunately Dr Schneider did not provide a description, so whether this observation refers to American, White-capped or an undescribed species of dipper is open to debate (Ridgely 1976). More recently some Czech observers repeatedly saw dippers, which in plumage resembled American Dippers, at a location in Carabobo State, Venezuela. Since this location is 1,600km from the presently-known range of the species, it is surely probable that an undescribed race is involved (Dungel & Sebela 1995).

VOICE Call, a short, sharp *jit* or *dzik* singly or in a short series. Song is a jumble or medley of single notes, repeated notes and trills, somewhat like the pattern of a Mockingbird or Thrasher (Kingery 1996); quality is sweet and bell-like but with raspy *jik* notes included. Song is very loud, audible over the sound of rushing water, and in quiet situations can be heard 1.5km away (Bent 1948). Both sexes sing, essentially indistinguishably.

HABITAT Fast-moving mountain streams and rivers; rarely more than 15m wide or 2m deep, but in winter will use wider and deeper streams (Kingery 1996). Nest-site availability also has an influence on distribution. After breeding season may occupy other habitats such as mountain lakes, beaver ponds etc. Winter habitats requires ice-free conditions. From near sea-level in the north to 3,500m in the central Rockies; in Costa Rica, breeds from 800–2,500m.

HABITS Typical for a dipper. Most food is taken by wading, swimming and diving in rushing water. Occasionally fly-catches. Dives can occur from a surface swimming start, or from rocks in a stream, or from mid-air as a bird flies across a stream, or from a wading start. Will dive both with and against the current. Most diving birds remain submerged for 10 seconds or less. 'Anting' has been observed only once, in Montana (Osborn 1998). Nests are frequently used for roosting; otherwise birds roost in crevices or similar sites near the nest. One example only of birds roosting in trees (Hendricks 2000).

STATUS AND DISTRIBUTION Breeds from Alaska, north to about 69°, including the Aleutian Islands west to Unalaska; Yukon territory, most of British Columbia including Vancouver and the Queen Charlotte Islands and south-western Alberta; interior western United States (Montana, Idaho, Wyoming, Utah, Colorado, northern New Mexico); coastal western United States south to central California including the Sierra Nevada. Also numerous small disjunct populations in Nevada, Arizona, New Mexico and the Black Hills of South Dakota. Mexico (Sierra Madre Occidental) with disjunct populations in Puebla, the Sierra Madre del Sur and the Chiapas-Guatemala highlands; highlands of south-eastern Honduras (one record, Monroe 1968) and north-western Nicaragua; Costa Rica (Cordillera de Talamanca and Pacific slope of Cordillera Central); Panama (Chiriquí and Veraguas). Also, very probably, Carabobo (Venezuela).

Vagrant to western Aleutians (Attu), Great Slave Lake (North-west Territories), Saskatchewan, Nebraska and Minnesota, southern California and Sonora, Mexico. The absence of the American Dipper from eastern North America, where there is abundant suitable habitat in the Atlantic Provinces, New England and the Appalachians, is puzzling; one plausible explanation is that the species was unable to recolonise after the last Ice Age due to a wide belt of inhospitable terrain in the Prairies and Great Plains.

BREEDING Nest is a typical dipper construction, a spherical or elliptical ball with a side-entrance, usually with a short portal. Outer layer is mostly moss and grass, inner chamber globular with woven cup of grass, leaves and bark. If nest-site is closely overhung (as in a nestbox or some bridge sites) the roof may be absent, giving an open nest. Diameter 20–25cm, internal dimensions about 14cm, cup diameter 5 x 7.5cm, entrance hole initially 5cm in diameter but enlarges with use. Nests usually located directly above deep or fast-flowing water, 2–6m, usually 2–3m. 66% of nests on cliff edges, 15% behind waterfalls and 10% on midstream boulders (Kingery 1996). Frequently uses man-made structures such as bridges or nestboxes, the provision of which may augment populations. Old nests are frequently refurbished. Nest-building by both sexes or mostly by female. Eggs glossy, unmarked white; in North America, usually four or five, occasionally three to six; in Costa Rica, two to four. Incubation by female alone, 14–17 days. Young fed by both sexes, fledging period 24–26 days. Nests early; first egg-laying from early March in coastal British Columbia to June in Colorado. Some birds are double-brooded. Generally monogamous, but polygyny does occur rather uncommonly. Polygynous males may feed two broods simultaneously or in a staggered manner. Itinerant breeding and mate switching (in this case a female which in one season raised one brood with one mate and then a second, with another male in a different watershed about 5km away) has been noted in one instance in Montana (Osborn 2000).

No information about Central American populations; in Costa Rica, nests from February to May.

FOOD Predominantly aquatic insects and larvae, especially caddis flies, stoneflies, mayflies and midges; also tadpoles, small fish and fish-eggs and beach-hoppers in seaweed. May cause significant damage in fish-hatcheries (Bent 1948). Has been observed to fly-catch and to take frozen insects from snowbanks.

MOVEMENTS Governed by availability of open water; see Status and Distribution.

MEASUREMENTS (*C. m. unicolor*) Wing of male 83–100, of female 79–92; tail of male 48–52, of female 41–55; exposed culmen of male 16–19, of female 16–18; tarsus of male 25–31, of female 26–30.

---

87   WHITE-CAPPED DIPPER
Cinclus leucocephalus   Plate 21

Cinclus leucocephalus Tschudi 1844 Jauja, Junín, Peru.

Alternative names: Spanish *Pájaro de Agua*

A spectacular bird, differing widely in plumage in different parts of its range, found in mountainous regions from Venezuela south to Bolivia.

IDENTIFICATION Length 15cm. Unmistakable. No other species in its range, or especially, its habitat, has any remote resemblance.

DESCRIPTION *C. l. leucocephalus*
Adult Crown and nape grey-white with blackish speckles on crown and streaks on nape. Back, shoulders, rump, flight-feathers and coverts uniformly dark blackish-brown. Chin, throat and upper chest whitish, sides of chest, belly and flanks dark blackish-brown. Lores, ear-

coverts and area behind eye dark blackish-brown. Underwing-coverts greyish-black; under surface of innerweb of secondaries with some white, visible from below. Iris brown, bill black, legs feet leaden grey.
Juvenile Lower back, rump and belly with pale feather-tips; breast-feathers streaked.

GEOGRAPHICAL VARIATION
  C. l. leucocephalus 'White-capped Dipper' (Andes of Peru [north of Molinopampa] and Bolivia) Described above.
  C. l. leuconotus 'White-backed Dipper' (western Venezuela, Colombia and Ecuador) Very different from the nominate race; white on underparts extends down to upper belly, and a large patch of white feathers in centre of back.
  C. l. rivularis 'Santa Marta Dipper' (Santa Marta

mountains, northern Colombia) Closer to *leucocephalus* (despite the separation of ranges); dark parts of plumage grey instead of blackish-brown, throat spotted with grey.

VOICE Call is a sharp *zeet-zeet*. Song is a loud musical trill, often hard to hear over the roar of the rushing water (Ridgely & Tudor 1989).

HABITAT Rushing mountain streams, including both wide rivers and small rivulets. Prefers clear water but will also occur where the waters are at least seasonally turbid. 1,000–3,900m (i.e. up to limits of *páramo*).

HABITS Much as other dippers. However, does not appear to dive into rushing water or swim as frequently as do both the North American and the Eurasian species. Foraging techniques involve wading into water on river margins, standing in rushing water at the lip of waterfalls etc., picking prey from rocks. Also forages in vegetation along stream-sides, apparently taking terrestrial prey such as earthworms (Tyler & Ormerod 1994).

STATUS AND DISTRIBUTION Generally quite common in suitable habitat, but very susceptible to pollution; has disappeared from some streams in Quito area, Ecuador due to degradation of water quality. Venezuela (Sierra de Perijá, Andes from Lara to Táchira); Colombia (Santa Marta mountains and all three Andean ranges); Ecuador (Andes from Carchí to Zamora-Chinchipe); Andes of Peru; Bolivia (La Paz, Cochabamba and north-western Santa Cruz).

BREEDING Relatively little information recorded. Two nests described in Ecuador. One was built into a cleft on a moss-covered rock cliff behind a waterfall, 1.3m above water level. It was roughly spherical with a diameter of 25cm, and consisted of an outer moss layer with a circular entrance-hole, and an inner cup mainly of dry leaves, strips of bark and strips of plastic. The diameter of the entrance-hole was 8cm (Tyler &

White-capped Dipper

Ormerod 1994). A second nest was in a narrow niche in a cliff-face beside a waterfall. Eggs two, no description of colour but presumably white. In Ecuador a nest held well-developed young at the end of September (Skutch 1972); eggs in March (Venezuela), November (Bolivia); fledglings October (Colombia), July (Peru), May (Bolivia) (Fjeldså & Krabbe 1990).

FOOD Little published information. Presumably aquatic invertebrates; also terrestrial prey from stream-side vegetation.

MOVEMENTS No information. Apparently sedentary, but not known if altitudinal movement occurs.

MEASUREMENTS Wing of male 82–89, of female 78–81; tail of male 41–47, of female 40–42; exposed culmen of male 12–13, of female 11–12; tarsus of male 29-33, of female 27–29.5.

---

88   RUFOUS-THROATED DIPPER
Cinclus schulzi

Plate 21

Cinclus schulzi Cabanis 1883 Cerro Bayo, Tucumán, Argentina.

Alternative names: Spanish *Mirlo de Agua Gorjirrufo*

The rarest of all the dipper species, found only in a few watersheds in northern Argentina and southern Bolivia, where its status is a source of considerable worry. Sometimes treated (rather implausibly) as a race of *C. leucocephalus*.

IDENTIFICATION Length 14–15cm. Not confusable with any other species in its range or habitat. Allopatric from the White-capped Dipper.

DESCRIPTION
Adult Entire upperparts dull brownish-grey, slightly more rufous on front of forehead and lores. Primaries, secondaries and rectrices slightly darker. Innerwebs of primaries grey-white along about half of exposed feather, giving a patch visible only on open wing. Chin

greyish, with contrasting orange-brown patch, starting on upper throat and extending and broadening to upper chest, contrasting sharply with dull grey chest. Remainder of underparts grey-brown, darkening on belly and flanks. Iris dark brown or black, bill black or dark grey, legs lead-grey.
Juvenile Very similar to adult but bill pink (Tyler 1994).

GEOGRAPHICAL VARIATION None; monotypic.

VOICE Call is a *zeet-zeet*. Song is similar to that of the White-capped Dipper, but more thrush-like (Tyler & Tyler 1996).

HABITAT Swift-flowing mountain streams and rivers. Seems to be restricted to watercourses in the alder zone, which is from about 1,400–2,500m (Collar *et al.* 1992).

HABITS In most respects similar to other dipper species. However, it does not appear to swim or dive, notwithstanding statements to the contrary. Neither does it seem

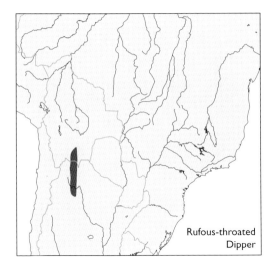

Rufous-throated
Dipper

to show the typical dipper 'dipping' behaviour; instead, the conspicuous pale webs of the primaries are flaunted by a wing-flicking motion.

STATUS AND DISTRIBUTION Restricted to watersheds in an area of northern Argentina (Jujuy, Salta, Catamarca and Tucumán) and southern Bolivia (Tarija) (Remsen & Traylor 1983). The known range is about 600km by 100km, but within this area there are gaps in distribution, and apparently suitable habitat in adjacent areas is not occupied. On some rivers or streams quite plentiful, with linear territories of about 650–1200m

(Tyler 1994). Susceptible to degradation of habitat by water impoundment, silting and eutrophication caused by farming and forestry etc; only a small section of the range is protected (in the Baritú National Park, Salta). Recent estimates of total world population are in the region of 1,000 pairs (Tyler 1994).

BREEDING Nest was not described until 1986 (Salvador *et al.* 1986); fewer than a dozen nests have been documented. Nest is a typical globular dipper construction, about 24cm high, 22cm wide and 14cm deep, with an entrance hole 7 x 5cm. It is double-layered, the outer shell being made of moss, grass stems, etc. Inside is a bowl of grass stems, leaves and in one case paper and plastic, the nesting cup being 8cm in diameter and 4cm deep. Nests are located in niches in rock-faces, in the stonework of bridges and on bridge supports, from 0.5–1.25m above rushing water. In late October in Argentina, one nest had freshly-laid eggs and another almost fledged young (Tyler 1994); freshly-laid eggs also on 21 December (Salvador *et al.* 1986). Eggs two, glossy white without markings. Incubation and fledging period unknown; young fed by both parents.

FOOD Aquatic insects including beetles (museum data).

MOVEMENTS Apparently moves to lower altitudes on the same watershed in winter (Dinelli 1918).

MEASUREMENTS Wing of male 82–86, of female 75–79; tail of male 41–47, of female 32–40; exposed culmen of male 11.5–13, of female 12; tarsus of male 30.5–34, of female 28.0–32.5 (Tyler & Tyler 1996 and museum measurements).

DUMETELLA

Rather small mimid (less than 20cm) with a notably short bill, prominent rictal bristles, wing fairly short and rounded, tail long and rounded; plumage generally grey with very soft feathers. Monotypic, although merged with *Melanoptila* by some authors.

89   GREY CATBIRD
Dumetella carolinensis   Plate 22

Muscicapa carolinensis Linnaeus 1766 (based on the 'Cat Bird' of Catesby, 1731), (Carolinas).

Alternative names: Black Mockingbird, Blackbird (Bermuda); French *Moqueur chat*; Spanish, *Zorzal gato, Pájaro-gato Gris*

An abundant and familiar bird over most of eastern North America.

IDENTIFICATION Length 20.5–21.5cm. Unique in shape and coloration, and essentially not confusable with any other species of any family.

DESCRIPTION
Adult Forehead, crown and nape dull black, contrasting dark grey shoulders, back and rump. Shoulders and coverts concolor with back. Primaries, secondaries and tertials dull greyish-black with inconspicuous paler

edgings on outerweb. Rectrices dull greyish-black, darker than back and rump. Lores and ear-coverts medium-grey, contrasting with darker cap. Chin and throat pale grey, darkening on chest and flanks; belly somewhat paler. Crissum contrastingly deep chestnut-brown. Underwing dull grey. Iris deep brown, bill (including inside) and legs black.
Juvenile Plumage generally duller, feathers notably more fluffy, crissum feathers very diffuse and much less deep in colour; inside mouth yellowish at front.

GEOGRAPHICAL VARIATION Monotypic. Some authorities separate apparently paler western populations as the subspecies *ruficrissa*, and the isolated population on Bermuda has also been separated as *bermudianus*. Neither race is currently recognised by the American Ornithologists' Union.

VOICE Song is a long, pleasing and varied series of whistled and gurgled notes, interspersed with harsher notes, and continuing for several minutes with brief interruptions. May incorporate some mimicry of other species of birds and even of mechanical noises and the calls of amphibia.

Will sing during bright moonlit nights. Females also sing, albeit rather rarely and with less vigour than males; sometimes in duet with male. Calls include a harsh grating *chek chek* and a longer mewing note.

HABITAT Scrubland, woodland edges, overgrown farmland and abandoned orchards; frequently in well-vegetated suburban areas. Not generally in the interior of forest, and usually absent in coniferous woodland. In Bermuda most abundant in scrub and myrtle swamp (Cimprich & Moore 1995). On winter quarters found in various types of scrub, coffee and citrus plantations and forests, including montane and rainforest.

HABITS More often first detected by its call, but not excessively shy. Usually forages close to or on the ground, flicking over vegetation with sideways bill movements, but will also feed in mid or upper levels of trees and bushes. Flight is usually low and direct. The long tail is frequently flicked upwards. Threat displays include a 'head-up' posture which shows the crissum, and a 'head-down' attitude which emphasises the crown patch (Cimprich & Moore 1995).

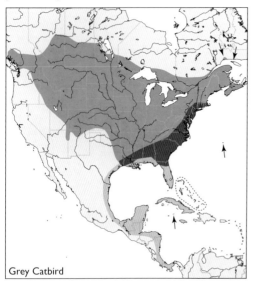

Grey Catbird

STATUS AND DISTRIBUTION Breeds over most of eastern North America, north to the Maritimes (including Prince Edward Island), southern Quebec, southern and central Ontario, across the Prairies to central Alberta and southern British Columbia; western Great Plains to northern Arizona and New Mexico, and across the central states south to central Louisiana, Georgia and the Carolinas northwards. Bermuda. Winters from the coastal states (rarely Massachusetts, through New York, Virginia, Georgia, Florida and Texas) south through the Caribbean drainage of Central America to Panama; also the Bahamas, Cuba, Jamaica, more rarely in Lesser Antilles. Vagrant in Colombia

(three records, Ridgely & Tudor 1989) and western Europe (Ireland, Channel Islands, England and Germany) (Long 1981, Rogers *et al.* 1987).

BREEDING Nest is a substantial cup-shaped construction, made of fine grasses, bark, rootlets, etc., the cup lined with finer materials including horsehair, built almost entirely by the female with very modest assistance from the male. Mean outside diameter 14cm, mean cup diameter 8.3cm, depth 4.5cm. Nests are located at an average height of 1.5m above the ground, but heights from ground level to 15m above the ground have been recorded (Cimprich & Moore 1995). Eggs one to six, average three or four, slightly higher in western part of the range and somewhat lower for later broods. Eggs are a bright blue-green colour, quite unlike those of any other North American passerine; rarely with fine red speckles. Incubation by female alone, sometimes fed by the male, 12–14 days. Young fed by both parents, mostly on invertebrates but with a small amount of fruit. Fledging period 8–12 days, average about 10.5 days. Double-brooded over most of range, triple-brooded in the south-eastern United States; in Ontario mainly single-brooded (Scott *et al.* 1988). Rarely parasitised by Cowbirds. Catbirds apparently learn to recognise Cowbird eggs as alien and eject them (Scott 1977).

FOOD Quite varied. Great varieties of invertebrates, including ants, caterpillars, grasshoppers and spiders; also fruit, berries and other vegetable matter. Birds in Ontario in autumn are frequently stained purple around the face from eating wild grapes. Vegetable component of diet greatest in autumn and least in spring (Cimprich & Moore 1995). Sometimes takes and eats eggs of other species such as Chipping Sparrow *Spizella passerina* or American Robin *Turdus migratorius* (Dixon 1930).

MOVEMENTS Highly migratory; withdraws from much of the breeding-range in winter. In southern Ontario usually arrives about 1 May, more rarely in late April, and leaves by mid-October. Banding encounters show that birds from the Maritimes and New England move in a generally south-westerly direction, wintering

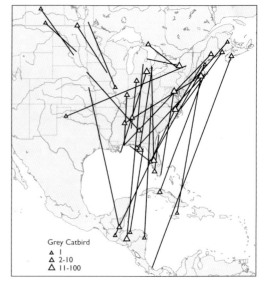

Grey Catbird
△ 1
△ 2-10
△ 11-100

in the southern states from Louisiana to Florida, and Central America; birds from the Prairie states and provinces move in a more south-easterly direction. The most distant banding recovery to date involves two birds banded in Bocas del Toro Province, Panama and recovered in Nova Scotia (Brewer *et al.* 2000).

MEASUREMENTS Wing of male 86–98, of female 84–91; tail of male 89–103, of female 82–97; exposed culmen of male 15–18, of female 15–17; tarsus of male 27–29, of female 27–28.5 (Ridgway 1907).

MELANOPTILA

Small mimid (length about 20cm), entirely black. Bill shorter than head, culmen mostly straight but decurved near tip; rictal bristles minute (in contrast to *Dumetella*). Wing rounded, sixth and seventh, or seventh and eighth primaries longest. Tail moderately long, rounded. Tarsus moderate in length, rather slender.

90   BLACK CATBIRD
Melanoptila glabrirostris   Plate 22

Melanoptila glabrirostris Sclater 1857, Omoa, Honduras.

Alternative name: Spanish *Pájaro-gato Negro*

A unique mimid, the only totally black member of the family, found in a restricted area of the Yucatán peninsula. Sometimes put into the genus *Dumetella* with the Grey Catbird.

IDENTIFICATION Length 19–20.5cm. Cannot be confused with any other mimid. Within this range there are several all-black birds – the Melodious Blackbird *Dives dives*, Bronzed Cowbird *Molothrus aeneus* and Giant Cowbird *Scaphidura oryzivora*. The last of these is much larger and the Bronzed Cowbird has bright red eyes. Confusion is most likely with the Blackbird. All these species have much more substantial bills and none has the attitude and mannerisms of a catbird.

DESCRIPTION
Adult Entire plumage glossy-black with purplish sheen; greater and lesser coverts glossy-black with greenish sheen. Primaries and secondaries duller black-brown with reduced sheen; rectrices black with slight greenish sheen. Iris red-brown, bill and legs black. Female similar to male but less glossy.
Juvenile Essentially identical to adult.

GEOGRAPHICAL VARIATION None; monotypic.

VOICE Song is a squeaky to sweet scratchy warble, often repeated over and over, often with metallic clicking buzzes thrown in; less often, prolonged warbling (Howell & Webb 1995). Calls are varied, some very reminiscent of the Grey Catbird; a gruff *chehr*, a harsh *rrriah* etc.

HABITAT Scrubland, wood-edge, abandoned farmland etc.; semi-arid to humid.

HABITS Very similar to those of the Grey Catbird; spends much time low down in vegetation and can be quite secretive. It will, however, sing from exposed perches.

STATUS AND DISTRIBUTION Restricted to the Yucatán peninsula, including some offshore islands (Cozumel, Isla Mujeres, Ambergris Cay, Cay Corker, Lighthouse Reef and Glover's Reef, Belize). On the

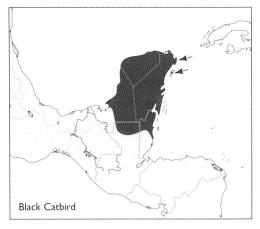

Black Catbird

mainland south to northern Guatemala (Petén) and northern Belize, west to central Campeche. The type specimen was taken in extreme north-western Honduras in 1855 or 1856. There have been no proven records in Honduras since, specimens labelled Honduras apparently having come from British Honduras (Belize) (Monroe 1968). There is a curious record in Brownsville, Texas in June 1892, based on a specimen taken by a reputable collector; this remains a source of controversy, currently being accepted by the Texas State Records Committee but not by the American Birding Association (G. W. Lasley pers. comm.).

BREEDING Nest is a cup-like structure of twigs, rootlets and finer material, placed in bushes or small trees. Eggs two, blue. Details of incubation and fledging periods, parental care and number of broods not known.

FOOD Nothing recorded; presumably a mixture of animal and vegetable matter as in related species.

MOVEMENTS Apparently entirely sedentary, at least under normal circumstances.

MEASUREMENTS Wing of male 88–93, of female 86–97; tail of male 89–97, of female 81–94; exposed culmen of male 16.5–21.5, of female 16–20; tarsus of male 26.5–30, of female 26–30 (Ridgway 1907).

MELANOTIS

Fairly large mimids, unique in the bright blue of the plumage and in juvenile plumage being substantially different from the adult. Bill not as long as *Toxostoma*, quite stout, with ridged culmen, slightly curved, with well-developed rictal bristles. Wing short and relatively rounded (fifth to seventh primaries longest). Rectrices broad, tail very rounded.

91 BLUE MOCKINGBIRD
Melanotis caerulescens   Plate 22

Orpheus caerulescens Swainson 1827, 'Mexico'.

Alternative name: Spanish *Mulato Azul*

A characteristic and fairly common Mexican species, endemic apart from a few vagrant records in the United States; a notable songster. Sometimes considered conspecific with the Blue-and-white Mockingbird.

IDENTIFICATION Length 24–26.5cm. Essentially different from all other species in its range. The dull grey juveniles may be somewhat confusing, but by shape and behaviour are obviously mimids. Allopatric with the Black Catbird.

DESCRIPTION *M. c. caerulescens*
Adult Crown deep blue with azure centres to feathers, especially above eye; centre of crown darker. Back, shoulders, wing-coverts and rump deep blue. Rectrices, primaries and secondaries deep blue-black. Lores, upper eyelid, area behind and below eye and ear-coverts black. Chin black, throat deep blue with azure streakings down to upper chest. Chest deep blue, becoming darker on belly and vent. Iris deep red, bill and legs black.
Juvenile Dull blackish-grey all over with bluish tint only very slightly discernible, mostly on flight feathers. Feathers of belly and vent fluffy and hair-like.

GEOGRAPHICAL VARIATION
M. c. caerulescens (eastern and south-central Mexico [Veracruz, Oaxaca, Puebla, Morelos, México and southern Tamaulipas]) Described above.
M. c. effuticus 'Chihuahua Blue Mockingbird' (northern and western Mexico [Chihuahua, Sonora and Durango south to Guerrero and Michoacán]) Similar to *caerulescens* but paler, especially on the underparts.
M. c. longirostris 'Tres Marias Blue Mockingbird' (Tres Marías Islands, Nayarit, Mexico) Similar to *effuticus* but smaller, with a much larger bill.

VOICE Song a varied arrangement of rich phrases, often with repetition, can be hard to distinguish from Ocellated or Curve-billed Thrashers (Howell & Webb 1995). Songs frequently incorporate imitations of other species. Calls a loud rich *choo* or *cheeoo*, a nasal mewing *meeahr*, a loud rich *wee-cheep* or *whieep*, a low *chuk*, etc.

HABITAT Woods, humid forest, riparian thickets, scrub, pine-oak and second growth; sea-level (in the Tres Marías and on Pacific coast) to 3,000m.

HABITS Typically rather skulking and difficult to see; feeds mostly low down or on ground. Usually sings from within cover, but will also sing from exposed perches.

Blue Mockingbird

STATUS AND DISTRIBUTION Quite common over much of its range. Mexico from Sonora south to central and eastern Oaxaca, in the east north to southern Tamaulipas; absent from arid central plateau; also Tres Marías Islands. Vagrant to southern Arizona and southern California.

BREEDING Nest is an untidy construction of twigs, with a cup of finer material, located in shrubs or bushes at low or medium height. Eggs two, immaculate pale blue. Incubation and fledging periods not recorded.

FOOD Omnivorous, including both animal (mostly invertebrate) and vegetable matter.

MOVEMENTS Presumably largely sedentary; however, the records from Arizona and California (about 200km and 900km respectively from the known Mexican range of the species) may indicate some tendency to wander.

MEASUREMENTS Wing of male 108–119, of female 98–110; tail of male 116–132, of female 105–125; exposed culmen of male 21–25, of female 22–24; tarsus of male 28.5–33, of female 28–31 (Ridgway 1907).

210

Melanotis hypoleucus Hartlaub 1852, Guatemala.

Alternative names: White-breasted Blue Mockingbird;
Spanish *Mulato Pechiblanco*

The most striking of all the Mimids, found only in a
limited area of southern Mexico, Guatemala and
Honduras. Sometimes treated as a race of the more
widespread Blue Mockingbird.

IDENTIFICATION Length 25.5–28cm. Quite unlike
any other bird in its range; the pure white chest, deep
blue back and dark face-patch is unique.

DESCRIPTION
Adult Crown deep blue with fine azure streaks in centres
of feathers. Back, shoulders, wing-coverts and rump
deep blue. Primaries, secondaries and rectrices blackish,
with hint of blue, especially on outerwebs of primaries.
Lores, areas below and behind eye and ear-coverts black,
contrasting with crown, chin and shoulders. Chin,
throat, chest and belly white; flanks and vent dark blue-
grey. Iris deep red, bill and legs black. Fully adult
plumage not attained in the first year; may breed in sub-
adult plumage.
Juvenile Very different from adult. Dull blackish grey
above and below, throat and breast with white markings,
abdominal feathers white with grey tips, iris dark brown.
This plumage is only maintained for two months or so
before moulting into an immature plumage that closely
resembles the full adult, but somewhat duller.

GEOGRAPHICAL VARIATION None; monotypic.

VOICE Song consists of a variety of short musical
phrases, each repeated a number of times, and rarely
contains imitations of the notes of other birds or harsh
interjections. At other times the song is a medley of
churr's, *cluck*'s, screeches and other harsh notes mingled
with clearer whistles and trills (Skutch 1950). Apparently
only the male sings. Calls include a loud, rich *tcheeoo* or
whee-oo, and *chweet*, *chrr*, a low hollow *chuck*, a gruff growl
followed by hollow clucking, *ahrr took-took-took*, etc.
(Howell & Webb 1995).

HABITAT 1,000–3,000m. Habitat varies with altitude.
In central Guatemala, open woodland of oak and pine
with dense undergrowth, scrubland, etc., of a fairly
humid nature. At lower altitudes in dryer or even semi-
arid bushland.

HABITS A shy and retiring bird, more often heard than
seen, although on occasion the male will sing from a

tree-top perch. Feeds mostly on ground, sweeping leaf-
litter aside with lateral movements of the bill. Generally
in pairs or family parties, more rarely in small groups of
up to six birds.

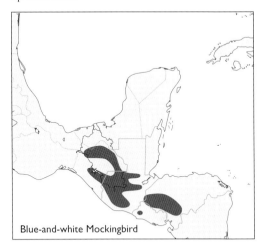
Blue-and-white Mockingbird

STATUS AND DISTRIBUTION Southern Mexico
(Chiapas), central Guatemala, southern Honduras and
extreme northern El Salvador. In suitable habitat quite
common.

BREEDING Nest is a shallow, untidy, rather insubstantial
cup of coarse sticks, lined with fibrous material, placed
in dense thickets or saplings, at heights of 1–5m.
Apparently built by female alone. Eggs immaculate light
blue; two in highland Guatemala (Skutch 1950) three
at lower altitudes (Salvin & Godman 1879). Incubation
by female only, period not recorded; young fed by both
parents, fledging period 14–15 days. Nesting period in
highland Guatemala from mid-May to early July; at lower
altitudes as late as September.

FOOD Omnivorous; both animal (mainly invertebrate)
and vegetable matter taken, including green berries of
viburnum.

MOVEMENTS Apparently entirely sedentary.

MEASUREMENTS Wing of male 105–116, of female
107–108; tail of male 128–139, of female 135–137;
exposed culmen of male 22–24.5, of female 23.5–24;
tarsus of male 32–34.5, of female 32–34.

MIMUS

Medium to large mimids, with relatively short bills (much shorter than heads), only slightly decurved and with
well-developed rictal bristles. Wing long but quite rounded. Tails typically long and rounded, legs and feet quite
sturdy. Usually grey or grey-brown with darker markings on wings; often with prominent white areas on flight-
feathers, both wings and tail.

Turdus polyglottos Linnaeus 1758, based on 'The Mockingbird' of Mark Catesby, Natural History of Carolina, 1731.

Alternative names: Mocking Thrush, Mocker, Mock-bird Nightingale (Jamaica), English Thrasher (Bahamas); Spanish *Centzontle Norteño* (Mexico), *Ruiseñor* (Caribbean); French *Moqueur polyglotte, Rossignol* (Caribbean)

With the probable exception of the American Robin, possibly the best-known and best-loved bird of North America. The State Bird of half a dozen states from Texas northwards.

IDENTIFICATION Length 23–25.5cm. Not readily confused with any other species, with the possible exception of the Tropical Mockingbird (q.v.) in those very limited areas of overlap. In plumage superficially resembles a Northern or Loggerhead Shrike, but the totally different behaviour precludes any confusion even before details of plumage are noted. In the Bahamas and Jamaica the Bahama Mockingbird occurs (q.v.).

DESCRIPTION *M. p. polyglottos*
Adult Crown, back, shoulders and rump dark grey. Wing-coverts darker grey with greyish-white edgings on lesser primary coverts. Base of primaries on both webs with large white areas, giving a conspicuous white flash on opened wing. Primaries and secondaries otherwise dull blackish-grey. Rectrices dull blackish, the outer ones largely white, the next two pairs mostly white with dark on outerwebs. Chin and throat whitish-grey, becoming more buff-grey on chest. Belly and vent grey. Underwing greyish-white with darker markings on underwing-coverts. Iris light green-yellow to yellow, occasionally orange, bill black, blackish-brown at base; legs dusky.
Juvenile Similar to adult, but with indistinct streaks on back and more pronounced spots and streaks on chest. Iris grey or grey-green.

GEOGRAPHICAL VARIATION
   M. p. polyglottos (eastern North America, from eastern Nebraska to Nova Scotia, south to eastern Texas and Florida) Described above.
   M. p. leucopterus 'Western Mockingbird' (western North America from north-western Nebraska and western Texas to the Pacific Coast, south through Mexico to the Isthmus of Tehuantepec; recently Socorro Island [Revillagigedo group]) Similar to *M. p. polyglottos* but larger, with relatively shorter tail; upperparts paler and more buff, underparts with stronger tinge of buff.
   M. p. orpheus (includes *elegans, delenificus* and *dominicus*) (Bahama Islands, Greater Antilles east to the Virgin Islands) Similar to *M. p. polyglottos* but generally smaller, grey of back paler, and underparts with little if any buff.

VOICE Song is an enormously varied series of strong, musical notes, often very prolonged, and incorporating imitations of a large variety of other species. Frequently sings during the night, especially in urban areas with artificial light. Individual birds have differing spring and fall repertoires, with little overlap (Derrickson &

Breitwisch 1992). Both sexes sing. A variety of call-notes; a harsh *chakk* or *churr*, a rasping *hew*, etc.

HABITAT Open bushland, abandoned farmsteads, forest edge; has adapted very well to suburban landscapes as long as there is sufficient cover for nesting. Does not occur in interior dense forest.

HABITS Confident and conspicuous. Spends a lot of time on the ground where the gait is a run or a hop. Invertebrate food is often taken on the ground, although it will hawk in the manner of a flycatcher though usually at no great height. Has been seen to capture large cicadas by striking them in flight with its wings then grabbing with the bill (Derrickson & Breitwisch 1992).
   Very aggressive during the breeding season; will mob and physically attack intruders such as crows or cats which approach the nest.

Northern Mockingbird

STATUS AND DISTRIBUTION Found year-round in most of its range; Canada from the Maritimes, irregularly to Newfoundland, through southern Ontario (sparse away from the Niagara peninsula where common), westwards to British Columbia; essentially the whole of the continental United States where suitable habitat exists and most of Mexico south to eastern Oaxaca and Veracruz; Bahamas, Hispaniola, Cuba, Jamaica, Puerto Rico and the Cayman and Virgin Islands. Range has expanded recently; in Ontario, first recorded as a breeding bird in 1883, and as recently as 1965 only a rare summer resident in the Niagara Peninsula where it is now common; has now nested as far north as Cochrane and probably Moosonee on the James Bay coast. First proven nesting in Quebec 1960. In the Cayman Islands, formerly found only on Grand Cayman, but colonised Cayman Brac prior to 1956, and Little Cayman in 1966 (Bradley 1985). Colonised Socorro Island in the Revillagigedo group off western Mexico between 1978 and 1981.

Vagrant in Great Britain (three records). Introduced to Hawaiian Islands in the 1970s, (subsequently colonised French Frigate Shoal on its own (Berger 1972)), St Helena and Tahiti (Derrickson & Breitwisch 1992).

Generally speaking the Northern Mockingbird has benefited from human-caused habitat change; expansion northward in California was aided by suburban development (Arnold 1980), while colonisation of Socorro Island was probably made possible by the artificial provision of water (Jehl & Parkes 1983).

BREEDING Nest is an open cup of dead twigs lined with grasses etc.; the foundation is built mostly by the male, the lining mostly by the female. Most nests in shrubs or bushes, to 3m above the ground, though up to 19m recorded. More rarely nests are located in buildings or cavities. Eggs two to six, bluish-grey or greenish-white to darker shades of blue and green, heavily marked with various shades of brown; rarely immaculate pale blue (Derrickson & Breitwisch 1992). In Puerto Rico, usually three or four eggs, rarely seven (Bowdish 1903, Biaggi 1983). Incubation by female only, 12–13 days. Young fed by both parents, fledging period 12–15 days unless disturbed into earlier departure. Two or three broods per year. Nest building begins late February to March in Florida, late March to mid-April in Pennsylvania; in Puerto Rico, nest with well-developed young on 12 March (Bowdish 1903).

Usually monogamous, but bigamy and trigamy has been recorded. Rarely parasitised by cowbirds (Brown-headed, Bronzed and Shiny).

FOOD Omnivorous. Arthropods (beetles, ants, bees, wasps, grasshoppers), earthworms, occasionally small lizards; and vegetable matter, especially berries. Diet is more animal in summer and vegetable in winter. Artificial provision of fruit especially Multiflora Rose *Rosa multiflora* may have had a major influence on range expansion (Derrickson & Breitwisch 1992).

MOVEMENTS Although present in most of its range

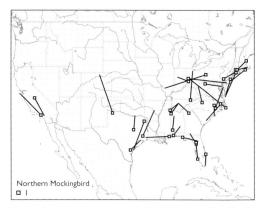

Northern Mockingbird

throughout the year, obviously prone to occasional long-distance wandering, as evidenced by occurrences in Europe, the Northwest Territories of Canada (including islands in Hudson's Bay) and the colonisation of Socorro Island. In Sonora, north-western Mexico, observed to migrate over coastal areas in March. Populations in north-western Mexico are obviously augmented by winter visitors (Russell & Monson 1998). An analysis of banding encounters shows that the Northern Mockingbird is irregularly nomadic rather than truly migratory. Of a total of 1,450 encounters only 30 show movements of more than 200km, and only 10 more than 500km. In contrast to both Grey Catbird and Brown Thrasher, a glance at the map of long-distance recoveries does not indicate obvious north-south displacements in the pattern of most medium-distance North American migrants, but instead more randomised movement with a major east-west component (data from Bird Banding Laboratory).

MEASUREMENTS Wing of male 106–120, of female 100–111.5; tail of male 110–134, of female 100.5–114.5; exposed culmen of male 17–18.5, of female 16–18; tarsus of male 29.5–34, of female 30.5–34 (Ridgway 1907).

94 TROPICAL MOCKINGBIRD
Mimus gilvus

Plate 23

Turdus gilvus Vieillot 1807 'dans la Guyane' (probably French Guiana).

Alternative names: Graceful Mockingbird; Spanish *Centzontle Sureño*; Portuguese *Sabiá-da-praia*; Suriname *Dagoefowroe*; Nightingale, *Pied Carreau*, *Grive Blanche* (West Indies)

An abundant and familiar bird of much of northern South America and parts of the West Indies, where it occupies the same suburban niche as does the Northern Mockingbird in North America.

IDENTIFICATION Length 23–25.5cm. Distinguished from the Northern Mockingbird, in the small area of possible overlap in southern Mexico, by the lack of conspicuous white wing-flashes and reduced amount of white on sides of tail. In South America the only allopatric Mockingbird is the Chalk-browed, a much more

brown (as opposed to grey) bird with a wider supercilium and more obviously streaked dorsally. The ranges of the two species overlap in parts of coastal Brazil. Hybrids between Northern and Tropical Mockingbird have been reported in southern Mexico (Howell & Webb 1995).

DESCRIPTION *M. g. gilvus*
Adult Crown, back, shoulders and rump medium grey. Wing-coverts, primaries, secondaries and tertials blackish-grey. Rectrices blackish-grey, the outer ones broadly tipped with off-white. Broad grey-white supercilium in front of and behind the eye. Lores and ear-coverts dark grey. Chin and throat off-white, chest grey, belly and vent off-white. Underwing-coverts grey-white with white edges. Iris pale yellowish or olive-green, bill and legs blackish.
Juvenile Conspicuous dark spots on chest, iris dark brown.

GEOGRAPHICAL VARIATION

M. g. gilvus (Suriname and French Guiana) Described above.

M. g. antelius 'Blue-gray Mockingbird' (eastern Brazil from Rio de Janeiro to Pará) Longer-tailed than *gilvus*, white tips on rectrices reduced, upperparts paler grey, flanks more heavily streaked.

M. g. antillarum 'Antillean Mockingbird' (Lesser Antilles from Nevis south to Grenada; introduced on Barbados) Darker above than *gilvus*, white on wing-coverts wider and less sharply defined, little grey on breast.

M. g. tobagensis 'Tobago Mockingbird' (Trinidad and Tobago) Darker above than *gilvus*, markings on wing-coverts wider, lateral rectrices with more extensive white tips, bill stouter though not longer.

M. g. melanopterus 'Black-winged Mockingbird' (northern South America from Guyana, Venezuela south to the Orinoco Valley, Margarita and Los Testigos Islands, northern Colombia) Larger than *gilvus*, white on outer rectrices more extensive, upperparts paler grey, underparts almost pure white.

M. g. rostratus 'Curacao Mockingbird' (islands north of Venezuela [Aruba, Curaçao, Bonaire, La Orchila, Tortuga, La Blanquilla]) Similar to *melanopterus* but with heavier bill.

M. g. tolimensis 'Tolima Mockingbird' (Colombia, from Cauca northwards, except where occupied by *melanopterus*) Similar to *melanopterus* but larger, with longer wings and tail.

M. g. gracilis 'Guatemalan Mockingbird' (southern Mexico [Veracruz, Chiapas], western Guatemala, Honduras) Similar to *melanopterus* but upperparts more brown, wing-coverts tipped white rather than grey, chest buffy-grey.

M. g. leucophaeus 'Yucatan Mockingbird' (Yucatán Peninsula, including Belize, Cozumel and other off-shore islands, Campeche and north-eastern Tabasco) Closest to *gracilis* but upperparts more clear grey, edgings on wing-coverts narrow and grey, white on lateral rectrices more extensive.

VOICE Song is loud and varied, probably not distinguishable from that of the Northern Mockingbird; apparently it appears to be less prone to mimic other species, although in Brazil it has been claimed that some birds learn to sing the National Anthem (!) (Sick 1993). Sometimes sings at night. Calls, a harsh *chek* etc.

HABITAT Open and semi-open country, including farmyards, suburban areas with lawns, savanna etc., sea-level to at least 2,400m in Guatemala and 2,500m in Colombia in cleared areas. In parts of the Caribbean, quite dry or semi-arid areas.

HABITS Much like those of the Northern Mockingbird; confiding and fearless, frequently seen running around grassy areas; habitually patronises bird-feeders where it may be very aggressive towards other species. Has the same 'wing-flashing' habit as other members of the family, raising the wings above the back when pausing from running.

STATUS AND DISTRIBUTION Over much if its range common or abundant; has probably benefited from

Tropical Mockingbird

human clearance of forest and the provision of well-watered suburbs, for example in the Canal Zone of Panama. Southern Mexico, from extreme eastern Veracruz and Oaxaca through the Yucatán Peninsula (including offshore islands such as Isla Mujeres, Holbox and Cozumel), Belize, central Guatemala and Honduras to north-eastern Nicaragua, Panama, in the Canal Zone from Colón to Panama City, and in adjacent areas, almost certainly as a result of a deliberate introduction (Chapman 1941). The Panama birds are probably referable to the race *melanopterus* rather than the more adjacent *tolimensis*. Northern South America from western Colombia across northern Venezuela, the Guianas and north-eastern Brazil; disjunctly south of the Amazon in coastal Brazil from Pará to Rio de Janeiro. Lesser Antilles from Guadelupe to Grenada; Barbados (introduced); Trinidad, Tobago and islands north of Venezuela from Aruba to Los Testigos.

Given the popularity of the species as a cage-bird, some extralimital records (e.g. from the Bay Islands, Honduras) are suspect.

BREEDING Nest is an open cup of sticks in thick bushes or shrubbery, usually at no great height. Eggs usually two or three, bluish with reddish-brown spots. Incubation and fledging periods not recorded. In Belize breeds in May and June (Russell 1964); in Suriname throughout the year (Haverschmidt 1968).

FOOD Invertebrates including caterpillars, spiders etc., and seeds and berries; frequently comes to feeders where it will take a variety of offerings including soaked rice.

MOVEMENTS Apparently sedentary.

MEASUREMENTS Wing of male 98–106.5, of female 95.5–105.5; tail of male 94–113.5, of female 94–111.5; exposed culmen of male 17–19, of female 17–18.5; tarsus of male 29.5–33.5, of female 30–33.5 (Ridgway 1907).

Mimus magnirostris Cory 1887, St Andrew Island (Isla San Andrés), Colombia.

Alternative names: Large-billed Mockingbird, 'Nightingale'

An isolated form confined to Isla San Andrés, an island only 13km long and 4km wide located in the Caribbean about 200km off the coast of Nicaragua. Several authorities regard it as a race of the Tropical Mockingbird; we have followed Bond (1971) and Ridgway (1907) in giving it full specific status pending further investigation.

IDENTIFICATION Length 28cm. On San Andrés no other species resembles it. It differs from the Tropical Mockingbird in its much larger size and obviously heavier bill.

DESCRIPTION
Adult Crown light grey with slight streaking. Back, shoulders and rump light grey. Greater and lesser coverts dull blackish with white tips. Primaries and secondaries blackish with grey edgings on outerweb, widest on secondaries. Rectrices dull blackish-grey with conspicuous white tips on outer four feathers, most extensive on outermost rectrix. Lores dark grey, ear-coverts paler grey, supercilium indistinct and pale grey-white. Throat, chest and belly off-white. Iris yellowish, bill and legs black.
Juvenile Heavy blackish-grey streaks on throat and upper chest.

GEOGRAPHICAL VARIATION None; monotypic.

VOICE Song like that of Northern Mockingbird but not known to mimic other birds. Alarm notes less harsh than those of the Northern Mockingbird (Bond 1971).

HABITAT Copses and orchards, chiefly in the hills (Bond 1971).

San Andres Mockingbird

HABITS Very similar to those of the Tropical Mockingbird.

STATUS AND DISTRIBUTION Confined to San Andrés. In 1950 it was described as surprisingly uncommon (Bond 1950). In 1972 'many' were seen (Russell *et al.* 1979). Since 1972 there has been extensive development on San Andrés; no recent information.

BREEDING Nest and eggs undescribed.

MOVEMENTS Sedentary.

FOOD No information recorded.

MEASUREMENTS Wing of male 118.5–126.5, of female 116–126; tail of male 133.5–139.5, of female 125.5–139; exposed culmen of male 26.5–28, of female 26–27.5; tarsus of male 36.5–37.5, of female 34.5–37 (Ridgway 1907).

---

96   **BAHAMA MOCKINGBIRD**
     Mimus gundlachii   Plate 23

Mimus gundlachii Cabanis 1855 'Cuba' (Cayo Santa María, north coast of Cuba).

Alternative names: Spanish Nightingale, Salt Island Nightingale, Spanish Thrasher (Jamaica); Spanish *Sinsonte Prieto, Sinsonte Carbonero*

A common species of the Bahamas, Turks and Caico Islands and parts of Cuba and Jamaica. Coexists in parts of its range with the Northern Mockingbird.

IDENTIFICATION Length 28cm. Only similar species in its range are Northern Mockingbird, which has conspicuous white wing flashes, but lacks dark whisker mark, conspicuous dark stripes on back and flanks, and Pearly-eyed Thrasher, which has darker upperparts and a yellow bill. Brown Thrasher, a sparse visitor to the

Bahamas, has rich rufous-brown upperparts.

DESCRIPTION *M. g. gundlachii*
Adult Crown, nape, back and shoulders dull grey-brown with indistinct darker lateral streaking. Lower back and rump warmer grey-brown with less streaking. Primaries and secondaries dull dark grey-brown with narrow paler edging on outerwebs. Greater and lesser primary and secondary coverts narrowly edged with whitish-grey giving indistinct wing-bars on closed wing. Rectrices dull grey-brown, the outermost ones with whitish tips. Chin, throat and chest grey-white, with a narrow grey-brown malar stripe extending to upper chest; a variable amount of grey-brown speckling on lower throat and upper chest. Flanks and lower belly with dark grey-brown streaks. Ear-coverts mottled off-white and grey-black. Iris

yellow, bill blackish with paler base, legs blackish.
Juvenile Underparts more heavily spotted throughout
than in adult, malar stripe usually less well defined.

GEOGRAPHICAL VARIATION
M. g. gundlachii 'Gundlach's Mockingbird' (Cays,
off northern Cuba; Bahama Islands, Turks and
Caicos Islands) Described above.
M. g. hilli 'Hill's Mockingbird' (southern Jamaica)
Similar to *gundlachii* but streaking on back more
distinct; white tips to rectrices larger.

VOICE Song is a series of low reiterated syllables interspersed with occasional trills and chuckles (Aldridge
1984). Less strident than Northern Mockingbird. Does
not mimic. May sing antiphonally with adjacent territorial
males, and with females. Males respond aggressively to
taped male songs, but ignore female songs. Alarm call a
low sharp chirp; also growls during territorial disputes.

HABITAT Scrubland, woodland, including modified
habitat. In many areas shares habitat with Northern
Mockingbird, but tends to live in areas of more dense
and taller vegetation; Northern Mockingbird tends to
be more common near human habitation and in more
open areas. In Jamaica, confined to semi-arid limestone
country (Bond 1971).

HABITS Feeds at all levels but on average higher up
than Northern Mockingbird; when on ground runs
rapidly, only pausing to snatch prey items. Responds
aggressively to intruding males of its own species. Aggression towards Northern Mockingbird is rare during times
of food abundance, but more common in times of
scarcity; during such encounters the larger Bahama
Mockingbird tends to come off best. Unlike Northern
Mockingbird only rarely flashes wings (Aldridge 1984).

STATUS AND DISTRIBUTION Common or abundant

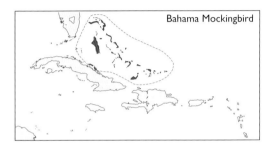

in much of its range. Most of Bahama group, but sight
records only on Grand Bahama and Great Abaco; Turks
and Caicos Island, Great Inagua; cays off the northern
coast of Cuba; southern Jamaica (Hellshire Hills).
Vagrant to Florida (April and May).

BREEDING Nest is a cup, made of twigs and bark and
lined with palm fibre, outer diameter 20–24cm, located
in bushes or shrubs at a height of about 1.5m. Both sexes
bring nest material, but not known whether both
actually build (Aldridge 1984). Eggs two, cream-white
with reddish-brown spots and blotches concentrated at
large end (Raffaele *et al.* 1998). Incubation and fledging
periods not recorded. Breeds from February to June.

FOOD Varied. Insects, caterpillars, small Anolis lizards,
agave nectar, and a variety of fruits and seeds (Aldridge
1984).

MOVEMENTS Resident over all its range; however, vagrant records in the Florida Keys and on Grand Bahama
obviously indicate some movement or dispersal.

MEASUREMENTS Wing of male 115–125.5, of female
112.5–116.5; tail of male 125–131.5, of female 118.5–
131.5; exposed culmen of male 20.5–24, of female 21–
22; tarsus 37.5–41, of female 37.5–39.5.

97   CHILEAN MOCKINGBIRD
Mimus thenca   Plate 24

Turdus thenca Molina 1782, Chile.

Alternative names: Spanish *Calandria Chilena, Tenca*

A well-known and quite common species in Chile, occurring in no other country; a popular and attractive songster.

IDENTIFICATION Length 27cm. Over most of its range
the only mockingbird. Two species occur as occasional
visitors, the very different White-banded Mockingbird,
and the Patagonian Mockingbird. The latter, which may
be sympatric in the south of the country, has more white
on the wing and is smaller, with a shorter tail and no
malar stripe.

DESCRIPTION
Adult Crown medium brown with obscure darker
streaks. Back and shoulders dull grey-brown becoming
slightly more rufescent on rump. Greater and lesser
primary and secondary coverts edged dull white, giving
two wing-bars on closed wing. Primaries and secondaries
dull grey-brown, tertials the same with dull whitish tips.
Rectrices dull blackish-brown, the outer four with off-

white tips, most extensive on outer feathers. Lores dull
grey; broad area behind eye off-white, contrasting strongly with adjacent feathers. Ear-coverts mottled grey-brown.
Chin and throat off-white. Cheeks whitish, mottled black;
malar stripe blackish, narrow near bill and broadening
below ear-coverts where mottled with brown. Chest grey-
brown, belly paler, flanks with broad diffuse blackish
streaks. Vent pale buffy-white. Underwing buffy-white.
Iris yellow to yellow-green, bill and legs black.
Juvenile Similar to adult, but with a buff wash on the
chest and streaked underparts.

GEOGRAPHICAL VARIATION None; monotypic.

VOICE Song is an attractive series of notes with numerous imitations of other species. Said to be the best song
of any Chilean bird, although inferior to that of the
White-banded Mockingbird (Johnson 1967).

HABITAT Found in various types of shrub and scrubland, though less common in cultivated areas (Fjeldså
& Krabbe 1990). Usually below 700m.

HABITS Similar to other members of the genus.

STATUS AND DISTRIBUTION Chile, from southern Antofagasta to Valdivia; over much of its range, fairly common to common.

BREEDING Nest is a cup in the fork of a thorn tree or cactus; some thorns may be used for the outside of the nest, the cup being lined with moss or sheep's wool. Eggs three or four, rarely two, bluish-green, heavily spotted with purplish-red (Johnson 1967). Eggs laid in November (Fjeldså & Krabbe 1990). Incubation and fledging periods not recorded.

FOOD No information recorded.

MOVEMENTS No evidence of migration recorded.

MEASUREMENTS Wing of male 112–122, of female 108–112; tail of male 108–127, of female 112–116; exposed culmen of male 16–18, of female 15.5–17.5; tarsus of male 35–39.5, of female 35–38.

Chilean Mockingbird

98   LONG-TAILED MOCKINGBIRD
Mimus longicaudatus

Plate 24

Mimus longicaudatus Tschudi 1844 Peru (probably Lima).

Alternative names: Spanish *Calandria Colilargo*

An abundant and very conspicuous part of the fauna of arid coastal Ecuador and Peru, where it is the only species of mockingbird. Most resembles the Chilean Mockingbird, and probably forms a superspecies group with that form.

IDENTIFICATION Length 29.5cm. The only mimid in its range, with little resemblance to any other species.

DESCRIPTION *M. l. longicaudatus*
Adult Crown and nape dull grey-brown with diffuse blackish-brown streaks. Back, rump and shoulders dull grey-brown with some streaking on upper portions. Primary and secondary greater and lesser coverts with pale edgings. Bases of primaries dull whitish giving a patch of off-white on extended wing; remainder of primaries and secondaries dull blackish-brown. Rectrices dull dark brownish-black, the outer feathers tipped with dirty white. Lores and area before and behind eye dull blackish; supercilium grey in front of eye, broader and whitish-grey behind. Ear-coverts mottled greyish, area behind ear-coverts off-white. Narrow black malar stripe, broadening below ear-coverts. Chin grey, chest dull greyish-brown with paler tips to feathers, belly and vent whitish, lower flanks with diffuse darker streaks. Underwing greyish-white. Iris hazel, bill and legs black. Juvenile Similar; chest with obvious dark longitudinal streaks.

GEOGRAPHICAL VARIATION
  M. l. longicaudatus (Peru, from the Ecuadorian border south to Arequipa) Described above.
  M. l. albogriseus 'Ecuadorian Long-tailed Mockingbird' (western Ecuador north to central Manabí) Smaller than *longicaudatus*, with blacker lores and ear-coverts and more white on tail.

  M. l. platensis 'La Plata Island Mockingbird' (Isla La Plata, Manabí, Ecuador) Similar to *albogriseus* but bigger, with a larger bill.

VOICE Song is loud and long-continued, with many chuckling and gurgling notes and little obvious pattern; often given right through the day (Ridgely & Tudor 1989).

HABITAT Arid scrubland and woodland, often with cactus; also in agricultural areas and isolated patches of vegetation in desert. Sea-level to 2,000m.

HABITS Rather demonstrative, frequently perching on exposed trees. In flight frequently glides over long distances with wings outstretched and tail spread (Ridgely & Tudor 1989).

Long-tailed Mockingbird

STATUS AND DISTRIBUTION Rather common in parts of its range. Ecuador from Manabí south through

217

most of coastal Peru to Arequipa; an isolated interior population in La Libertad, Peru.

BREEDING Nest and eggs apparently not described.

FOOD Stomach contents include marine invertebrates, small cashew nuts and plant fragments (Ecuador).

MOVEMENTS Apparently sedentary.

MEASUREMENTS Wing of male 119–128, of female 117–123; tail of male 132–138, of female 122–133; exposed culmen of male 21–23, of female 36–41; tarsus of male 39–41.5, of female 36–41.

99   CHALK-BROWED MOCKINGBIRD
Mimus saturninus
                                                                   Plate 24

Turdus saturninus Lichtenstein, 1823 Rio Tapajóz, Pará, Brazil.

Alternative names: Spanish *Calandria Grande*; Portuguese *Sabiá-do-campo*

An abundant, familiar and well-liked bird, commonly found in suburban areas of cities like Buenos Aires as well as in more rural areas.

IDENTIFICATION Length 25–26cm. In its extensive range it overlaps with several other species of mockingbird. In coastal Brazil it is sympatric with the Tropical Mockingbird. It differs from that species by the more brown cast of its plumage and by having streaks on the back. White-banded and Brown-backed Mockingbirds have prominent white flashes on the wings; and Patagonian Mockingbird has a less prominent supercilium, unstreaked grey back and buff-grey area of breast.

DESCRIPTION *M. s. frater*
Adult Crown, nape, back, shoulders and rump dull grey with very diffuse darker streaking, paler on rump. Alula and lesser coverts, and primary greater coverts with grey-white edges; bases of primaries white, remainder of primaries, and secondaries, blackish-grey with pale edges on outerwebs; tertials with rusty edgings and off-white tips. Rectrices dull brownish-black, the four outer feathers with broad off-white tips, most extensive on outer feathers. Supercilium buffy-white before eye, broader and more prominent behind, contrasting strongly with adjacent feathers. Lores and area behind eye dull brownish-black, ear-coverts mottled buffy-brown. Chin whitish, throat, chest, flanks and belly grey, becoming slightly more buff on vent. Underwing buff-white. Iris yellow or yellow-green, bill and legs black.
Juvenile Similar to adult; iris grey or grey-yellow, chest with dark streaks, supercilium less prominent, back feathers with buffy edges.

GEOGRAPHICAL VARIATION
M. s. frater 'Brazilian Mockingbird' (eastern Bolivia and Brazil from Maranhão south to Rio de Janeiro and Matto Grosso) Described above.
M. s. saturninus 'Lower Amazonian Mockingbird' (northern Brazil [Pára]) Very similar to *frater*, but upperparts less brownish and rump more buff-coloured.
M. s. arenaceus 'Chapman's Mockingbird' (eastern Brazil [Bahia]) Similar to *frater* but bill larger.
M. s. modulator 'Argentine Mockingbird' (southern Brazil [Rio Grande do Sul], Uruguay, Paraguay, south-east Bolivia and Argentina) Similar to *frater*

but spotting on pileum and upper back darker, flank streaking lighter or absent and rump more rufescent.

VOICE Song is very variable, frequently with imitations of other species, sometimes with phrases repeated. While there is no comparison to the song of the White-banded Mockingbird, some individuals have very good songs. Call is a characteristic sharp *chripp chripp*.

HABITAT Probably the most adaptable of the South American mockingbirds; suburban areas including parks and gardens, open areas with trees, bushy scrub. Not found in either total forest or totally treeless areas. Sea-level to (mostly) 1,000m, occasionally to 2,500m in Argentina (Ridgely & Tudor 1989).

HABITS The most confident and least shy of the genus in South America, frequently seen running around lawns and parks. Feeds mostly on the ground and in low bushes. Singing birds may indulge in a short song-flight similar to that of the Northern Mockingbird, consisting of a vertical jump, followed by a slow flapping descent; otherwise frequently sings from an exposed perch. Sometimes aggressive towards other species, especially Shiny Cowbird *Molothrus bonariensis*.

STATUS AND DISTRIBUTION Common or abundant

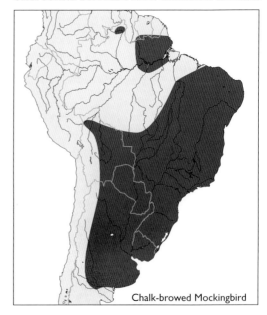

Chalk-browed Mockingbird

in many parts of its range. Argentina from Río Negro north through Uruguay and Paraguay to eastern Bolivia and most of southern and eastern Brazil north to Maranhão; isolated populations in Pará and Roraima and southern Suriname (Sipalwini savanna).

BREEDING Nest is a large open cup of twigs lined with fibres (Fraga 1985), frequently with shiny twigs on the outside, and usually situated in isolated shrubs or trees with dense foliage at a height of 0.5–3.7m above the ground. Eggs, three or four, are rather variable, base colour pale bluish-green to intense bluish-green, spotted with various shades of chestnut, heaviest round the blunt end. Incubation period 14–15 days; fledging period 12–15 days.

Parasitism by Shiny Cowbirds very common; in a study in Córdoba province, Argentina, 88% of mockingbird nests held cowbird eggs (Salvador 1984); other studies have found somewhat lower figures (Fraga 1985). Shiny Cowbirds lay two types of eggs, heavily marked (more resembling those of mockingbirds) and unmarked white or pale blue. Mockingbirds may eject alien eggs, especially those which differ in appearance from their own; the success rate of immaculate eggs in a study in Buenos Aires province was close to zero (Fraga 1985).

Nesting period in Córdoba province early October to early January, mostly October and November (Salvador 1984). Although there is no documented evidence of cooperative nesting sometimes additional birds will join a nesting pair in nest defence (Fraga 1985).

FOOD Little published information. Invertebrates and some vegetable matter.

MOVEMENTS Apparently sedentary; in Buenos Aires province, birds banded in the breeding season were frequently captured in exactly the same site in winter (Fraga 1985). Not known if any movement occurs at extreme southern end of range.

MEASUREMENTS (*M. s. frater*) Wing of male 105–112, of female 102–108; tail of male 105–118, of female 103–109; exposed culmen of male 17–19, of female 17–19; tarsus of male 33.5–35, of female 32–35.

---

100 PATAGONIAN MOCKINGBIRD
Mimus patagonicus
Plate 25

Orpheus patagonicus Lafresnaye and d'Orbigny 1837 Río Negro, Patagonia.

Alternative names: Spanish *Calandria Mora, Calandria Gris, Calandria Chica*

The southern most of the South American mockingbirds, extending to about 50°S in southernmost Patagonia.

IDENTIFICATION Length 22–25cm. Sympatric (at least during part of the year) with several other mockingbird species, but the greatest overlap is with Chalk-browed Mockingbird, which is larger, longer-tailed and with a very prominent pale supercilium. White-banded Mockingbird is immediately distinguished by the large amounts of white on wing and tail, as is the Brown-backed Mockingbird, a mountain species of northern Argentina and Bolivia.

DESCRIPTION
Adult Crown, back, shoulders and rump medium grey-brown, the crown with small, diffuse darker streaks, the rump somewhat more rufescent. Alula and primary and secondary coverts blackish tipped with white, the greater coverts edged with tawny on outerweb. Primaries and secondaries blackish with whitish tips, the primaries edged whitish on the outerweb, the secondaries and tertials tawny. Rectrices blackish, all feathers except central pair tipped white, most extensive on outermost feathers. Lores and area behind eye dark grey-black; supercilium behind eye buffy-white. Ear-coverts rufous-grey with darker mottling. Hint of darker malar stripe. Chin grey, becoming grey-buff on chest and more cinnamon-buff on belly, thighs and vent. Underwing greyish-white. Iris olive-green, bill and legs black.
Juvenile Similar to adult; throat and chest with obvious dark diffuse streaks, back feathers with tawny edges, edgings to coverts less pure white.

GEOGRAPHICAL VARIATION None; monotypic. Some authorities have separated the north-western populations as a race, *M. p. tricosus*, on the basis of a greyer back but the validity of this race is not generally accepted.

VOICE Song, although not as loud or forceful as that of the Chalk-browed Mockingbird is varied, a 'bewitching call, mixed with lower twittering notes, with amazing imitations' (Ochoa de Masramón 1975). Frequently sings from exposed perches in trees.

HABITAT Arid and semi-arid bushy scrub, including atriplex, creosote bush and greasewoods; arid gravel hills where water is wholly lacking (Wetmore 1926a). Less common around settlements than Chalk-browed Mockingbird (Ridgely & Tudor 1989).

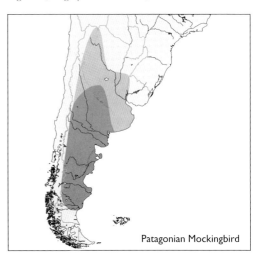

Patagonian Mockingbird

HABITS Much like other mockingbirds; less terrestrial than Chalk-browed Mockingbird.

STATUS AND DISTRIBUTION Quite common. Breeds from central Argentina (San Luis, Córdoba) south to southern Santa Cruz; barely into Chile (Aysén and Magallanes, casually to northern Tierra del Fuego) (Bernath 1965). Withdraws from southern part of range in winter; then found as far north as Jujuy and Salta (about 22°S).

BREEDING Nest is a cup, at no great height above the ground. Eggs are greenish, with spots and speckles of chestnut or dull greyish (Ochoa de Masramón 1975). Clutch size, incubation and fledging periods and num-

ber of broods per year not recorded. A common host of the Shiny Cowbird *Molothrus bonariensis* (Pereyra 1937).

FOOD No data recorded; presumably similar to other members of the genus.

MOVEMENTS Migrates north during the austral winter, reaching almost to the Bolivian border. Exact southern limits of winter distribution not recorded; leaves Chile completely in winter (Venegas & Jory 1979), returning at the end of September.

MEASUREMENTS Wing of male 105–118, of female 99–106; tail of male 91–105, of female 90–99; exposed culmen of male 16.5–17, of female 16.5–17; tarsus of male 35.5–37, of female 33–35.

---

101 WHITE-BANDED MOCKINGBIRD
Mimus triurus

Plate 25

Orpheus tricaudatus Lafresnaye & d'Orbigny 1837, Chiquitos, eastern Bolivia.

Alternative names: Spanish *Calandria Real*, *Calandria de tres Colas*; Portuguese *Calandra-de-tres-babos*

The most striking of all the South American mockingbirds; the tail, mostly white with a black centre, is responsible for its vernacular Spanish, Portuguese and its scientific name, 'the Three-tailed Mockingbird'.

IDENTIFICATION Length 20-23cm. Immediately distinguished from all other similar sympatric species by extensive white markings on wing and tail, obvious even when perched and very striking in flight. Most closely resembles Brown-backed Mockingbird, with which it is extensively sympatric in winter. That species has much less white on the wing.

DESCRIPTION
Adult Crown, nape, back and shoulders uniform grey-brown, becoming more rusty on lower back and rusty-orange on rump. Primary coverts largely white. Primaries black; secondaries extensively white on both webs, with variable amount of black towards tip, giving a large area of white on the closed wing. Tertials brownish-black with extensive rusty edgings. Outer two rectrices entirely white, the next two largely so, the remainder blackish. Lores buffy, narrow supercilium off-white, ear-coverts grey-brown. Chin off-white, chest and belly pale buffy-white, vent buffy. Underwing white contrasting sharply with black primaries. Iris coffee-brown, upper mandible black, lower mandible black with leaden base, legs black.
Juvenile Very similar to adult; primary coverts black with extensive white edgings.

GEOGRAPHICAL VARIATION None; monotypic.

VOICE Song, 'a diamond among stones' (W. H. Hudson). A long-continued stream of strong, pure melodic notes, interspersed with near-perfect imitations of various other songbirds (Ridgely & Tudor 1989). Song is sometimes given in a slow, flapping song-flight, but more often from cover.

HABITAT Various types of bushland, open woodland,

steppe with scattered bushes etc.; also around farms and other habitation, mostly sea-level to 500m, though up to 1,950m in wintering-grounds in Bolivia. During the breeding season tends to be found in areas of denser vegetation (Ochoa de Masramón 1975). In wintering-grounds in Brazil often near water (Sick 1993).

HABITS Similar to other mockingbirds; not particularly secretive. Feeds mostly on or near the ground. During display the male runs a few steps on the ground while singing, then opens wings and tail and jumps up a foot or so, bringing the body nearly horizontal, then drops and runs a few steps further (Fjeldså & Krabbe 1990).

STATUS AND DISTRIBUTION Quite common in many parts of its range; breeds in north-central Argentina, from northern Río Negro to Salta, with populations also in Paraguay and Bolivia. Extent of northern parts of breeding range imperfectly known. In winter, over much

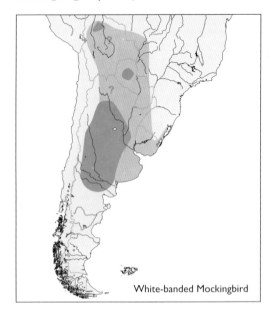

White-banded Mockingbird

of lowland Bolivia, Paraguay, Uruguay and adjacent parts of Brazil (Matto Grosso and coastal Rio Grande do Sul).

BREEDING In lowlands mainly in December. Nest is the usual mockingbird type, fairly low down in a bush, often a spiny one. Eggs usually four, of a very pale blue or slightly greenish colour, with reddish speckles especially concentrated around the blunt end (Ochoa de Masramón 1975). Incubation and fledging periods and number of broods per year not recorded. Frequently parasitised by the Shiny Cowbird *Molothrus bonariensis* (Pereyra 1937).

FOOD Little information; stated to take bees, wasps, butterflies, etc. (Ochoa de Masramón 1975).

MOVEMENTS Quite migratory; in southern winter moves into Bolivia, parts of Brazil, Paraguay and Uruguay. Southern limits of winter range not precisely recorded.

MEASUREMENTS Wing of male 102–109, of female 99–104; tail of male 102–110, of female 96–100; exposed culmen of male 15.5–17, of female 14–16.5; tarsus of male 32–34, of female 31–34.

102 BROWN-BACKED MOCKINGBIRD
Mimus dorsalis
Plate 25

Orpheus dorsalis Lafresnaye and d'Orbigny 1837 'in Andiis, rep. Boliviana' (Cochabamba, Bolivia).

Alternative names: Bolivian Mockingbird; Spanish *Calandria Castaña*

Perhaps the least well-known of all the South American mockingbirds, restricted to dry highland areas of Northern Argentina and Bolivia.

IDENTIFICATION Length 21–25.5cm. During the breeding season largely allopatric from most other *Mimus* species. In winter the White-banded Mockingbird shares part of its range. It differs from that species by having much less white on the wing, obvious in flight and at rest, and by having a more rufous back. Chalk-browed Mockingbird has no obvious white wing flashes, and a more prominent supercilium.

DESCRIPTION
Adult Crown dark rufous-brown with diffuse darker streaks. Back, shoulders and rump rufous-brown, becoming warmer in tone towards rump. Primary coverts white; secondary coverts black with narrow white tips. Primaries black, with extensive white bases giving a conspicuous white flash on closed wing. Secondaries black with reduced white bases and pale tips in unworn plumage, tertials dull black with tawny edging on both webs. Three outer rectrices white, fourth largely white, remainder entirely black. Supercilium buffy-white, broader and paler behind eye. Lores and area behind eye dull black. Ear-coverts grey with fine darker speckles. Chin buffy-white, chest and lower belly darker buffy-white. Under-wing white, contrasting with black and white flight feathers. Iris dark brown or brownish-yellow, bill and legs black.
Juvenile Chest extensively covered with diffuse brown spots, tertials broadly fringed rusty, tips on secondary coverts rusty, base of bill yellowish-green.

GEOGRAPHICAL VARIATION None; monotypic.

VOICE Song varied, mostly of harsh notes *terett terett tett tett* (Fjeldså & Krabbe 1990).

HABITAT Arid mountain scrubland, sometimes with scattered cacti, often near villages 1,700–4,200m.

HABITS Alone, or in pairs or family groups. Feeds on

the ground, often with cocked tail. During display flies up to spread wings and tail (Fjeldså & Krabbe 1990).

STATUS AND DISTRIBUTION Quite common in some areas. Northern Argentina (Jujuy and Salta) and central Bolivia north to Cochabamba and La Paz. One sight record in northern Chile (Fjeldså & Krabbe 1990); the validity of this record is, however, disputed (A. Jaramillo pers. comm.).

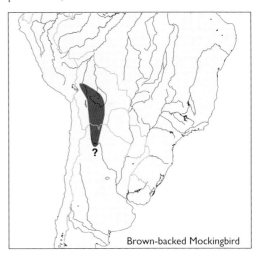
Brown-backed Mockingbird

BREEDING Nest and eggs apparently undescribed. Eggs in November in northern Argentina, recently fledged birds in December, January and March (Bolivia).

FOOD No information recorded.

MOVEMENTS No information recorded; presumably largely sedentary, but data on altitudinal movements lacking.

MEASUREMENTS Wing of male 120–124, of female 113–116; tail of male 109–116, of female 105–115; exposed culmen of male 19–22.5, of female 19.5–22; tarsus of male 37.5–40, of female 34.5–38.

NESOMIMUS

Medium to large mimids. Bill as long as the head or nearly so, rather slender and moderately decurved. Wings quite long and pointed, sixth to eighth primaries the longest. Tail fairly long and strongly rounded. Tarsus long and slender. Plumage brown or grey-brown. Four species endemic to the Galápagos Islands.

The separation of *Nesomimus* from *Mimus* is not upheld by some authorities, and indeed in captivity the two genera have interbred (Bowman & Carter 1971). A feature of *Nesomimus* which has not so far been observed in mainland populations is a well-developed system of cooperative breeding which has been the subject of much detailed study.

103 GALAPAGOS MOCKINGBIRD
Nesomimus parvulus   Plate 26

Orpheus parvulus Gould 1837, Galápagos Islands.

Alternative names: Mocking Thrush; Spanish *Cucuve de los Galápagos*

The most widely distributed of the four species found on the Galápagos Islands, occurring on most of the northern and western members of the group, and all of the largest islands. The best-studied of all the species, with a complex social system involving group defence of territory and cooperative breeding.

IDENTIFICATION Length 25.5cm. Each species and race is allopatric; identification is established simply by location.

DESCRIPTION *N. p. parvulus*
Adult Crown dark blackish-brown. Nape grey-brown, contrasting with crown and with dark brown back and shoulders. Lower back and rump dark brown, becoming paler on rump. Greater and lesser coverts dull dark brown with off-white tips to feathers forming two wing-bars on closed wing. Primaries and secondaries dull dark brown with paler edges on outerwebs and paler tips on secondaries. Rectrices dark brown with off-white tips on outer pair. Lores, area below eye and ear-coverts solid chocolate-brown, contrasting with chin, paler supercilium and pale buff area in front of shoulders. Chin and throat off-white, chest dull grey, belly off-white with dull brown streaks on flanks. Vent off-white. Underwing off-white with darker markings. Iris yellowish, bill and legs black.
Juvenile Spotted and streaked on breast.

GEOGRAPHICAL VARIATION
N. p. parvulus 'Albemarle Island Mockingbird' (Isabella [Albemarle Island], Fernandina [Narborough Island], Daphne Island, Baltra [South Seymour Island], Santa Cruz [Indefatigable Island]) Described above.
The remaining races of the Galápagos Mockingbird are distributed as follows.
N. p. hulli (Culpepper Island [Darwin])
N. p. bauri (Tower Island [Genovesa])
N. p. wenmani (Wenman Island [Wolf])
N. p. personatus (includes *N. p. bindloei*) (Pinta [Abingdon Island], Marchena [Bindloe Island], James Island [Santiago, San Salvador], Jervis Island [Rabida])
N. p. barringtoni (Barrington Island [Santa Fe])

VOICE Song is loud and melodious, the call strident and attention-drawing (Harris 1974).

HABITAT Over most of the habitats of the islands of its range; abundant in arid lowlands, a semi-vegetation-type with a few deciduous tree species, *Opuntia* cacti and various shrubs and vines. Also moister, higher forest on all islands; apparently only absent from the highest zones on Santa Cruz (Curry & Grant 1990).

HABITS Extraordinarily tame; Darwin (1839) recounts a bird drinking from a tortoiseshell held in his hand. Lives in groups holding collective territories which are vigorously defended with a characteristic display involving the cocking and fanning of the tail, flicking of the wings away from the body and giving loud distinctive calls. Attachment of individuals to a group and group territory is strong and faithful; most wandering individuals are young females searching for breeding vacancies. A 'territorial group', which consists of all birds resident in a defined territory, may include up to four breeding females. These 'reproductive units' operate within the territorial group, and are more fluid; whereas birds only rarely leave a territorial group, individual birds within that group may act as a breeder in one reproductive unit and a helper at another, or by being a breeder or a helper at more than one. Some birds, not themselves breeding, do not help other breeding pairs, while others may assist a pair with one brood but not with subsequent broods. Recruitment for the population of a territorial group comes from young produced within the territory, with the exception of small numbers of young wandering females. A system of rank, a linear dominance hierarchy, is well developed; the dominant male in any group is invariably the oldest individual, while females (which are substantially smaller) rank lower than males other than their own sons. Breeding pairs tend to be birds of equal rank; however, incestuous relationships between brother and sister, father and daughter, mother and son do occur and result in successful rearing of young. For detailed studies of the social organisation and reproductive strategy of the Galapagos Mockingbird see Curry 1988a, 1988b; Kinnaird & Grant 1982; Curry & Grant 1989, 1990.

STATUS AND DISTRIBUTION Found in all the islands in the north and west of the Galapagos group; Barrington (Santa Fe), Santa Cruz (Indefatigable), James (Santiago), Fernandina (Narborough), Genovesa (Tower) Marchena (Bindloe). Pinta (Abingdon), Wenman (Wolf) and Culpepper (Darwin) and various smaller islands; absent from Duncan (Pinzon) except for two records. Generally common to abundant on

Galapagos Mockingbird

cactus plant, from 1–6m above the ground. Eggs three or four, average 3.9, (nests with up to seven eggs were attended by more than one female), blue-green with brown markings. Incubation 12–13 days or 15 days (Castro & Phillips 1996). Young fed by a variable number of parents and helpers (Curry & Grant 1990). In good years double-brooded (Grant & Grant 1979).

FOOD Very varied. Most kinds of invertebrates, crickets, centipedes, spiders, caterpillars; has also been seen to steal invertebrate prey from a large centipede (Curry 1986); lizards; some vegetable matter, including fruits and flowers of cacti. Also carrion (dead land iguanas, seabirds, regurgitated fish in seabird colonies, sea lions, goats, etc.) and iguana faeces. Will clean ticks off land iguanas *Conolophus cristatus* and *C. pallides*, a seemingly symbiotic relationship since the iguanas cooperate (Christian 1980); also dead skin from live iguanas. Blood-drinking from wounds on both land and marine iguanas *Amblyrhynchus subcristatus* has been observed on some, but not all, islands (Curry & Anderson 1987). Also feeds on eggs, including smaller eggs of species like those of Darwin's Finches *Platyspiza crassirostris* which they are capable of breaking into unaided, and cracked or damaged eggs of seabirds (Bowman & Carter 1971); also 'attracted to scrambled eggs in open pan' (!)

MOVEMENTS Very sedentary; studies of colour-banded birds show that most males remain in their natal territories, although females are somewhat more mobile (Curry & Grant 1990). There are two records on Duncan (Pinzon) which is more than 10km from the closest island on which the species breeds.

MEASUREMENTS Wing of male 105–111, of female 99–103; tail of male 103–113, of female 97–105; exposed culmen of male 19–20, of female 19–20; tarsus of male 35–37.5, of female 33–36 (Ridgway 1907).

many islands; on Genovesa, territories (occupied by groups of birds) ranged from 0.1–3.5ha, with an average of 0.95ha, larger groups tending to have larger territories. Isabella is less densely populated, possibly due to predation on nests by Black Rats.

BREEDING Breeds cooperatively with a complex social system (see under Habits). Breeding season heavily dependent on amount of rain; normally December to May, but in El Niño years extending to July, while in drought years breeding may not occur at all (Curry & Grant 1990). Nest is similar to that of *Mimus* mockingbirds, a substantial cup placed in a bush, low tree or

---

104 CHARLES MOCKINGBIRD
Nesomimus trifasciatus

Plate 26

Orpheus trifasciatus Gould 1837 Galápagos Islands.

Alternative names: Three-banded Mockingbird, Floreana Mockingbird; Spanish *Cucuve de Floreana*

The only species of the Galápagos Islands mockingbird group to be seriously endangered; now confined to two tiny islands. The type specimen was collected by Charles Darwin.

IDENTIFICATION Length 25.5cm. The only mockingbird in its minute range. Characteristic dark brown patches at side of breast.

DESCRIPTION
Adult Crown, nape, back and rump dark chocolate-brown, most feathers having lighter edges. Greater and lesser primary and secondary coverts dark dull brown with off-white edges giving wing-bars on closed wing. Primaries and secondaries blackish-brown, the primaries with pale edges to outerwebs, the secondaries when unworn with broad white tips. Rectrices dull blackish-brown with obscure pale tips on outer feathers. Lores

dark brown, ear-coverts buff, area below eye buff with dark brown mottling. Chin and throat buffy; chest buffy-white with solid blackish-brown areas at sides. Lower chest and belly off-white with large blackish-brown spots at sides and on flanks. Vent off-white, underwings greyish with dark brown markings. Iris seal-brown, bill and legs blackish.

GEOGRAPHICAL VARIATION None; monotypic.

VOICE No information recorded.

HABITAT Arid scrubland.

HABITS Apparently similar to the species on other islands although less well studied. Lives in groups with territories defended by the group. Feeds both on the ground and in low vegetation.

STATUS AND DISTRIBUTION Now entirely restricted to two islets, Champion (Iolia) and Gardner-near-Floreana. In 1968 Harris estimated the population on both islets at not more than 150 birds; recent estimates on Gardner

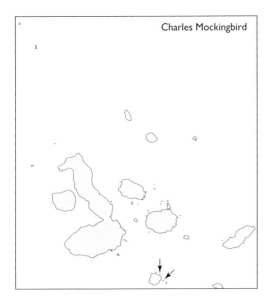
Charles Mockingbird

was estimated at 4.9 birds per ha, with all terrestrial habitat filled. The Champion population is estimated to have a less than 50% chance of long-term viability, although this estimated is improved if other figures for female fecundity are used. Populations are apparently subject to sudden crashes, which occur during El Niño years, due to outbreaks of avian pox (D. Capper, pers. comm.). Common on Floreana (Charles) in the middle of the nineteenth century, but by 1888 had disappeared, probably due to the introduction of Black Rats *Rattus rattus*.

BREEDING On Champion, nests in several species of tree and in *Opuntia* cactus; on Gardner-near-Floreana, nests mostly in *Croton* and *Cordia* trees.

FOOD Omnivorous. Food includes invertebrates, fruit and vegetable matter (including *Opuntia* fruit and Convolvulus flowers), carrion (dead seabirds, lizards and sea lions). Has not been seen to drink blood. May take eggs, but precise instances not so far observed; has been seen to eat broken eggs (Bowman & Carter 1971).

MOVEMENTS Sedentary.

are 200–300 birds (1988; Collar *et al.* 1992) and on Champion, 28–53 individuals between 1980 and 1991 (Curry & Grant 1991). Population density on Champion

MEASUREMENTS Wing of male 121–126, of female 121–125; tail of male 110–120, of female 114–117; exposed culmen of male 27, of female 26.5–27; tarsus of male 40–41, of female 38–38.5 (Ridgway 1907).

105 HOOD MOCKINGBIRD
Nesomimus macdonaldi
Plate 26

Nesomimus macdonaldi Ridgway 1890, Hood (Española) Island, Galápagos.

Alternative names: Spanish *Cucuve de Española*

The endemic mockingbird on Hood, an island noted for large colonies of seabirds and marine mammals, where it has developed some bizarre feeding habits.

IDENTIFICATION Length 28cm. The only mockingbird on Hood. A large-billed bird with reduced pale tips to the rectrices.

DESCRIPTION
Adult Crown, nape, back, shoulders and rump dark dull brown, each feather having greyish or tawny edges, giving a variegated appearance. Greater and lesser coverts dark brown with off-white tips and tawny edges. Primaries and secondaries dark brown with lighter edges to outerwebs. Rectrices dull dark brown. Lores blackish-brown, ear-coverts mottled blackish-brown and buffy-grey, diffuse malar stripe blackish-brown. Chin and throat off-white, chest off-white with a variable quantity of large dark brown spots, especially on sides. Lower chest and belly off-white. Thighs off-white with dull brown barring. Underwing dull grey with dull brown marks. Iris yellow, bill black, legs black.
Juvenile Spotted underparts.

GEOGRAPHICAL VARIATION None; monotypic.

VOICE Calls include a raucous squeak and faint rattle.

HABITAT Arid scrubland, but also spends substantial time in seabird colonies.

HABITS Like all the other mockingbirds of the Galápagos, confiding and curious, investigating unfamiliar objects (such as human beings and their impedimenta) with a fearless inquisitiveness. Usually encountered in groups larger than in the related species, sometimes numbering up to 40 individuals (Castro & Phillips 1996); breeding biology presumably involves similar cooperation to other species. Groups defend a group territory. Within a group there is a set hierarchy which is established and maintained by stereotyped behaviour, including a begging display to indicate submission. Apparently birds recognise each other by facial markings (Hatch 1966). Group size tends to be larger for groups whose territories include shoreline, perhaps as a response to the increased food sources there. The Hood Mockingbird, probably in response to its sparse habitat (Hood is one of the islands with a relatively impoverished flora [Bowman & Carter 1971]) has, more than any other species, exploited alternative and non-traditional food sources, and has developed behaviour patterns for this purpose. Notable examples are blood-drinking from live mammals and birds and egg pecking.

Hood Mockingbirds are very rapidly attracted by the sight of blood, on marine mammals, large seabirds and iguanas. Indeed they are rather catholic and indiscriminating in their tastes as individuals 'twice attempted to drink blood from superficial wounds on the legs of field investigators' (Curry & Anderson 1987). Large marine mammals, such as sea-lions *Zalophus californianus*, wounded in fights are immediately attractive to

224

mockingbirds; one injured bull sea-lion with lacerations in the genital area was surrounded by six birds which drank directly from the open wounds. When the sea-lion moved away the birds fed on the congealed blood on the sand. Birds have also been seen to glean dried blood from the scene of a kill of an iguana by a Galapagos Hawk *Buteo galapagoensis*. Wounded nestling seabirds, such as Masked Boobies *Sula dactylatra* are also a source of fresh blood; mockingbirds may stand on the nestling, probing the wound with their bills. Also seen to drink from wounds in Marine Iguanas *Amblyrhynchus subcristatus*.

The origins of blood-drinking are uncertain. Mockingbirds frequently tear ticks and small pieces of dead skin from iguanas, sometimes creating small wounds in the process; drinking blood from wounds thus created may be a logical progression. Other possibilities include the birds having acquired a taste for blood from the afterbirth of marine mammals and by picking engorged blood-sucking ectoparasites from large animals. Blood-drinking is only found in some *Nesomimus* populations (the habit being far more prevalent in the Hood Mockingbird than in other species) and there may be a correlation between the habit and the occurrence of the Galapagos Hawk *Buteo galapagoensis*, with the opportunities created by wounded iguanas (Curry & Anderson 1987). The occurrence of suitable predators, however, and the presence or absence of blood-drinking tendencies among the local mockingbird population is not totally clear-cut.

Egg-pecking has been observed in several of the Galápagos mockingbirds, but the habit seems to be much more pronounced in the Hood Mockingbird than in others. The bill of the Hood species is substantially more powerful than that of other members of the genus, although it is not powerful enough to break open the eggs of larger seabirds such as the Waved Albatross *Diomedea irrorata* or Blue-footed Booby *Sula nebouxii*. Cracked eggs, however, are enthusiastically attacked and devoured. Smaller eggs, such as those of Swallow-tailed Gull *Creagrus furcatus* may be broken into. Large eggs are turned over by sweeping sideways movements of the bill, even in the presence of the rightful owner.

STATUS AND DISTRIBUTION Confined to Española (Hood) Island where it seems to be abundant, parties of 40 birds having been observed (Hatch 1966).

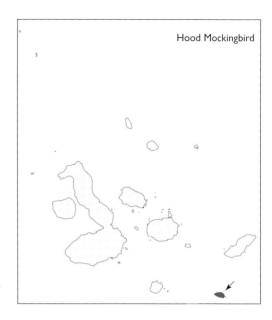

Hood Mockingbird

BREEDING No information recorded on nest or eggs but doubtless similar to those of the other *Nesomimus* species. Apparently at least double-brooded, the peak of breeding being usually in February (Venables 1940).

FOOD More varied, or more opportunistic, than other members of the genus; besides invertebrates and vegetable matter, eggs, blood and frequently carrion and faeces, associated with colonies of seabirds and marine mammals. An enthusiastic camp follower to humans, the local group immediately 'taking over' any temporary settlement and snapping up any unconsidered trifles arising therefrom.

MOVEMENTS Sedentary apart from very short distance movements between groups.

MEASUREMENTS Wing of male 113–125, of female 114.5; tail of male 103–115, of female 102; exposed culmen of male 31.5–33, of female 31.5; tarsus of male 38–38.5, of female 38 (Ridgway 1907).

106 CHATHAM MOCKINGBIRD
Nesomimus melanotis   Plate 26

Orpheus melanotis Gould 1837, Galápagos Islands.

Alternative names: Spanish *Cucuve de San Cristóbal*

The smallest of the Galápagos mockingbirds, with a smaller bill than the Hood Mockingbird; has not been seen to feed on eggs.

IDENTIFICATION Length 25.5cm. The only mockingbird on Chatham (San Cristóbal) Island.

DESCRIPTION
Adult Crown, nape, back and shoulders dark brown, each feather with greyish or tawny edges giving a variegated appearance; rump buffy-brown, uppertail-coverts darker. Greater and lesser coverts and alula blackish-brown with off-white tips to feathers giving two wing-bars on closed wing. Primaries and secondaries dull blackish-brown with tawny edges on outerwebs and off-white tips on secondaries. Rectrices dark-brown with off-white tips to outer three feathers, most extensive on the outermost. Indeterminate pale supercilium, lores dark-brown; ear-coverts buff heavily mottled with blackish-brown. Chin and throat off-white or very pale buffy-white. Chest off-white with very small medium brown spots at sides; lower chest, belly and vent off-white.

Underwing greyish with darker brown markings. Iris yellowish, bill and legs black.

Juvenile Similar; back feathers with extensive tawny edges, wing-bars tawny, chest heavily spotted with dark brown.

GEOGRAPHICAL VARIATION None; monotypic.

HABITAT Habitat on San Cristóbal includes semi-desert scrub in coastal areas, better watered areas at medium elevation and grassy 'downs' still higher up. Mocking-birds are found in all of these (Venables 1940).

HABITS Much as other members of the genus. Very tame and curious. Some birds are very aggressive around the nest, others less so. Wing-flashes (Hundley 1963). Territories are defended by a 'posture dance'. Since this may involve up to three birds (Venables 1940) it may be inferred that group territories and defence occur with this species as with others. Feeding behaviour involves scratching over leaf-litter on the scrubland floor. Has not been seen to attack eggs of seabirds, but this may simply be due to lack of opportunity, there being no major colonies of suitable species on the mainland of San Cristóbal. The relatively small bill would presumably make this species a less efficient predator of eggs than the Hood Mockingbird. Will peck at Marine Iguanas *Amblyrhynchus suberistatus* but blood-drinking from live iguanas has not been observed, and iguanas on San Cristóbal did not show any wounds consistent with mockingbird attack (Curry & Anderson 1987).

STATUS AND DISTRIBUTION Confined to San Cristóbal (Chatham) Island, where it appears to be common despite the presence of Black Rats *Rattus rattus*.

BREEDING Nest, built by both sexes, is an untidy structure with a foundation of dry twigs, the bulk being made of orchilla moss and dry weed and grass stems, lined with finer grass-stems (Rothschild *et al.* 1902), situated in crotches of trees about 4–5m above ground-level, lower at higher elevations where the trees are smaller. Multiple nests may be built (Venables 1940).

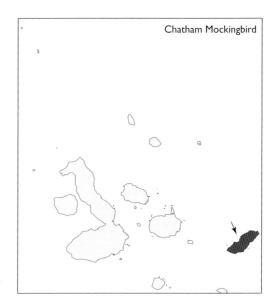
Chatham Mockingbird

Eggs usually four, sometimes two to five, light greenish, more or less frequently marked with reddish-brown patches and spots (Rothschild *et al.* 1902). Incubation by female alone, period not recorded. Young fed by both sexes, fledging period not recorded. Probably double-brooded. Egg dates usually January to March, later at higher elevations (Venables 1940).

FOOD Seen to take insects, caterpillars and spiders and to peck marine iguanas. Carrion-eating, blood-drinking and egg-predation not observed.

MOVEMENTS Presumably largely sedentary.

MEASUREMENTS Wing of male 109–113, of female 107–114; tail of male 95–104, of female 92–105; exposed culmen of male 24, of female 22–24; tarsus of male 37–38, of female 37–38 (Ridgway 1907).

MIMODES

Medium-sized mimid with dull coloured plumage. Bill short and rather stout, not decurved, with distinct rictal bristles. Wings short and rounded, with fifth and sixth primaries the longest. Tail fairly long, somewhat rounded. Legs quite long and rather slender. The precise relationships of *Mimodes* to *Mimus* and *Toxostoma* remain obscure (Gulledge 1975) but anatomically it seems in some ways to link the two genera. One species, found only on Socorro Island, Revillagigedo group, Mexico.

107 SOCORRO MOCKINGBIRD
Mimodes graysoni   Plate 27

Harporhynchus graysoni Lawrence 1871, Socorro Island, Revillagigedo group, Mexico.

Alternative names: Socorro Thrasher, Grayson's Mimodes; Spanish *Cenzontle de Socorro*

An endemic species and monotypic genus, confined to Socorro Island in the Revillagigedo archipelago west of

the Mexican mainland. Formerly very common, it is now, tragically and quite unnecessarily, hovering on the verge of extinction.

IDENTIFICATION Length 24–26.5cm. The only similar species on Socorro island is the recently-arrived Northern Mockingbird which is immediately distinguished by its conspicuous white wing-flashes and tail markings.

DESCRIPTION

Adult Forehead, crown, back, shoulders and rump uniform dull grey-brown. Primaries and secondaries dark grey-brown, the outerweb of the primaries with narrow paler edgings; tertials edged dull rusty. Rectrices dull greyish-brown with very obscure narrow barring, not visible in field. Outer feathers with dull grey-white tips. Lores dark brown, ear-coverts dull grey-brown with obscure mottling. Chin dull grey-white, chest dull buffy-white, belly dull grey-white, lower flanks dull grey-brown with obscure darker brown, longitudinal streaks. Vent dull brownish-white. Iris amber-yellow, bill and legs blackish.

Juvenile Indistinct greyish-brown spots on chest, iris duller.

GEOGRAPHICAL VARIATION None; monotypic.

VOICE Song is more of a mockingbird than thrasher type. A varied, scratchy to rich warble (Howell & Webb 1995), soft and full of rich melody (Anthony 1898). May now mimic the songs of the Northern Mockingbird. Calls include a rich *whi-choo* and *whi-chee-oo*. Calls of females a guttural *chunk* and a nasal *nya nya* (Martínez Gómez & Curry 1995).

HABITAT Formerly found all over the island, now more restricted. At lower elevations almost entirely restricted to the vicinity of large fig groves, habitat which is now rare (Jehl & Parkes 1982). Formerly abundant in higher wooded areas, now mostly found in wooded canyons and chaparral scrub at middle and higher elevations.

HABITS All earlier observers commented on the extreme tameness of the species, which would feed from the hand and sing perched on the observer's shoulder (Jehl & Parkes 1982). Forages on the ground, in vegetation and in the canopies of trees; will also chase and catch flying insects on the wing.

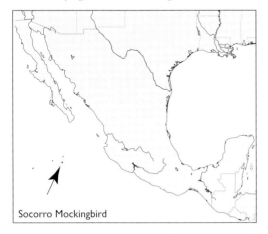

Socorro Mockingbird

STATUS AND DISTRIBUTION Critically endangered. The recent history of the Socorro Mockingbird is indeed a sad story. All earlier visitors to the island agreed that it was abundant (e.g. McLellan 1926), a situation that prevailed until at least 1958. Over the next twenty years the species declined catastrophically; by 1978 only a very few individuals could be found (Jehl & Parkes 1982). More recently, comprehensive surveys of the island produced an estimate of about 50–60 pairs in 1988–1990 (Castellanos & Rodríguez-Estrella 1993), and between 100 and 300 individuals; in 1993 and 1994 a total of 215 birds were banded (Martínez Gómez & Curry 1995).

Several reasons for the decline of the species have been postulated. The Northern Mockingbird colonised Socorro naturally by 1978, and within three years was abundant. Competition from this species has been cited as a cause for the decline of its endemic relative, but this argument seems very unconvincing (Jehl & Parkes 1983). Almost certainly the true cause has been the introduction, about 1958 following the establishment of a military garrison, of the domestic cat, which has now established a feral population; and habitat destruction by introduced sheep. It is clear that the future of the Socorro Mockingbird and other endangered species still present, such as Townsend's Shearwater *Puffinus auricularis*, depends on the control of alien mammals; the endemic Socorro Dove *Zenaida graysoni* is already extinct in the wild.

BREEDING Nesting was described for the first time only as recently as 1995 (Martínez Gómez & Curry 1995). Five nests were found; all were at altitudes of 750–850m above sea-level, in trees about 15m in height. Nests were open cups constructed of twigs and lined with mosses and epiphytes, averaging 16m in external diameter, with the cup about 8cm wide and 4cm deep. Three nests were placed in the foliage of outer branches, one in the forked bole of a large tree, and one in a shallow cavity in the side of the trunk of a large tree, with an average height of about 4m above the ground. Eggs three (two nests), bluish-green with large brown spots (and hence more typical of *Mimus* than *Toxostoma*). Incubation apparently by female alone, probably no more than 15 days; young fed by both parents, fledging period 14 days or less. Young leave the nest before being capable of sustained flight and hence are very vulnerable to feral cats. No evidence of cooperative breeding. Nests with well-grown young in late March; two nests with eggs in April. However, it is likely that the breeding period is more protracted, possibly from November through July.

FOOD Very varied. Observed to feed young on small insects, moths, small butterflies and caterpillars. Adults seen to take blowflies from sheep carcasses, land crabs, eggshells and other matter; one small blue lizard in stomach contents (Anthony 1898). Much vegetable matter, including rosehips and blackberries and other fleshy fruits. May be predatory on small birds' nests (Parkes 1990). Will come to 'hand-outs', taking bread from the hand of the observer and being especially fond of cheese.

MOVEMENTS Sedentary; one colour-banded juvenile was observed 1.6km from the banding location two months later (Martínez Gómez & Curry 1995).

MEASUREMENTS Wing of male 104–110, of female 99–108; tail of male 110–120, of female 111–120; exposed culmen of male 18–22, of female 19–21; tarsus of male 36–38.5, of female 34–38 (Ridgway 1907 and museum measurements).

Rather small mimids (about 20cm), notably smaller than *Toxostoma*, with seventh or eighth primary the longest. Tail much shorter and less rounded than in *Toxostoma*. Bill shorter and not decurved, in shape more resembling that of a *Turdus* thrush than most thrashers. One species only, breeding in dry areas of western North America; strongly migratory. DNA hybridisation evidence suggests a closer relationship to *Mimus* than *Toxostoma*, despite plumage similarities to several species of thrasher (Sibley & Ahlquist 1984).

108 SAGE THRASHER
Oreoscoptes montanus   Plate 27

Orpheus montanus Townsend, 1837 'Plains of the Rocky Mountains' (probably Big Sandy River, Wyoming).

Alternative names: Mountain Mockingbird, Sage Mockingbird; Spanish *Cuitlacoche de Chias, Cuitlacoche de Artemisia*; French *Moqueur des Armoises*

A small thrasher of arid areas of the western United States and marginally into western Canada. A sagebrush obligate or nearly so, as a breeding bird largely confined to areas dominated by Big Sagebrush *Artemisia tridentata*.

IDENTIFICATION Length 20.5–23cm. Not readily confused with other thrashers, or indeed with any other species. It differs from *Toxostoma* thrashers in overall shape and form, being shorter-tailed, longer-winged and with a more thrush-like bill. Of the south-western thrashers with which it shares habitat, in at least some part of the year, Bendire's and Curve-billed are most likely to cause confusion. It differs from both by its more sharply demarcated markings on the chest, by more obvious wing-bars, shorter bill and very obvious white-tipped tail. Brown Thrasher is a much richer chestnut-brown on top.

DESCRIPTION
Adult Crown, shoulders and back dull brownish-grey, becoming more washed-out on rump. Wing-coverts grey-brown with narrow buff-brown edgings, giving a wing-bar on closed wing. Primaries, secondaries and tertials dull grey-brown. Rectrices brownish-grey, the three outermost tipped broadly with white. Lores, area under eye and ear-coverts mottled buff-grey. Chin off-white, flanked by narrow blackish malar stripe. Chest and belly off-white with conspicuous blackish spots, thickest on chest, becoming larger and more scattered on upper belly. Vent buffy. Underwing grey-buff. Iris lemon-yellow, bill dull brown-grey, base of lower mandible pinkish. Legs dull olivaceous-brown.
Juvenile Similar to adult; back brown with dusky streaks, tertials with broad whitish-buff edgings (Pyle 1997).

GEOGRAPHICAL VARIATION None; monotypic.

VOICE The song, delivered from a prominent perch or in a song-flight is a prolonged series of warbled soft syllables, quite musical and generally without harsh notes, continuing for up to $2^1/_2$ minutes at a stretch. Only rarely mimics other species, and then only briefly. Other calls include a sharp *chuck*, a high *churr* and a whistled *whee-er*.

HABITAT As a breeding bird, largely confined to areas where the dominant species is Big Sagebrush *A. tridentata*, although in Utah and Nevada, black greasewood

Sarcobatus vermiculatus and in Washington, bitterbrush *Purshia tridentata* (Reynolds *et al.* 2000). In winter found in much more varied habitat types, including Sonoran and Chihuahuan desert communities and various other types of arid and semi-arid brushland.

HABITS Generally much more wary than any other North American member of its family, though this shyness will evaporate when abundant food in the form of berries is present (Kennedy 1911). Spends a lot of time on the ground, where it runs, breaking into a sprint with upturned tail when alarmed; frequently avoids intruders by rushing into nearby cover. When alarmed characteristically flicks up tail and then more slowly lowers it. Takes most invertebrate prey on ground, although berries are taken where growing. Generally rather solitary, although in winter it may occur in small groups or flocks (Russell & Monson 1998).

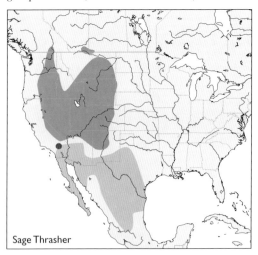
Sage Thrasher

STATUS AND DISTRIBUTION Partial migrant. Breeds from southern British Columbia (Osoyoos, White Lake) and extreme southern Saskatchewan (Govenlock, East-end) southwards in suitable habitat from interior Washington and Oregon through Nevada, eastern California, northern Arizona, north-western New Mexico, western Colorado, Wyoming, Montana and southern Idaho; birds also seen in breeding season in Chihuahua, Mexico, without actual proof of breeding (Reynolds *et al.* 2000). Winters mostly south of the breeding range, from southern parts of California, Arizona, New Mexico and Texas south to Michoacán, México and Hidalgo. Vagrant over much of eastern

North America, with records from Illinois, Michigan, Wisconsin, Minnesota, southern Ontario, the eastern seaboard from Massachusetts to North Carolina, and the Gulf coast from eastern Texas to north-western Florida (Reynolds *et al.* 2000); also on Guadalupe Island, Baja California.

Over much of its breeding range reasonably common; some local population decreases due to conversion of habitat to rangeland. Populations may be reduced if larger bushes are removed since these are preferentially used for nesting. The small Canadian population is considered to be endangered due to habitat modification, as in some other political jurisdictions.

BREEDING Nest, built by both sexes, is a bulky structure built of coarse twigs and lined with finer material including grasses, horsehair or fur, about 20cm in diameter, with a cup of about 11cm diameter, on the ground under a bush or in bushes of a variety of species, especially sagebrush; height of nests in bushes 10–40cm (Reynolds *et al.* 2000). Eggs usually four or five, rarely one to seven, deep rich blue or greenish-blue, boldly spotted with large, well-defined spots or blotches of various shades of brown or cinnamon (Bent 1948). Incubation by both sexes; fledging period 8–14 days, usually 10–11 days. Young are often not capable of sustained flight when they leave the nest. Fed by both parents after fledging. Double-brooded at least occasionally. Dates of first eggs vary from 4 April in Washington to late May in British Columbia; second broods in Idaho in early June to early July.

Rarely parasitised by Cowbirds; Sage Thrashers reject Cowbird eggs and there are no known instances of Cowbirds being raised by this species.

FOOD Mainly invertebrate, of a great variety of families, but especially ants and beetles. Some vegetable matter (Reynolds *et al.* 2000) Reported as doing serious damage to cultivated berries and grapes in Washington (Kennedy 1911).

MOVEMENTS Migratory; apart from an area of south-eastern California, breeding-range is almost entirely vacated in winter. Average arrival dates on breeding-grounds between 23 March in eastern Washington to late May in Canada. Numerous occurrences as a vagrant (see above).

MEASUREMENTS Wing of male 92–103, of female 93–97; tail of male 77–92, of female 76–92; exposed culmen of male 10.3–14.0, of female 10.9–13.3; tarsus of male 27.4–31.4, of female 26.3–31.3 (Reynolds *et al.* 2000).

TOXOSTOMA

Medium to large mimids (total length 23–30cm), with rounded wings, notably long and rounded tails, heavy legs and long to very long bills, frequently down-curved, with strong rictal bristles. Plumage generally brown, grey-brown or grey, frequently with prominent spots on underparts. Confined entirely to North America and Mexico, from about latitude 55°N in western Canada to about 17°N in Mexico, with the greatest abundance of species in south-western USA and north-western Mexico.

Speciation within the group probably occurred in the late Pliocene or early Pleistocene. Studies based on nucleic acids and on some morphological characters suggest that the species fit into related groups; namely the Rufous-Long-billed-Cozumel group, the Le Conte's-Crissal-California group, and the Bendire's-Grey group. The relationships of Curve-billed and Ocellated Thrashers are less clear. The closest relationships outside the genus *Toxostoma* appear to be with the Sage Thrasher (Zink *et al.* 1999).

109 BROWN THRASHER
Toxostoma rufum
Plate 28

Turdus rufus Linnaeus 1758, based on the 'Fox-coloured Thrush' of Mark Catesby, Natural History of Carolina.

Alternative names: Spanish *Cuitlacoche rojizo*; French *Moqueur roux*.

The only thrasher to occur in eastern North America, a very familiar and popular species of brushland, open woodland and some suburban areas.

IDENTIFICATION Length 25.5–28cm. Over most of its range unmistakable. The Wood Thrush, the only other species with heavily spotted breast and rufous upperparts, has a shorter tail, dark eye, pink legs, slighter bill and no wing-bars. For distinctions from Long-billed Thrasher in areas of sympatry, see under that species.

DESCRIPTION *T. r. rufum*
Adult Crown deep rufous-brown, becoming warmer and more rufescent on back and rump. Shoulders and wing-coverts reddish-brown, with conspicuous broad off-white tips to greater and lesser coverts, giving two wing-bars on closed wing. Primaries and secondaries dark brown, with warm rufous-brown on outerwebs; tertials warm brown with narrow buff-white edgings. Rectrices warm brown. Lores and ear-coverts mottled grey-brown. Chin and throat whitish, chest buff-white with conspicuous teardrop-shaped markings, blackish in centre of chest and reddish-brown at sides. Belly whitish with few spots; flanks buff-white with fewer, but more elongated, blackish spots. Vent buffy. Underwing-coverts buffy-white with dark markings. Iris yellow, bill brownish with flesh-coloured base to lower mandible, legs brownish.
Juvenile Similar to adult, but plumage of a looser, more fluffy texture (especially the undertail-coverts), indistinct buff spotting on upperparts, iris greyish or greyish-olive.

GEOGRAPHICAL VARIATION

T. r. rufum (eastern United States and Canada, from New Brunswick and Maine west to central Ontario, south to Florida) Described above.

T. r. longicauda 'Western Brown Thrasher' (western Ontario to southern Alberta, south to north-eastern New Mexico and central Oklahoma) Upperparts more cinnamon-rufous, wing-bars whiter than in *rufum*.

VOICE Song is a loud musical series of clear phrases, each phrase usually repeated two of three times, the whole sometimes given continuously for minutes at a time. There may be some elements of mimicry of other species, but not nearly so marked as in the Northern Mockingbird. Call is a sharp, abrupt *chakk*; alarm calls include a whistle, and a series of harsh, slurred notes. A soft sub-song may be heard in autumn (Bent 1948).

HABITAT Brushy areas, abandoned farmlands and orchards, forest plantations with small trees, hedgerows and wood-edge. Suburban areas of low density, but less inclined to live in close proximity to housing than the Grey Catbird. Generally absent from densely wooded areas.

HABITS Usually found alone or in pairs. Not a shy bird, although it has a great ability to slip away unnoticed. Flights are usually low, from clumps of bush to clumps of bush, the bird usually diving into cover. Birds will sing from cover, but frequently from an exposed perch high in a tree. Feeds mostly low down or actually on the ground, where it both hops and runs. Probes into soft ground with its bill; will also hammer acorns to remove the shell, and scatters leaf-litter with a sideways sweeping motion. Can be extremely aggressive in defence of the nest, not hesitating to attack intruders up to and including the size of human beings.

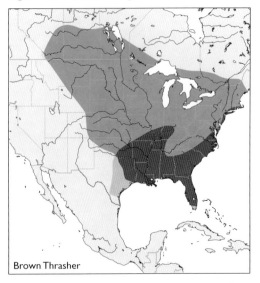

Brown Thrasher

STATUS AND DISTRIBUTION Summer visitor from southern Maine, Quebec to southern Alberta, south to Florida, Louisiana, Texas, Oklahoma and New Mexico. Occasionally further north (James Bay, Ontario). Winters from coastal Massachusetts, New York, the Carolinas to Texas, north to southern Illinois and Indiana. Occasionally winters north to Ontario (James *et al.* 1976). Vagrant to England (Incledon 1968), Cuba (Garrido and Garcia Montaño 1965), Newfoundland, Churchill, Manitoba, and the islands in Hudson's Bay (Godfrey 1986), Point Barrow, Alaska, Bermuda, Bahamas and Mexico south to Nayarit (Howell & Webb 1995).

Probably benefited from the clearing of forests for agriculture (the one area in southern Ontario where it does not breed is the Algonquin Highlands, an area of extensive unbroken forest), and further benefited from the abandonment of farmland. In Ontario in the last fifty years there has been a northwards extension of the breeding range (Curry, in Cadman *et al.* 1987). However, there has been a consistent and significant decline in population as estimated from counts of migrant birds at Long Point, Ontario; a comparison of annual totals averaged over the years 1961 to 1988, and 1988 to 1997 (to eliminate short-term inconsistences) shows a cumulative decline of almost 40%, or 2.5% a year, an observation which is consistent with results obtained from the Ontario Breeding Bird Survey (Francis & Hussell 1998).

BREEDING Nest is a bulky open structure, with a base of thorny twigs and a cup of dry leaves, grass stems etc.; outside diameter about 30cm, height 10cm, diameter of cup about 9–10cm, depth 2.5cm. Nests may be on the ground or as high as 6m in trees; usually about 0.6–2.1m. Ground-nesting varies within the range of the species; half of the nests found in New England were on the ground whereas in Tennessee only one out of 109 in one sample (Bent 1948). Nest is built by both sexes. Eggs three to five, rarely two, pale bluish-white, sometimes with a greenish tinge, evenly covered with fine reddish-brown dots and spots, more rarely without spots, and very rarely, a dark green colour with bright reddish spots. Incubation by both sexes, 11–14 days, usually 12–13 days. Young fed by both sexes. Double-brooded; pairs may change partners in between broods (Harrison 1975). One of the largest species routinely parasitised by Brown-headed Cowbird *Molothrus ater.*

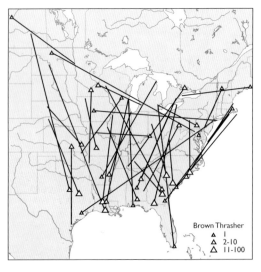

Brown Thrasher
△ 1
△ 2-10
△ 11-100

FOOD Quite varied, both animal and vegetable. Beetles, caterpillars, grasshoppers, wire-worms, spiders, crawfish etc.; also small frogs, lizards, salamanders and snakes. Proportion of vegetable matter increases in fall; especially berries (holly, elder, blueberries, pokeberries etc.) but also acorns, corn, wheat etc. Will visit bird-tables, especially in winter.

MOVEMENTS Strongly migratory. Withdraws from northern parts of range in winter; in southern Ontario, most migration occurs from the second week of September through to mid-October, rarely to late October (Bradstreet & Holroyd 1969). Banding encounters show that birds from the New England states travel south-westwards in winter, to the Carolinas and Georgia; birds from the central states east of the Mississippi winter further west, from Georgia to Arkansas; and those from the Dakotas and the prairie Provinces move in a more south-easterly direction to eastern Texas and Louisiana. There are additionally a small number of encounters showing large east-west displacements, for example, from New York to Texas, and Maryland to North Dakota (data from Bird-banding Laboratory, Laurel MD and Canadian Wildlife Service).

MEASUREMENTS Wing of male 99.5–115, of female 95.5–114; tail of male 116–137, of female 109–141; exposed culmen of male 23–29, of female 22–29; tarsus of male 33.5–35.5, of female 32.5–35 (Ridgway 1907).

110 LONG-BILLED THRASHER
Toxostoma longirostre   Plate 28

Orpheus longirostris Lafresnaye 'Mexique et de la Californie' 1838.

Alternative names: Sennett's Thrasher (*T. l. sennetti*); Spanish *Cuitlacoche Piquilargo*

A close relative of the widespread Brown Thrasher, restricted to a limited range in southern Texas and north-eastern Mexico.

IDENTIFICATION Length 26.5–29cm. Very similar to Brown Thrasher (which although allopatric in breeding range does enter the Long-billed Thrasher's range in winter). Differs from Brown Thrasher by having greyish, not rufous, sides to the face; an all-dark lower mandible (that of the Brown Thrasher is whitish or yellowish at base); more white, less buffy underparts; richer-coloured, more orange eye; and longer bill. The sympatric Curve-billed Thrasher is quite distinct, being a grey-brown bird lacking the sharp, prominent breast markings and wing-bars of the Long-billed Thrasher. The Sage Thrasher, which winters in the range of the Long-billed, is a smaller, greyer bird with a shorter bill and prominent white tips to the rectrices. The Ocellated Thrasher of central Mexico apparently does not overlap with the Long-billed, either in range or in habitat.

DESCRIPTION *T. l. sennetti*
Adult Crown greyish-brown in front, becoming more rufous at rear. Back, shoulders and rump cold rufous-brown. Greater and lesser primary coverts with broad white tips giving two conspicuous wing-bars on closed wing. Primaries and secondaries dull brown with broad rufous-brown edges on outerweb, giving the closed wing a rufous appearance. Rectrices dull rufous-brown. Area around eye and ear-coverts greyish-brown. Chin and throat white or pale buffy-white; chest and belly the same, with heavy, sharply defined oval blackish spots, becoming more elongated at sides and on flanks. Vent buffy. Underwing buffy-white. Iris orange or orange-yellow, bill dull brown, base of lower mandible pinkish-grey.
Juvenile Dusky streaking on rump, loosely textured and buffy undertail-coverts (Pyle 1997).

GEOGRAPHICAL VARIATION
   T. l. sennetti 'Sennett's Thrasher' (southern Texas and Río Grande Valley and Mexican states of Tamaulipas. Nuevo León and San Luis Potosí) Described above.
   T. l. longirostre (southern part of range; Mexican states of Querétaro, Veracruz, México and Puebla) Smaller than *sennetti*; generally darker and more rufescent, with buffy-white underparts.

VOICE Song is a rich loud warble, very similar to that of the Brown Thrasher, but with less repetition (Tweit 1997). Calls, a soft *verrs*, and a harsh, scolding *tsuck*, given during territorial disputes, both similar to the corresponding calls of the Brown Thrasher; a mellow, descending *kleak* and an ascending *toe-ree*, neither like any call of the Brown Thrasher.

HABITAT In Texas, riparian woodland and dense thickets containing mesquite and other species; in Mexico arid to semi-humid brushy woodland, scrubby thickets and hedges (Tweit 1997).

HABITS General behaviour similar to that of Brown Thrasher. Forages on ground by rapidly sweeping bill from side to side in leaf-litter, tossing litter upwards and behind, then scratches for food (Tweit 1997). Although sometimes difficult to see in dense bush, not excessively wary; frequently sings from an obvious and exposed post. Flights generally of short duration and close to the ground. Frequently aggressive to other species in its territory; will defend its nest vigorously, including against humans.

STATUS AND DISTRIBUTION Resident in southern Texas north to San Antonio and Aransas, south through north-western Mexico to central Veracruz, east to eastern Coahuila, San Luis Potosí and Hidalgo. In suitable habitat quite common; breeding density highest in lower Río Grande valley (Tweit 1997). Formerly abundant or numerous in the lower Río Grande valley. Much of the original habitat has been removed for agriculture, resulting in a major decrease in population between 1930s and early 1970s. However, some human activity, resulting in the invasion of former grassland by scrub, may benefit the species; possibly expanding range westwards to Big Bend area. Vagrant to New Mexico and Colorado.

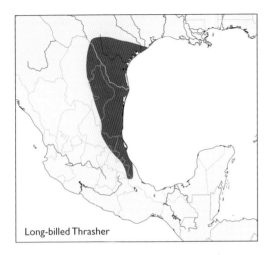

Long-billed Thrasher

average in Texas 3.7, in Mexico 3.8. In Texas egg-laying mostly in April (36% of clutches taken) and May (54%), latest date 24 June; in Mexico 37% in May, 53% in June, latest date 3 July (Tweit 1997).

Incubation by both sexes, 13–14 days. Young fed by both sexes, initially entirely on invertebrates; some vegetable matter given to older nestlings. Fledging 12–14 days. Rarely parasitised by Brown-headed Cowbird *Molothrus ater* and Bronzed Cowbird *M. aeneus*. Breeding territories vary in size from just over 1ha to 3ha (Tweit 1997).

FOOD Predominantly invertebrate; crickets and grasshoppers, beetles, other insects and Crustacea, snails and slugs, but also with a significant amount of vegetable matter, especially berries.

MOVEMENTS Apparently entirely sedentary; all recoveries of banded birds were in the same or immediately adjacent 10-minute block (data from Bird-banding Laboratory, Laurel, MD). In a study in southern Texas, 48% of birds banded were retrapped close to the banding location the following year (Fischer 1981).

BREEDING Nest is a cup of thorny twigs lined with grasses and straw, well-hidden in dense parts of thorny bush; in Texas 1.2–2.4m above the ground, average 1.7m. Outside diameter 18–20.5cm, inside cup 9.5–11cm, inside depth 6cm (Fischer 1980). Eggs two to five,

MEASUREMENTS (*T. l. sennetti*) Wing of male 95–105, of female 92–102; tail of male 120–132, of female 118–128; exposed culmen (sexes combined) 25.3–29.0 (Pyle 1997).

111 COZUMEL THRASHER
Toxostoma guttatum

Plate 28

Harporhynchus guttatus Ridgway 1885 Cozumel Island, Quintana Roo, Mexico.

Alternative name: Spanish *Cuitlacoche de Cozumel*

The most restricted of all the thrashers, found only on the 45km island of Cozumel, where its present status is the cause of some anxiety.

IDENTIFICATION Length 21.5–24cm. No other thrasher occurs on the island; most likely to be confused with the migrant Wood Thrush *Catharus mustelinus*, which is immediately distinguished by its lack of wingbars, shorter bill and different shape.

DESCRIPTION
Adult Crown, back, shoulders and rump warm brown, becoming more rufous on lower back and rump. Greater and lesser coverts warm brown with conspicuous white tips, preceded by a narrow black bar. Primaries and secondaries grey-brown with warm rufous-brown outerwebs. Rectrices warm-brown. Lores and ear-coverts mottled grey-brown. Chin and throat off-white, flanked by a blackish partial malar stripe. Chest buffy-white with conspicuous black teardrop-shaped spots. Belly offwhite, the flanks having larger black spots. Vent buffy. Underwing buffy-white with darker markings. Iris yellowish, bill grey-brown, legs dull brown.
Juvenile Plumage not recorded; presumably differs from adult in a corresponding manner to Brown and Long-billed Thrasher juveniles.

GEOGRAPHICAL VARIATION None; monotypic.

VOICE Song is a rich varied warbling, slightly scratchy

and with little repetition (Howell & Webb 1995). Call not described.

HABITAT Low and medium deciduous and semi-deciduous woodland (T. Macouzet, pers. comm.).

HABITS Little recorded; much like other thrashers.

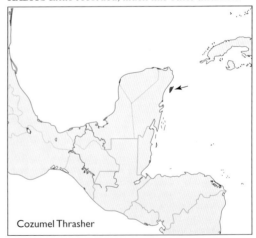

Cozumel Thrasher

STATUS AND DISTRIBUTION Restricted to Isla Cozumel, which is about 45km long and 20km wide. Formerly apparently quite common, but following hurricanes in 1988 and 1995 now very rare and possibly threatened or endangered. There have been some sight records since 1988 (S. Howell pers. comm.; G. Speight pers. comm.), but these are very few in number. During a year's work on Cozumel in 1994–1995, sampling various vegetative types with mist-nets, only three individuals were caught (T. Macouzet pers. comm.). The reason for this rarity is not immediately apparent. Although there has been much tourist-related development on Cozumel, the bulk of the island is little changed. The thrasher is not taken by local people as a cage-bird. None of the other Cozumel endemics seem to have been seriously affected by hurricane damage. Enquiry among the local population suggests that the species is now most likely to be encountered near the Mayan ruins of San Gervasio.

BREEDING Nest and eggs undescribed.

FOOD No information recorded.

MOVEMENTS Presumably entirely sedentary.

MEASUREMENTS Wing of male 88.5–94.5, of female 83–85.5; tail of male 105–113.5, of female 92.5–103.5; exposed culmen of male 27.5–29, of female 26.5–29; tarsus of male 30.5–31.5, of female 29.5–32 (Ridgway 1907).

---

112 GREY THRASHER
Toxostoma cinereum   Plate 27

Harporhynchus cinereus Xantus 1859 Cape San Lucas, Lower California.

Alternative names: Ash-colored Thrasher; Spanish *Cuitlacoche peninsular, Cuitlacoche Ceniciento*

An endemic of the Baja California peninsula.

IDENTIFICATION Length 24–26.5cm. Not readily confused with other species. The only two thrashers which occur in Baja California are Le Conte's, an extremely pale, sandy bird with dark eyes and no spotting on the breast, and, in winter, Sage, which is smaller, shorter-tailed and smaller-billed, with prominent white sides to the tail.

DESCRIPTION *T. c. cinereum*
Adult Crown, nape, back, shoulders and rump dull brown-grey, becoming warmer and more cinnamon on rump. Greater and lesser coverts dull dark brownish with narrow off-white tips forming two thin wing-bars on closed wing. Primaries, secondaries and tertials dull grey-brown, the tertials with narrow pale tips. Rectrices dull brown, the outer two or three with inconspicuous off-white tips. Lores and area below eye mottled grey and dark brownish; ear-coverts dark brownish with paler mottling. Throat white; sides of throat and upper chest with fine blackish spots, which become larger, more dense and triangular on chest and upper belly. Lower belly immaculate buffy-white with blackish streaks on flanks. Vent and thighs buff. Underwing buffy-white with dark brown markings. Iris golden-yellow, bill and legs greyish-black.
Juvenile Iris colour duller, edgings to wing-coverts and tertials pale buff-brown.

GEOGRAPHICAL VARIATION
    T. c. cinereum 'San Lucas Thrasher' (Baja California, from 28°30' N to Cabo San Lucas) Described above.
    T. c. mearnsi 'Mearn's Thrasher' (Baja California from 28°30' N to 31°N) Darker above than *cinereum*, with spotting on underparts heavier and darker.

VOICE Song is a loud, fairly scratchy warbling with frequent two or three-fold repetition of phrases, and occasional rich notes thrown in (Howell & Webb 1995). Call, a rolled rippling to rough *whirr-rr-rr* and a gruff *chrek*.

HABITAT Desert and semi-desert areas with scattered scrub, sea-level to 1,500m. Some presence of small cacti seems to be necessary (Bancroft 1930). Absent from sand-dune areas.

HABITS The two races are said to differ somewhat in both habits and nesting behaviour (Bancroft 1930). The northern race *mearnsi*, is apparently much more skulking, while *cinereum* is stated to be 'not notably wary'. Both feed low down much of the time but will sing from exposed perches.

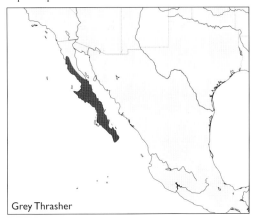

Grey Thrasher

STATUS AND DISTRIBUTION Endemic to the Baja California peninsula from about San Antonio del Mar south to Cabo San Lucas. No information on numbers but apparently reasonably common in suitable habitat.

BREEDING The two races differ somewhat in breeding habits. *Mearnsi* breeds from March to April. The nests are almost invariably located in small cactus bushes of various species at a height of about 1m; individual pairs seem always to nest in the same species. *Cinereum* nests in May or June, uses a greater variety of sites – cacti, mesquite, cardón or other species – and pairs do not seem tied to any one species. The nest of both forms is a typical thrasher construction, a bulky and untidy structure of twigs and grass lined with finer material. Eggs of both races usually two to three, rarely four; *mearnsi* clutches tend to average three eggs, *cinereum* two. Eggs whitish, pale blue or blue-green with grey, brown or reddish-brown speckles. Incubation and fledging periods and details of parental involvement not known.

FOOD No information available.

MOVEMENTS Apparently sedentary.

MEASUREMENTS Wing of male 96–104.5, of female 95.5–102.5; tail of male 98–109, of female 101.5–110.5; exposed culmen of male 24.5–29, of female 27–28.5; tarsus of male 33–34.5, of female 30–33 (Ridgway 1907).

113 BENDIRE'S THRASHER
Toxostoma bendirei
Plate 29

Harporhynchus bendirei Coues 1873 Tucson, Arizona.

Alternative names: French *Moqueur de Bendire*; Spanish *Cuitlacoche Sonorense, Cuitlacoche Piquicorto*

Etymology: Named by Elliot Coues for its discoverer, Major Charles E. Bendire (1836–1897), one of the most colourful characters in the history of American ornithology, who took the first specimen at Fort Lowell, Arizona, an area now close to the centre of the city of Tucson. Bendire (born Karl Emil Bender in Germany) joined the US Army in 1854 at the age of eighteen. After the American Civil War he became a renowned Indian fighter, once marching boldly into the camp of Cochise in an attempt to bring an end to the conflict. On retirement from the military he began a massive work, *Life Histories of North American Birds*, a project cut short by his early death (Mearns & Mearns 1998).

The last species of mimid to be described from the United States, Bendire's Thrasher is also one of the least known. Breeds only in a limited range of the south-western United States and north-eastern Mexico.

IDENTIFICATION Length 24–25.5cm. Very similar to the more abundant and widely-distributed Curve-billed Thrasher *Toxostoma curvirostre*. "Indeed, when the redoubtable Major Bendire sent Fort Lowell specimens to Washington, they were identified as the female of the latter species. It was only upon the Major's insistence that the nests and eggs of the two were entirely different that Elliot Coues finally described the species as new" (Phillips *et al.* 1964). Adult Bendire's Thrashers are distinguished from Curve-billed by having smaller and more-sharply defined spots, often in the form of arrowheads as opposed to the larger and more rounded spots of the Curve-Billed. However, Curve-billed also tend to have some pointed spots above and below the rounded spots in the centre of the chest. Iris colour is a fairly good distinguishing feature; a deeper, more orange in most Curve-billed, a paler, more yellow in Bendire's. However, it should be noted that some adult Curve-billeds also have yellow rather than orange eyes. Consistently the base of the lower mandible of Bendire's is pale, and the rest of the bill is dark grey, whereas in Curve-billed the entire bill is blackish. The bill-shape is, in adults, usually diagnostic, but requires care. In Bendire's the lower surface of the lower mandible is close to straight, whereas in Curve-billed it has a distinct downward curve. In both species the cutting edges and the culmen are curved downwards, more so in Curve-billed. The overall bill length of Curve-billed is substantially greater, best judged by the relative length of bill and the head-size. The gonydeal angle made by the rami is, at all ages, rounded in Bendire's, acutely-angled in Curve-billed (Phillips *et al.* 1964). This is not, however, a character of any use in the field. Adult Bendire's have obviously pale tips to the outer rectrices, a distinction from the race *palmeri* of the Curve-billed Thrasher, with which it has areas of sympatry, but not *oberholseri*.

The majority of these distinctions fail when applied to young birds. Curve-billed Thrashers take some time to acquire the full bill size, and before this time the bill-shape is also much closer to Bendire's. Iris colour in young birds is also very muted, and the breast spotting is likewise much less well-marked, with streaks rather than the full rounded spots of the adult. The calls of young birds remain diagnostic (Kaufman 1990).

Bendire's Thrasher also bears some resemblance to the Sage Thrasher, which has a shorter bill, more prominent wing-bars and white on the tail and more prominent marks on the lower underparts.

DESCRIPTION *T. b. bendirei*
Adult Crown, back, shoulders and rump dull brownish, becoming warmer on rump. Wing-coverts grey-brown. Primaries, secondaries and tertials dull greyish-brown, more cinnamon on outerwebs. Lores and ear-coverts mottled grey-brown. Rectrices dull grey-brown, the outer ones with inconspicuous whitish tips. Chin and throat off-white, flanked by a diffuse mottled grey-brown malar stripe. Chest dull brownish-grey with numerous small arrowhead blackish-grey markings which cease on lower belly, and become more diffuse on flanks. Lower belly and vent buff. Underwing grey-buff. Iris generally yellow, sometimes orange-yellow. Upper mandible dark grey, lower mandible grey with horn base, legs dark grey.
Juvenile Very similar, spots on chest smaller and less extensive.

GEOGRAPHICAL VARIATION There is some dispute as to the validity of races of Bendire's Thrasher. *T. b. rubricatum* and *T. b. candidum* are not recognised by the American Ornithologists' Union (1957).
> *T. b. bendirei* (south-western US and adjacent northern Sonora) Described above.
> *T. b. rubricatum* (central and south Sonora) Stated to be more reddish and darker.
> *T. b. candidum* (central and western Sonora) Paler, less rufous than *rubricatum* and with whiter underparts (Van Rossem 1942).

VOICE Song is a sweet-voiced continuous warble (Kaufman 1990), quite distinct from that of Curve-billed Thrasher, which is abrupt and contains some guttural notes. Much variation in song between different individuals. Call is *cheep, cheep-cheep*; also a plaintive *wheet* rising at the end.

HABITAT From sea-level in Sonora to 1,800m in Utah. Generally in relatively open grassland, with scattered junipers. Sometimes in degraded desert-grassland with various xerophytic plants but little grass (England & Laudenslayer 1993).

HABITS Not particularly shy. Feeds mostly on or near the ground; locomotion is a walk or run, often with tail cocked upwards. Flies readily, often considerable distances and quite high up. Probes the ground with its bill and occasionally digs. Sings from prominent perches.

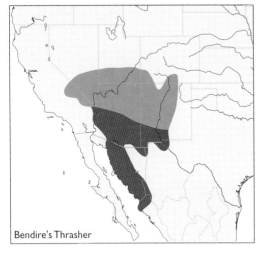
Bendire's Thrasher

STATUS AND DISTRIBUTION Partial migrant. Breeds from southern Nevada, southern Utah and south-western Colorado south to central Sonora. Withdraws from the northern part of the range in winter, and then occurs sparsely to Sinaloa; status as a visitor to Baja California unclear. Casual winter visitor west of the desert in California. Vagrant to Manitoba and Saskatchewan (Godfrey 1986). Varies from rather common to local in Arizona (Phillips *et al.* 1964). Where the two species occur together, usually much less common than Curve-billed Thrasher.

BREEDING Nest is a typical thrasher bowl-shaped construction, made of grass and twigs, with a cup lined with finer grass, animal hair and feathers; dimensions up to 30cm in diameter, up to 23cm deep, with a cup of from 5.7–8.9cm diameter and 3.8–8.9cm depth (England & Laudenslayer 1993). Usually located in bushes or shrubs, 1–3m above the ground. Rarely in other locations, such as on a beam in a carport or in an abandoned Flicker *Colaptes* nest-hole. Eggs pale grey-green to greenish-white (rarely bluish-green) in ground colour, irregularly spotted and blotched with well-defined markings of drab fawn and vinaceous-buff, heavier around the larger end (Bent 1948). Clutch size usually three, quite often four, rarely five. Incubation period not recorded. Young fed by both parents; fledging period about 12 days. In Arizona usually at least double-brooded, occasionally triple-brooded. First set of eggs (in Arizona) laid late February to early March, in California late March; second brood by late May or early June, (England & Laudenslayer 1993), and one example of a third brood on 25 July (Gilman 1915). In Sonora, nests found from 28 February to 18 July (Russell & Monson 1998).

FOOD Largely invertebrate; ants, termites, caterpillars, some vegetable matter including seeds and fruit (Bent 1948).

MOVEMENTS Partially migratory. Withdraws from northerly part of range in winter. In the Mojave desert, California, migration begins as soon as breeding is complete in late July, with breeding areas vacated by late August. Arrives on breeding grounds early, in Tucson area from late January; leaves northern Arizona by the end of August and southern Arizona by September (England & Laudenslayer 1993). In Sonora, winter visitors arrive in early September and depart from February to March (Russell & Monson 1998).

MEASUREMENTS Wing of male 103–107.5, of female 97.5–108.5; tail of male 108–115, of female 101.5–115.5; exposed culmen of male 21.5–25.5, of female 21.5–25.5; tarsus of male 33.0–34.5, of female 31.5–34.5 (Ridgway 1907).

114 OCELLATED THRASHER
Toxostoma ocellatum

Plate 30

Harporhynchus ocellatus Sclater 1862, Oaxaca, Mexico.

Alternative names: Spanish *Cuitlacoche Manchado*

An endemic thrasher of the highlands of south-central Mexico, so far relatively little studied.

IDENTIFICATION Length 26.5–29.5cm. Not readily confused with any thrasher or any other bird found in its limited range. Differs from the Curve-billed Thrasher by its heavy black spotting on the chest and more prominent supercilium. The Sage Thrasher, which barely overlaps its range in winter, is shorter-tailed, lacks the heavy breast spotting and has more prominent white edgings to the tail feathers.

DESCRIPTION
Adult Crown, back, shoulders and rump dull dark

brown. Wing-coverts dark brown with narrow white tips. Primaries, secondaries and tertials dull dark brown. Rectrices dark brown, the outer ones with narrow off-white tips. Lores greyish, ear-coverts mottled grey-brown, postocular supercilium greyish. Throat and chest white, the chest with large conspicuous circular black spots. Belly off-white, the spots becoming smaller, and absent on lower belly. Vent buffy. Underwing grey with darker markings. Iris dark brown, bill and legs blackish-grey. **Juvenile** Spots on underparts more diffuse, wing-bars and tail spots tinged buffy, iris brownish.

GEOGRAPHICAL VARIATION None; monotypic.

VOICE Song is a rich series of notes, often grouped in twos or threes, similar to other thrashers. Calls are a harsh *chak*, *chekk*, etc.

HABITAT Brush, secondary growth and understorey of open forest, generally of a rather dry nature, 1,400–3,000m.

Ocellated Thrasher

HABITS Not always easy to see, usually feeding on the ground or quite close to it, and frequently rather wary. Will, however, respond to taped songs and will sing from an obvious and prominent perch.

STATUS AND DISTRIBUTION Endemic to Mexico; from eastern Guanajato through México, Morelos and Puebla south to central Oaxaca. In some locations fairly common.

BREEDING Nest is a typical thrasher construction, a substantial cup-shaped structure of grass, twigs etc., usually located below about 2m in a bush or small tree. Eggs two, greenish-blue, heavily speckled with browns and greys (Howell & Webb 1995). Incubation and fledging periods unknown.

FOOD Little information recorded. Presumably a mixture of vegetable and invertebrate animal.

MOVEMENTS Apparently entirely sedentary.

MEASUREMENTS Wing of male 100–104, of female 96–99; tail of male 136–144, of female 130–135; exposed culmen of male 32–33.5, of female 31–33; tarsus of male 37–38.5, of female 35.5–36.5 (Ridgway 1907).

115 CURVE-BILLED THRASHER
Toxostoma curvirostre

Plate 29

Orpheus curvirostris Swainson 1827, 'Table-land of Mexico'.

Alternative names: Spanish *Cuitlacoche Pico Curvo*; Piman, *Kud Vil*

The common thrasher of the arid south-west, a characteristic and conspicuous element of the fauna of semi-desert regions from Texas to Arizona and much of the drier regions of central Mexico.

IDENTIFICATION Length 25.5–28cm. A medium-sized grey-brown bird, immediately distinguished as a thrasher by its long tail, long curved bill and short wings. The only serious identification problem is with Bendire's Thrasher, which see for distinctions. Other sympatric and potentially co-occurring species are Crissal, which has a distinctive rufous crissum and obvious moustache stripe; Le Conte's, which is very pale, with a dark tail (neither species has any spotting on the underparts). In southern Texas, resident Long-billed Thrasher, and wintering Brown Thrasher, both of which have warm rufous upperparts and prominent dark marks on underparts. In central Mexico, Ocellated Thrasher with very obvious dark chest spots; and in winter, Sage Thrasher, a smaller bird with shorter bill, more conspicuous white tips to the rectrices and heavy, clearly defined dark marks on chest. Other thrashers are allopatric.

DESCRIPTION *T. c. oberholseri*
Adult Crown, back, shoulders and rump dull grey-brown. Wing-coverts dull grey-brown, the tertials with narrow greyish tips. Rectrices dull blackish-brown, the outer feathers with diffuse off-white tips. Lores greyish, ear-coverts mottled grey. Chin and throat off-white, sides of throat and chest grey-brown, the chest with diffuse,

circular grey-brown spots. Belly buffy-grey, flanks with dull grey-brown streaks. Vent buffy. Underwing buffy-grey with darker markings. Iris orange, or with an orange outer ring and reddish centre; bill blackish-brown, base of lower mandible pale brown, legs dark brown.
Juvenile Lacks pale tips to rectrices, abdominal feathers loose and fluffy, upperparts and breast washed rufous (Pyle 1997).

GEOGRAPHICAL VARIATION Opinions have varied widely over the years as to the validity of several races. However, subspecies fall into two groups which are substantially different from each other, in the field as well as in the hand. The eastern group of races, including the nominate *curvirostre* is more conspicuously spotted on the chest, has more white on the tips of the rectrices and obvious wing-bars; the western group, typified by *T. c. palmeri*, has less well-marked spotting on the chest, less defined wing-bars and less obvious pale tips to the rectrices. Recent DNA work indicates that the separation of the two groups is of long standing, perhaps as much as a million years, resulting in a level of genetic divergence similar to that in such currently-recognised species-pairs as Mourning and MacGillivray's Warblers (*Oporornis philadelphia* and *O. tolmei*); hence full species treatment for each group is plausible. Given the very obvious plumage differences between the eastern and western groups this is hardly surprising. What is, however, unexpected is that DNA results also indicate a substantial divergence in the populations in southern Mexico (Puebla and Oaxaca), which do not exhibit great plumage differences from their northern neighbours. Further work is required to clarify this situation. (Zink & Blackwell-Rago 2000; Omland 2001.)

The eastern group:

T. c. oberholseri 'Brownsville Thrasher' (south-eastern Texas, north-eastern Mexico [Tamaulipas, Coahuila and Nuevo León]) Described above.

T. c. curvirostre (central and south-central Mexico south to Puebla, Oaxaca and Veracruz) Similar to *oberholseri*, but with longer wings and tail and less slaty body-colour.

T. c. celsum 'Plateau Thrasher' (south-eastern Arizona, southern New Mexico, Mexico from eastern Chihuahua south to Guanajuato and Jalisco) Dubiously distinct from *curvirostre*, but larger, more buff on lower parts, pale tips to rectrices more white (Moore 1941).

The western group:

T. c. palmeri 'Palmer's Thrasher' (southern Arizona, northern Sonora and Chihuahua) Differs from *oberholseri* by much less distinct spots on breast, less white on tail.

T. c. occidentale 'Mazatlan Thrasher' (western Mexico, from Sinaloa to Nayarit and Jalisco) Larger than *curvirostre* with a longer tail; upperparts more brown.

T. c. maculatum 'Spotted Thrasher' (north-western Mexico [southern Sonora, south-western Chihuahua]) Similar to *occidentale* but smaller and darker.

T. c. insularum 'San Esteban Thrasher' (Islands of San Esteban [formerly] and Tiburón, Gulf of California) Similar to *palmeri* but paler and more grey, with better defined breast spotting.

VOICE Song is a prolonged, reasonably melodious series of warbles and low trills, similar to that of the Brown Thrasher but more continuous. Distinct from the 'feverish, rollicking music' of Bendire's Thrasher (Stafford 1912). Birds in the *curvirostre* group include some mimicry of other species in their songs, in contrast to *palmeri*; there is also a differential response to play-back between the two groups (Tweit 1996).

Usual call is a loud whistled *whit-wheet*, one of the characteristic early morning sounds in south-western deserts. Other calls include a scolding *churr* and a wren-like chatter.

HABITAT Relatively catholic in its requirements. Sea-level to 3,000 m. The *palmeri* group of subspecies is found especially in the Sonoran desert vegetation type, characterised by palo verde, ocotillo, creosote bush and various cacti, especially cholla and saguaro. The presence of cholla (a favourite nesting-site) is necessary in creosote-bush habitat (Tweit 1996). Occurs with reasonable density in suburban areas provided the basic nature of the vegetation is largely unchanged. Absent from the more extreme desert habitat of Le Conte's thrasher.

In New Mexico in a variety of vegetative types, including open oak and pinyon woodland at higher elevations. In Texas, varied habitat-types including prickly-pear thickets, yuccas, etc. (usually found in more open areas than the Long-billed Thrasher).

HABITS A typical *Toxostoma* thrasher in its behaviour. Not especially wary; spends a lot of time on the ground, where it runs rapidly from cover to cover. Flights are usually low-down from bush to bush. Will come to feeding stations where it will aggressively expel other species such as Inca Dove *Scardafella inca*.

STATUS AND DISTRIBUTION Resident from southern and western Arizona through central New Mexico to extreme south-eastern Colorado, south-western Kansas, Oklahoma, western Texas to the Gulf coast, coastal Mexico as far south as central Tamaulipas, and inland to Oaxaca, coastally from Sonora to Nayarit. In many habitats very common. Although in some areas decreases due to gross habitat destruction or modification have occurred, seems to be relatively tolerant to minor changes. In Arizona it will remain in widely-spaced suburbs; if cholla cacti are no longer present may withdraw to nearby areas where they still occur to breed (Phillips *et al.* 1964).

Vagrant to California, South Dakota, Minnesota, Iowa, Wisconsin, New Hampshire, Louisiana and Florida. Two Canadian records, both of birds which over-wintered at feeders, one in Manitoba and the other in Alberta (Whelan 1999). One vagrant in north-western Florida was subspecifically identified as *palmeri*, and several Iowa vagrants as *curvirostre* type (Tweit 1996).

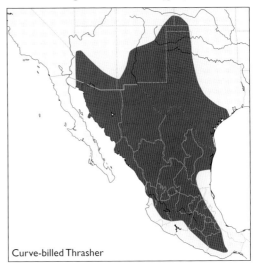

Curve-billed Thrasher

BREEDING Nest is an open cup with a base of spiny twigs, the cup lined with finer material and horsehair. Usually situated in a spiny bush, in Arizona especially cholla cactus, but also in prickly pear, yucca and a variety of other plants including organ-pipe cactus; height above the ground usually 1–1.5m, rarely to 12m (Russell & Monson 1998). More rarely in holes in sycamore and saguaro (Bent 1948). Eggs, usually three to five in south Texas, average 3.8; in Arizona, average variously quoted by different authors as 2.5 to 3.2 (Tweit 1996). Ground-colour of eggs bluish-green to pale yellowish-blue, profusely spotted with reddish-brown (Oberholser 1974). Incubation by both sexes, fledging period 11–16 days (average 14 days) in Texas, 14–18 days in Arizona. Young fed by both sexes (but generally more by female). Timing of breeding somewhat variable, in Arizona affected by amount of winter rains (which can be very variable); may be as early as February, with a broad peak in March to May. Dry winters may result in later nesting. Probably multiple-brooded in good years; latest egg date in Arizona, 30 July, the later dates indicating subsequent broods (Russell & Monson 1998). Only rarely parasitised by cowbirds.

FOOD Predominantly invertebrate; beetles, Hymenoptera, butterflies and moths, woodlice, snails, etc.; a certain amount of vegetable matter and berries. Vagrants in Canada in mid-winter quickly become addicted to bird-feeders (Whelan 1999). Young fed on invertebrates (especially crickets and grasshoppers), with some vegetable matter such as saguaro fruit.

MOVEMENTS Generally sedentary; however, the widespread occurrence of vagrants (see above) may indicate dispersal of young birds. In Sonora it occurs in fall and winter in areas where it does not nest (Russell & Monson 1998).

MEASUREMENTS Wing of male 101–109, of female 98–105; tail of male 102–117, of female 99–107.4 ; exposed culmen of male 25.9–31.8, of female 23.1–27.8; tarsus of male 32.0–35.1, of female 29.9–34.0 (Tweit 1996).

116 LE CONTE'S THRASHER
Toxostoma lecontei

Toxostoma le contei (sic) Lawrence 1852, junction of Gila and Colorado Rivers, Arizona.

Alternative names: Desert Thrasher; Spanish *Cuitlacoche Pálido*

Etymology: Named after Dr John L. Le Conte (1825–1883) a medical doctor who never actually practiced medicine but who became president of the American Association for the Advancement of Science. Confusingly, Le Conte's Sparrow *Ammodramus lecontei* is named after his cousin, also Dr John Le Conte (1818–1891), who among other things operated a gunpowder factory on the Confederate side during the American Civil War (Choate 1985).

A generally uncommon bird, the palest and most terrestrial of all the thrashers, found in some of the harshest desert habitat in southern California, Nevada, Arizona and Sonora, and disjunctly in Baja California. Two species may be involved.

IDENTIFICATION Length 26.5–29cm. Readily distinguished from all other thrashers by its extremely pale appearance, lack of spotting on the underparts, dark (not yellow or orange) iris, dark tail and deep buff crissum.

DESCRIPTION *T. l. lecontei*
Adult Crown, back, shoulders and rump pale sandy-grey. Primaries and secondaries grey-brown, paler on outerwebs. Rectrices darker grey-brown, contrasting with body plumage. Lores and ear-coverts mottled grey-brown. Throat off-white, with trace of darker malar stripe. Chest and belly pale buffy-grey, becoming a warmer buff on vent and undertail-coverts. Underwing grey-buff. Iris chestnut-brown, bill black, legs dark horn, almost black.
Juvenile Upperparts darker brown, feathers of a looser and more fluffy texture, especially on vent.

GEOGRAPHICAL VARIATION
T. l. lecontei (California, Nevada, Arizona, northern Sonora and northern Baja California) Includes *T. l. macmillanorum*, whose separation does not seem to be justified either on morphological or biochemical grounds. Described above.
T. l. arenicola 'Rosalia Thrasher' (western Baja California between about 26° to 28°N) Upperparts and chest darker and more grey than nominate race, tail shorter. Recent DNA studies strongly suggest that *arenicola* is a distinct species (Zink *et al.* 1997). Probably geographically disjunct from *lecontei*. If this 'split' is upheld, a suggested English name is Vizcaino Thrasher.

VOICE Song is a loud, rich, prolonged and greatly varied series of notes, typical of the genus, audible at some distance and somewhat similar to that of Curve-billed Thrasher, but 'higher pitched and marked by clear rest intervals' (Hardy *et al.* 1987). Song is frequently delivered from an exposed perch, usually in the morning or evening, and sometimes at night. Female song occasionally heard; similar to the sub-song of young males. Calls include a short whistle note *suuuweeee* or *hew-eep*, and the distress call, a double-noted whistle (Sheppard 1996).

Apparently no data from the range of *arenicola*; a comparison of vocalisations of this population with those of the nominate form would obviously be of great interest.

HABITAT Inhabits some of the harshest desert environment on the North American continent, where 'the sun beats down with torrid fury on the white sand' (Bent 1948) and annual precipitation is between 4–20cm. Sparsely vegetated desert flats, dunes, alluvial fans or gently rolling hills with saltbush, chollas and other low vegetation (Sheppard 1996). Altitudinal range from 80m below sea-level (in Death Valley, California) to about 1,600m, average about 500m. During the summer many areas have temperature that do not drop below 35°C for many weeks, with frequently substantially higher figures. Does not generally coexist with other *Toxostoma* species which require a less harsh, more vegetated habitat.

HABITS Largely terrestrial; runs with surprising speed, outpacing a trotting horse (Mearns 1886). Observers familiar with both species are immediately reminded of the Hoopoe Lark *Alaemon alaudipes*, an old-world species of similar habitat. When running the dark tail is frequently held upwards exposing the buffy crissum. Feeds mostly on ground, digging small pits in leaf-litter while searching for prey. Generally found throughout the year in pairs; juveniles may form small parties of from two to eight birds. Males may give a visual display to other intruding males by adopting a head-down position, showing the conspicuous crissum while disappearing slowly head first into a saltbush (Sheppard 1996). Does not need to drink; in fact liquid water is only very rarely available in typical habitat, and only one actual observation recorded of a bird drinking.

STATUS AND DISTRIBUTION Resident from southeastern California, southern Nevada, western and southwestern Arizona to coastal Sonora south to about the same latitude; disjunctly (*arenicola*) in western Baja

lecontei group
arenicola group

Le Conte's Thrasher

California between about 26°N and 28°N. Nowhere very common, absent from considerable areas within the indicated range, and usually occurring at relatively low densities even in prime habitat.

Although non-migratory, occasional individuals are seen outside the normal range; however, no long-distance vagrancy.

BREEDING Nest is quite a bulky affair consisting of an outer layer of twigs, a middle layer of smaller twigs, grasses and rootlets and an inner layer of insulating materials, frequently composed of fuzzy plant seeds, leaves or flowers, rarely feathers and sometimes artificial material (Sheppard 1996). This inner layer is diagnostic

and not found in other desert thrashers (Pemberton 1916). Overall nest dimensions 14–28cm wide, 9–23cm deep, with cup 8–9cm wide, 6–7cm deep. Nest is typically located in spiny bush such as cholla or saltbush, more rarely in artificial site (e.g. abandoned vehicle or shed), always in a shaded situation; nest heights average about 0.8m, highest 2.4m above ground. Nest built by both sexes but amount of participation by male variable. In California, egg dates from February (rarely earlier) to the end of May; in Sonora, from December to April (Russell & Monson 1998). Eggs light bluish-green, sometimes without markings, or with very fine pinpoint spots of pale brown to yellowish-brown, occasionally heavier (Bent 1948). Clutch size (*lecontei*) two to five, mean 3.31; *arenicola*, only five clutches described, two of two eggs and three of three. Incubation by both sexes, 14–15 days, mean 15.8 days. Young fed by both parents, fledging period 12–20 days, mostly 14–16.5 days. Fledglings fed for a further 15–18 days. Young birds may briefly form small groups (Sheppard 1996).

Not apparently a cooperative breeder; however, in Sonora three birds, one a probable juvenile, observed building a nest (Russell & Monson 1998).

FOOD Stomach contents from Arizona, California and Utah were over 90% arthropods, remainder seeds and fruits. Also small snakes and lizards, and occasionally eggs, including those of its own species.

MOVEMENTS Sedentary. Young birds disperse only 5–8km (Sheppard 1996).

MEASUREMENTS Wing of male 93.0–107.3, of female 93.0–103.9; tail of male 109.2–132.1, of female 106.7–131.9; bill (nostril to tip) of male 23.3–31.1, of female (nostril to tip) 24.3–30.9; of male tarsus 28.2–33.1, of female 27.9–32 (Sheppard 1998).

117 CALIFORNIA THRASHER
Toxostoma redivivum

Plate 30

Harpes rediviva Gambel 1845 Monterrey, in upper California.

Alternative names: Spanish *Cuitlacoche Californiano*

This, the largest member of its genus, confined geographically to the two Californias, was first actually collected in 1786 by the Compte de la Pérouse.

IDENTIFICATION Length 28–30cm. Has only very limited areas of sympatry with similar thrashers. Le Conte's Thrasher is very pale, with little evidence of a superciliary stripe. Crissal Thrasher has a very obvious chestnut crissum, no superciliary and yellowish eyes. Both these species occur very close to the range of California Thrasher but are usually separated. Curve-billed Thrasher, a vagrant to California, has yellow-orange eyes, diffuse spotting on the chest and a sickle-like bill. In Baja California there is an area of sympatry with Grey Thrasher, which is immediately distinguished by its grey upperparts and heavily spotted underparts.

DESCRIPTION *T. r. redivivum*
Adult Crown, back, shoulders and rump dull medium-brown. Wing-coverts dull brown with inconspicuous

narrow buff tips. Primaries and secondaries dull brown, the outerwebs more rufous. Rectrices brownish-black. Lores grey. Ear-covers dark greyish with pale grey streakings. Throat whitish, chest dull grey, belly buff-cinnamon, flanks buff-grey, lower belly and vent warm buff. Underwing grey-brown. Iris brown, bill black or blackish, paler at base of lower mandible, legs brown, greyish-brown or blackish-brown.
Juvenile Buffy-cinnamon edgings to greater coverts and tertials; crissum plumage loosely textured (Pyle 1997).

GEOGRAPHICAL VARIATION
    T. r. redivivum (southern section of the species' range, from north-western Baja California north to near Monterrey Bay) Described above.
    T. r. sonomae 'Sonoma Thrasher' (remainder of range from Santa Cruz County northwards) Larger and darker than *redivivum*, with a pale chest-band and darker belly (Grinnell 1915).

VOICE The song consists of vigorous and cheerful phrases variously repeated, delivered in continuous sequence for 3 to ± 10 seconds, with brief pauses between successive sequences (Cody 1998). A very accomplished mimic, including in its song imitations of a wide variety of other species, from flickers to hawks to orioles, as well as such noises as coyote howls, frog calls and whistles (Bent 1948). Calls, a dry *chak* and a sharp *leek*.

HABITAT Chaparral, a bush-land including scrub oak, sumac, lilac and sugarbush; also in lesser density, California Sagebrush, and in other vegetation types including Piñon Pine, Joshua tree etc. Frequently found close to Le Conte's Thrasher, but the two species are always sharply demarcated by habitat type. Sea-level to about 1,600m (Cody 1998).

HABITS Largely terrestrial; runs, or rather rushes, in short dashes with elevated tail; on stopping this is usually wagged up and down. Frequently responds to intruders by running away rather than by flying. Flights are usually short and low, with much laboured flapping, the head and tail drooping. Spends much time digging in the earth, leaving characteristic little pits in wet soil and sweeping loose litter with sideways movements of the long bill.

California Thrasher

STATUS AND DISTRIBUTION Resident, from north-central California to central Baja California, south to about 29°30'N (Anthony 1895). One record in southern Oregon. In many locations quite common. Can coexist to a degree with suburban development, but habitat fragmentation has resulted in population losses. Population density in optimal habitat about 0.5 pairs/ha; total population estimated at about 3 million (Cody 1998).

BREEDING Nest is a robust platform of coarse twigs, 3–10mm in diameter; the cup made of fine twigs and roots, lined with finer material; the whole nest 20–30cm in diameter, the cup averaging 10.5cm in diameter and 3.8–5cm in depth. Well hidden in shrubs, average height about 2.25m. Eggs pale blue with spots and blotches of various shades of brown; rarely immaculate pale blue. Clutch size one to six, but the great majority three or four (most usually three). Incubated by both parents, 14 days. Incubating birds usually arrive and depart from the nest on foot, slipping away through the vegetation to the ground. Fledging period 12–17 days, usually 12–14 days. Double-brooded (Cody 1998). Breeding season very protracted; active nests recorded from November to July, with a peak for first broods in February or March (Bent 1948). Not subject to Cowbird parasitism.

FOOD Varied. Arthropods, including very large insects such as crickets, beetles, ants, bees and wasps, caterpillars, spiders etc.; also a large proportion of vegetable matter, especially seeds, berries and fruit, including grapes and rotting windfall oranges. Frequent at bird-feeders when it takes meat scraps, suet and fruit (Cody 1998).

MOVEMENTS Apparently very sedentary; the great majority of banding returns show no or trivial movement, the longest displacement being 60km (Cody 1998).

MEASUREMENTS Wing of male 97–106.5, of female 96–105.5; tail of male 120–138, of female 124–132.5; exposed culmen of male 32–39.5, of female 34–39; tarsus of male 35.0–40.5, of female 35.5–38.5 (Ridgway 1907).

118 CRISSAL THRASHER
Toxostoma crissale

Plate 30

Toxostoma dorsale Henry 1858, Fort Thorn, New Mexico.

Alternative names: Red-vented Thrasher; Spanish *Cuitlacoche crisal*; French *Moqueur cul roux*.

Note: the specific name *dorsale* was given as a result of a printer's error (*dorsale* actually being a new form of Junco). For many years this was maintained by the principle of precedence, but was eventually corrected in 1983.

One of the less well-known of the North American thrashers, notwithstanding its impressive appearance and superb song, doubtless as a result of its furtive and retiring habits.

IDENTIFICATION Length 28–30.5cm. Most similar to the allopatric California Thrasher, which is larger, olive-brown rather than ash-brown above and lacks the dark

chestnut-red crissum. Le Conte's Thrasher, which overlaps in geographic range but in different habitats, is notably pale, without the crissum. Curve-billed and Bendire's Thrashers have pale eyes, spotted chests and again lack the chestnut crissum. Does not overlap with Grey Thrasher.

DESCRIPTION *T. c. crissale*
Adult Crown, back, shoulders and rump uniform dull greyish-brown. Primaries and secondaries dull grey-brown, rectrices somewhat darker. Lores and ear-coverts mottled dark and light grey. Chin and throat off-white. Diffuse malar stripe greyish-black. Chest and belly buffy-grey, darkening on lower flanks. Crissum deep reddish-brown, contrasting with remainder of underparts. Underwing buffy-grey. Iris brown, bill blackish, legs blackish or dusky-horn colour.

Juvenile Buffy-cinnamon edging to greater coverts and tertials, and fluffy-textured plumage, especially on vent.

GEOGRAPHICAL VARIATION

T. c. crissale (Arizona, southern New Mexico and western Texas) Described above.

T. c. coloradense (Colorado desert of south-eastern California to south-eastern Nevada and south-western Utah, south to Baja California Norte and north-western Sonora) Paler above than *crissale*, crissum more yellowish-brown with little hint of chestnut-brown.

T. c. dumosum (Mexico, from Coahuila and Durango to Hidalgo) Smaller and darker than *crissale*, with a darker crissum.

T. c. trinitatis 'Trinidad Thrasher' (Valle de Trinidad, Baja California) Similar to *coloradense* but larger, darker and more slaty-grey above and below.

VOICE One of the most accomplished songsters of the arid south-west, although the singer is frequently hidden in thick vegetation. Song consists of melodious and distinct phrases, variously repeated, given in bouts about a minute long; phrases are less harsh, and delivery less staccato and emphatic than California Thrasher (Cody 1999). Call is a characteristic two or three syllable *pitcheree*, *chi-deary*, or *pitchree*, quite distinct from the *whit-wheet* of the Curve-billed Thrasher.

HABITAT Various types of scrubland, but especially fond of riparian scrub along the banks of marshes and streams. May coexist with other Thrasher species (such as Curve-billed and Bendire's), but in these cases tends to occupy the densest vegetation. Unlike Curved-billed Thrasher it does not adapt well to suburban-modified habitat, but will occur in revegetated riparian areas following removal of salt cedar (Cody 1999). Occurs as low as 60m above sea-level in California, but generally at higher elevations with more plentiful rainfall; up to 2,400m in northern Mexico.

HABITS By far the most retiring of the south-western thrashers; were it not for its characteristic call would more often go undetected. It may sing from exposed perches, or from cover, but spends a lot of its time on the ground, where it hops or runs rapidly. On being disturbed it is far more prone to flee on foot than by wing, sprinting into thick cover where it is remarkably difficult to observe. Forages among leaf-litter by probing and sweeping with the long bill; does not kick away vegetation in the manner of a towhee. Probes the ground where soft enough. May visit bird-feeders, but less so than other thrasher species, and more circumspectly, often sneaking in at dawn.

STATUS AND DISTRIBUTION In suitable habitat, south-eastern California, southern Nevada, central and southern Arizona, southern New Mexico, western Texas; Mexico from the US border south to Hidalgo and Zacatecas; northern Sonora (rather sporadically); disjunctly in Valle de Trinidad, Baja California.

Not especially rare, but vulnerable to habitat destruction. Much of the range is relatively unsuitable for human development, but in California the species is listed as one of 'special concern' (Cody 1999).

BREEDING Nest is a typical thrasher construction of

Crissal Thrasher

coarse twigs, lined with finer material; notably smaller than that of other sympatric thrashers. Nest diameter 18–32cm, depth 10–15cm, cup diameter 7.5–8.2cm, depth 4–4.5cm. Nests are located in dense cover, usually about 1m or so up. Eggs two or three, sometimes one to four, unspotted blue or blue-green (unusual for a thrasher); similar to those of American Robin but somewhat darker and greener (Bent 1948). Incubation by both sexes, about 14 days. Young fed by both sexes; fledging period 11–16 days. Double-brooded. Nesting season ranges from early January in New Mexico, February in California and Arizona, with second broods as late as July; breeding starts later at higher elevations. Average clutch dates in different parts of California 27 March and 9 April, in Arizona and New Mexico 5 May (Cody 1999). In contrast to some other thrasher species, rejects cowbird eggs, removing them from its nest.

FOOD Primarily invertebrate; beetles, crickets, ants, bees and wasps, grasshoppers, etc.; one small lizard reported in stomach contents. Also vegetable matter, especially berries and some seeds.

MOVEMENTS Generally held to be sedentary; all 27 recoveries of banded birds up to 1995 were found locally (data from Bird-banding Laboratory, quoted by Cody 1999). However, Russell & Monson (1998) point out that in Sonora, Mexico it occurs in winter in locations where it does not nest, implying movement from further north.

MEASUREMENTS Wing of male 92.9–108, of female 94–107.8; tail of male 125.1–140.1, of female 120–139.4; exposed culmen of male 26.9–31.7, of female 26.4–31.8; tarsus of male 22.2–31.0, of female 25.0–29.8 (Cody 1999).

CINCLOCERTHIA

Medium to large mimids, with a notably long, rather fine bill, straight for most of its length and gently downcurved at the end, with small or obsolete rictal bristles; cranium flattened; wings fairly long, the sixth and seventh primaries the longest; tail fairly long and strongly rounded; legs quite sturdy. Two species, confined to the Lesser Antilles, sexually dimorphic in bill-length.

119 BROWN TREMBLER
Cinclocerthia ruficauda   Plate 31

Stenorhynchus ruficauda Gould, 1835 (locality unknown).

Alternative names: French *Grive Trembleuse, Trembleur Brun, Cocobino* (French Islands)

An extraordinary and rather aberrant mimid of the Lesser Antilles, noted for its peculiar habit of drooping and then violently trembling its wings. Frequently regarded as conspecific with the Grey Trembler; we have followed Storer (1989) and other authorities and maintained the two as separate species.

IDENTIFICATION Length 23–25.5cm. Essentially unlike any other species within its range. Scaly-breasted and Pearly-eyed Thrashers and Forest Thrush all have scaled or scalloped underparts.

DESCRIPTION *C. r. ruficauda*
Adult Crown and nape dull blackish-brown, becoming dark olivaceous-brown on shoulders and increasingly rufescent on lower back and rump. Shoulders and coverts dark rufescent-brown; remiges somewhat more rufescent, especially on outerwebs. Rectrices dark rufous-brown. Lores (especially) and ear-coverts darker than crown. Throat dull grey-brown, chest slightly darker, lower chest and belly orange-brown, becoming darker on flanks and vent. Underwing-coverts dull rufescent-brown. Iris light yellow, bill black, legs brown. Females have noticeably longer bills than males.
Juvenile Chest faintly spotted with dusky-grey.

GEOGRAPHICAL VARIATION
   C. r. ruficauda (Dominica) Described above.
   C. r. tremula (Saba, Montserrat, St Kitts, Nevis, Barbuda, Guadeloupe) Larger than *ruficauda*, but similar in coloration. Includes *C. r. pavida*.
   C. r. tenebrosa (St Vincent) Much darker above than *ruficauda*; underparts extensively suffused with greyish.

VOICE Several different song types have been identified. The full song consists of loud phrases uttered at approximately two second intervals; some rather harsh, others rich and warbled, and others high and squeaky. Subsong consists of a quiet series of complicated phrases, lasting about five seconds, and 'excitement' song (during territorial disputes) is a loud jumble of notes (Zusi 1969). Calls a rasping *yeeeak* and a sharp *cht* or *chip*.

HABITAT Wet forest with epiphytes, especially bromeliads and aroids, less common in mossy elfin forest on mountain ridges; also grapefruit and cacao plantations; rarely in banana plantations (Zusi 1969).

HABITS Feeds at all levels, from the crowns of large forest trees 40m or more high to ground level. Takes a lot of fruit in season in forest canopy; forages amongst epiphytes, probing into bromeliad clumps. Will also cling to branches and tree-trunks in the manner of a Woodcreeper (Dendrocolaptidae) while probing into cavities. On the ground it hops, often with tail cocked, removing dead leaves by picking them up with its bill rather than sweeping them aside; also probes into wet earth. The eponymous trembling so characteristic of the species consists of drooping both wings then rapidly bringing back into position frequently accompanied by a nervous jerking movement of the tail in the manner of a waterthrush *Seiurus*; the function of trembling is not entirely clear, but it occurs much more frequently when birds are in groups (Markowsky *et al.* 1994).

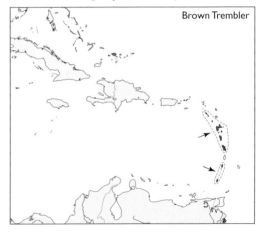

Brown Trembler

STATUS AND DISTRIBUTION Lesser Antilles from Saba and Barbuda south to St Vincent and Grenada; vagrant to Antigua and Virgin Islands (St Thomas). Both species of Trembler occur on Martinique, although it is not known if there is any differentiation in habitat requirements between them (H. Raffaele, pers. comm.). On many islands much reduced due to habitat destruction; still abundant in parts of Dominica, common on Guadeloupe and Saba, less common on other islands. Probably extinct on St Eustatius except as a vagrant.

BREEDING Nest is a cup of rootlets, lined with finer rootlets and dead leaves, placed in the base of a palm frond, in the cavity of a tree or in the hollow stump of a treefern (Bond 1971); will use nestboxes (Zusi 1969). Other reports state that the nest is domed, with a side-entrance, unusual in a mimid (Raffaele *et al.* 1998). Eggs two or three, unmarked greenish-blue. Incubation and fledging periods and details of parental involvement not recorded. Breeding season from March to July.

FOOD Very varied. A large variety of invertebrates; beetles, cockroaches, spiders, scorpions and snails, also tree-frogs and small lizards. Fruit and berries including seed-pods.

MOVEMENTS Presumably sedentary, although it does occur as a vagrant on some islands (e.g. St Thomas, St Eustatius and Antigua) where it does not breed.

MEASUREMENTS Wing of male 87–102, of female 88–98; tail of male 71–84, of female 70–83; exposed culmen of male 30.5–35, of female 36–41; tarsus of male 27–31, of female 26–31 (Storer 1989).

120 GREY TREMBLER
Cinclocerthia gutteralis

Plate 31

Ramphocindus gutteralis Lafresnaye 1843 'Antilles'.

Alternative names: French *Moqueur trembleur, Grive Trembleuse, Trembleur Gris* (Martinique), *Trembleur* (St Lucia)

The Trembler of Martinique and St Lucia, formerly regarded as conspecific with Brown Trembler by many authorities. Less sexual dimorphism in bill-length than in the Brown Trembler.

IDENTIFICATION Length 23–25.5cm. White-breasted Thrasher has all-white underparts, a stouter bill and red eyes; other species such as Scaly-breasted Thrasher have scaled or scalloped underparts.

DESCRIPTION *C. g. gutteralis*
Adult Crown, nape, back, rump, wings and tail sooty-greyish-brown, lightest on the lower back but without any real demarcation. Shafts of rectrices dark brown or blackish above, white below. Lores (especially) and ear coverts darker than crown. Slightest hint of subtle, very faint greyish superciliary stripe, especially over lores. Throat creamy white, blending into softly greyish breast-band, that blends into soft, light greyish-brown flanks. Centre of belly creamy white. Vent warm greyish-brown, centres of feathers slightly darker than edges, giving faint mottled effect. Underwing-coverts dull, creamy-whitish, in contrast to dark remiges. Iris whitish or yellow, bill black, legs dark brown or grey.
Juvenile Upperparts browner, chest indistinctly mottled with greyish-brown, wing-coverts edged light brown.

GEOGRAPHICAL VARIATION
 C. g. gutteralis (Martinique) Described above.
 C. g. macrorhyncha (St Lucia) Similar to *gutteralis* but underparts dull, buffy whitish.

VOICE Wavering, whistled phrases; also harsh scold and call notes (Raffaele *et al.* 1998).

HABITAT Mature moist forests both lowland and mountain; less often in second growth, dry scrub and open woodlands (Raffaele *et al.* 1998). More general in habitat than the Brown Trembler (Diamond 1973).

HABITS Mostly arboreal; probes with the long bill among clumps of vegetation. Less well-studied than the Brown Trembler.

STATUS AND DISTRIBUTION Confined to the islands of Martinique and St Lucia; on the latter at least it is widespread and abundant (Diamond 1973).

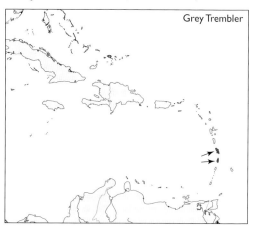
Grey Trembler

BREEDING Nest is domed with a side-entrance, built of dry grass, often in a palm, but sometimes nests in a tree cavity. Eggs two or three, unmarked greenish-blue. Breeds in March and April (Raffaele *et al.* 1998).

MOVEMENTS Apparently sedentary.

FOOD Little information recorded; presumably similar to that of the Brown Trembler, a mixture of invertebrates, small vertebrates and fruit.

MEASUREMENTS Wing of male 99–115.5, of female 97–111; tail of male 81–96, of female 83.5; exposed culmen of male 34–37.5, of female 39.5; tarsus of male 31.5–34, of female 29 (Storer 1989).

RAMPHOCINCLUS

Medium-sized mimid, with rather short tail, with notably long gently decurved bill, about as long as, or slightly shorter than, head; rictal bristles distinct. Wing quite long, sixth primary usually the longest. Tail shorter than wing, distinctly rounded. Tarsus rather narrow.

Turdus brachyurus Vieillot 1818 Martinique, West Indies.

Alternative names: French *Moqueur Gorge-blanche, Gorge Blanc*

A striking and unique mimid, confined to two islands in the Lesser Antilles, on both of which it is critically endangered.

IDENTIFICATION Length 23–24cm. Not confusable with any other species in its limited range. The Grey Trembler lacks the striking white underparts and has a yellow eye and notably longer bill; the Tropical Mockingbird has a much longer tail and is grey above.

DESCRIPTION *R. b. brachyurus*
Adult Forehead, crown, nape, wing-coverts, back and rump blackish-brown, becoming slightly more rufescent on lower back and rump. Primaries, secondaries, tertials and rectrices brownish-black. Lores and ear-coverts dull black. Chin, throat, chest and belly white; flanks blackish-brown, vent dark brown. Iris red or reddish-brown, bill black with brown base to lower mandible, legs dark green.
Juvenile Entirely warm brown, developing a creamy white patch on the breast as it gets older (Raffaelle *et al.* 1998).

GEOGRAPHICAL VARIATION
R. b. brachyurus (Martinique, West Indies) Described above.
R. b. sanctaeluciae (St Lucia, West Indies) Larger and darker than *brachyurus.*

VOICE Song, a series of short phrases *te-ru-ti, ti-a-ritu* (Bond 1971). Calls, a harsh *chek-chek-chek-chek.*

HABITAT Dense thickets in semi-arid woodland with no ground cover and abundant leaf-litter, and in riverine forest; probably, formerly, also in deeper and wetter forest (Collar *et al.* 1992).

HABITS Largely terrestrial. Feeds amongst leaf-litter, vigorously sweeping it aside with its bill; will also pluck berries from trees while clumsily fluttering (Diamond 1973). May droop and twitch wings when agitated, but does not tremble them.

STATUS AND DISTRIBUTION Confined to the islands of Martinique and St Lucia; both populations are critically endangered. On Martinique it was widespread and common in the nineteenth century, but decreased rapidly in the latter half; a specimen was taken in 1896, but for fifty years it was considered extinct. It was first rediscovered in 1950. Recent estimates of the population are tiny, varying between 15–40 pairs (Collar *et al.* 1992). The present Martinique population is confined to the Caravelle peninsula, where some 500ha is protected as

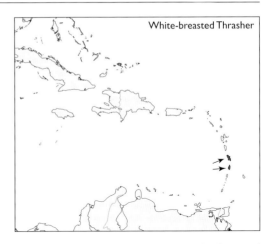

White-breasted Thrasher

a nature reserve. The St Lucia race has also decreased drastically. In 1872 it was 'constantly to be met' in pairs or small flocks of four or five pairs, but by 1931 it was feared to be extinct (Collar *et al.* 1992). By 1971 the population was confined to five ravines in the north-east of the island, and was estimated at 75 pairs. An estimate in 1987 gave a population of 57 pairs, while a detailed survey in 1992 estimated a total of 46 pairs (Ijsselstein 1992). The rate of population decline seems to be accelerating, from 2.5% per year for 1971 to 1987 to 4.1% per year for 1987 to 1992. Recommendations to reverse this decline have been made. Postulated causes of the decline have included habitat destruction, predation by introduced mongooses and rats and (in St Lucia) aggressive competition from the recently colonised Bare-eyed Thrush (*Turdus nudigenis*).

BREEDING Nest is a bulky cup in a shrub or tree, 1.5–5m up. Eggs two, immaculate greenish-blue. Breeds April to August. Incubation and fledging periods, and details of parental care, unknown. Young apparently leave the nest before being capable of prolonged flight.

MOVEMENTS Appears to be highly sedentary, a factor which may hinder its conservation since it may not move between patches of now- isolated habitat in different valleys.

FOOD Primarily insect, although it has been seen to eat berries (Diamond 1973).

MEASUREMENTS Wing of male 91–102, of female 89–105; tail of male 69–84, of female 69–83; exposed culmen of male 27.3–30.7, of female 26–28.6; tarsus of male 29–32, of female 30–32 (Storer 1989).

MARGAROPS

Large mimids with a large, stout, compressed bill nearly as long as head, straight over much of its length and strongly decurved terminally, with distinct rictal bristles. Wing long and pointed, sixth and seventh primaries the longest. Tail relatively shorter than in Mimus, slightly rounded. Tarsus rather short and stout. Two species, endemic to the West Indies.

Muscicapa fusca Müller 1776 Martinique, West Indies.

Alternative names: Black-billed Thrush, Grive. French *Grivotte, Moqueur Grivotte*

An endemic to the Lesser Antilles, formerly placed in the monotypic genus *Allenia*.

IDENTIFICATION Length 22.5–23cm. Only confusable species in its range is the Pearly-eyed Thrasher, a larger bird with a more massive, yellow bill and no obvious wing-bar. Scaly-breasted Thrasher is much more thrush-like in form.

DESCRIPTION *M. f. fuscus*
Adult Crown, shoulders and back medium brown, the feathers having darker centres giving a streaky appearance. Lower back and rump similar, somewhat more rufescent; uppertail-coverts with small off-white central spots and whitish tips. Remiges dull brownish-black, the tertials with off-white tips, the secondaries with rufous edging on outerweb. Rectrices dull blackish-brown with grey tips on innerweb of outer feathers. Sides of face, lores, malar region and ear-coverts mottled dull dark brown. Chin and throat off-white with diffuse dull brownish streaks, becoming more prominent and coalescing on chest; belly off-white with dull brown streaks, darker on sides. Vent dull greyish-white with brown markings. Underwing-coverts greyish-brown with darker mottling. Iris white to yellowish, bill blackish, legs blackish-brown.
Juvenile Similar to adult; eyes dark.

GEOGRAPHICAL VARIATION
M. f. fuscus (Dominica and Martinique, disjunctly in Grenada and as a vagrant the Grenadines) Described above.
M. f. atlanticus (Barbados [possibly extinct]) Similar to *fuscus*, but dorsum more reddish-brown, white on tail reduced.
M. f. hypenemus (northern Lesser Antilles from Saba and Barbuda [possibly also St Martin] south to Guadeloupe and Marie-Galante) Larger and paler than *fuscus*.
M. f. schwartzi (St Lucia) More white on tail than *fuscus*, with a longer wing.
M. f. vincenti (St Vincent) Darker on underparts than other races, especially on chin and throat; flank spots larger and darker.

VOICE Repeats phrases in a manner similar to a

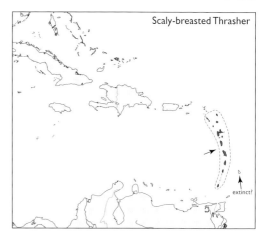

Scaly-breasted Thrasher

extinct?

Tropical Mockingbird, but with less vigor (Raffaele *et al.* 1998).

HABITAT Forests, semi-arid woodlands and in settled areas (Buden 1993).

HABITS Arboreal and retiring, but not especially shy (Raffaele *et al.* 1998).

STATUS AND DISTRIBUTION On many islands quite common. Rare and local on Grenada; status on Barbuda and St Eustatius unclear. The endemic race on Barbados may be extinct; several specimens were collected in the 1920s, but the most recent published record is of one seen in 1987 (Buden). A search of one of the known localities in July 1998 revealed no birds (A. D. Brewer pers. obs.).

BREEDING Nest is cup-shaped, situated in a tree (Raffaele *et al.* 1998). Eggs, two or three, greenish-blue; nests in May and June. Incubation, fledging periods and other details of breeding not recorded.

FOOD Largely frugivorous.

MOVEMENTS Resident on all islands; occurrences as a visitor to the Grenadines suggests some tendency to wander.

MEASUREMENTS (Means) Wing of male 117.6, of female 117.5; tail of male 91.8, of female 91.5; of exposed culmen of male 17.5, of female 17.7 (Buden 1993).

Turdus fuscatus Vieillot 1807, Santo Domingo, Porto Rico.

Alternative names: Jack Bird, Paw-paw Bird, Mango Bird, Sour-sop Bird, Black Thrasher, Wall-eyed Thrush (West Indies); French *Grosse Grive, Moqueur Corossol* (French

islands); Spanish *Chucho, Truche, Zorzal Pardo, Zorzal de Palmares* (Puerto Rico)

A very common, raucous and conspicuous inhabitant of the southern Bahamas and Lesser Antilles.

IDENTIFICATION Length 28cm. In the Bahamas, only likely to be confused with the Bahama Mockingbird, which has a dark eye, dark bill and paler back. In the Lesser Antilles, the Scaly-breasted Thrasher is a lot smaller, with a relatively shorter, black bill and a pale wing-bar and edgings to the tertials.

DESCRIPTION *M. f. fuscatus*
Adult Crown, shoulders and back medium brown, the feathers having darker centres giving a streaky appearance. Lower back and rump similar, somewhat more rufescent; uppertail-coverts with small off-white central spots and whitish tips. Remiges dull brownish-black, the tertials with off-white tips, the secondaries with rufous edging on outerweb. Rectrices dull blackish-brown with grey tips on innerweb of outer feathers. Sides of face, lores, malar region and ear-coverts mottled dull dark brown. Chin and throat off-white with diffuse dull brownish streaks, becoming more prominent and coalescing on chest; belly off-white with dull brown streaks, darker on sides. Vent dull greyish-white with brown markings. Underwing-coverts greyish-brown with darker mottling. Iris whitish-grey or yellowish-grey, bill yellow-ochre, darker above, legs brown to ochraceous.
Juvenile Very similar to adult.

GEOGRAPHICAL VARIATION
M. f. fuscatus (Bahamas from Eleuthera southwards to Puerto Rico and northern Leeward Islands [Antigua]) Described above.
M. f. densirostris 'Darker Pearly-eyed Thrasher' (southern Lesser Antilles [Montserrat to St Vincent]) Similar to *fuscatus* but darker on upperparts, and more broadly streaked on underparts.
M. f. bonairensis (Bonaire and [formerly] La Horquilla Island, southern Caribbean) Differs from both *fuscatus* and *densirostris* in being more greyish-olive, rather than brownish, above and below.
M. f. klinikowskii (St Lucia) Breast markings more contrastingly dark brown and white than either *fuscatus* or *densirostris*; white on tips of rectrices and secondaries more extensive.

VOICE Song is a series of one to three syllabled phrases with fairly lengthy pauses separating them. Often sings well into the day and during clear nights. Also many raucous call notes, including a guttural *craw-craw* and a harsh *chook-chook* (Raffaele *et al.* 1998).

HABITAT Quite varied. Wooded areas, scrubland, plantations, abandoned orchards and suburban areas; at sea-level palm and mangrove forest. On Bonaire, restricted to fruit plantations during the dry season, but widespread after rains (Voous 1983).

HABITS At times raucous and conspicuous, at others very secretive. Forages from ground level to 5m or more in trees. An extraordinarily aggressive bird. Habitually attacks the eggs and young of a variety of species such as Red-legged Thrush *Mimocichla plumbea* (Rolle 1965a) and White-crowned Pigeon *Columba leucocephala*, inflicting severe wounds on nestlings and breaking eggs (Wiley & Wiley 1979). On Mona Island, Puerto Rico, it was considered a 'plague' because of the damage it inflicted on the scarce avifauna (Biaggi 1983). In the Luquillo Forest, Puerto Rico, it was considered by far the most important of the nest predators of the critically

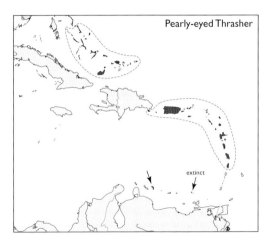

Pearly-eyed Thrasher

extinct

endangered Puerto Rican Parrot *Amazona vittata* (Snyder & Taapken 1977), habitually entering the nest-holes of the parrot and destroying the eggs, and on one occasion dragging out a nestling parrot almost its own weight. In one instance 26 thrashers were shot over a period of time when they were attempting to enter a guarded parrot nest. A more effective strategy has been to provide deep, dark boxes which are suitable for the parrots but not used by the thrashers, while siting nearby a shallower box which the thrashers use; the territorial thrashers then drive away others of their own species while not interfering with the parrots.

STATUS AND DISTRIBUTION Generally common over most of its range, and in Puerto Rico expanding both in numbers and into previously unoccupied habitats (Snyder & Taapken 1977). Rare on Martinique; became extinct on La Horquilla Island, Venezuela, prior to 1908 (Meyer de Schauensee & Phelps 1978). Bahamas, from Exuma and Cat Island south; Turks and Caicos Islands, Lesser Antilles from Beata Island, south of Hispaniola (but rare on Hispaniola itself) through Puerto Rico and the Lesser Antilles south to St Lucia. Bonaire (Netherlands Antilles). Vagrant on Jamaica and Barbados (Raffaele *et al.* 1998).

BREEDING Unusual among thrashers in being a cavity-nester. Nest is a bulky construction made of sticks, dry grass and roots, usually placed in a cavity, including nestboxes; more rarely in an open situation in a bush; on Mona Island, between Hispaniola and Puerto Rico, in niches in rocks in the roofs of caves (Bowdish 1903). Eggs, two or three, deep glossy blue. Incubation and fledging periods not recorded. Breeding recorded from December to September.

FOOD Very varied; in the absence of several families of North American birds, seems to have expanded into a variety of ecological niches. Insects, fruit and berries of all kinds, eggs and young of numerous other species of birds, carrion, house mice etc. Will store food impaled on barbed wire or thorns in the manner of a shrike *Lanius*, or jammed into the crotch of a bush; on one occasion 13 white rats, apparently laboratory escapees, were found. Birds may return on consecutive days to stored food (Rolle 1965b). Has been seen to catch and kill a Bananaquit *Coereba flaveola* (Voous 1983). Lizards are taken on some islands, but curiously never on others (McLaughlin & Roughgarden 1989).

MOVEMENTS Resident on all the islands where it occurs; vagrancy on Jamaica and Barbados (the former some 500km from the nearest breeding population)

presumably indicates some tendency to wander.

MEASUREMENTS Wing of male 124.5–143.5, of female 132–142; tail of male 94.5–120.5, of female 104.5–118.5; exposed culmen of male 26–30, of female 25–30; tarsus of male 32.5–38.5, of female 34–37 (Ridgway 1907).

DONACOBIUS

An enigmatic and controversial genus, consisting of one species only, native to much of lowland northern South America. Originally described by Linnaeus in 1766 as a thrush, *Donacobius* was for many years regarded as an aberrant mockingbird, a reasonable viewpoint considering its size, long tail, short rounded wings, heavy feet and legs and generally extroverted and rambunctious behaviour; the nest, an open cup, is also consistent with a mimid origin. However, the social structure of *Donacobius* is unusual for a mockingbird, and the duetting vocalisations and mutual display are highly reminiscent of *Campylorhynchus* wrens (Kiltie & Fitzpatrick 1984); furthermore, anatomical data strongly suggest a relationship closer to wrens rather than mimids (Clench *et al.* 1982). Notwithstanding all of this, recent DNA studies suggest that *Donacobius* is in fact neither a wren nor a mockingbird, but an aberrant *Sylvioid*, a member of a group including the Old World warblers and babblers (F. K. Barker, pers. comm.).

124 DONACOBIUS
Donacobius atricapillus   Plate 32

Turdus atricapilla Linnaeus 1766, location in error, actually eastern Brazil.

Alternative names: Black-capped Donacobius, Black-capped Mockingthrush, Black-capped Reed Wren; French *Troglodyte à miroirs, Troglodyte à calotte noir*; Spanish *Paraulata de Agua, Donacobio*; Portuguese *Japacanim, Batuquira*; Suriname *Zwampoe Fowroe*

Note: We, in common with several authors, have shortened the name; since the name Donacobius is unique, the qualifying 'Black-capped' is superfluous (precedents being Phainopepla and Pyrrhuloxia).

An extraordinary marshland bird, found over much of the northern half of South America from eastern Panama to Argentina. It clearly has no close relatives, and its taxonomic position is still vigorously debated.

IDENTIFICATION Length 21.5–22cm. Essentially unmistakable; the black cap, staring yellow eye, white wing-flash and long white-tipped tail resemble no other Neotropical species.

DESCRIPTION *D. a. atricapillus*
Adult Crown, nape and shoulders glossy jet-black, back with brownish suffusion, rump dark brownish-olive. Rectrices black with white tips, narrow on central rectrices, becoming broader at sides with outer rectrices three-quarters white; outer pairs of rectrices much shorter than inner. Chin buffy-white, throat and chest warm buffy-yellow, deepening slightly on belly. Upper flanks with narrow, sharply-defined black bars; lower flanks dull blackish at sides. Primaries and secondaries dusky black with a broad pure white base to primaries, giving a conspicuous flash on closed and extended wing. Iris bright staring yellow; bill black; legs greenish-dusky, darker anteriorly; cheek pouch deep yellow.
Juvenile Crown dark dusky-brown, supercilium behind eye whitish-grey, back medium brown with rufous-brown edgings to feathers, greater and lesser primary coverts with narrow white or brownish edgings, underparts

much duller than adult without black barring on flanks.

GEOGRAPHICAL VARIATION
D. a. atricapillus (northern Venezuela, the Guianas, most of Brazil south to the Rio Paracai, Paraguay, extreme north-eastern Argentina) Described above.
D. a. brachypterus 'Short-winged Mocking-Thrush' (eastern Panama [Darién], northern Colombia, Magdalena Valley south to northern Tolima, and Santa Marta region) Similar to *atricapillus* but slightly smaller, with paler rump and lighter underparts.
D. a. nigrodorsalis (south-eastern Colombia, eastern Ecuador and Peru south to Madre de Dios) Similar to *atricapillus* but darker above.
D. a. albovittatus 'White-browed Mocking-Thrush' (eastern Bolivia [Beni, Cochabamba and Santa Cruz] and western Brazil [Aere]) Differs from other races by having prominent white superciliaries in adult plumage (in all other subspecies these are found only in juvenile plumage).

VOICE The song is an utterance more noteworthy for the power and excitement that it suggests than for its beauty (Skutch 1968). Both sexes sing, antiphonally, but the song of each is different and readily distinguishable; the male gives a series of ringing, liquid whistles slurred upwards *who-it who-it who-it* while the female makes a lower, sizzling or grating sound (Kiltie & Fitzpatrick 1984). During song both sexes, but especially the male, inflate their bare yellow throat patches. During batches of mutual song pairs sit close to one another, waving the fanned tail rhythmically from side to side. Alarm call is a grating scold. Occasionally other members of the cooperative group (see Breeding) may also sing, again with a song-type specific to their sex. Does not, apparently, mimic other species' songs.

HABITAT Mainly confined to brushy areas along river-edges, especially when the formation of ox-bow lakes has left successional vegetation invading standing water;

also artificial water impoundments as they become overgrown. May forage in adjacent areas away from standing water, but for breeding marsh is essential. In one study in Peru (Kiltie & Fitzpatrick *loc. cit.*) territories occupied by breeding groups were sometimes only one hundred metres long, and very narrow.

HABITS Vociferous and conspicuous, frequently greeting the intruder with a chorus of raucous calls. Pairs perform ritualised mutual displays, flirting and wagging the tail, fanned out to show the conspicuous white tips from side to side; a more intense display involves a hunched-back posture, head and tail held down, while the throat is grotesquely distended (Skutch 1968). Sometimes the wings may also be opened to display the white flash on the primaries. Feeds at low or medium heights above the water surface, picking insect prey from the surfaces of leaves; also occasionally hawks for flying insects such as dragonflies.

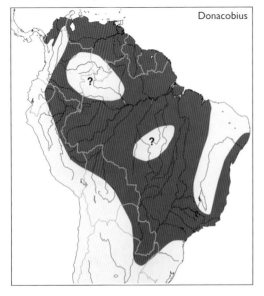

Donacobius

STATUS AND DISTRIBUTION Quite common where suitable habitat exists; prime habitat may have a high density of birds. From eastern Panama (Darién) through northern Colombia, northern Venezuela and the Guianas to north-eastern Brazil (Maranhão); Amazonian Ecuador, Peru and Bolivia (being absent from the Pacific Coast) south to eastern Paraguay and extreme northern Argentina; and along the Atlantic coast of Brazil from Rio de Janeiro to Paraiba; most of Amazon basin. Sea-level mostly to 600m, occasionally to 1,400m in Ecuador (Ridgely in press).

BREEDING A cooperative nester, at least in situations where the population is reasonably dense. In a study in Amazonian Peru (Kiltie & Fitzpatrick 1984) breeding groups consisted of the mated pair, and from zero to two additional helpers which are offspring from last season's breeding, or from the season before that. The helpers assisted in the defence of the territory, feeding the young and guarding the nest. Unassisted pairs did not fledge more than one young, whereas in all cases where two young were fledged there were helpers at

the nest. Breeding occurred during the rainy season (October onwards), with the bulk of fledgings in November–January. The nest is a deep, bulky cup, about 10–15cm in external length and width, the nesting cavity being about 6cm deep and 7.5–8cm in diameter. Nests are made of grass, vegetable fibres, etc., and frequently incorporate snake skins, moth-cocoons and other extraneous material (Young 1925, Skutch 1968). Building birds frequently pilfer materials from the nests of other species such as Vermilion-crowned Flycatchers *Myiozetetes similis*. Nests are located in vegetation, sometimes over standing water, at heights of 0.25–1m, sometimes at the edge of a pond, and sometimes in other situations such as the edge of a sugar-cane plantation (Young 1925). Nests not over water may be situated higher, up to 2m from the ground. Nest-building seems to be predominantly the responsibility of the female. Eggs are two in number (although one clutch of three recorded in Venezuela; in São Paulo State, Brazil, broods of three quite common [Ragusa-Netto 1996]), purplish-white, almost wholly covered with reddish and purplish spots and blotches (Haverschmidt 1968). Incubation, by the female alone, 16–18 days. Young are hatched without down, and have a conspicuous (and almost unique in the Neotropical region) pattern on the inside of the pinkish mouth consisting of three black spots, one anterior and two posterior (Skutch 1968). The adults cool naked nestlings by wetting them with their own feathers, soaked by immersion in water, rather in the well-known manner of sandgrouse *Pterocles*, albeit without any special feather modifications (Ragusa-Netto 1998). Young are fed by both sexes and by any available helpers and leave the nest in 17–18 days. Broods which are fed by more than two adults are more productive, apparently as a result of a higher survival rate of nestlings after fledging (Ragusa-Netto 1996). Incubation and fledging periods in *Donacobius* are considerably more protracted than in most wrens or mimids. Nesting in northern Venezuela has been observed over the first nine months of the year (Schafer & Phelps 1954), although May to July seems commonest: in Guyana, March to August: and in Suriname, January to July. Apparently single-brooded aside from clutches laid as replacements for those lost.

FOOD Almost entirely invertebrate, gleaned from leaf-surfaces, but also including some flying insects taken on the wing. In Suriname recorded orders include Coleoptera, Hymenoptera, Orthoptera, Neuroptera and Arachnoidea (Haverschmidt 1968).

MOVEMENTS Apparently entirely sedentary; in the Peruvian study, no evidence was found of marked birds moving between suitable patches of habitat only 2km away.

MEASUREMENTS (*D. a. atricapillus*) Wing of male 77–88, of female 75–86; tail of male 87–105, of female 82–89; bill of male 18.5–23, of female 17.5–21; tarsus of male 31–37, of female 31–35.

BIBLIOGRAPHY

Abdusalyamov, I.A. 1973. *Fauna of the Tadjik Soviet Socialist Republic.* Academy of Sciences of the Tadjik SSR, Dushanbe.

Aldrich, J.W. 1946. White eggs of the Long-billed Marsh Wren. *Auk* 63: 442–443.

Aldridge, B.M. 1984. Sympatry in two species of mockingbirds on Providenciales Island, West Indies. *Wilson Bull.* 96: 603–618.

Allen, A.A. 1914. The Red-winged Blackbird: a study in the ecology of a cat-tail marsh. *Abstr. Proc. Linn. Soc. New York:* nos. 24 & 25.

Alvarez-Lopéz, H., Heredia-Flores, M.D. & Hernández-Pizarro, M.C. 1984. Reproducción del Cucarachero Común (*Troglodytes aedon;* Aves: Troglodytidae) en el Valle del Cauca. *Caldasia* 14: 85–123.

Anderson, A.H. & Anderson A. 1957–1962. Life History of the Cactus Wren Parts I–III and Part V. *Condor* 59:274–296; 61:186–205; 63: 87–94; 64:192–212.

Anderson, A.H. & Anderson, A. 1973. *The Cactus Wren,* University of Arizona Press, Tucson, Arizona.

Anonymous 2000. Bird Sightings from the Hotlines, February–March 2000. *Winging It,* 12 (4): 10.

Anthony, A.W. 1895. The birds of San Fernando, Lower California. *Auk* 12: 134–143.

Anthony, A.W. 1898. Avifauna of the Revillagigedo Islands. *Auk.* 15: 311–318.

AOU 1957. *Checklist of North American Birds,* Fifth Edition. American Ornithologists' Union, Washington DC.

AOU 1998. *The AOU checklist of North American Birds,* Seventh Edition, American Ornithologists' Union, Washington DC.

Armstrong, E.A. 1953. Nidicoles and parasites of the Wren. *Irish Naturalists' Journal* 11: 57–64.

Armstrong, E.A. 1955. *The Wren.* Collins, London.

Armstrong, E.A. & Whitehouse, H.L.K. 1977. Behavioural adaptations of the wren (*Troglodytes troglodytes*). *Biol. Rev.* 52: 235–294.

Arnold, J.R. 1980. Distribution of the Mockingbird in California. *Western Birds* 11: 97–102.

Asami, R. & Haga, R. 1983. A study of the population ecology of the brown dipper *Cinclus pallasii* at the Tokachi river system. *Tori* 32: 75–94.

Aspinall, R.J. & Aspinall, S.J. 1987. The past and present status, distribution and ecology of the Fair Isle Wren (*Troglodytes troglodytes fridarensis*). Report submitted to the British Ecological Society Ecological Affairs Committee.

Atkinson, P.W., Whittingham, M.J., Gómez de Silva Garza, H., Kent, A.M. & Maier, R.T. 1993. Notes on the Ecology, Conservation and Taxonomic Status of *Hylorchilus* Wrens. *Bird Conserv. Int.* 3: 75–85.

Austad, S.N. & Rabenold, K.N. 1986. Reproductive enhancement by helpers and an experimental enquiry into its mechanism in the Bicolored Wren. *Behav. Ecol. Sociobiol.* 17: 19–27.

Aveledo, R. & Gines, R.H. 1952. Cuatro aves y dos extensiones de distribución para Venezuela, de Perijá. *Noved. Cient. Mus. Hist. nat. Caracas (Zool)* 6: 1–15.

Badzinski, D., 2001. Vanishing Grasslands, Declining Birds – an Ecosystem in Peril. *Birdwatch.* 16: 1–2. Bird Studies Canada, Port Rowan, ON.

Baker, E.C.S. 1932. *The nidification of birds of the Indian Empire, Vol. 1.* Taylor and Francis, London.

Bailey, F.M. 1904. Twelve Rock Wren nests in New Mexico. *Condor* 6: 68–70.

Bailey, F.M. 1922. Cactus Wrens' nests in southern Arizona. *Condor* 24: 163–168.

Baird, S.F. 1864. *Review of American Birds in the Museum of the Smithsonian Institution.* Washington DC 1:122–130.

Bancroft, G. 1930. Breeding birds of Central Lower California. *Condor* 32: 20–49.

Bancroft, G. 1946. Geographic variation in the eggs of Cactus Wrens in Lower California.*Condor* 48:124–128.

Bangs, O. & Peters, J.L. 1927. Birds from the rainforest region of Veracruz. *Bull. Mus. Comp. Zool.* 67: 471–487.

Bannerman, D.A. & Bannerman, W.M. 1958. Birds of Cyprus. Oliver and Boyd, Edinburgh and London.

Barbour, T. 1926. A remarkable new bird from Cuba. *Proc. New England Zool. Club* 9:73–75.

Barbour, T. 1928. Notes on three Cuban birds. *Auk* 45: 28–32.

Barker, F.K. 1999. The evolution of cooperative breeding in *Campylorhynchus* wrens; a comparative approach. PhD dissertation, University of Chicago.

Barlow, J.C. 1978. Another colony of the Guadeloupe House Wren. *Wilson Bull.* 90: 635–637.

Barnés, V. 1939. Contribución ornitológica. Exploración preliminar de la Sierra de Imataca. *Revista de fomento* 19: 437-500.

Barnett, J.M. & Kirwan, G.M. 1999. Neotropical Notebook. *Cotinga* 11: 103.

Bart, J. & Tornes, A. 1989. Importance of monogamous male birds in determining reproductive success. Evidence for House Wrens and a review of male-removal studies. *Behavioral Ecology and Sociobiology* 24: 109-116.

Bates, J.M., Parker, T.A. III, Capparela, A.P. & Davis, T.J. 1992. Observations on the campo, cerrado and forest avifauna of eastern Bolivia, including 21 species new to the country. *Bull. Brit. Orn. Club* 112: 658-662.

Bates, R.S.P. & Lowther, E.H.N. 1952. *Breeding Birds of Kashmir.* Oxford University Press, London.

Beal, F.E.L., McAtee, W.L., & Kalmbach, E.R. 1916. Common birds of the southeastern United States in relation to agriculture. US Dept. Agr. *Farmer's Bull.* 755.

Beebe, W. 1917. *Tropical Wildlife in British Guiana.* New York Zoological Society, NY.

Beebe, W. 1949. *High Jungle.* Duell, Sloan and Pearce. New York.

Belcher, C. & Smooker, G.D. 1937. Birds of the colony of Trinidad and Tobago. *Ibis,* 14th ser., 1: 504–550.

Belles-Isles, J-C. & Picman, J. 1986. House Wren nest-destroying behavior. *Condor* 88: 190–193.

Belles-Isles, J-C. & Picman, J. 1987. Suspected adult intra-specific killing by House Wrens. *Wilson Bull.* 99: 497–498.

Bennett, A.G. 1935. Two records from the Falkland Islands. *Ibis* 87: 436.

Bent, A.C. 1948. *Life Histories of North American Nuthatches, Wrens, Thrashers and their Allies.* Bulletin 195, U.S. Nat. Mus.

Berger, A.J. 1972. *Hawaiian Birdlife.* University of Hawaii Press, Honolulu.

Bernath, E.L. 1965. Observations in southern Chile in the southern hemisphere autumn. *Auk* 82: 95–101.

Biaggi, V. 1983. *Las Aves de Puerto Rico.* Editorial de la Universidad de Puerto Rico.

Binford, L.C. 1989. A distributional survey of the birds of the Mexican state of Oaxaca. *Ornithological Monographs* No.43, American Ornithologists' Union, Washington DC.

Blake, E.R. 1953. *Birds of Mexico.* University of Chicago Press, Chicago and London.

Boggs, G.O. 1961. Notas sobre las aves de 'El Centro' en el valle medio de Río Magdalena. *Colombia. Noved. Colombianas* 1: 401-423.

Bond, J. 1941. Nidification of the birds of Dominica B.W.I. *Auk* 74: 259-260.

Bond, J. 1950. Birds of St Andrew and Old Providence Islands, Colombia. *Proc. Acad. Nat. Sciences Philadelphia* 102: 43-68.

Bond, J. 1971. *Birds of the West Indies.* Collins, London.

Bond, R.M. 1940. Sleeping posture of the Rock Wren. *Condor* 42: 122.

Borrero, J.I. 1953. Status actual de *Zenaida auriculata* y *Leptotila plumbeiceps* en el Dept. de Caldas y *Cistothorus apolinari* en la región de Bogotá. *Lozania* 6: 1–6.

Borror, D.J. 1956. Variation in Carolina Wren songs. *Auk* 73: 211–229.

Bowdish, B.S. 1903. Birds of Porto Rico. *Auk* 20: 10–23.

Bowman, R.I. & Carter, A. 1971. Egg-pecking behaviour in Galápagos mockingbirds. *Living Bird* 10: 243–270.

Bradley, P. 1985 *Birds of the Cayman Islands.* P.E. Bradley, Georgetown, Grand Cayman.

Bradstreet, M.S.W. & Holroyd, G.L. 1969. *Long Point Bird Observatory Ten Year Report.* Port Rowan, Ontario.

Brandt, H. 1945. A new wren from Arizona. *Auk* 62: 574–577.

Brattstrom, B.H. 1990 Biogeography of the Islas Revilla-gigedo, Mexico. *J. Biogeogr.* 17: 177–183.

Brattstrom, B.H. & Howell, T.R. 1956. The birds of the Revilla Gigedo (sic) Islands, Mexico. *Condor* 58: 107–120.

Brewer, A.D.1977. *The Birds of Wellington County.* Guelph Field Naturalists' Special Publication #1, Guelph, Ontario.

Brewer, A.D., Diamond, A.W.,Woodsworth, E.J., Collins, B.T. & Dunn, E.H. (2000) *Canadian Atlas of Bird Banding* Vol.1. Canadian Wildlife Service, Ottawa.

Brodkorb, P. 1939 Rediscovery of *Heleodytes chiapensis* and *Tangara cabanisi. Auk* 56: 447.

Brodkorb, P. 1943. The Rufous-browed Wrens of Chiapas, Mexico. *Occ. Papers Museum Zoology, University of Michigan* No. 480: 1–3.

Brown, R.N. & Lemon, R.E. 1979. Structure and evolution of song form in the wrens *Thryothorus sinaloa* and *Thryothorus felix. Behav. Ecol. Sociobiol.* 5: 111–113.

Brown, R.N. & Lemon, R.E. 1980. The effect of sympatric relatives on the evolution of song. *Acta XVII Congressus Internationalis Ornithologicii,* 742–747. Verlag der Deutschen Ornithologen Gesellschaft, Berlin.

Brumfield, R.T. & Capparella, A.P. 1996. Genetic differentiation and taxonomy in the House Wren species group. *Condor* 98: 547–556.

Brumfield, R.T. & Remsen, J.V., Jr. 1996. Geographic variation and species limits in *Cinnycerthia* Wrens of the Andes. *Wilson Bull.* 108: 205–227.

Bruner, S.C. 1934. Observaciones sobre *Ferminia cerverai* (Aves: Troglodytidae). *Mun. Soc. Poey* 8: 97–102.

Bryant, W.E. 1887. Additions to the Ornithology of Guadelupe Island. *Bull. California Acad. Sci.* 2:269–318.

Buden, D.W. 1993. Geographic variation in the Scaly-breasted Thrasher with descriptions of three new subspecies. *Bull. Brit. Orn. Club* 113: 75-84.

Bump, S.R. 1986. Yellow-headed Blackbird nest defense; aggressive responses to Marsh Wrens. *Condor* 88: 328-335.

Burns, J.T. 1982. Nests, territories and reproduction of Sedge wrens (*Cistothorus platensis*). *Wilson Bulletin* 94 : 338–349.

Burt, D.E. 1970. Habitat selection and species interactions of some marsh passerines. MSc thesis, Iowa State University, Ames, Iowa.

Bystrak, D. 1979. The breeding bird survey. *Sialia* 1:74–87.

Cabanis, 1847. *Arch. F. Naturg* 13(1): 206.

Cadman, M.D., Eagles, P.J.F. & Helleiner, F.M. 1987. *Atlas of the Breeding Birds of Ontario.* University of Waterloo Press, Waterloo, Ontario.

Carriker, M.A. 1910. An annotated list of the birds of Costa Rica including Cocos Island. *Annals of the Carnegie Museum of Natural History* 6: 314–915.

Carriker, M.E. 1935. Description of new birds from Peru and Ecuador, with critical notes on other little-known species. *Proc. Acad. Nat. Sci. Philadelphia* 87: 337.

Castellanos, A. 1935. Observaciones de algunas aves de Tierra del Fuego e Isla de los Estados. *Hornero* 6: 390

Castellanos, A. & Rodríguez-Estrella R.1993. Current status of the Socorro Mockingbird. *Wilson Bull.* 105: 167–171.

Castro, I. & Phillips, A. 1996. *A Guide to the Birds of the Galápagos Islands.* Christopher Helm, London.

Chapman, F.M. 1900. *Bird Studies with a Camera.*

Chapman, F.M. 1914. Diagnosis of some apparently new Colombian birds. *Bull. Amer. Mus. Nat. His.* 33: 635.

Chapman, F.M. 1917. The distribution of bird-life in Colombia; a contribution to a biological survey of South America. *Bull. Amer. Mus. Nat. His.* 36: 1–729.

Chapman, F.M. 1921. Descriptions of apparently new birds from Bolivia, Brazil and Venezuela.*Amer. Mus. Novit.* 2: 6.

Chapman, F.M. 1929. *My Tropical Air Castle.* Appleton, New York.

Chapman, F.M. 1936. The Composer. *Bird Lore* 38: 267–273.

Chapman, F.M. 1941. Mockingbirds in Panama. *Auk* 58: 98–99.

Cherrie, G.K. 1893. Exploraciones zoológicas efectuadas en el Valle del Río Naranjo. *Anales Inst. Físico-Geog. Nac. Costa Rica* 6: 69–73

Cherrie, G.K. 1916. A contribution to the ornithology of the Orinoco region. *Mus. Brooklyn Inst. Arts and Sci., Sci. Bull.* 2: 133a–374.

Choate, E. A. 1985. *The Dictionary of American Bird Names.*

Revised edition. The Harvard Common Press, Harvard and Boston, Massachusetts.

Christian, D.G. & Roberts, D. 2000. First description of nest and nesting behavior of *Microcerculus marginatus* (Troglodytidae). *Wilson Bull.* 112: 284–287.

Christian, K.A. 1980. Cleaning/feeding symbiosis between birds and reptiles of the Galápagos Islands; new observations of inter-island variability. *Auk* 97: 887–889

Chubb, C. 1921. *The Birds of British Guiana*, Vol II. Bernard Quaritch, London.

Cimprich, D.A. & Moore F.R. 1995. Grey Catbird (*Dumetella carolinensis*). In Poole, A. & Gill, F. (eds) *The Birds of North America*. No. 167. The Academy of Natural Sciences, Philadelphia and The American Ornithologists' Union, Washington DC.

Clench, M.H., Gullidge, J.L. & Parkes, K.C. 1982. The Black-capped Donacobius is a wren, not a mimid. Abstract. One hundredth stated meeting, American Ornithologists' Union, Chicago.

Cody, M.L. 1998. California Thrasher (*Toxostoma redivivum*). In Poole, A. & Gill, F. (eds) *The Birds of North America* No. 323, The Academy of Natural Sciences, Philadelphia, Pennsylvania and American Ornithologists' Union, Washington DC.

Cody, M.L. 1999. Crissal Thrasher (*Toxostoma crissale*). In Poole, A. & Gill, F. (eds) *The Birds of North America* No. 419 The Birds of North America Inc., Philadelphia, Pennsylvania.

Collar, N.J., Crosby, M.J. & Stattersfield, A.J. 1994. Birds to watch 2: the world list of threatened birds. *Birdlife Conservation Series* no. 4. Birdlife International, Cambridge.

Collar, N.J., Gonzaga, L.P., Krabbe, N., Madroño Nieto, A., Naranjo, L.G., Parker, T.A. & Wege, D.C. 1992. *Threatened Birds of the Americas: the ICBP/IUCN Red Data Book.* ICBP, Cambridge.

Colyer, E. 2000. Tweets for my sweet. *New Scientist* 2233: 34–37.

Contreras, B.A.J. & Trevino, S.C.H. 1987. Notas sobre predación de Aves en reptiles. *Southwest. Nat.* 32: 505–506.

Cory, C.B. 1886. The birds of the West Indies, including the Bahama islands, the Greater and Lesser Antilles, excepting the islands of Trinidad and Tobago. *Auk* 3: 1–59.

Cramp, S. (ed.) 1988. *Handbook of the Birds of Europe, the Middle East and North Africa; Birds of the Western Palearctic* Vol. 5, Oxford University Press, Oxford.

Crawford, R.D. 1977. Polygamous breeding of Short-billed Marsh Wrens. *Auk* 94: 359–362.

Crawshay, R. 1907. *The Birds of Tierra del Fuego.* Bernard Quaritch, London.

Creaser, C.W. 1925. The egg-destroying activity of the House Wren in relation to territorial control. *Bird-Lore* 27: 163-167.

Creutz, G. 1952. Einemsen ('anting') bei *Cinclus. J. Ornithol.* 93: 174.

Crossin, R.S. & Ely, C.A. 1973. A New Race of Sumichrast's Wren from Chiapas, Mexico. *Condor* 75: 137-139.

Curry, R. 1987. Northern Mockingbird, in Cadman M.F., Eagles, P.F.J. & Helleiner, F.M. *Atlas of the breeding birds of Ontario.* University of Waterloo Press, Waterloo, Ontario.

Curry, R.L. 1986. Galapagos Mockingbird kleptoparasitizes centipede. *Condor* 88: 119–120.

Curry, R.L. 1988a. Influence of kinship and helping behaviour of Galápagos Mockingbirds. *Behav. Ecol. Sociobiol.* 22: 141–152.

Curry, R.L. 1988b. Group structure, within-group conflict, and reproductive tactics in co-operatively-breeding Galápagos Mockingbirds *Nesomimus parvulus. Anim. Behav.* 36: 1708–1728.

Curry, R.L. & Anderson, D.J. 1987. Interisland variation in blood drinking by Galápagos Mockingbirds. *Auk* 104: 517–521.

Curry, R.L. & Grant, P.R. 1989. Demography of the co-operatively breeding Galápagos Mockingbird, *Nesomimus parvulus*, in a climatically variable environment. *J. Anim. Ecol.* 58:441–464.

Curry, R.L. & Grant, P.R. 1990. In: Stacey, P.B. & Koening, W.D.K. (eds) *Cooperative breeding in birds: long-term studies of ecology and behaviour.* Cambridge University Press, Cambridge.

Darlington, P.J. 1931. Notes on the birds of Río Frío (near Santa Marta), Magdalena, Colombia. *Bull. Mus. Comp. Zool.* 71: 349–421.

Darwin, C. 1839. Narrative of the Surveying Voyages of Her Majesty's Ships *Adventure* and *Beagle* between the years 1826 and 1836. '*Journal and Remarks*' Vol III 1908 edition, J. M. Dent, London.

Darwin, C. 1859. *On the Origin of Species by Means of Natural Selection.* John Murray, London.

Davis, T.J. 1986. Distribution and Natural History of some birds from the Department of San Martín and Amazonas, Northern Peru. *Condor* 88: 50–56.

Davis, W.B. & Russell, R.J. 1953. Aves y Mamíferos del Estado de Morelos. *Rev. Soc. Mex. Hist. Nat.* 14: 82 and 104.

Dementiev, G.P. & Gladkov, N.A. (eds) 1966 *Birds of the Soviet Union* Vol. 6. Israel Programme for Scientific Translation, Jerusalem.

Derrickson, K.C. & Breitwisch, R. 1992. Northern Mockingbird. In Poole, A., Steltenheim, A.P. & Gill, F. (eds) *The Birds of North America* No. 7. The Academy of Natural Sciences, Philadelphia, Pennsylvania and The American Ornithologists' Union, Washington DC.

Diamond, A.W. 1973. Habitats and feeding stations of St Lucia forest birds. *Ibis* 115: 313-328.

Dickerman, R.W. 1973. A review of the white-breasted woodwrens of México and Central America. *Condor* 75: 361–363.

Dickerman, R.W. 1975. Revision of the Short-billed Marsh Wren (*Cistothorus platensis*) of Mexico and Central America. *Novitates* 2569: 1–8.

Dickey, D.R. & Van Rossem, A.J. 1938. Birds of El Salvador, Field Museum of Natural History, 23: 434.

Dinelli, L. 1918. Notas biológicas sobre las aves del noreste de la República Argentina. *Hornero* 1: 57–68.

Dixon, E. 1930. Catbird robs Chipping Sparrow. *Oologist* 47: 126.

Dolgushin, I.A., Korelov, M.N., Kuzmina, M.A., Gavrilov, E.I., Gavrin, V.F., Kovshar, A.F., Borodikhin, I.F. & Rodionov, E.F. 1970. *Ptitsy Kazakhstana, Tom. III.* Izdatel'stvo 'Nauka' Kazakhskoi SSR, Alma-Ata.

Downer, A. & Sutton, R. 1990. *Birds of Jamaica.* Cambridge University Press, Cambridge.

Drilling, N.E. & Thompson, C.F. 1984. The use of nest-boxes to assess the affect of selective logging on House Wren populations. 188–196 in McComb, W.C.(ed). *Proceedings of the workshop on management of non-game species and ecological communities.* Lexington, KY.

Dungel, J. and Sebela, M. 1995. American Dipper *Cinclus mexicanus* in Venezuela. *Bull. Brit. Orn. Club* 115: 191-192.

Edwards, E.P. & Lea, R.B. 1955. Birds of Monserrati area, Chiapas. *Condor* 57: 31–54.

Edwards, E.P. & Martin, P.S. Further notes on birds of the Lake Patzcuaro region, México. *Auk* 72: 174-178.

Eisenmann, E. 1950. Behavior and habitat of *Thryophilus leucotis* in Central Panama. *Wilson Bull.* 62: 216.

Eisenmann, E. 1955. The species of Middle American birds. *Trans. Linn. Soc. New York*: 7.

Eisenmann, E. 1957. Notes on birds of the province of Bocas del Toro, Panama. *Condor* 59: 247–262.

Emlen, J.T. 1974. An urban bird community in Tucson, Arizona: derivation, structure, regulation. *Condor* 76: 184–197.

England, A.S. & Laudenslayer, W.F., Jr. 1993. Bendire's Thrasher (*Toxostoma bendirei*). In Poole, A. & Gill, F.(eds) *The Birds of North America* No. 71. The Academy of Natural Sciences, Philadelphia, Pennsylvania and American Ornithologists' Union, Washington DC.

Everett, W.T. 1988. Notes from Clarion Island. *Condor* 90: 512-519.

Farabaugh, S.M. 1982. In Kroodsma, D.E. & Miller, E.H. (eds) *Acoustic Communication in Birds* Vol. 2: 85–124. Academic Press, New York.

Farabaugh, S.M. 1984. A comparative study of duet song in tropical *Thryothorus* wrens. *Dissertation Abstr. int. B* 45: 484.

Farley, G.H. 1995. Thermal, social and distributional consequences of night-time cavity roosting in *Campylorhynchus* wrens. PhD dissertation, University of New Mexico, Albuquerque New Mexico.

ffrench, R. 1973. *A Guide to the Birds of Trinidad and Tobago.* Livingstone, Wynnewood, Pennsylvania.

Fitzpatrick, J.W., Terborgh, J.W. & Willard, D.E. 1977. A new species of Wood-wren from Peru. *Auk* 94: 195–201.

Fischer, D.H. 1980. Breeding biology of Curve-billed Thrashers and Long-billed Thrashers in southern Texas. *Condor* 82: 392–397.

Fischer, D.H. 1981. Wintering ecology of thrashers in southern Texas. *Condor* 83: 340–346.

Fjeldså, J. & Krabbe, N. 1990. *Birds of the High Andes.* Zoological Museum, University of Copenhagen, Copenhagen.

Flaspohler, D.J. 1994. Nest site selection by birds in Acacia trees in a Costa Rican dry deciduous forest. *Wilson Bulletin* 106: 162–165.

Fleischer, R.C. & Tarr. C.L. 1995. Plain Wren destroys egg of Dusky Antbird. *J. Field Ornithol.* 66: 404–405.

Fleming, R.L., Fleming, R.L. & Bangdel,L.S. 1976. *Birds of Nepal.* R.L. Fleming Sr. & Jr., Box 229, Kathmandu, Nepal.

Flint, P.R. & Stewart, P.F. 1983. *The Birds of Cyprus.* British Ornithologists' Union, London.

Fraga, R.M. 1985. Host-parasite interactions between Chalk-browed Mockingbirds and Shiny Cowbirds. Neotropical Ornithology. *Ornithological Monographs No.* 36: 829-844. American Ornithologists' Union, Washington DC.

Francis, C.M. & Hussell, D.J.T. 1998. Changes in numbers of land birds counted in migration at Long Point Bird Observatory, 1961–1997. *Bird Populations* 4: 37–66.

Freed, L.A. 1986. Usurpatory and opportunistic bigamy in tropical House Wrens. *Anim. Behav.*34: 1894–1896.

Freed, L.A. 1987. Rufous-and-white Wrens kill House Wren nestlings during a food shortage. *Condor* 89: 195–197.

Friedmann, H. 1947. A new wren from Chiapas. Mexico. *Auk* 64:128.

Friedmann, H., Griscom, L. & More, R.T. 1957. Distributional checklist of the birds of Mexico. *Pacific Coast Avifauna* No. 33, Cooper Ornithological Society.

Garrido, O.H. & García Montaña, F, 1965. Aves Nuevas para Cuba. *Poeyana* Serie A 10: 1-6.

Garrido, O.H. & García Montaña, F. 1975. *Catálogo de las Aves de Cuba.* Academia de Ciencias de Cuba, Havana.

Garrido, O.H. & Remsen, J.V. Jr 1996. A new subspecies of the Pearly-eyed Thrasher *Margarops fuscatus* (*Mimidae*) from the island of St Lucia, Lesser Antilles. *Bull. Brit. Orn. Club* 116: 75-80.

Gibbons, D.W., Reid, J.B. & Chapman, R.A. 1993. *The New Atlas of Breeding Birds in Britain and Ireland.* T. & A.D. Poyser, London.

Gilardi, J.D. & von Kugelgen, K, 1991. Bird/ant/acacia symbioses in a mature neotropical forest. *Wilson Bull.* 103: 711–712.

Gilman, M.F. 1915. A forty-acre bird census at Sacaton, Arizona. *Condor* 17: 86–90.

Gochfield, M. 1978 Ecological aspects of habitat selection by two sympatric mockingbirds, *Mimus* spp, in Patagonia. *Ibis* 120: 61–65.

Gochfield, M. 1979. Nest description and plumage variation of the Sepia-brown Wren *Cinnycerthia peruana.* *Bull. Brit. Orn. Club* 99(2): 45–46.

Godfrey, W.E. 1986. *The Birds of Canada.* National Museums of Canada, Ottawa, Ontario.

Gómez de Silva,G. 1995. Canyon Wren *Catherpes mexicanus* in humid lowlands of Mexico, with notes on near sympatry with other rock-loving wrens. *Bull. Brit. Orn. Club* 115: 132–133.

Gómez de Silva Garza, H. 1997a. Distribution and Conservation Status of *Hylorchilus* Wrens (Troglodytidae) in Mexico. *Bird Conserv. Int.* 7: 409–418.

Gómez de Silva Garza, H. 1997b. Comparative Analysis of the Vocalisations of *Hylorchilus* Wrens (Troglodytidae). *Condor* 99: 981–984.

Gonzáles, H. 1982. Localización de *Ferminia cerverai* (Aves: Troglodytidae) en la Ciénaga de Zapata. *Miscelanea Zoologica* 16:4.

Gould, J. 1836. *Proc. Zool. Soc. London* 4:89.

Gould, J. & Darwin, C. 1841. *The Zoology of the voyage of HMS 'Beagle'.* Part 3 Birds: 8-145.

Gould, J. 1987. Sedge Wren. In Cadman, M.F., Eagles, P.F.J. & Helleiner, F.M. (eds). *Atlas of the breeding birds of Ontario.* University of Waterloo Press, Waterloo, ON.

Graber, J.W. & Graber, R.R. 1979. Severe winter weather and populations in southern Illinois. *Wilson Bull.* 91: 88–103.

Grant, P.R. 1966a. Late breeding on the Tres Marías Islands. *Condor* 68: 249–252.

Grant, P.R. 1966b. The coexistence of two wren species of the genus *Thryothorus*. *Wilson Bull.* 78: 266–278.

Grant, P.R. & Grant, N. 1979. Breeding and feeding of Galápagos Mockingbirds *Nesomimus parvulus*. *Auk* 96: 723–736.

Graves, G.R. 1980. Relationship of white facial feathering to age and locality in Peruvian *Cinnycerthia peruana*. *Bull. Brit. Orn. Club* 100(2): 149–150.

Graves, G.R. 1985. A recent record of the endangered St. Lucia Wren *Troglodytes aedon mesoleucus*. *Bull. Brit.Orn. Club* 105: 69–71.

Grayson, A. J. 1868. Exploring expedition to Socorro Island from Mazatlán, Mexico. *The Californian Farmer and Journal of Useful Sciences* 29: 7

Green, C. 1996. *Birding Ecuador*. Clive Green, Tucson, Arizona.

Grinnell, J. 1915. A distributional list of the birds of California. *Pacific Coast Avifauna* No. 11.

Grinnell, J. 1928 Notes on the systematics of West American birds. *Condor* 30: 155–156.

Griscom, L. 1923. Notes on Donacobius. *Auk* 40: 214–217.

Griscom, L. 1930. The races of the Spotted-breasted Wren (*Thryothorus maculipectus*). *Proc. New England Zool. Club* 12: 7.

Griscom, L. 1932a. The distribution of bird-life in Guatemala. *Bull. Amer. Mus. Nat. Hist.* 64.

Griscom, L. 1932b. New birds from Honduras and Mexico. *Proc. New England Zool. Club* 13: 61.

Griscom, L. 1932c. Revision of the races of Rock Wren. *Bull. Amer. Mus. Nat. Hist.* 64: 297.

Griscom, L. 1932d. The ornithology of the Caribbean coast of extreme eastern Panama. *Bull. Mus. Comp. Zool.* 72: 359.

Gross, A.O. 1968. Albinistic eggs of some North American birds. *Bird Banding* 39: 1–6.

Gulledge, J.L. 1975. A Study of phenetic and phylogenetic relationships among the mockingbirds, thrashers and their allies. PhD dissertation, City University of New York, New York.

Guzmán-Velasco, A., Contreras-Balderas, A.J., García-Salas, J.A. & González-Rojas, J.I. An unusual Cactus Wren *Campylorhynchus brunneicapillus* nest. *Cotinga* in press.

Haffer, J. 1967. On the birds from the northern Chocó region, northwestern Colombia. *Veröff. Zool. Staatsamml.* München 11: 123–149.

Haffer, J. 1975. Avifauna of northwestern Colombia, South America. *Bonner Zool. Monogy* 7: 18.

Haggerty, T.M. & Morton, E.S. 1995. Carolina Wren (*Thryothorus ludovicianus*) in Poole, A & Gill, F. (eds). *The Birds of North America* No. 188. The Academy of Natural Sciences, Philadelphia and the American Ornithologists' Union, Washington DC

Hardy, J.W., Barlow, J.C. & Coffey, B.B., Jr. 1987 *Voices of all the mockingbirds, thrashers and their allies.* ARA Records, Gainesville, Florida.

Hardy, J.W. & Coffey B.B.Jr. 1991. *Voices of the wrens, family Troglodytidae*. ARA records, Gainesville Florida.

Hardy, J.W. & Delaney, D.J. 1987. The vocalisations of the Slender-billed Wren (*Hylorchilus sumichrasti*); who are its close relations? *Auk* 104: 528–530.

Harris, M.P. 1974. *A Field Guide to the Birds of the Galapagos*. Collins, London.

Harrison, H.H. 1975. *A Field Guide to Birds' Nests*. Houghton Mifflin, Boston, Massachusetts.

Hartert, E. 1910. *Die Vögel der palaärktischen Fauna*. Friedlander, Berlin.

Hatch, J.J. 1966. Collective territories in Galápagos mockingbirds, with notes on other behavior. *Wilson Bull.* 78: 198–207.

Haverschmidt, F. 1952. Nesting behaviour of the southern House Wren in Surinam. *Condor* 54: 292–295.

Haverschmidt, F. 1968. *The Birds of Surinam*. Oliver and Boyd, Edinburgh and London.

Haverschmidt, F. & Mees, G.F. 1994. *Birds of Suriname*. Evaco, Uitgeversmaatschappij, Paramaribo.

Hawthorn, I. & Mead, C.J. 1975. Wren movements and survival. *Brit. Birds* 68: 349–358.

Hejl, S. & Holmes, J.A. 2000. Winter Wren (*Troglodytes troglodytes*) in Gill, F & Poole, A (eds) *The Birds of North America* The Birds of North America Inc., Philadelphia, Pennsylvania.

Hellmayr, C.E. 1903. Bemerkungen über Neotropische Vögel. *J. Ornithol.* 51: 527–534.

Hellmayr, C.E. 1908. *Thryothorus genibarbis intercedens* subsp. nov. *Nov. Zool.* 15: 17–18.

Hellmayr, C.E. 1924–1949. Catalogue of birds of the Americas and the adjacent islands. *Field Mus. Natural Historical Publication* 330, Zool. Ser. 13: 1–531 (p. 141).

Hellmayr, C.E, 1924–1949. Birds of North and Middle America, *Bull.* 50, United States National Museum.

Hellmayr, C.E. 1929. A contribution to the ornithology of northeastern Brazil, *Field Mus. Nat. Hist. Zoology.* 12: 253.

Hendricks, P. 2000. Arboreal Nocturnal Roosting Behavior of a Fledgling American Dipper. *Wilson Bulletin* 112: 148–150.

Herkert, J.R. 1994. The effects of habitat fragmentation on Midwestern grassland bird communities. *Ecol. Appl.* 4: 461–471.

Hilty, S.L. & Brown, W.L. 1986. *A Guide to the Birds of Colombia*. Princeton University Press, Princeton New Jersey.

Hilty, S.L. 1994. *Chloropingus flavovirens* rediscovered ,with notes on other Pacific Colombian and Cauca Valley birds. *Auk* 111: 44–49.

Hollom, P.A.D. 1952. *The Popular Handbook of British Birds*. H. F. & G. Witherby, London.

Howard, R. & Moore, A. 1984. *A Complete Checklist of the Birds of the World*. Macmillan, London.

Howell, A.H. 1932. *Florida Bird Life*.

Howell, S.N.G. & Webb, S. 1989. Additional notes from Isla Clarión, Mexico. *Condor* 91: 1007–1008.

Howell, S.N.G. & Webb, S. 1992. New and noteworthy bird records from Guatemala and Honduras. *Bull. Brit. Orn. Club* 112: 42–49.

Howell, S.N.G. & Webb, S. 1995. *A Guide to the Birds of Mexico and Northern Central America*. Oxford University Press, Oxford.

Howell, T.R. 1957 The Birds of the second growth rainforest area of Nicaragua. *Condor* 59: 73–111.

Hudson, W.H. 1920. *Birds of La Plata*. London, J.M. Dent & Sons.

Huguet, P. & Tostain, O. 1990. *Forêt de l'Amazone.* [1 CD] Sitelle Eds.

Humphrey, P.S., Bridge, D., Reynolds, P.W. & Peterson, R.T. 1970. *Birds of the Isla Grande (Tierra del Fuego).* Smithsonian Institution, Washington DC.

Hundley, M.H. 1963. Wing-flashing in the Galápagos Mockingbird. *Auk* 80: 372.

Ijsselstein, C. 1992. Report on the censussing of the St Lucia White-breasted Thrasher, *Ramphocinclus brachyurus sanctaeluciae.* International Council for Bird Preservation, Cambridge, UK.

Incledon, C.S.L. 1968. Brown Thrasher in Dorset; a species new to Britain and Ireland. *Brit. Birds* 61: 550–553.

Jaeger, M.J. 1980. Breeding songbird associations in a southern Wisconsin wetland. *Passenger Pigeon* 42: 64–66.

James, R.D., McLaren, P.L., Barlow, J.C. 1976. Annotated checklist of the Birds of Ontario. *Life Sci. Misc. Publ.,* Royal Ontario Museum, Toronto.

Jehl, J.R. & Parkes, K.C.1982. The status of the avifauna of the Revillagigedo Islands, Mexico. *Wilson Bull.* 94: 1–19.

Jehl, J.R. & Parkes, K.C. 1983. 'Replacements' of landbird species on Socorro Island, Mexico. *Auk* 100: 551–559.

Jenni, L. 1998. An incredible Dipper story; nestling *Cinclus cinclus aquaticus* from Switzerland moves 1055km to Poland and breeds with a Swedish *C. c. cinclus. Euring Newsletter* 2: 49.

Johnson, A.W. 1967. *The Birds of Chile and adjacent regions of Argentina, Bolivia and Peru,* Vol. II., Platt Establecimientos Gráficos S.A., Buenos Aires.

Johnson, L.S. 1998. House Wren (*Troglodytes aedon*). In Poole, A. & Gill, F. (eds.) *The Birds of North America* No. 380, The Academy of Natural Sciences, Philadelphia PA and The American Ornithologists' Union, Washington DC.

Johnson, L.S., Kermott, L.H. & Lein, M.R. 1993. The cost of polygamy in the House Wren. *Journal of Animal Ecology* 62: 669-682.

Johnson, L.S., Kermott, L.H. & Lein, M.R. 1994. Territorial polygamy in House Wrens; are females sufficiently compensated for the cost of mate sharing? *Behavioral Ecology* 5: 98- 104.

Johnson, L. S., Merkle, M. S. & Kermott, L.H. 1992. Experimental evidence for importance of male parental care in monogamous House Wrens. *Auk* 109: 662-664.

Jones, S.L. & Dieni, J.S. 1995. Canyon Wren in Poole, A. & Gill, F. (eds) *The Birds of North America* No. 197. The Academy of Natural Sciences of Philadelphia, Pennsylvania and The American Ornithologists' Union, Washington DC.

Joyce, F.J. 1993. Nesting success of rufous-naped wrens (*Campylorhynchus rufinucha*) is greater near wasp nests. *Behav. Ecol. Sociobiol.* 32: 71–77.

Jullien, M. & Cariveau, D.P. First description of the nest of the Wing-banded Wren *Microcerculus bambla* in French Guiana (South America) and new comments on its behavioral ecology. In press.

Kale, H.W. 1965. Ecology and bioenergetics of the Long-billed Marsh Wren *Telmatodytes palustris griseus* in Georgia salt marshes. *Publ. Nuttall Ornithol. Club* no. 5.

Kashkarov, D. Yu., Lanovenko, Ye. N., Fottler, E.R.,

Ostanenko, M.M., Sagitov, A.K., Shernazarov, E., Bakayev, S.B., Tretyakov, G.P., Mitropol'skii, O.V. & Meklenburtsev, R.N. 1995. *Ptitsy Uzbekistana Tom. III.* Izdatel'stvo 'Fan', Akademia Nauk Respubliki Uzbekistan, Tashkent.

Kattan, G.H. 1993. Albino eggs in a tropical population of the House Wren (*Troglodytes aedon*). *Hornero* 13: 305–306.

Kaufman, K. 1990. *Advanced Birding.* Houghton Mifflin, Boston.

Keith, A.R. 1997. *The Birds of St. Lucia, West Indies.* British Ornithologists' Union, Tring.

Kennedy, C.H. 1911. Notes on the fruit-eating habits of the sage thrasher in the Yakima valley. *Auk* 28: 225–228.

Kennedy, E.D. & White, D.W. 1997. Bewick's Wren in Poole, A. & Gill, F(eds), *The Birds of North America* No. 315. The Academy of Natural Sciences, Philadelphia, Pennsylvania and American Ornithologists' Union, Washington DC.

Kiltie, R.A. & Fitzpatrick, J.W. 1984. Reproduction and social organisation of the Black-capped Donacobius (*Donacobius atricapillus*) in southeastern Peru. *Auk* 101: 804–811.

King, H. 1969. Shetland Wren in Aberdeenshire. *Scottish Birds* 7: 391.

Kingery, H.E. 1996. American Dipper (*Cinclus mexicanus*). In Poole, A.& Gill, F. (eds). *The Birds of North America* No. 229 The Academy of Natural Sciences, Philadelphia PA and The American Smithsonian Institution, Washington DC.

Kinnaird, M.F. & Grant, P.R. 1982. Cooperative breeding by the Galápagos Mockingbird, *Nesomimus parvulus. Behav. Ecol. Sociobiol.* 10: 65–73.

Kirwan, G. 1996. Neotropical Notebook, *Cotinga* 6:33.

Krabbe, N. & Sornoza, M.F. 1994. Avifaunistic results of a subtropical camp in the Cordillera del Condor, south-eastern Ecuador. *Bull. Brit. Orn. Club* 114(1): 55–61.

Kratter, A.W. and Garrido, O. 1996. A new subspecies of *Margarops fuscus* (Scaly-breasted Thrasher) from St Vincent, Lesser Antilles. *Bull. Brit. Orn. Club* 116: 189-193.

Kroodsma, D.E. 1974. Song learning, dialects and dispersal in the Bewick's Wren, *Z. Tierpsychol.* 35: 352–380.

Kroodsma, D.E. 1980. Winter Wren singing behavior; a pinnacle of song complexity. *Condor* 82: 357-365.

Kroodsma, D.E. 1985. Geographic variations in songs of the Bewick's wren; a search for correlations with avifaunal complexity. *Behav. Ecol. Sociobiol.* 16: 143–160.

Kroodsma, D.E. 1988. Two species of Marsh Wren in Nebraska? *Birding* (60: 371–374.

Kroodsma, D.E. 1998. Marsh Wren (*Cistothorus palustris*). In Poole, A. & Gill, F. (eds) *The Birds of North America* No. 308. The Academy of Natural Sciences, Philadelphia, Pennsylvania and American Ornithologists' Union, Washington DC.

Kroodsma, D.E., Miller, E.H. & Ouellet, H. (eds) 1982. *Acoustic Communication in Birds.* Volume 1. Academic Press, New York.

Kroodsma, D.E. & Momose, E.H. 1991. Songs of the Japanese population of the Winter Wren (*Troglodytes troglodytes*). *Condor* 93: 424–432.

Kroodsma, D.E., Salas, V. & Muradian, R. Singing behaviour of the Merida Wren, *Cistothorus meridae*. In preparation.

Lafresnaye, Baron N.F.A.A. de 1845. *Rev. Zool.* 8: 337.

Land, H.C. 1970. *The Birds of Guatemala*. Livingstone, Wynnewood Pennsylvania.

Lanyon, W.E. 1960 Relationship of the House Wren (*Troglodytes aedon*) of North America and the Brown-throated Wren (*Troglodytes brunneicollis*) of Mexico. *Proc. Int. Congr. Orn.* 12: 450–458.

Laskey, A.R. 1948. Some nesting data on the Carolina Wren at Nashville, Tennessee. *Bird-Banding* 19: 101–121.

La Touche, J.D. 1925. *A Handbook of the Birds of Eastern China*. Taylor and Francis, London.

Lawrence, G.N. 1887. Birds of south-western Mexico collected by Francis E. Sumichrast for the United States National Museum. *Bull. U S Nat. Mus.* 4: 5–56.

Lawrence, G.N. 1871. On the specimens collected by Col. A J Grayson in the Revillagigedo Islands, Mexico. *Am. Lyc. Nat. Hist. New York*, 10: 1-21.

Lea, R.B. & Edwards, E.P. 1950. Notes on birds of the Lake Patzcuaro region, Michoacán, México. *Condor* 52: 260–267.

Lentino, R.M. 1978. Extensiones de distribución de ocho especies de aves de Venezuela. *Memoria Soc. Cienc. nat. La Salle* 38: 113–118.

Leonard, M.L. & Picman, J. 1987. The adaptive significance of multiple nest-building by male Marsh Wrens. *Anim. Behav.* 35: 271–277.

Lesson, R.-P. 1834. *L'Institut* 2 Paris, 72: 316.

Levin, R.N. 1988. The adaptive significance of antiphonal song in the Bay Wren *Thryothorus nigricapillus*. *Nagasaki Daigaku Suisanga Kubu Kenkyu Hokoku* 48: 3514.

Levin, R.N. 1996. Song behaviour and reproductive strategies in a duetting wren, *Thryothorus nigricapillus*: 2. Playback experiments. *Animal Behaviour* 52: 1107–1117.

Levin, R. & Wingfield, J.C. 1992. The hormonal control of territorial aggression in tropical birds. *Ornis Scandinavica* 23: 284–291.

Linton, C.B. 1908. *Salpinctes obsoletus pulverius* restricted to San Nicholas Island. *Condor* 10: 129.

Loetscher, F.W., Jr. 1952. Striped Cuckoo fed by Rufous-and-white Wren in Panamá. *Condor* 54: 169

Lofberg, L.M. 1931. 'Office Aids' in Nest Building. *Condor* 33: 245–246.

Long, R. 1981. Catbird in the Channel Islands. *Brit. Birds* 74: 526-527.

Low, J.B. 1943. Wrens use duck down as nest lining. *Auk* 63: 593–594.

Lowery, G.H. 1940. Geographic variation in the Carolina Wren. *Auk* 57: 95–104.

Lowery, G.H. & Newman, R. J. 1949. New birds from the State of Veracruz and the Tuxtla mountains of Veracruz, Mexico. *Occ. Papers Louisiana S.U.* 22: 4–5.

Manci, K.M. & Rusch, D.H. 1988. Indices to distribution and abundance of some inconspicuous waterbirds in Horicon Marsh. *J. Field Ornithol.* 59: 67–75.

Manson-Bahr, P. 1959. Recollections of some famous British ornithologists. *Ibis* 101: 53–64.

Marchant, S. 1960. The breeding of some SW Ecuadorian birds. *Ibis* 102: 349–382.

Markowsky, J.K., Glanz, W. & Hunter, M. 1994. Why do Brown Tremblers tremble? *J. Field Ornithology* 65: 247-249.

Martin, R.F. 1971. The Canyon Wren (*Catherpes mexicanus*) raiding food storage of trypoxylid wasp. *Auk* 88: 677.

Marshall, D.B. & Horn, K. 1973. Adaptations of two desert birds to clearcut areas in the Oregon Cascades. *Murrelet* 54 (3): 35–36.

Marshall, J.T. 1956. Summer birds of the Rincon Mountains, Saguaro National Monument, Arizona. *Condor* 58: 81–97.

Martínez García, O. & Martínez García, A. 1991. Primer registro de nidificación y observaciones ecoetológicas de *Ferminia cerverai* (Aves: Troglodytidae). *Revista Biológica* 5: 91–93.

Martínez-Gómez, J.E. & Curry, R.L. 1995. First description of the nest and eggs of the Socorro Mockingbird. *Wilson Bull.* 107: 551–555.

Martínez-Sánchez, J.C. 1989. Records of new little-known birds for Nicaragua. *Condor* 91:468–469.

Mayr, E. 1946. History of the North American bird fauna. *Wilson Bulletin* 58: 3–41.

McAtee, W.L. 1950. The Carolina Wren, *Thryothorus ludovicianus*, as a mimic. *Wilson Bull.* 62: 136.

McLaughlin, J.F. & Roughgarden, J. 1989. Avian predation on *Anolis* lizards in the northeastern Caribbean; an inter-island contrast. *Ecology* 70: 617-628.

McLellan, M.E. 1926. Birds and Mammals. In: Expedition to the Revillagigedo Islands, Mexico, in 1925. *Proc. Calif. Ac. Sci. S. Francisco* 15: 279-322.

Mead, C.J. & Clark, J.A. 1988. Report on bird-ringing for 1988. *Ringing and Migration* 10: 158–196.

Meanley, B. 1952. Notes on the ecology of the Short-billed Marsh Wren in the lower Arkansas rice paddies. *Wilson Bull.* 64: 22-25.

Mearns, B. & Mearns, R. 1998. *The Bird Collectors*. Academic Press, San Diego.

Mearns, E.A. 1886. Some birds of Arizona. *Auk* 3: 289–307.

Mees, G.F. 1968. First record of the Wing-banded Wren in Surinam. *Gerfaut* 58: 101–107.

Meinertzagen, R. 1924. A note on Scottish wrens (*Troglodytes*) with characteristics of a newly defined Hebridean race. *Scottish Naturalist* September–October 1924.

Merola, M. 1995. Observations of the nesting and breeding behaviour of the Rock Wren. *Condor* 97: 585–587.

Metz, K.J. 1991. The enigma of multiple nest-building by male Marsh Wrens. *Auk* 108: 170–173.

Meyer de Schauensee, R. 1946a. Colombian Zoological Survey part II, Notes on Colombian Crows, Wrens and Swallows. *Notulae Naturae* 161: 1–14.

Meyer de Schauensee, R. 1946b. A new species of wren from Colombia. *Notulae Naturae* 182: 1–2.

Meyer de Schauensee, R. 1964. *The Birds of Colombia*. Livingstone, Narberth, Pennsylvania.

Meyer de Schauensee, R. 1984. *The Birds of China*. Smithsonian Institution Press, Washington DC.

Meyer de Schauensee, R. & Phelps, W.H., Jr. 1978. *A Guide to the Birds of Venezuela*. Princeton University Press, New Jersey.

Miller, A.H. 1947. The tropical avifauna of the upper Magdalena valley. *Auk* 64: 351–381.

Miller, A.H. 1948. Further observations of variations in the Canyon Wren. *Condor* 50: 83–85.

Miller A. H. 1963. Seasonal activity and ecology of the avifauna of an American equatorial cloud forest. *Univ. Calif. Pub. Zool.* 66: 1–74.

Miller, A.H., Friedmann, H., Griscom, L. & Moore, R.T. Distribution checklist of the birds of Mexico, Part 2. *Pacific Coast Avifauna* 33, Cooper Ornithological Society.

Miller, W. de W., & Griscom, L. 1925. Descriptions of new birds from Nicaragua. *Am. Mus. Nov.* No. 159.

Mirsky, E.N. 1976. Ecology of coexistence of a wren-wrentit-warbler guild. PhD dissertation. University of California.

Mitchell, M.H. 1957. *Observations on Birds of South-eastern Brazil.* University of Toronto Press, Toronto, Ontario.

Mitford, R.H. 1882. Dipper breeding in Middlesex. *The Zoologist* 6:109.

Monroe, B.L., Jr. 1963. New birds from Honduras. *Occ. Papers Mus. Zool. Louisiana S. U.* 26: 5–6.

Monroe, B.L., Jr. 1968. A distributional survey of the birds of Honduras. *Ornithological Monographs* No.7. American Ornithologists' Union.

Monroe, B.L. & Sibley, C.G. 1993. *A World Checklist of Birds.* Yale University Press, New Haven CT.

Moore, R.T. 1941. Notes on *Toxostoma curvirostre* of Mexico, with description of a new race. *Proc. Biol. Soc. Washington.* 54: 211–216.

Morton, E.S. 1980. Close range sounds. *Acta XVII Congressus Internationalis Ornithologii*, 736–741. Verlag der Deutschen Ornitholigen Gesellschaft, Berlin.

Morton, E.S. 1982. In Kroodsma, D.E. & Miller, E.H. *Acoustic Communication in Birds*, Vol. 1 Academic Press, New York.

Morton, E.S. & Farabaugh, S.M. 1979. Infanticide and other adaptations of the nestling Striped Cuckoo *Tapera naevia. Ibis* 121: 212–213.

Morton, E S. & Shalter, M.D. 1977. Vocal response to predators in pair-bonded Carolina Wrens. *Condor* 79: 222–227.

Mousley, H. 1934. A study of the home life of the Short-billed Marsh Wren (*Cistothorus stellaris*). *Auk* 51: 439–445.

Narosky, T. & Yzurieta, D. 1987. *Guía para la identificación de las aves de Argentina y Uruguay.* Asoc. Ornitológica del Plata, Buenos Aires.

Nelson, E.W. 1897. Preliminary descriptions of new Birds from Mexico and Guatemala in the collection of the United States Department of Agriculture. *Auk* 14: 42–76.

Nordstrom, W. 1978. Short-billed Marsh Wrens in Alberta. *Blue Jay* 36: 200–206.

Norton, R.L. 1994. Reports from the Caribbean region. *American Birds* 48: 156–158.

Oberholser, H.C. 1904. A review of the wrens of the genus *Troglodytes. Proc. U.S. Nat. Mus.* 27, no. 1354.

Oberholser, H.C. 1934. A revision of the North American House Wrens. *Ohio Journal of Science* 34 (2): 86-96.

Oberholser, H.C. 1974 *The Bird Life of Texas*, Vol. 2. University of Texas Press, Austin, Texas.

Ochoa de Masramón, D. 1975. Contribución al estudio de las aves de San Luís. *Hornero*, 11 (4): 309–310.

Olivares, A. 1969. *Aves de Cundinamarca.* Universidad Nacional de Colombia, Bogotá, Colombia.

Olrog, C.C. 1948. Observaciones sobre la avifauna del archipiélago de Cabo de Hornos. *Acta Zoológica Lilloana* 5: 437–531.

Omland, K.E. 2001. Gleanings from the technical literature; thrashing out species limits in the Southwest. *Birding* 33: 320-328.

Osborn, S.A.H. 1998. Anting by an American Dipper. *Wilson Bull.* 110: 423–425.

Osborn, S.A.H. 2000. Itinerant breeding and mate switching by an American Dipper. *Wilson Bull.*112(4): 539–541.

Paessler, R. 1928. *Beitr. Fortpfl.-Biol. Vog.* 4: 30.

Parker, T.A. III, Parker, S.A. & Plenge, M.A. 1982. *An Annotated Checklist of Peruvian Birds.* Buteo Books, Vermillion, South Dakota

Parker, T.A. III & O'Neill, J.P. 1980. Notes on little-known birds of the upper Urubamba valley, southern Peru. *Auk* 97: 167–176.

Parker, Theodore A. III & O'Neill, J.P. 1985. A new species and a new subspecies of *Thryothorus* wren from Peru. *Neotropical Ornithology*, AOU Monograph no. 36: 9-15.

Parker, T.A. III, Remsen, J.V. , Heindel, J.A. 1980. Seven bird species new to Bolivia. *Bull. Brit. Orn. Club* 100: 160–162.

Parker, T.A. III, Schulenberg, T.S. ,Graves, G.R. & Braun, M.S. 1985. Avifauna of the Huancabamba region, northern Peru. *Neotropical Ornithology.* AOU Monograph No. 36: 182–183.

Parkes, K.C. 1990. Was the Socorro Mockingbird (*Mimodes graysoni*) a predator on small birds? *Wilson Bull.* 102: 317–320.

Paynter, R.A. 1955. The Ornithogeography of the Yucatán Peninsula, Peabody Mus. Nat. Hist., *Yale University Bull.* 9:1–347.

Paynter, R.A., Jr. 1957. Taxonomic notes on the New World forms of *Troglodytes. Breviora* 71: 1–15.

Paz, U. 1987. *The Birds of Israel.* Stephen Greene, Lexington, Massachusetts.

Pemberton, J.R. 1916. Nesting of the Leconte Thrasher. *Condor* 18: 219–221.

Pernety, A.J. 1771. *The history of a voyage to the Malovine (or Falkland) Islands.* Translated for T. Jeffreys, London.

Pereyra, J.A. 1937. Contribución al estudio y observaciones ornitológicas de la zona norte de la Gobernación de la Pampa. Mun. Jardin Zool. *La Plata* 7; 198–326.

Pérez-Villafana, M., Gómez de Silva Garza, H. & Desucre-Medrano, A. 1997. Sexual Dimorphism in the Song of Sumichrast's Wren *Hylorchilus sumichrasti. Wilson Bull.* 111: 128–130.

Peters, J.L. 1931–1986. *Checklist of Birds of the World.* Harvard University Press, Cambridge, Massachusetts.

Pettingill, O.S. Jr. 1973. *Living Bird* 12: 113-115.

Phelps, W.H. & Phelps, W.H. Jr. 1947. Ten new subspecies of birds from Venezuela. *Proc. Biol. Soc. Washington.* 60: 149–164.

Phillips, A.R. 1986. *The known birds of North and Middle America, part 1: Hirundinidae to Mimidae.* Allan R. Phillips, Denver, Colorado.

Phillips, A.R., Marshall, J. & Monson, G. 1964. *The Birds of Arizona.* University of Arizona Press, Tucson, Arizona.

Picman, J. 1980a. A new trap for Long-billed Marsh Wrens. *North American Bird Bander* 5: 8–10.

Picman, J. 1980b. Impact of Marsh Wrens on reproductive strategy of Red-winged Blackbirds. *Can. J. Zool.* 58: 337–350.

Picman, J. 1980c Response of Red-winged Blackbirds to nests of Long-billed Marsh Wrens. *Can. J. Zool.* 58: 1821–1827.

Picman, J. 1986. Attempted nest parasitism of the Marsh Wren by a Brown-headed Cowbird. *Condor* 88: 381-382.

Picman, J. & Picman, A. K. 1980. Destruction of nests by the Short-billed Marsh Wren. *Condor* 82: 176–179.

Picman, J., Pribil, S. & Picman, A.K. 1996. The effect of intraspecific egg destruction on the strength of Marsh Wren eggs. *Auk* 113 : 599–607.

Piper, W.H. 1994. Courtship, copulation, nesting behaviour and brood parasitism in the Venezuelan Stripe-backed Wren. *Condor* 96:654–671.

Piper, W.H. & Slater, G. 1993. Polyandry and incest-avoidance in the cooperative Stripe-backed Wren of Venezuela. *Behaviour* 124: 227–235.

Pyle, P. 1997. *Identification Guide to North American Birds: Part 1.* Slate Creek Press, Bolinas, California.

Rabenold, K.N. 1984. Cooperative enhancement of reproductive success in tropical wren societies. *Ecology* 65: 871885.

Rabenold, K.N. 1985. Cooperation in breeding by non-reproductive wrens: kinship, reciprocity and demography. *Behav. Ecol. Sociobiol.* 17: 1–17.

Rabenold, K.N. 1990. *Campylorhynchus* wrens: the ecology of delayed dispersal and cooperation in the Venezuelan Savanna. Pp. 158-196 in Stacey, P.B. & Koenig, W.D. (eds) *Cooperative breeding in birds.* Cambridge University Press, Cambridge.

Raffaele, H., Wiley, J., Garrido, O., Keith, A. & Raffaele, J. 1998. *A Guide to the Birds of the West Indies.* Princeton University Press, Princeton, New Jersey.

Ragusa-Netto, J. 1996. Nestling development, size and juvenile survival in *Donacobius atricapillus* (Passeriformes; Troglodytidae). *Ararajuba* 4: 81–85.

Ragusa-Netto, J. 1998. Wetting the nestlings: a possible kind of parental care in *Donacobius atricapillus* (Passeriformes; Troglidytidae). *Ararajuba* 6: 52–53.

Ramadan-Jaradi, G.H. & Ramadan-Jaradi, M. 1999. An updated checklist of the birds of the Lebanon. *Sandgrouse* 21 (2): 132-170.

Ramsay, A.O. 1987. Thermal adaptations of the Carolina Wren. *North American Bird Bander* 12: 64.

Ray, M.S. 1904. A fortnight on the Farallones. *Auk* 21: 425–442.

Remsen, J.V. & Brumfield, R.T. 1998. Two new subspecies of *Cinnycerthia fulva* (Aves: Troglodytidae) from the southern Andes. *Proc. Biol. Soc. Washington* 111: 1008–1015.

Remsen, J.V. Jr. & Traylor, M.A. Jr. 1983. Additions to the avifauna of Bolivia, Part 2. *Condor* 85: 95–98.

Renaud, W.E. 1979. The Rock Wren in Saskatchewan; status and distribution. *Blue Jay* 37: 138–148.

Reynolds, T.D., Rich, T.D. & Stephens, D.A. 2000 Sage Thrasher (*Oreoscoptes montanus*). In Poole, A & Gill, F. (eds). *The Birds of North America* No 463. The Birds of North America Inc., Philadelphia, Pennsylvania.

Rice, N.H., Peterson, A.T. & Escalona-Segura, G. 1999. Phylogenetic patterns in montane *Troglodytes* wrens. *Condor* 101: 446–451

Richard, M.A. In Cadman, M.A., Eagles, P.F.J. & Helleiner, F.M. (eds) 1987. *Atlas of the breeding birds of Ontario.* University of Waterloo Press, Waterloo, Ontario.

Richardson, F. 1965. Breeding and feeding habits of the Black Wheatear *Oenanthe leucura* in Southern Spain. *Ibis* 107: 1–16.

Ridgely, R.S. 1976. *A Guide to the Birds of Panama.* Princeton University Press, Princeton, New Jersey.

Ridgely, R.S. & Gaulin, S.J. C. 1980. Birds of Finca Merenberg, Huila Department, Colombia. *Condor* 82: 379–391.

Ridgely, R.S. & Greenfield, P. (2001). *The Birds of Ecuador.* Vols I & II. Cornell University Press, Ithaca, New York.

Ridgely, R.S. & Tudor, G.E. 1989. *The Birds of South America* Vol. 1 University of Texas Press, Austin, Texas.

Ridgway, R. 1876. Ornithology of Guadelupe Island, based on notes and collections of Dr Edward Palmer. *Bull. Hayden Surv. Terr.* Pt 2:183–195.

Ridgway, R. 1878. *Thryothorus felix lawrencii* sp. nov. *Proc. U. S. Nat. Mus.* 1: 252.

Ridgway, R. 1904. *The Birds of North and Middle America, Part III,* Government Printing.

Ridgway, R. 1907. The birds of North and Middle America Part IV. *US Nat. Mus. Bull.* no. 50.

Rogers, M.J. & the Rarities Committee 1987. Report on rare birds in Great Britain in 1986. *Brit. Birds* 80: 516–571.

Rolle, F.J. 1965a. Destruction of Red-legged Thrush nest by Pearly-eyed Thrasher. *Auk* 82: 643.

Rolle, F.J. 1965b. An observation of heavy predation by Pearly-eyed Thrasher. *Wilson Bull.* 77: 296-297.

Rosenberg, K.V., Ohmart, R.D., Hunter, W.C. & Anderson, B.W. 1991. *Birds of the Lower Colorado River Valley.* University of Arizona Press, Tucson, Arizona.

Rosene, W. 1954. Nesting in the Carolina Wren. *Alabama Bird-Life* 2: 23–25.

Rothschild, W., Hartert, E. & Jordan, K. 1902. Further notes on the Fauna of the Galapagos Islands. *Novitates Zoologicae* 9: 382.

Rowley, J.S. 1935. Notes on some birds of Lower California, Mexico. *Condor* 37: 163–168.

Rowley, J.S. 1984. Breeding records of land birds in Oaxaca, Mexico. *Western Foundation of Vertebrate Zoology* 2 (3): 171–172.

Russell, S.M. 1964. A distributional study of the birds of British Honduras. *Ornithological Monographs* No. 1, American Ornithologists' Union.

Russell, S.M. & Monson, G. 1998. *The Birds of Sonora.* University of Arizona Press, Tucson, Arizona.

Russell, S.M., Barlow, J.C. & Lamm, D.W. 1979. Status of some birds on Isla San Andrés and Isla Providencia, Colombia. *Condor* 81: 98-100.

Saether, B.-E., Tufto, J., Engen, S., Jerstad, K., Røstad, O.W. & Skåtan, J.E. 2000. Population dynamical consequences of climate change for a small temperate songbird. *Science* 287: 854–856.

Sage, B.L. 1956 A note on variation in the colour of the legs and plumage of the Wren *Troglodytes troglodytes troglodytes* (Linnaeus) *Bull. Brit. Orn. Club* 76: 32.

Salvador, S.A. 1984. Estudio de parasitismo de cría del Renegrido (*Molothrus bonariensis*) en Calandria (*Mimus saturninus*) en Villa María, Córdoba. *Hornero* 12(3): 141-149.

Salvador, S., Narosky, S. & Fraga, R. 1986. First description of the nest and eggs of the Rufous-throated Dipper (*Cinclus schulzi*) in northwestern Argentina. *Gerfaut* 76: 63–66.

Salvin, O. 1861. Description of three new species of bird from Guatemala. *Proc. Zool. Soc. London* 202.

Salvin, O. 1864. Two new species of wren from Costa Rica. *Proc. Zool. Soc. London* 580.

Salvin, O. & Godman, F.D. 1879. *Biologia Centrali-Americana. Aves* Vol. 1, Taylor and Francis, London.

Schafer, E. & Phelps, W.H. 1954. Las aves del Parque Nacional 'Henri Pittier'(Rancho Grande) y sus funciones ecológicas. *Bol. Sociedad Venezolana de Ciencias Naturales.* Vol. 16 no. 83.

Schaldach, W.J., Jr. 1963. The avifauna of Colima and adjacent Jalisco, Mexico. *Proc. West. Found. Zool.* 1: 1–100.

Schalow, H. 1998. Die Vögel der Sammlung Plate. *Zoologischen Jahrbuchen Jena*, Supple. 4 (3): 641–748.

Schönwetter, M. 1963–1974. *Handbuch der oologie*. Berlin, Akademie-Verlag

Sclater, P.L. 1860a. *Thryothorus mystacalis* sp. nov. *Proc. Zool. Soc. London* 28: 64.

Sclater, P.L. 1860b. *Proc. Zool. Soc. London* 28: 74.

Sclater, P.L. 1860c. Characters of ten new species of American birds. *Proc. Zool. Soc. London* 28: 461–467.

Sclater, P.L. & Salvin, O. 1879. On the birds collected by T. K. Salmon in the State of Antioquia, Colombia. *Proc. Zool. Soc.* London 1879: 486–550.

Scott, D.M. 1997. Cowbird parasitism on the Gray Catbird at London, Ontario. *Auk* 94: 18-27.

Scott, D.M., Darley, J.A. & Newsome, A.V. 1988. Length of the laying season and clutch size of Gray Catbirds at London, Ontario. *J. Field Ornithol.* 59: 355-360.

Selander, R.K. 1964. Speciation in Wrens of the Genus *Campylorhynchus. University of California Publications in Zoology* 74: 1–259.

Selander, R.K. 1965. Hybridization of Rufous-naped Wrens. *Auk* 82: 206–214.

Seneca, J.J. 1985. A record of extreme leucism in the Carolina Wren. *Wilson Bull.* 97: 244.

Seutin, G. & Chartier, B. 1989. The Rock Wren *Salpinctes obsoletus* breeding at Churchill, Manitoba. *Can. Field-Naturalist* 103:416–417.

Sharpe, R.B. 1881. *Cat. Birds of the Brit. Mus.* 6: 184.

Steiger, J.A. 1940. Dipper, wilderness dweller. *Bird-Lore* 42: 10-14.

Sharrock, J.T.R. (ed) 1976. *The Atlas of Breeding Birds in Britain and Ireland.* T. & A.D. Poyser, Berkhampstead.

Sheppard, J.M. 1996. Le Conte's Thrasher (*Toxostoma lecontei*) in Poole, A. & Gill,F. (eds) *The Birds of North America* No. 230. The Academy of Natural Sciences, Philadelphia, Pennsylvania and American Ornithologists' Union, Washington DC.

Sherman, A.R. 1925. Down with the house wren boxes. *Wilson Bull.* 37: 5-13.

Short, L.L. & Morony, J.J., Jr. 1969. Notes on some birds of central Peru. *Bull. Brit. Orn. Club* 89: 112–115.

Shuler, J.B. 1965. Duet singing in the Carolina Wren. *Wilson Bull.* 77: 405.

Sibley, C.G. & Ahlquist, J.E. 1984. The relationship of Starlings (Sturnidae: Sturnini) and Mockingbirds (Sturnidae: Mimini). *Auk* 101: 230–243.

Sibley, C.G. & Ahlquist, J E. 1990. *Phylogeny and Classification of Birds.* Yale University Press, New Haven, Connecticut.

Sibley, C.G., Corbin, C.W., Ahlquist, J.E. & Ferguson, A. 1974. In Wright, C.A. (ed.) *Biochemical and Immunological Taxonomy of Animals.* 80-176., Academic Press, London.

Sick, H. 1993. *Birds in Brazil: a Natural History.* Princeton University Press, Princeton, New Jersey.

Skutch, A.F. 1940. Social and sleeping habits of Central American Wrens. *Auk* 57: 292–312.

Skutch, A.F. 1950. Life history of the White-breasted Blue Mockingbird. *Condor* 52: 220–227.

Skutch, A.F. 1953. Life History of the Southern House Wren. *Condor* 55: 121–149.

Skutch, A.F. 1960. Life Histories of Central American birds II. *Pacific Coast Avifauna* 34: 130–182 Berkeley, Cooper Ornithological Society.

Skutch, A.F. 1968. The nesting of some Venezuelan birds. *Condor* 1968: 66–82.

Skutch, A.F. 1972. *Studies of Tropical American Birds.* Publications of the Nuttall Ornithological Club, No. 10.

Skutch, A.F. 1976. *Parent Birds and Their Young*, University of Texas Press, Austin, Texas.

Skutch, A.F. 1979. *Aves de Costa Rica.* Editorial Costa Rica, San José.

Slud, P. 1958. Observations of the Nightingale Wren in Costa Rica. *Condor* 60: 243–251.

Slud, P. 1960. The birds of finca 'La Selva', a tropical wet forest locality. *Bull. Am. Mus. Nat. Hist.* 128.

Slud, P. 1964. The birds of Costa Rica: distribution and ecology. *Bull. of the Am. Mus. of Nat. Hist.* 134: 261–296.

Smith, F.B. 1966. *The Birds of Tikal.* AMNH Natural History Press, Garden City, New York.

Smith, P.W. Jr., 1904. Nesting habits of the Rock Wren, *Condor* 6: 109–110.

Snyder, D.E. 1966. *The Birds of Guyana.* Salem, Massachusetts.

Snyder, N.F.R. & Taapken, J.D. 1977. Puerto Rican Parrots and nest predation by Pearly-eyed Thrashers. In *Endangered birds, Management techniques for preserving threatened species.* (S.A. Temple, ed.) University of Wisconsin Press, Madison WI.

Squires, W.A. 1952. *The Birds of New Brunswick.* New Brunswick Museum, Saint John, New Brunswick.

Stafford, E.F. 1912. Notes on Palmer's Thrasher (*Toxostoma curvirostre palmeri*). *Auk* 29: 363–368.

Steineger, L. 1905. Birds of the genus *Cinclus* and their geographical distribution. *Smithsonian Misc. Coll.* 47: 421–430.

Stevenson, H.M. 1973. An undescribed insular race of the Carolina Wren. *Auk* 90: 35–38.

Stiles, F.G. 1983. The Taxonomy of *Microcerculus* wrens (*Troglodytidae*) in Central America. *Wilson Bull.* 95: 169–183.

Stiles, F.G. !984. The songs of *Microcerculus* wrens in Costa Rica. *Wilson Bull.* 96: 99–103.

Stiles, F.G. & Skutch, A.F. 1989. *A Guide to the Birds of Costa Rica*. Cornell University Press, Ithaca, New York.

Storer, R.W. 1989. Geographic variation and sexual dimorphism in the Tremblers (*Cinclocerthia*) and White-breasted Thrasher (*Ramphocinclus*). *Auk* 106: 249-258.

Stone, R. 1918. Birds of the Panama Canal Zone with special reference to a collection made by Mr Lindsey L. Jewel. *Proc. Acad. Nat. Sci. Philadelphia* 70: 271.

Sunquist, M.E. 1974. Territory size and nesting habits of Brown Dippers *Cinclus pallasii*. *Ibis* 118: 577–578.

Sutton, G.M. 1948. The nest and eggs of the White-bellied Wren. *Condor* 50: 101–112.

Swarth, H.S. 1914. A study of certain island forms of the genus *Salpinctes*. *Condor* 16: 211–217.

Taczanowski, L. 1884. *Ornithologie du Perou*, Vols 1 and 2. Typographie Oberthur, Rennes, France.

Tashian, R.E. 1952. Some birds of the Palenque region of northeastern Chiapas. *Auk* 69: 60–66.

Taylor, L.C. 1951. Prior description of two Mexican birds by Andrew Jackson Grayson. *Condor* 53: 194-197.

Terborgh, J.W., Fitzpatrick, J.W. & Emmons, L. 1984. Annotated checklist of bird and mammal species of Cocha Cashu Biological Station, Manu National Park, Peru. *Fieldiana Zool. Mus. Nat. Hist.* 21: 1–29.

Thomas, B.T. 1979. The birds of a ranch in the Venezuelan llanos. Pp 213–232 in Eisenberg, J.F. (ed.) *Vertebrate Ecology in the Northern Neotropics*. Smithsonian Institution. Press, Washington DC

Todd, W.E.C. 1913. *Pheugopedius genibarbis bolivianus* subsp. nov. Bolivia. *Proc. Biol. Soc. Washington.* 26: 170.

Todd, W.E.C. & Carriker, M.A., Jr. 1922. The birds of the Santa Marta region of Colombia; a study in altitudinal distribution. *Ann. Carnegie Mus.* 14.

Tostain, O. 1980. Contribution á l'ornithologie de la Guyane. *Oiseau* 50: 47-62.

Tostain, O., Dujardin, J.-L., Erard, C. & Thiollay, J.M. 1992. *Oiseaux de Guyane*. Soc. Étud. Orn., Brunoy..

Townsend, C.W. 1909. A Carolina Wren invasion of New England. *Auk* 26: 263–269.

Tramontano, J. 1964. Comparative studies of the Rock and Canyon Wren. Ms thesis, University of Arizona, Tucson, Arizona

Traylor, M.T., Jr. 1988. Geographic variation and evolution in South American *Cistothorus platensis* (Aves: Troglodytidae). *Fieldiana* No. 48. Publication No. 1392 of the Field Museum of Natural History, Chicago, Illinois.

Tremoleras, J. 1934. Tres notas ornitológicas. *Hornero* 5: 390-396.

Tweit, R.C. 1996. Curve-billed Thrasher (*Toxostoma curvirostre*) in Poole, A. & Gill, F (eds). *The Birds of North America* No. 235. The Academy of Natural Sciences, Philadelphia, Pennsylvania and American Ornithologists' Union, Washington DC.

Tweit, R.C. 1997. Long-billed Thrasher (*Toxostoma longirostre*). In Poole, A. & Gill, F (eds) *The Birds of North America* No. 317. The Academy of Natural Sciences, Philadelphia, Pennsylvania and American Ornithologists' Union, Washington DC.

Tyler, S.J. 1994. The Yungas of Argentina; in search of Rufous-throated Dippers (*Cinclus schulzi*). *Cotinga* 2: 38–41.

Tyler, S.J. & Ormerod, S.J. 1994. *The Dippers*, T & A.D. Poyser, London.

Tyler, S.J. & Tyler, L. 1996. The Rufous-throated Dipper (*Cinclus schulzi*) on rivers in north-west Argentina and southern Bolivia. *Bird Conserv. Int.* 6: 103–116.

Unitt, P. 1996. Taxonomy of the Marsh Wren in Southern California. *Proc. San Diego Soc. Nat. Hist.* No. 31.

Van Rossem, A.J. 1930a. New birds from Northwestern Mexico. *Trans. San Diego Soc. Nat. Hist.* 6:225.

Van Rossem, A.J. 1930b. New Sonora races of *Toxostoma* and *Pheugopedius*. *Trans. San Diego Soc. Nat. Hist.* 6: 207–208.

Van Rossem, A.J. 1942. Notes on some Mexican and Californian birds, with descriptions of six undescribed races. *Trans. San Diego Soc. Nat. Hist.* 9: 377–384.

Van Vegten, J.A. & Schipper, W.J.A. 1968. First observation of the Wren on São Miguel, Azores. *Ardea* 56: 194-195.

Varty, N., Adams, J., Espin, P. & Hambler, C. (eds) 1986. An ornithological survey of Lake Tota, Colombia, *ICBP Study Report* 12, Cambridge.

Vaurie, C. 1959. *Birds of the Palaearctic Fauna; passeriformes*. H.F. & G. Witherby, London.

Velásquez-Tibatá, J.I., Gutiérrez, A. & Carillo, E. 2000. *Primer registro de parasitismo reproductivo en el Cucarachero de Pantano* Cistothorus apolinari *por el Chamón Maicero* Molothrus bonariensis. *Cotinga* 14: 102.

Venables, L.S.V. 1940. Nesting behaviour of the Galapagos Mockingbird. *Ibis* 82: 629–639.

Venegas C,C. & Jory H,J. 1979. *Guía de campo para las Aves de Magallanes*. Instituto de la Patagonia, Punta Arenas.

Verner, J. 1964. Evolution of polygamy in the Long-billed Marsh Wren. *Evolution* 18: 252–261.

Verner, J. 1965. Breeding biology of the Long-billed Marsh Wren. *Condor* 67: 6–30.

Verner, J. 1980. Interspecific aggression between Yellow-headed Blackbirds and Long-billed Marsh Wrens. *Condor* 82: 328–331.

Voloshina, I. V. 1977. *Gnezda i Gnezdovye Uchastki Sibirskoi Buroi Olyapki*. VII Vsesoyuznaya Ornitologicheskaya Konferentsia. Akademii Nauk Uk SSR Kiev.

Voloshina, I.V. & Myslenikov A.I. 1980. Oologicheskie i Yuvenil'nye Priznaki Sibirskoi Buroi Olyapki (*Cinclus pallasii pallasii*). *Zoologicheskie Zhurnal* 4: 621–624.

Voous, K. H. 1983. *Birds of the Netherlands Antilles*. De Walburg Pers, Zuphen.

Walkinshaw, L.H. 1935. Studies of the Short-billed Marsh Wren (*Cistothorus stellaris*) in Michigan. *Auk* 52: 362–369.

Wapple, G.T. & Smith, A.R. 1982. First sight record of the Cactus Wren in Saskatchewan and Canada. *Blue Jay* 40: 203–204.

Waters, E. 1964. Observations on the St. Kilda Wren. *Brit. Birds* 57: 49–64.

Webster, M. 1976. *A New Guide to the Birds of Hong Kong*. Sino-American Publishing Co., Hong Kong.

Weir, R.D. 1983. The nesting season. *American Birds* 37: 982–985.

Welter, W.A. 1935. The natural history of the Long-billed Marsh Wren. *Wilson Bull.* 47: 3–34.

Wetmore, A. 1926a. Birds of Argentina, Paraguay, Uruguay and Chile. *Smithsonian Inst. Bull.* 353.

Wetmore, A. 1926b. Observations on the birds of Argentina, Paraguay, Uruguay and Chile. *Bull. US Nat. Mus.* 113: 1–448.

Wetmore, A. 1939. Observations on the birds of northern Venezuela. *Proc. U. S. Nat. Mus.* 87: 523–581.

Wetmore, A., Pasquier, R.F. & Olson, S.L. 1984. *The Birds of the Republic of Panama, Part 4, Passeriformes:* Fringillidae. Smithsonian Institution Press, Washington, DC.

Wheatley, N. 1994. *Where to watch birds in South America.* Christopher Helm, London.

Wheatley, N. & Brewer, A.D. (in press) *Where to watch birds in Central America and the Caribbean.* Christopher Helm, London.

Whelan, P. *Globe and Mail.* Toronto March 27, 1999.

Whitehall, M. H. 1957. *Observations on Birds of Southeastern Brazil.* University of Toronto Press, Toronto, Ontario.

Whittingham, M.J. & Atkinson, P.W. 1996. A species split in Mexico: Sumichrast's and Nava's Wren, *Hylorchilus sumichrasti* and *H. navai. Cotinga* 5: 20–22.

Wilbur, S.R.1987. *Birds of Baja California.* University of California Press, Berkeley, California.

Wiley, J.W. & Wiley, B.N. 1979. The biology of the White-crowned Pigeon. *Journal of Wildlife Management* Monograph 64, 43: 41-43.

Wiley, R.H. & Wiley, M.S. 1977. Recognition of neighbors' duets by Stripe-backed Wrens *Campylorhynchus nuchalis. Behaviour* 62: 10–34.

Williamson, K. 1958. Population and breeding environment of the St Kilda and Fair Isle Wrens. *Brit. Birds* 51: 369–393.

Willughby, F. & Ray, J. 1676. *Ornithologiae libri tres.* Royal Society, London (English translation 1678).

Winker, K., Klicka, J.J. & Voelker, G. 1996. Sexual dimorphism in birds from southern Veracruz, Mexico; *Thryothorus maculipectus* and *Henicorhina (leucosticta) prostheleuca. J. Field Ornithol.* 67: 236–251.

Woods, R.W. 1975. *The Birds of the Falkland Islands.* Anthony Nelson, Oswestry.

Woods, R.W. 1993. Cobb's Wren *Troglodytes (aedon) cobbi* of the Falkland Islands. *Bull. Brit. Orn. Club* 113: 195–207.

Woods, R. & Woods, A. 1997. *Atlas of Breeding Birds of the Falkland Islands.*, Anthony Nelson, Oswestry.

Yanushevich, I.A., Tyurin, P.S., Yakovleva, I.D., Kydyralev, A. & Semenova, N.I. 1960. *Ptitsy Kirgizii Tom. II.* Izdatel'stvo Akademii Nauk Kirgizskoi SSR, Frunze.

Young, B,E., Kaspari, M. & Martin, T.E. 1990. Species-specific Nest Site Selection by Birds in Ant-Acacia Trees. *Biotropica* 22: 310–315.

Young, C.G. 1925. The nest of *Donacobius atricapillus. Ibis* 67: 473.

Zack, S. & Rabenold, K.N. 1989. Assessment, age and proximity in dispersal contests among cooperative wrens: field experiments. *Anim. Behav.* 38: 235–247.

Zimmer, J.T. & Phelps, W.H. 1946. Twenty-three new subspecies of birds from Venezuela and Brazil. *Amer. Mus. Novit.* 1312: 17–18.

Zimmer, J.T. & Phelps, W.H. 1951. New subspecies of birds from Surinam and Venezuela. *Amer. Mus. Novit.* 1511:6

Zimmerman, D.A. 1957. Some remarks on the behaviour of the Yucatan Cactus Wren. *Condor* 59: 53–58.

Zink, R.M., Blackwell, R.C. & Rojas-Soto, O. 1997. Species limits in the Le Conte's Thrasher. *Condor* 99: 132–138.

Zink, R.M. & Blackwell-Rago, R.C. 2000. Species limits and recent population history of the Curve-billed Thrasher. *Condor* 102: 881-886.

Zink, R.M., Dittmann, D.L., Klicka, J. & Blackwell-Rago, R.C. 1999. Evolutionary patterns of morphometrics, allozymes and mitochondrial DNA in Thrashers (genus *Toxostoma*). *Auk* 116: 1021–1038.

Zusi, R.L., 1969. Ecology and adaptations of the Trembler on the island of Dominica. *The Living Bird, eighth annual of the Cornell Laboratory of Ornithology,* 137-164. Cornell University, Ithaca, NY.

INDEX

Species are listed by their vernacular name (e.g. Brown Dipper) and by their scientific name. Specific scientific names are followed by their generic name as used in the book (e.g. *pallasii, Cinclus*) and subspecific names are followed by both the specific and generic names (e.g. *tenuirostris, Cinclus pallasii*). Numbers in *italic* refer to the first page of the relevant systematic entry. Numbers in **bold** type refer to the colour plate numbers.

White-breasted Thrasher **32** 86, *244*
White-breasted Wood Wren **17** 56, *188*
White-breasted Wren. *See* Buff-breasted Wren
White-browed Cactus Wren. *See* Bicolored Wren
White-browed Equatorial Wren. *See* Mountain Wren
White-browed Mocking-Thrush. *See* Donacobius
White-browed Wood Wren. *See* Grey-breasted Wood
    Wren
White-browed Wren **8** 38, *134*
White-capped Dipper **21** 64, *205*
White-eared Wren. *See* Buff-breasted Wren
White-headed Wren **3** 28, *100*
White-sided Wood Wren. *See* White-breasted Wood
    Wren
White-throated Canyon Wren. *See* Canyon Wren
White-throated Dipper,. *See* Eurasian Dipper
Wing-banded Wren **18** 58, *195*
Winter Wren **13** 48, *165*
Worthington's Marsh Wren. *See* Marsh Wren
Wren. *See* Winter Wren

xerampelinus, Thryothorus spadix 136
xerophilum, Campylorhynchus rufinucha 98

yananchae, Thryothorus mystacalis 142
yavii, Troglodytes rufulus 183
Yucatan Cactus Wren. *See* Yucatan Wren
Yucatan Mockingbird. *See* Tropical Mockingbird
Yucatan Spotted-breasted Wren. *See* Spot-breasted Wren
Yucatan Wren **1** 24, *91*
yucatanicus, Campylorhynchus 24, 91

Zapata Wren **16** 54, *130*
zeledoni, Thryothorus 46, 159
Zeledon's Wren. *See* Canebrake Wren
Zempoaltepec Wren. *See* Brown-throated Wren
zetlandicus, Troglodytes troglodytes 48, 166
zimmeri, Campylorhynchus griseus 96
zonatus, Campylorhynchus 30, 104
zonatus, Campylorhynchus zonatus 104
Zulia Wren. *See* Buff-breasted Wren
zuliensis, Thryothorus leucotis 160

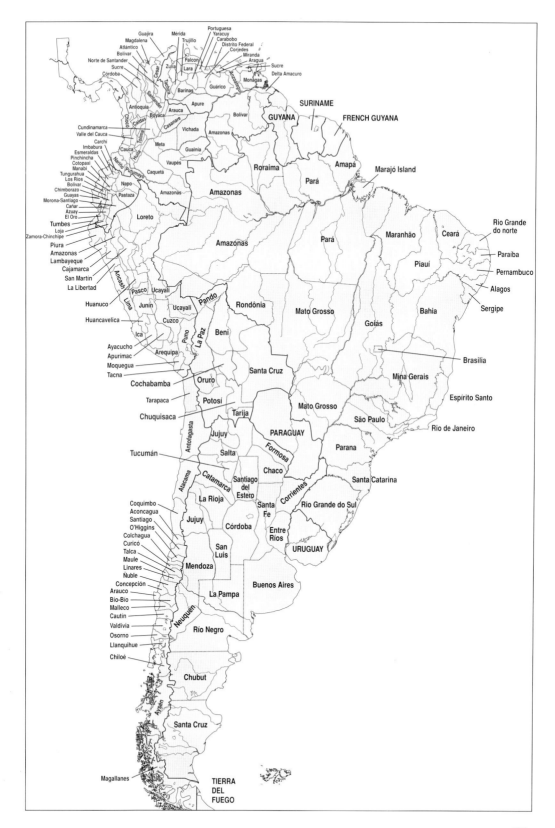

Guajira
Magdalena
Atlántico
Bolivar
Norte de Santander
Sucre
Córdoba

Mérida
Trujillo
Falcón
Zulia
Lara

Portuguesa
Yaracuy
Carabobo
Distrito Federal
Corjedes
Miranda
Aragua
Sucre
Delta Amacuro

Cesar
Tachira

Barinas

Guárico

Monagas

SURINAME

Antioquia
Boyacá
Arauca
Apure

Bolivar

GUYANA

FRENCH GUYANA

Chocó
Caldas
Cundinamarca
Valle del Cauca
Carchi
Imbabura
Esmeraldas
Pinchincha
Cotopaxi
Manabí
Tungurahua
Los Ríos
Bolivar
Chimborazo
Guayas
Morona-Santiago
Cañar
Azuay
El Oro
Tumbes
Loja
Zamora-Chinchipe
Piura
Amazonas
Lambayeque
Cajamarca
San Martin
La Libertad
Huanuco
Huancavelica

Santander
Cauca
Huila
Tolima
Nariño
Putumayo
Napo
Pastaza

Vichada
Meta
Guainía
Vaupés
Caquetá
Amazonas

Amazonas

Roraima

Amapá

Marajó Island

Pará

Amazonas

Pará

Maranhão

Ceará

Rio Grande
do norte

Paraíba

Pernambuco

Alagos

Sergipe

Piauí

Loreto

Ancash
Pasco
Ucayali
Lima
Junin
Ucayali
Cuzco
Ica
Puno
Pando

Rondônia

Mato Grosso

Goiás

Bahia

Brasilia

Ayacucho
Apurimac
Moquegua
Tacna

La Paz
Arequipa
Beni

Santa Cruz

Mina Gerais

Cochabamba
Oruro
Tarapaca
Potosí
Chuquisaca

Tarija

Mato Grosso

São Paulo

Espírito Santo

Rio de Janeiro

Antofagasta
Jujuy
Salta
PARAGUAY

Formosa

Parana

Tucumán

Atacama
Catamarca

Chaco

Santa Catarina

Coquimbo
Aconcagua
Santiago
O'Higgins
Colchagua
Curicó
Talca
Maule
Linares
Ñuble
Concepción
Arauco
Bio-Bio
Malleco
Cautin
Valdivia
Osorno
Llanquihue
Chiloé

La Rioja
Jujuy

Santiago
del
Estero

Córdoba

San
Luis

Santa
Fe

Corrientes

Rio Grande do Sul

Entre
Ríos

URUGUAY

Mendoza

Buenos Aires

La Pampa

Neuquén

Río Negro

Chubut

Aysén

Santa Cruz

Magallanes

TIERRA
DEL
FUEGO

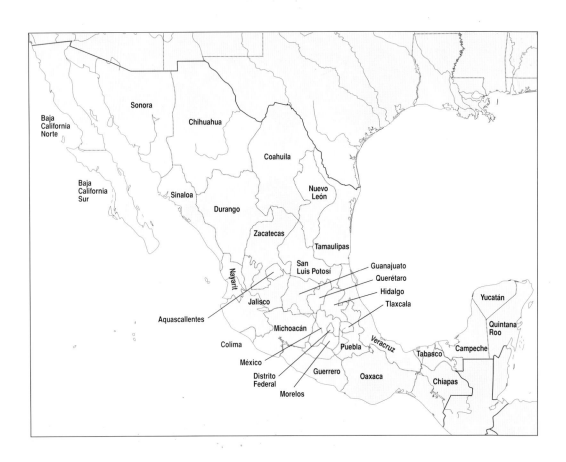

Baja
California
Norte

Sonora

Chihuahua

Coahuila

Baja
California
Sur

Sinaloa

Nuevo
León

Durango

Zacatecas

Tamaulipas

Nayarit

San
Luis Potosí

Guanajuato

Querétaro

Hidalgo

Jalisco

Tlaxcala

Aquascallentes

Yucatán

Michoacán

Quintana
Roo

Colima

Veracruz

Puebla

México

Campeche

Tabasco

Distrito
Federal

Guerrero

Oaxaca

Chiapas

Morelos

272